Basic Mathematics Simplified

OLIVO AND OLIVO

4TH EDITION

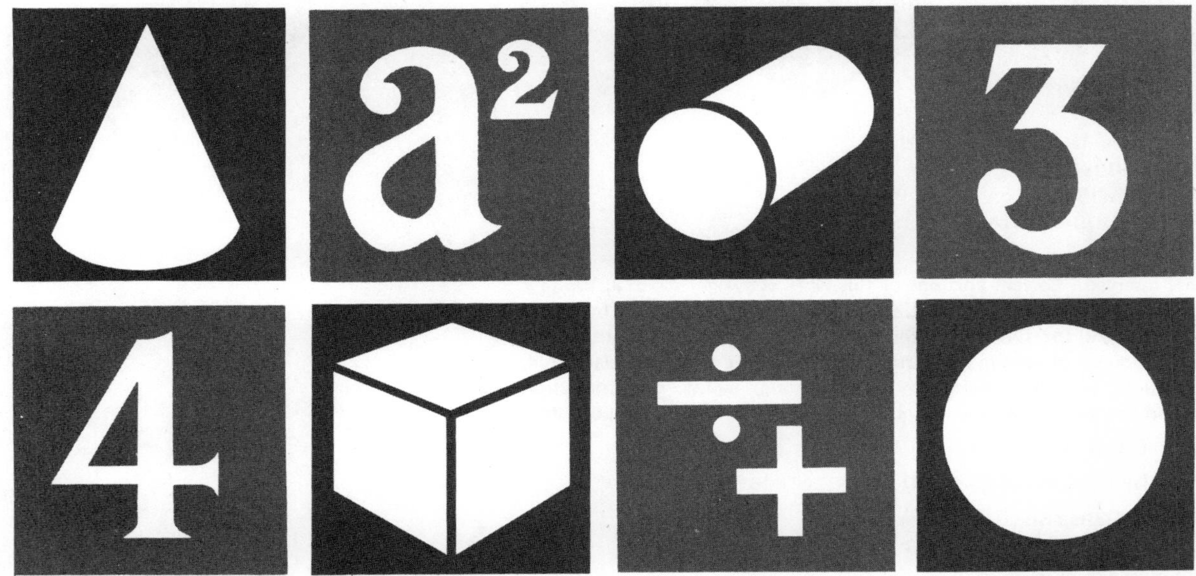

Basic Mathematics Simplified

4TH EDITION

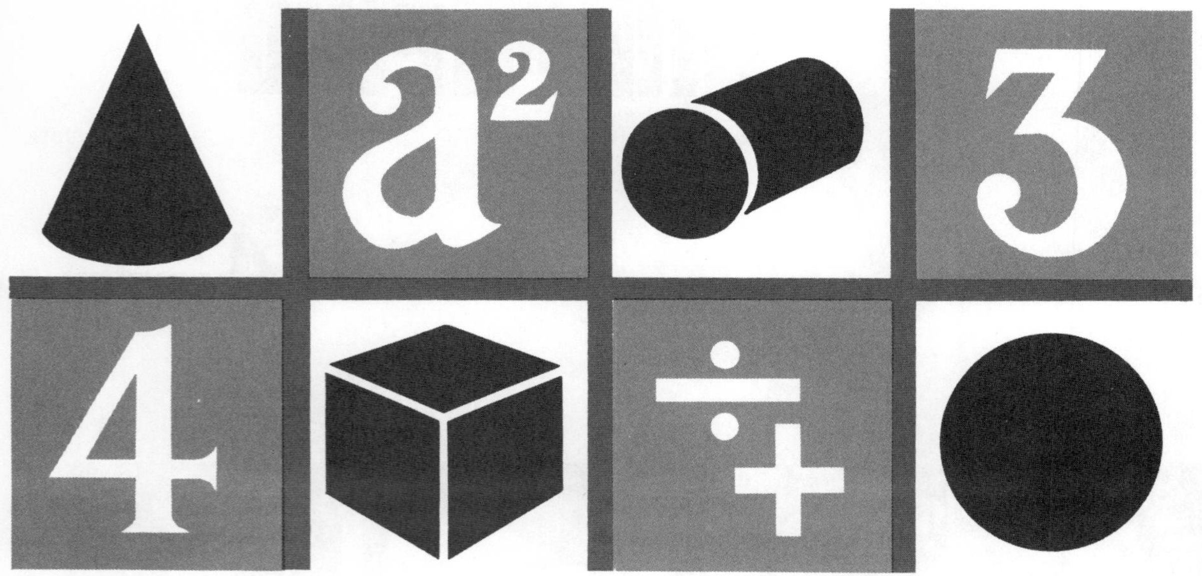

DELMAR PUBLISHERS

4TH EDITION

10 9 8 7 6 5 4 3

LIBRARY OF CONGRESS CATALOG CARD NUMBER: 76-3941

Printed in the United States of America
Published Simultaneously in Canada by
Delmar Publishers, A Division of
Van Nostrand Reinhold, Ltd.

C. THOMAS OLIVO
Professor
Temple University

THOMAS P. OLIVO
Curriculum Coordinator
Board of Cooperative
Education Services
Suffolk County, New York

DELMAR PUBLISHERS • ALBANY, NEW YORK 12205
A DIVISION OF LITTON EDUCATIONAL PUBLISHING, INC.

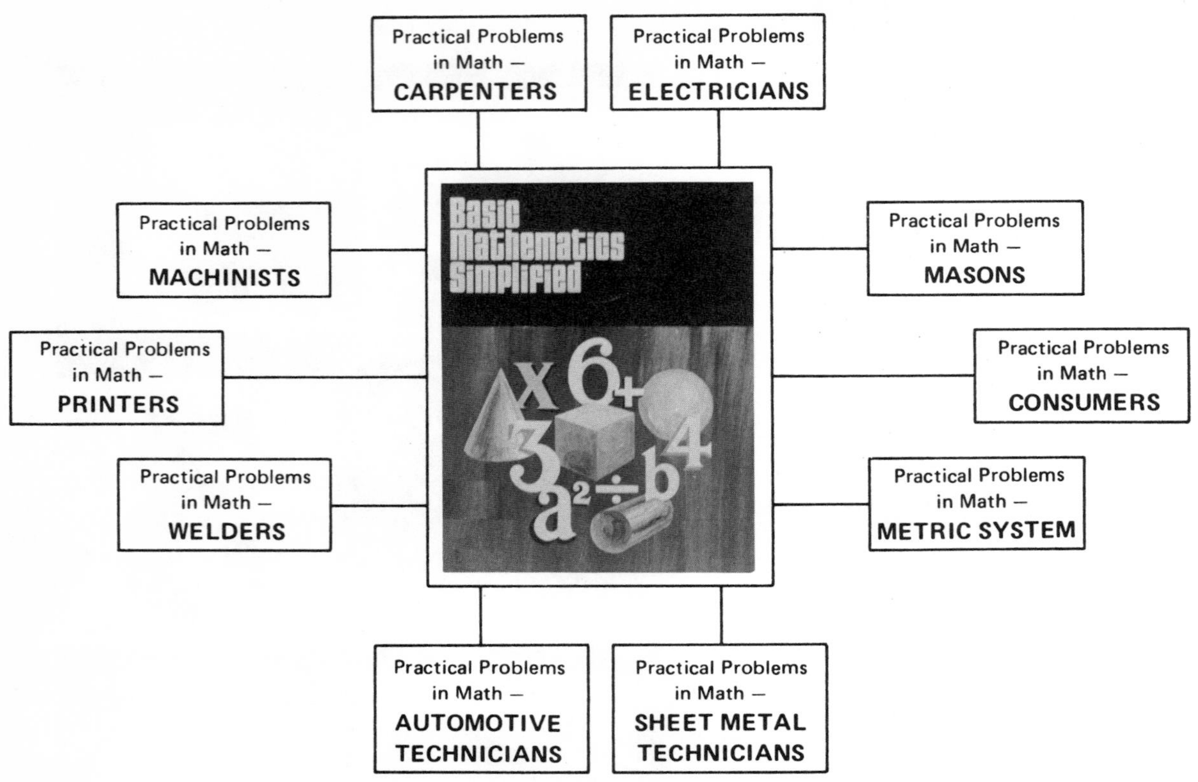

As the accompanying diagram indicates, *Basic Mathematics Simplified* is the basic text on which successful use of each of the *Practical Problems in Mathematics* books depends. The textbook is designed to give the student a solid background in the fundamental concepts, processes, and general applications of mathematics. The ancillary books supply him with specific application in whichever of the seven career areas he has chosen.

Basic Mathematics Simplified may be used to teach a complete mathematics course or to teach a refresher course. The content is widely varied to meet many student needs. The four basic arithmetic processes are outlined as they are used with whole numbers, fractions, and decimals. Material on algebraic equations, geometric shapes and constructions, and trigonometric functions is included. The metric system of measurement and methods of converting between the metric and English systems are presented. The use of the slide rule for computation is introduced.

Presentation of the material follows a consistent format: discussion of a concept, statement of rules, step-by-step examples, and immediate application. This consistency, plus the use of screening, aids the learning process and simplifies review.

Each of the *Practical Problems in Mathematics* books contains material selected to meet the interests and needs of students in a particular career area. The related mathematics problems involve such areas as determining measurements, estimating materials, costs, and time allotments, and using appropriate laws and formulas. Each application is keyed to the unit in *Basic Mathematics Simplified* where the relevant concept and process may be found.

Answers and complete solutions for all problems are included in the instructor's guides which are provided for the textbook and each of the ancillary books.

PREFACE

Mathematics is the heritage of all people. The position of leadership and service to which a nation rises depends largely on the ability of all its people to understand and apply simple mathematical truths. Beyond this level of competence and application are the contributions of the relatively few, by comparison, who need to apply the more advanced branches of mathematics.

Every word in the title *Basic Mathematics Simplified* is descriptive of the purpose, organization and scope of this book. Each unit, each section and each part is the result of extensive study. Occupational and human resource analyses were made to establish the basic mathematical skills needed by individuals in preparation for satisfactory careers and social adjustment. The fundamental question, "How much mathematics does a person need to earn a living and to live a meaningful life?" is answered in this book.

Basic Mathematics Simplified provides instructional material for a well-balanced, continuous and integrated program of mathematics based on concrete life needs. The scope is broad enough to permit adaptation of content to meet the varying needs and capabilities of students at different age levels and stages in career development.

The pattern used in each instructional unit makes it possible to continuously adjust and reorganize programs and methods. These changes recognize variations in individual ability and motivation in applying mathematics to important real problems.

This edition has been changed significantly. The changes reflect broader demands for mathematical competence. These result from scientific and technical developments, the accelerating trend toward metrication, changing concepts of consumer needs, emphasis on career planning and growth, and the common use of electronic calculators.

The major changes cover the following:

- Each of the five parts in the previous edition has been expanded. New materials and new problems are introduced. Others are updated or changed. The additional problems provide applications in different occupations.

- Three new parts are added. Part 2 relates to fundamentals of SI Metrics and conventional metric systems. There is considerable expansion of the material that was earlier contained in a single detailed unit on the (customary) metric system of measurement. The three units and the Achievement Review in Part 2 deal in depth with the most recent developments in metrication.

- Part 7 is a new addition on *Electronic Calculators.* There are two units and an Achievement Review in this part. Collectively, the principles, processes and applications cover electronic computers and their use in basic mathematical processes. Algorithms are introduced to extend the application of commonly used calculators to advanced mathematical processes.

- Part 8 is another new addition of two units and two Achievement Reviews. These provide a practical, concentrated approach in applying mathematics to consumer and career planning and development needs.

- The units following Part 2, in which metric systems are treated, include a considerable number of practical problems in both the conventional metric system and SI Metrics. The measurement systems and standards that are incorporated are those most widely used by producers, consumers and various other standards setting groups.
- The twelve technical reference tables are expanded to fifteen. The new tables and changes in the original tables reflect increasing emphasis on metrication, electronic calculators and processes, career and consumer needs, and other technical developments.
- A Glossary is now a part of the Appendix. Current measurement terms, mathematical expressions and quantities, concepts in SI Metrics, conventional metric systems and customary units are described.
- The Index is updated and expanded to reflect the changes and newer applications as discussed earlier.
- All changes and additions in the textbook which require revision and extension of solutions and answers in the "Instructors Guide" are incorporated in that publication. Selected answers are also contained in the assignment section at the end of each unit.

The emphasis on developing multi-measurement system mathematical capability is evident. Whenever SI Metrics is accepted by federal legislation it will be the "dominant" system of measurement. A word of caution is in order. SI Metrics will not be the "sole" system of standards in the United States. Conversion to SI Metrics by producers and consumers, professional bodies, and others will be voluntary.

Like all other measurement systems, SI Metrics is a constantly evolving, coherent system of measurement. Standards are proposed, modified, adopted and then applied. Standards in SI involve compromises among responsible scientific, engineering, and other international professional groups and representatives. From concept to implementation represents a span of many, many years. The practices suggested in this text lead toward the development of essential mathematical competencies in the individual in applying the commonly accepted units of measure.

This edition of *Basic Mathematics Simplified* is rededicated to Hilda G. Olivo, an outstanding teacher, and to Connie, Tom and Judi. As a member of the family each has continued to share generously through the years in the numberless hours which were needed in the successive stages of research, outlining, developing, testing, refining and preparing final manuscript. This book is a tribute to them. Special recognition is made to Thomas P. Olivo (Tom) as coauthor, whose significant contributions are incorporated in this extensively-revised edition, and to Stephanie B. Olivo for her editorial assistance.

C. Thomas Olivo

Albany, New York
1976

TO THE INSTRUCTOR

Basic Mathematics Simplified serves a three-fold purpose:

1. The content is organized around concrete life needs in preparation for work.
2. The scope is sufficiently broad to include the everyday consumer mathematics needed by individuals to develop functional competency as citizens.
3. The instructional units include all the basic principles that are required in each branch to make mathematics function.

The scope of the instructional units, the sequence in which they are given, the step-by-step form in which each basic principle is explained and applied, and the problem material are based on sound analyses of need and tested, successful, teaching/learning experiences.

SCOPE OF INSTRUCTIONAL MATERIAL

Basic Mathematics Simplified includes five branches of mathematics. These branches are related to eight major areas of application. The areas are identified as "Parts." Part One deals with Fundamentals of Basic Mathematics; Part Two, Fundamentals of SI Metrics and Conventional Metric Systems; Part Three, Fundamentals of Applied Algebra; Part Four, Fundamentals of Applied Geometry; Part Five, Fundamentals of Applied Trigonometry; and Part Six, Fundamentals of Advanced Mathematics (Slide Rule). Part Seven covers Fundamentals of Electronic Calculators; Part Eight, Fundamentals of Mathematics Applied to Careers and Consumer Needs.

Each "Part" contains a number of sections. The Sections represent major divisions, areas or blocks of mathematics. Each Section, in turn, includes a number of Instructional Units. These are arranged in the natural order of dependence of one new principle or skill on another.

BASIC PRINCIPLE UNITS

Each new concept or principle in mathematics is introduced in such a manner as to establish a need for mastering it. This introduction is followed in each unit by a series of steps. The steps show how the simple rules relating to each principle are used. Immediate application of each rule or principle is made by using, where possible, a practical example. The procedures show and give meaning to each new rule or principle.

ASSIGNMENT UNITS

An Assignment Unit follows each Basic Principle Unit. Sufficient problem material is included in the Assignment Units to insure mastery of each new principle. Within each Assignment Unit, the problems follow a definite pattern, progressing from the simple to the complex.

Wherever practical, typical problems from technical, business, industry or other occupational sources are used. These give value to and create interest in developing greater mathematical skills. Accuracy and speed are built into the problems by specifying a degree of accuracy that is meaningful and valuable. Decimal and fractional values are to be carried throughout a solution. The final answer is then rounded, as required.

A series of ancillary *Practical Problems in Mathematics* publications is available. These provide additional problem material to meet needs in specific occupational career areas.

ACHIEVEMENT REVIEWS

A cumulative review of all the instructional material in a section is provided in the Achievement Test. Here, too, the sequence in which the practical problems are given is the same as the order of teaching/learning difficulty in the Basic Principle Units. In some instances, the Achievement Test may serve as a pre-test of a student's ability to apply the basic principles which are covered in one section. The combination of problems in the Assignment Units and those in the Achievement Tests is intended to develop mathematical skills, speed and accuracy. At the same time, they provide checkpoints on the effectiveness of instruction.

APPENDIX RESOURCE MATERIALS

- A series of tables, formulas and other handbook data which the student normally uses is contained in the Appendix. These make the book self-contained. The tables were especially selected and developed to provide valuable information required in solving everyday problems.
- The Glossary of the Appendix includes abbreviated pertinent statements of mathematical terms, values, quantities, systems, and other technical information. These are to be reviewed continuously to complement the text matter.
- Alternate answers appear in the assignment section at the end of each unit. These permit individual student checking and problem reworking, where needed. This procedure is intended to conserve valuable teaching/learning time.

SUGGESTED APPLICATIONS FOR *BASIC MATHEMATICS SIMPLIFIED*

This book is intended for those individuals who need to develop a practical understanding of basic mathematical skills for use either as producer mathematics in preparation for a vocation or for consumer mathematics to develop functional competencies as future citizens, or both. The organization and content provide a wealth of material to meet varying needs and capacities of individuals. A few applications are cited. These suggest places where the instructional material may be used.

1. As a mathematics text for students at varying age and career growth levels. The essential basic principles of mathematics are learned in relation to real problems that are meaningful to each student.
2. As a basic textbook which meets the need for practical instruction in mathematics in occupational, vocational, industrial and technical education. The contents are applicable for class instruction with homogeneous groups or individualized instruction for heterogeneous groups.

3. As a basic text for apprentice training and other business, industry and occupational training programs.
4. As a textbook for cooperative or diversified occupation students with either homogeneous or mixed groups.
5. As a source book or reference text for teacher training classes for the development of courses of study, analysis of teachable content and teaching/learning methods.
6. As a textbook or source book for adult programs and occupational extension classes where a sound working knowledge of mathematics is required.

Basic Mathematics Simplified provides a key to the development of mathematical competency. This key opens many opportunities for successful entrance into and progress in health and related occupations, business, distribution, industrial, and other sectors of society.

TO THE STUDENT

Mathematics is the foundation on which the everyday necessities of life depend. Modern heating and cooling, jet and aerospace transportation, oceanographic discoveries, laser developments, television and other mass communications, instantaneous computerized feedback – these are just a few of the limitless number of products and systems that make life more comfortable and secure. Each process, product, and material depends on mathematics.

Mathematics plays an essential part in the daily work, play, and living of each individual. In the development of complex products, higher mathematics is used by specially trained technologists, engineers and mathematicians. The simplest form of mathematics is known as arithmetic. It is used by all to solve most common problems.

Orderly procedures must be followed in mathematics. Thus, attention is directed to the value of developing desirable work habits.

DEVELOPING DESIRABLE WORK HABITS

Systematic work habits should be applied to the interpretation and solution of all problems. Such orderly and organized step-by-step procedures simplify the working out of each problem and insure greater accuracy. A simple list of practices to follow for all problems includes eight basic steps:

Step 1 Read the problem carefully to understand what is meant by every part of it.

Step 2 Determine what is asked for or required.

Step 3 Separate what is given in the problem and what solution is required. At the start, it may be advisable to write the given information in one column and what is required in another.

Step 4 Decide what arithmetical processes must be used to solve the problem.

Step 5 Perform all operations neatly and arrange the work in columns wherever practical.

Step 6 Label the answer in terms of the values on which it is based.

Step 7 Estimate what a reasonable answer must be.

Step 8 Check every step. Then, compare the computed answer with the estimated answer as a final check. If necessary, rework and recheck the problem.

CONTENTS

PART 1 FUNDAMENTALS OF BASIC MATHEMATICS

PART 2 FUNDAMENTALS OF SI METRIC AND CONVENTIONAL METRIC SYSTEMS

PART 3 FUNDAMENTALS OF APPLIED ALGEBRA

Section 9 Symbols

Section 10 Equations

Section 11 Ratio and Proportion

Section 12 Exponents

Section 13 Radicals

PART 8 FUNDAMENTALS APPLIED TO CONSUMER AND CAREER NEEDS

Section 1

WHOLE NUMBERS

Unit 1 ADDITION OF WHOLE NUMBERS

A. THE CONCEPT OF WHOLE NUMBERS

The term *whole numbers* refers to complete units where there are no fractional parts left over. Such numbers as 20 and 50; quantities like 144 machine screws, 10 spools, and 57 outlets; and measurements like 75 feet, or 10 inches, or $875, represent whole numbers because the values do not contain a fraction.

The four basic operations in arithmetic include addition, subtraction, multiplication, and division. Addition is, by far, the most widely used of the four operations. However, even before the basic principles of addition may be applied, the Arabic system of numbers must be understood.

B. THE ARABIC SYSTEM

The Arabic number system is the one which is widely used in this country and in many other parts of the world. This system includes ten digits: 0 1 2 3 4 5 6 7 8 9. These may be combined to express any desired number.

The ten digits make up what is sometimes called the *system of tens* or the *decimal system.* An important fact about this system is that the location or position of a digit in the written number expresses its value.

PLACE NAMES						
Millions	Hundred-Thousands	Ten-Thousands	Thousands	Hundreds	Tens	Units
9	8	7	6	5	4	3

The digit in the extreme right place of a whole number is said to be in the *units* column. The digit in the next position to the left is in the *tens* column; the third position, *hundreds,* and the like.

A whole number like 231 is a simple way of saying 200 + 30 + 1. The 231 means that every digit in the *units* column has its value multiplied by 1; every numeral in the *tens* column, by 10; and hundreds, by 100. The whole number is a shorthand way of representing the sum of the individual place values of the numerals.

Numbers may be written in words as three hundred thirty-six; in an expanded form, 300 + 30 + 6; or the numeral, 336.

C. ADDING WHOLE NUMBERS

Addition is simply the process of adding all the numbers in each column in a problem. The answer is called the *sum.*

RULE FOR ADDING WHOLE NUMBERS

- Write one number under another so the unit digits are in the units column, tens in the tens column, and the like.
- Add all the numbers in the *units* column.
- Write the result by placing the unit digit in the units column.

  NOTE: Where the sum of a column is greater than 9, put the second digit on the left in the *tens* column.
- Add all the numbers in the tens column. Write the last digit in this sum in the *tens* column.

  NOTE: If this sum is greater than 9, put the second digit on the left in the *hundreds* column.
- Continue to add each column of numbers. Find the sum of all columns by adding the numbers in the separate answers in each column.

EXAMPLE: Add 2765 + 972 + 857 + 1724.

Step 1	Arrange numbers in columns.		2	7	6	5
				9	7	2
				8	5	7
Step 2	Add all numbers in *units* column.		1	7	2	4
	(5 + 2 + 7 + 4 = 18)				1	8
Step 3	Add all numbers in *tens* column.					
	(6 + 7 + 5 + 2 = 20)			2	0	
Step 4	Add all numbers in *hundreds* column.					
	(7 + 9 + 8 + 7 = 31)		3	1		
Step 5	Add all numbers in *thousands* column.					
	(2 + 1 = 3)		3			
Step 6	Add the sums in each column.	Ans.	6	3	1	8

RULE FOR ADDING WHOLE NUMBERS (SIMPLIFIED FORM)

- Write the numbers one under another with each digit in the proper column.
- Add all the numbers in the *units* column.
- Write the last digit on the right in the units column.
- *Carry* the remaining digit (mentally) on the left to the *tens* column and add it with the rest of the numbers in this column.
- Continue the same process with the remaining columns.

EXAMPLE: Add 2765 + 972 + 857 + 1724.

Add Downward

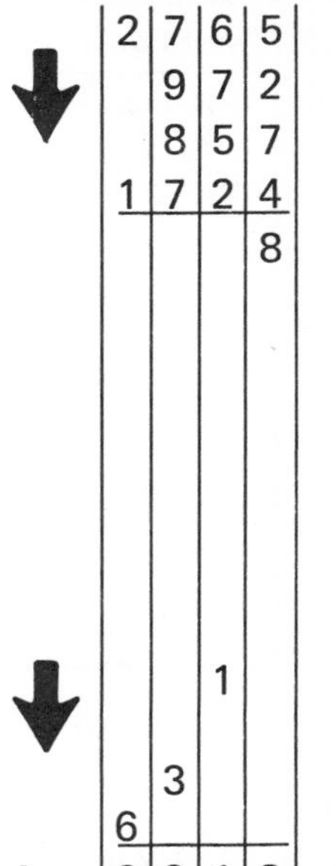

Step 1 Arrange numbers in columns.

Step 2 Add numbers in *units* column.

$(5 + 2 + 7 + 4 = 18)$

Place 8 in the *units* column. Carry the 1 (mentally) to the *tens* column.

NOTE: Add all columns downward from top to bottom.

Step 3 Add the numbers in the *tens* column and add the 1 carried over (mentally).

$(6 + 7 + 5 + 2) + (1) = 21$

Place 1 in the *tens* column and carry the 2 over to the *hundreds* column.

Step 4 Perform the same addition steps with the *hundreds* and *thousands* columns.

RULE FOR CHECKING ACCURACY

- Find the sum of the numbers in the units column by adding upward (or in the reverse direction).
- Continue to add the numbers in the *tens,* then *hundreds,* then *thousands* column.

  NOTE: If the sum of the numbers in the *units* column is more than 9, carry the number of tens to the tens column and add to the numbers in that column. Follow this same practice with the other columns.

6 3 1 8
2 7 6 5
9 7 2
8 5 7
1 7 2 4

Add Upward

- Compare the result (sum) with the sum obtained by adding in the reverse order.

  NOTE: If there is an error, repeat the addition step in the reverse order.

D. THE ROMAN NUMERAL SYSTEM

The Roman numeral system emerged toward the end of the sixteenth century as a second numerical system. This system uses seven basic symbols. These are combined to produce any required number or sequence of numerals.

This system is applied in the medical and allied health industry. Normally, the range in such occupations is from 1 to 100. There are other limited uses in architecture and design, different businesses, and for general consumer applications.

Many Roman numeral equivalents require more symbols and are more difficult to write and apply than Arabic numerals. Seven basic Roman numerals with their values (together with other general combinations from 1 to 1,000) are given in the table.

Note from the table that Roman numerals "I, II and III" correspond with Arabic numerals 1, 2 and 3. The value for four is written as "IV" (V – I, 5 – 1). Six is "VI"

Basic Roman Numerals and Equivalent Values		Common Roman Numeral Combinations and Equivalent Values					
Roman Numeral	Value	Roman Numeral	Value	Roman Numeral	Value	Roman Numeral	Value
I	1	I	1	X	10	C	100
V	5	II	2	XX	20	CC	200
X	10	III	3	XXX	30	CCC	300
L	50	IV	4	XL	40	CD	400
C	100	V	5	L	50	D	500
D	500	VI	6	LX	60	DC	600
M	1,000	VII	7	LXX	70	DCC	700
		VIII	8	LXXX	80	DCCC	800
		IX	9	XC	90	CM	900
						M	1,000

(V + 1, 5 + 1); seven, "VII" (V + II, 5 + 2); and eight "VIII" (V + III, 5 + 3). In the case of nine, the numeral is "IX" (X – I, 10 –1).

Forty is written "XL." This is the equivalent of L – X (50 – 10). Ninety is "XC" (C – X, 100 – 10); four hundred is "CD" (D – C, 500 – 100), and nine hundred is "CM" (M – C, 1,000 – 100). Intermediate numerals are stated as combinations of I, V, X, L, C, D and M. Symbols for the numerals may be in capitals or lower case, like: i, v, x, l, c, d and m. Capitals are usually used.

RULE FOR WRITING ROMAN NUMERALS

- Break the numeral down into appropriate digits: units, tens, hundreds, thousands.
- Determine the Roman numeral equivalent of the largest digit.
- Move to the next digit to the right. Again, determine the Roman numeral equivalent.
- Repeat these steps for the numerical value in each digit position.
- Combine the separate Roman numerals in each digit position.
- Write the combination of numerals in a continuous sequence. The answer is the equivalent Roman numeral value.

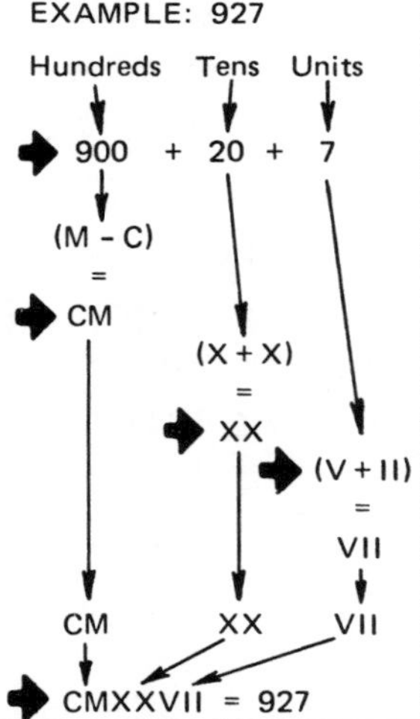

The rule is reversed to determine the equivalent numerical value in the Arabic system. The Roman numeral is broken down into its respective digits. The Arabic numeral equivalent of each digit value is determined. The separate numerals in each digit position are combined. The resulting Arabic numeral is equivalent to the Roman numeral.

ASSIGNMENT UNIT 1

A. THE CONCEPT OF WHOLE NUMBERS

1. Write each number in Arabic figures.

a. Fifty-nine
b. One hundred twenty
c. One thousand eight
d. Twelve thousand nine hundred eighty-seven

2. Write each number in words.

a. 12 b. 27 c. 140 d. 926 e. 1,700 f. 7,937

3. Write each expression in simplified form.

a. 50 + 7
b. 80 + 10 + 9
c. 100 + 3 + 2
d. 400 + 50 + 7
e. 1,000 + 600 + 50
f. 8,000 + 50 + 7

4. Write each number in expanded form.

a. 61 b. 103 c. 422 d. 1,006 e. 4,027 f. 6,931

5. State the equivalent Roman numeral for each Arabic numeral for values A through F.

A	B	C	D	E	F
6	24	49	94	444	1,976

Ans.: B. XXIV D. XCIV F. MCMLXXVI

6. Determine the equivalent Arabic numeral value for Roman numerals A through F.

A	B	C	D	E	F
XIX	XLIX	XCI	CXLIX	CDXCIX	MDCCCXC

Ans.: B. 49 D. 149 F. 1890

B. ADDING WHOLE NUMBERS

1. Add each column of numbers vertically. Check all answers.

A	B	C	D	E	F
17 20	35 35	67 24	96 48	900 65	808 15
G	**H**	**I**	**J**	**K**	**L**
925 96	474 888	72 94 53	83 94 40 12	110 87 215 468	9,765 4,372 8,988 1,009

Ans.: B. 70 D. 144 F. 823 H. 1362 J. 229 L. 24,134

2. Find the sum of (a) to (f) by adding horizontally. Check each answer.

a. 12 + 37
b. 56 + 25
c. 77 + 69
d. 962 + 829 + 13
e. 548 + 941 + 960
f. 827 + 633 + 569

Ans.: b. 81 d. 1804 f. 2029

C. ADDING WHOLE NUMBERS IN PRACTICAL PROBLEMS

1. The taillights of an automobile draw 2 amperes of current; the headlights, 11 amperes; the car heater, 9 amperes; and the ignition coil, 5 amperes. What is the total number of amperes drawn from the battery? **Ans.**: 27 amperes
2. The following amounts of fabrics are required for decorating certain rooms: 23 yards, 19 yards, 15 yards, and 8 yards. Determine the total yardage of fabric that is needed.
3. Six buildings are to be wired by electricians. The number of outlets that must be installed are 65, 75, 69, 81, 57, and 76, respectively. Find the total number of outlets that must be roughed-in. **Ans.**: 423 outlets
4. A carpenter laid 675 shingles in a half day; 1,425 the second day; and 1,540 the third day. How many shingles were laid in the 2 1/2 days? Label the answer and check.
5. A plumber made the pipe connections as illustrated. What was the total length of pipe used? (The end-to-end measurement of each pipe is given in inches.) **Ans.**: 67″

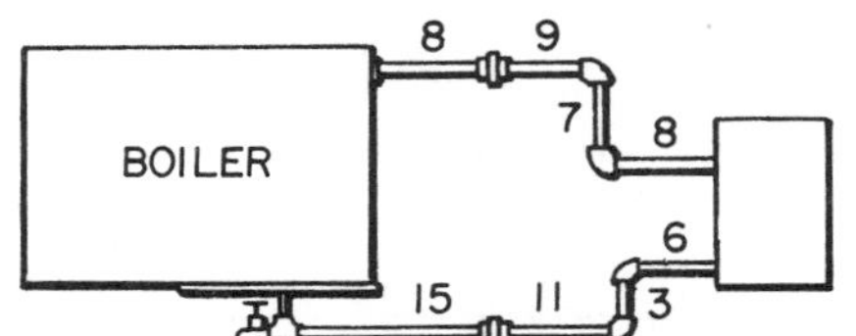

6. Three shipments of 1-inch native pine are received by a contractor: 7,556; 8,750; and 9,898 board feet, respectively. What is the total number of board feet of lumber delivered?
7. The monthly production of motors for refrigerators was as follows: Jan. 29,220; Feb. 32,416; Mar. 37,240; April 39,374; May 45,666; June 52,487; July 36,458; Aug. 35,000; Sept. 32,250; Oct. 51,750; Nov. 62,475; Dec. 50,525. Determine the total output for the year. **Ans.**: 504,861 motors
8. The kilowatt (kw) hours of electrical energy consumed monthly for six months were 1,412; 1,839; 27,000; 29,787; 32,496; and 1,934. Determine the total kilowatts of energy that were used.
9. A construction project required the quantities of fuel for four groups of equipment (A, B, C, and D) as shown in the table. (a) Find the number of gallons of diesel fuel used by each group. (b) Determine the total amount of fuel used by the four groups. **Ans.**: b. 54,599 gals.

Equipment (A)	Equipment (B)	Equipment (C)	Equipment (D)
1,210	4,605	3,202	1,369
989	5,925	3,998	2,787
1,868	9,879	4,687	4,695
		3,896	5,489

10. Examine the main floor plan of the house. Determine the total number of square feet in the master bedroom, living and kitchen/dining rooms, and deck.

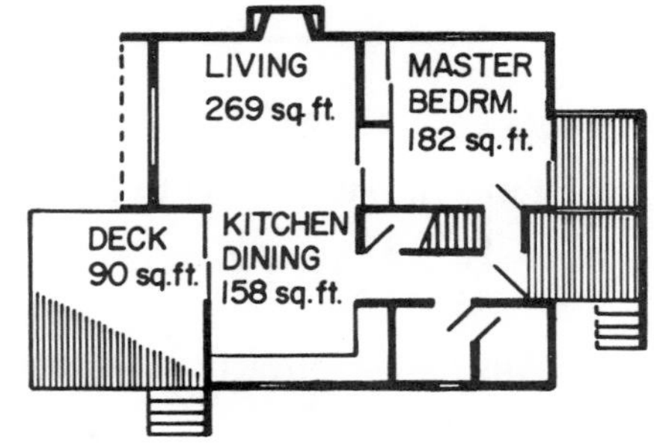

Unit 2 SUBTRACTION OF WHOLE NUMBERS

Subtraction is the process of determining the difference between two numbers or quantities. The number from which another number is to be taken (subtracted) is known as the *minuend.* The number to be subtracted is the *subtrahend.* The result of the process is called the *difference* or *remainder.*

RULE FOR SUBTRACTING WHOLE NUMBERS

- Write the larger of the two numbers as the *minuend.*
- Write the number to be subtracted *(subtrahend)* underneath the minuend, so the digits are in their respective columns: units with units, tens with tens.
- Start with the *units* column and subtract the number in the subtrahend from the minuend.
- Continue the same process with the *tens, hundreds,* and the other columns in the problem.

EXAMPLE: Subtract 346 from 988.

Step 1 Write the larger number as the minuend.

Step 2 Place the digits in the subtrahend in proper columns.

Step 3 Start with the *units* column and take 6 away from 8. Record the difference (2) in the units column.

Step 4 Continue in the same manner with the *tens* and *hundreds* column.

Step 5 The answer (642) is the difference between the two numbers.

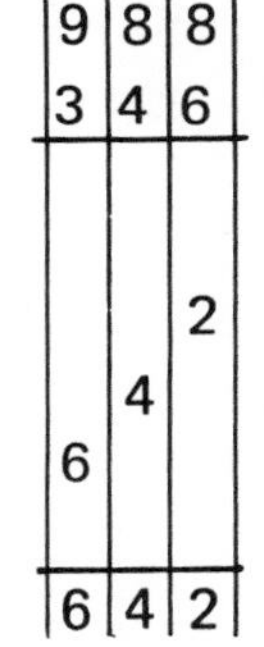

Many times the digits in one or more columns of the subtrahend are larger than the corresponding digits in the minuend. In such cases, numbers are *exchanged* from the minuend. The principle of *exchanging* is based on redistributing numbers. For instance, if 254 is to be subtracted from 723, the digits in both the units and tens places of the subtrahend are larger than those in the minuend.

RULE FOR "EXCHANGING" NUMBERS IN SUBTRACTION

- Consider the 723 as being equal to 700 + 20 + 3.
- Exchange one ten from the tens column for 10 units, adding these to the units column. The 723 is now equal to 700 + 10 + 13.
- Subtract the 4 in the subtrahend from 13.
- Exchange 100 from the *hundreds* column and add it to the 10 in the *tens* column. Thus, the 723 is now equal to 600 + 110 + 13.

  NOTE: The 5 in the *tens* column of the subtrahend means 5 times 10 or 50.
- Subtract the 50 in the minuend from the 110 in the subtrahend.
- Subtract the 2 in the *hundreds* column from the 6 in the same column of the minuend; 600 - 200 = 400.
- Simplify the result. 400 + 60 + 9 = 469.

To summarize, when 254 is subtracted from 723, consider the

minuend	= 600 + 110 + 13,	and the
subtrahend	= 200 + 50 + 4.	The
difference	= 400 + 60 + 9	or 469.

With continued practice, the steps in exchanging become automatic. At this point there is no need to write the steps in detail.

RULE FOR CHECKING THE SUBTRACTION OF WHOLE NUMBERS

- **Arrange the digits in the subtrahend and the answer in columns.**
- Add the subtrahend and the difference. When the difference is correct, the sum of the difference and the subtrahend is equal to the minuend.
- Recheck if the answers are not equal. Check first the addition, which is the easiest step. If the answers still do not agree, rework the original problem.

ASSIGNMENT UNIT 2

A. SUBTRACTING WHOLE NUMBERS AND CHECKING

1. Subtract each pair of numbers. Check each answer.

A	B	C	D	E	F
78 34	87 26	45 29	98 59	286 142	364 158
G	**H**	**I**	**J**	**K**	**L**
753 225	946 168	473 289	707 198	1,642 456	2,537 1,659

Ans.: B. 61 D. 39 F. 206 H. 778 J. 509 L. 878

2. Perform each operation as indicated. Check each answer.

A	246 - 134	E	3,015 - 2,127
B	727 - 415	F	6,007 - 5,188
C	965 - 847	G	4,112 + 705 + 1,293 - 2,097
D	1,752 - 1,263	H	15,625 + 16,596 + 8,989 - 7,349

Ans.: B. 312 D. 489 F. 819 H. 33,861

3. Determine the difference between each set of numbers and check each answer.

a. 19,264 and 11,156
b. 8,537 and 6,759
c. 10,065 feet and 9,047 feet
d. 20,003 miles and 13,365 miles

Ans.: b. 1,778 d. 6,638 miles

4. Subtract and check each answer.

a. 51,219 from 63,422
b. 9,655 from 13,004
c. 7,603 acres from 9,502 acres
d. 17,092 square miles from 25,001 square miles

Ans.: b. 3,349 d. 7,909 square miles

B. SUBTRACTING WHOLE NUMBERS IN PRACTICAL PROBLEMS

1. A contractor has 5,500 board feet of oak flooring. If 2,625 board feet are used on one house, how much flooring is left?
2. A customer's service bill for electricity shows that a total of 1,235 kilowatt hours was used. Of this total, 367 kilowatt hours were used for lighting service and the balance for domestic hot water. How many kilowatt hours were used for hot water? **Ans.**: 868 kwh
3. Determine the number of miles traveled for each of five weeks from the speedometer readings shown in the table.

Week	1	2	3	4	5
Reading (Start)	32,119	32,899	33,988	35,976	37,065
Reading (End)	32,899	33,988	35,976	37,065	39,001

4. A container (drum) holds 55 gallons of turpentine. In a one-month period, these quantities were used: 5 gallons, 10 gallons, 8 gallons, 7 gallons, 16 gallons, and 8 gallons. How much turpentine is left? **Ans.**: 1 gallon
5. The cubic yards of gas energy used for five projects for two processes (A and B) are given in the table.

Projects	1	2	3	4	5
Process (A)	99	365	1,277	3,018	41,605
Process (B)	87	246	1,098	1,129	32,719

   a. Find the increased number of cubic yards of energy required for process A over process B for projects 1 through 5.
   b. Determine the total cubic yards of energy required for process A. **Ans.**: b. 43,364 cubic yards
   c. Determine the total cubic yards for process B.
   d. Find the difference between the amounts of gas energy required for process A and process B for the total projects 1 through 5. **Ans.**: d. 11,085 cubic yards
   e. Show how the answer may be checked by a second method.

6. A time and motion study of three workers shows the production reported in the table for processes (A) through (E).

Workers	PRODUCTION FOR PROCESS				
	(A)	(B)	(C)	(D)	(E)
1	22	131	2,027	1,169	2,235
2	36	257	3,249	2,479	1,357
3	15	215	2,116	3,368	1,799

   a. Identify the fastest production worker for each process (A) through (E).
   b. Make a table and indicate the difference in production between the fastest worker and (1) the second fastest worker and (2) the slowest worker.

7. Complete the weekly garment sales chart. Compute the missing quantities for garment types A through D.

Type	Garments Received	Daily Sales – Week Ending June 20						Quantity on Hand June 22
		M	T	W	Th	F	S	
A	178	21	17	9	14	25	31	
B	2,347	345	196	187	294	468	613	
C		93	79	67	105	198	94	217
D		216	237	259	316	419	177	597

Ans.: B. 244 D. 2,221

8. a. Determine the difference in calories of food quantities A and B for each item (1, 2, 3 and 4).

b. Find the total food values for A and B. **Ans.:** B. 17,421

c. Indicate the total difference in calories between quantities A and B.

Item	Quantity Food Values in Calories		Difference in Calories
	A	B	
1	46	228	
2	2,280	1,682	
3	7,357	5,469	
4	9,874	10,042	
Total			

Unit 3 MULTIPLICATION OF WHOLE NUMBERS

Multiplication is a simplified method of adding a quantity a given number of times. For example, instead of writing a number like 27 nine times and adding a long column of numbers, the 27 may be multiplied by 9. The multiplication process saves time and simplifies the problem. The answer or result obtained by multiplication is usually called the *product.*

A. ARRANGING NUMBERS FOR MULTIPLICATION

When one number is multiplied by another number, the product is the same, regardless of how the numbers are arranged. For instance, the product of 22 x 11 is the same as 11 x 22. In either case, the number to be multiplied is called the *multiplicand* and the other number, the *multiplier.* The multiplication process is simplified when the smaller number is the multiplier and the larger, the multiplicand. Each digit in the multiplier and multiplicand (and those obtained by multiplying) should be placed in its proper column. This simple practice saves time and makes greater accuracy possible.

B. EXPLANATION OF THE MULTIPLICATION PROCESS

In the multiplication process every number in the multiplicand is multiplied by every number of the multiplier. When a number like 47 is to be multiplied by 26, the numbers in the units column of both multiplicand and multiplier are multiplied first.

Since the product of 7 times 6 is greater than 9, the second digit is mentally *carried over* to the *tens* column. In this instance, the 42 means 2 *units* and 4 *tens.* The 2 is written in the units column and the 4 is carried over and added to the result in the tens column.

Continue to multiply the number in the tens column of the multiplicand (4) by the same multiplier (6). To this product of (6 x 4) add the 4 that is carried over.

Write the 8 in the tens column. Since no other numbers in the multiplicand are to be multiplied by 6, the 2 is written in the hundreds column.

The same multiplication processes are carried out until every number in the multiplicand is multiplied by every number in the multiplier. When the number in the multiplier is in the tens place, the first digit in the product is written in this column. Thus, the next step is to multiply each number in the multiplicand by the number in the tens column of the multiplier.

Actually, the 7 in the multiplicand is multiplied by 20. If this were done, 0 would be written in the units column, 4 in the tens column, and 1 in the hundreds column.

Next, the 4 in the multiplicand represents 4 tens or 40. If the 40 is multiplied by the same 20 in the multiplier, the product is 800. The last step is to add 282 + 140 + 800 = 1222.

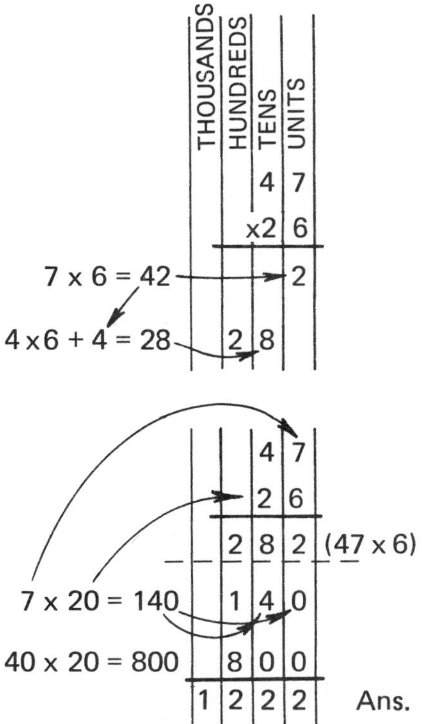

SHORTENING THE MULTIPLICATION PROCESS

The multiplication process is shortened and simplified by multiplying by the actual number in the tens column of the multiplier rather than by ten times that number. Then, enter the first right digit of the product in the tens column and carry over the remainder to the hundreds column. When multiplying by a number in the hundreds column, put the first right digit in the hundreds column, and so on.

C. MULTIPLYING WHOLE NUMBERS

Regardless of the number of digits in either the multiplicand or multiplier, the multiplication process is the same.

RULE FOR MULTIPLYING WHOLE NUMBERS

- Write the larger of the two numbers as the multiplicand; the smaller, the multiplier.
  NOTE: Place the numerals in both multiplicand and multiplier under each other in columns: tens in tens column, hundreds in hundreds column.
- Multiply the numbers in the units column of both multiplicand and multiplier. Write the units result in the units column and *carry over* the tens.
- Multiply the number in the tens column of the multiplicand by the number in the units column of the multiplier. Add the *tens remainder* to this product.
- Write the first digit on the right in the result in the tens column.
- Carry over any numerals representing hundreds and add to the next result.
  NOTE: If no other numbers are to be multiplied, write each digit in the result in the proper column.
- Continue to multiply every number in the multiplicand by every number in the multiplier.
- Add the results in each column.

EXAMPLE: Multiply 156 by 78.

Step 1 Write numbers in columns.

Step 2 Multiply every number in the multiplicand by 8.

Step 3 Multiply every number in the multiplicand by the number in the tens place of the multiplier (7).

Step 4 Add the numbers in each column. The result 12,168 is the product of 156 x 78.

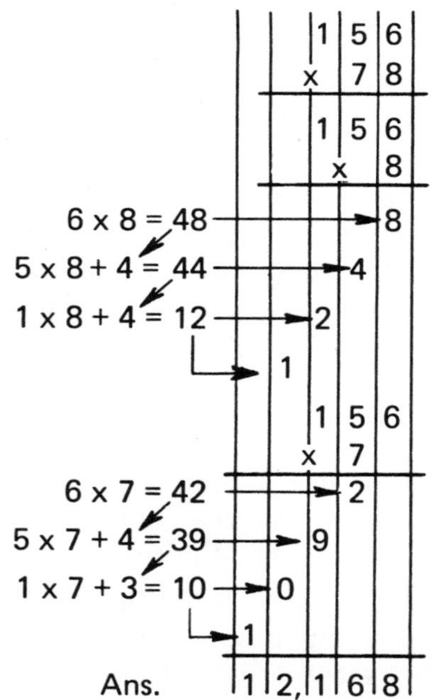

D. CHECKING THE MULTIPLICATION PROCESS

Two methods of checking multiplication problems are commonly used.

METHOD I (Checking Each Step)

- Multiply the numbers in the units column of both multiplicand and multiplier.
- Continue until all numbers in the multiplicand are multiplied by all the numbers in the multiplier.
- Check the product against the original product. If the products are not the same, recheck the steps.

METHOD II (Reworking)

- Write the multiplicand as the multiplier; the multiplier, as the multiplicand.
- Multiply each number. Check the final product against the original product.

Regardless of the method which is used, the checking process takes almost as much time and effort as the original problem. One of the principal places for error is in remembering the numeral to be carried over from one column to another. This difficulty may be overcome by writing the number to be carried lightly and very small over the number to be multiplied next. For instance, if 97 is to be multiplied by 7, the problem may be worked out as shown at the right.

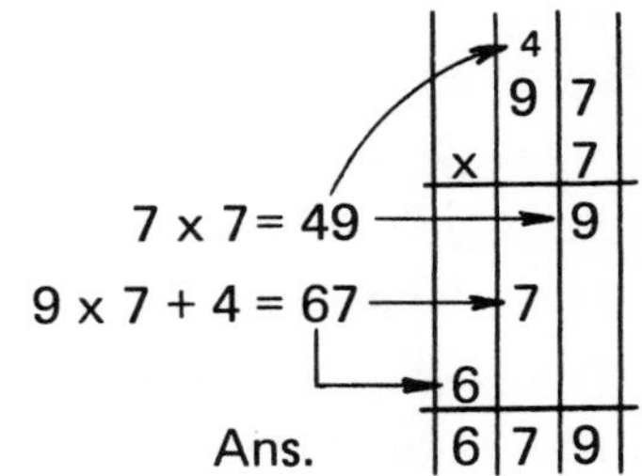

The multiplication process is simplified further by learning all the combinations of numbers in a multiplication table from 1 to 10. The product of any two of these numbers may then be given quickly without computation.

ASSIGNMENT UNIT 3

A. MULTIPLYING WHOLE NUMBERS

1. Multiply each set of numbers mentally.

A	B	C	D	E
14 6	22 7	78 9	240 8	121 7

Ans.: B. 154
D. 1,920

2. Multiply each set of numbers and check each product.

A	B	C	D	E
212 x 6	343 x 5	508 x 9	689 x 6	987 x 7
F	G	H	I	J
411 14	627 26	303 97	879 78	687 90
K	L	M	N	O
8,165 72	6,057 324	5,009 620	7,987 869	97,009 308

Ans.: B. 1,715 D. 4,134 F. 5,754 H. 29,391
J. 61,830 L. 1,962,468 N. 6,940,703

B. MULTIPLYING WHOLE NUMBERS IN PRACTICAL PROBLEMS

1. A gang of 17 men worked on a construction job 153 days of 8 hours each without a lost-time accident. How many accident-free man-hours did the gang work? **Ans.:** 20,808 man-hours
2. A bricklayer lays an average of 145 bricks an hour. At this rate, how many bricks can he lay in 37 hours?
3. A mason purchased 223 cubic yards of ready mixed concrete at $26.00 a cubic yard, 51 barrels of lime at $14.00 a barrel, and 38 cubic yards of sand at $6.00 per cubic yard. What was the total cost of materials? **Ans.:** $6,740
4. The cost of a certain size brass elbow is $1.17 per pound. Determine the cost of 147 pounds of elbows.
5. It takes 760 shingles per square (100 square feet) when laid 5 inches to weather. How many shingles will be needed to cover 37 squares with the same weathering? **Ans.:** 28,120 shingles
6. A bundle of white cedar shingles contains 250 shingles. How many shingles are there in 378 bundles?
7. Two magnets are wound. The first has 57 layers of 98 turns each; the second, 38 layers of 179 turns each. Give the total number of turns in both coils. **Ans.:** 12,388 turns
8. An electrical contractor purchased 196 conduit bodies at 49 cents each and 87 of another type for 76 cents each. Give the total cost of these materials.
9. A car has three 34 candlepower bulbs, two 26 candlepower, four 9 candlepower, and three 15 candlepower. Find the total candlepower. **Ans.:** 235 candlepower
10. A truck averages 42 miles an hour for 6 hours daily for 19 days. Another truck averages 37 miles an hour for 6 hours daily for 23 days. A third truck averages 39 miles an hour for 6 hours daily for 22 days. Determine the total mileage of the three trucks.
11. A power plant consumes an average of 17 gallons of fuel per hour. Determine the consumption (a) for a 24-hour day, (b) each week, and (c) for a 31-day month. **Ans.:** (b) 2,856 gallons

12. The hourly production for four different parts, A, B, C, and D, produced on three machines, 1, 2, and 3, is recorded in the chart.

Machine	Part A	Part B	Part C	Part D
1	4	10	100	234
2	6	11	120	247
3	9	17	132	379
Unit Cost	3	5	12	27

a. How many of each part are produced on each machine in an 8-hour shift?
b. What is the weekly production of each part on each machine for two shifts, each working a 36-hour week?
c. Determine the weekly cost for each part for the two shifts using the unit costs per part.

13. Compute the amount of material that is needed in the total order for

a. Hem and seam allowance
b. Cover length
c. Completed covers

COVER SPECIFICATIONS

MATERIAL: PERCALE MUSLIN
FINISHED LENGTH: 43"
HEM SEAM ALLOWANCE: 4"
QUANTITY: 725 COVERS

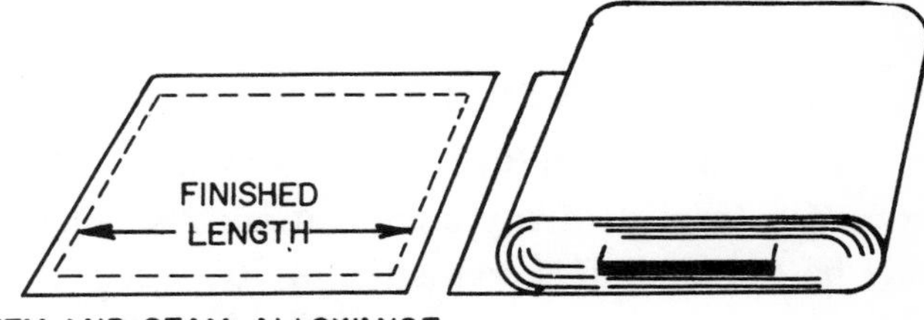

Ans.: c. 34,075″

Unit 4 DIVISION OF WHOLE NUMBERS

Division is a simplified method of subtracting a quantity a given number of times. For example, if 23 is subtracted from 92, the subtraction process is repeated four times until there is no remainder.

1. Subtract 23 from 92	92 − 23 = 69
2. Subtract 23 from 69	69 − 23 = 46
3. Subtract 23 from 46	46 − 23 = 23
4. Subtract 23 from 23	23 − 23 = 0

This method of repeated subtraction is long and becomes more involved as the numbers get larger. In its place, a shorter method known as division is used to save time and effort.

In any division problem, the number to be divided is called the *dividend*. The number by which the dividend is divided is the *divisor*. The number that indicates how many times the divisor may be subtracted from the dividend is the *quotient*. When the divisor cannot be subtracted from the dividend an even number of times, the number left over is referred to as the *remainder*. The two signs or symbols that are commonly used to denote the process of division are (÷) and ($\overline{)\quad}$).

$$\begin{array}{r} 4 \\ 23\overline{)92} \\ \underline{92} \end{array}$$

Divisor ▶ 23; 4 ◀ Quotient; 92 ◀ Dividend

A. THE DIVISION PROCESS

Division, like multiplication, is based on the fact that the dividend may be written in expanded form with any combination of smaller numbers. For instance, a number like 525 may be thought of as consisting of 500 + 25, or 350 + 175, or any other combination. The combination depends largely on the divisor. The first step is to break the dividend into a combination of numbers into which the divisor will divide evenly.

Returning to the 525, if this number is to be divided by 35, the division process is simplified when the 525 is considered as 350 + 175.

$$35\overline{)525} \quad = \quad 35\overline{)350} \quad + \quad 35\overline{)175} \quad = \quad (10 + 5) \quad = \quad 15 \text{ Ans.}$$

In this case, 525 is divided an even number of times by 35. If the number were to be divided by 25, instead of 35, the 525 may be considered in expanded form to be equal to 500 + 25.

$$25\overline{)525} \quad = \quad 25\overline{)500} \quad + \quad 25\overline{)25} \quad = \quad (20 + 1) \quad = \quad 21 \text{ Ans.}$$

Thus, in these two examples the dividend in expanded form is made up of different combinations of numbers depending on the divisor.

B. DIVIDING WHOLE NUMBERS

While this is the principle on which division is based, the actual process is simplified by following a few basic steps.

RULE FOR DIVIDING WHOLE NUMBERS

- Write the number to be divided as the dividend within the division frame; the divisor, outside.
- Determine how many times the numerals in the first few digits of the dividend may be divided by the divisor.
- Multiply the divisor by the *trial quotient.* The numeral in the units digit of the divisor is multiplied first, then tens, etc. The product is placed under the dividend.

  NOTE: If the *trial quotient* is larger than it should be, the product will be greater than the dividend. When this happens, change the quotient to the next lower number.
- Subtract the product from the dividend.
- Bring down the numeral in the next place in the dividend. If the remainder cannot be divided by the divisor, bring down the next numeral in the dividend.
- Repeat the division process until all the numerals in the dividend are used.

  NOTE: When the divisor does not divide evenly into the dividend, the number resulting from the last subtraction is the *remainder.*
- Express the quotient in terms of the quantities that are being divided.

Divisor)Dividend

Trial Quotient

Place Product Here

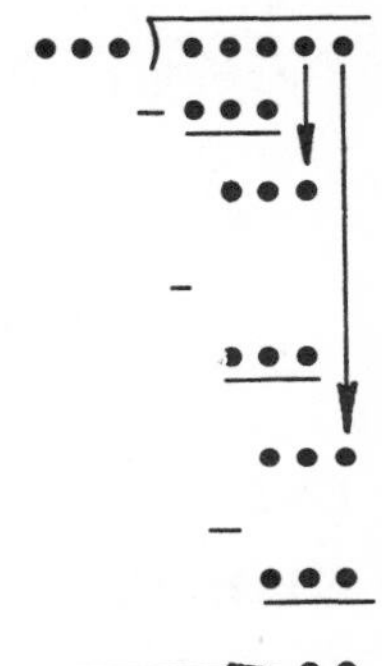

EXAMPLE: Case 1 (Without a remainder) Divide 1984 by 64.

Step 1 Write as a division problem.

Step 2 Determine what the trial quotient is. Try (4 x 64 = 256). This is greater than 198 in the dividend.

Step 3 Drop the trial quotient back to 3. Then, multiply the divisor by 3. (3 x 64 = 192).

Step 4 Place the first number (3) in the quotient over the proper number in the dividend. Write the product under the first three numerals in the dividend.

Step 5 Subtract the product from the dividend.

Step 6 Bring down the next numeral from the dividend.

Step 7 Determine the next trial quotient. In other words, how many times will the divisor (64) go into the remainder (64)?

Step 8 Insert the next numeral (1) in the quotient (1 x 64 = 64). Since there is no remainder, 64 may be divided equally into 1984 thirty-one times. The answer is 31.

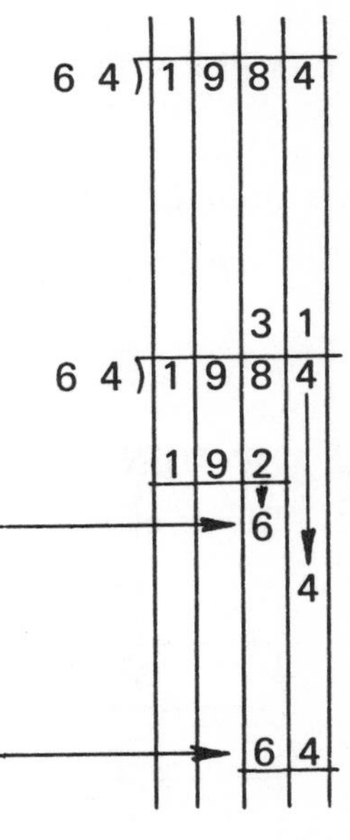

The division process is simplified if the expanded form of a number is constantly considered. In this instance, the first 3 in the quotient is actually 30. Multiplying the divisor 64 by 30 = 1920. Subtracting this from the original 1984 leaves 64. The second numeral in the units column is 1, so the quotient is equal to 30 + 1 or 31.

EXAMPLE: Case 2 (With a remainder) Divide 3900 by 47.

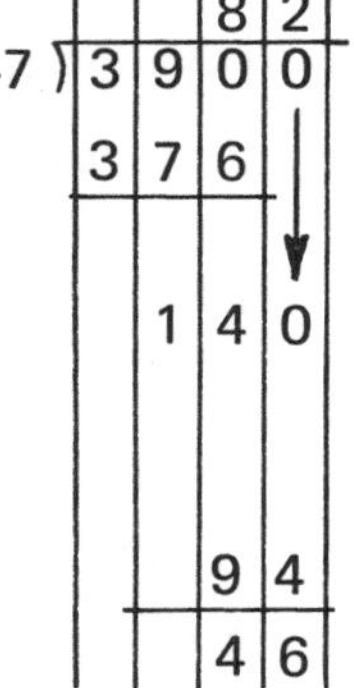

Step 1 Determine the trial quotient. Try 9. (9 x 47 = 423)

Step 2 Drop back to 8 as 9 is too large. (8 x 47 = 376)

Step 3 Subtract. Then, bring down the next numeral in the dividend.

Step 4 Determine the next numeral in the trial quotient. Try 2. (2 x 47 = 94)

Step 5 Subtract 94 from 140. The difference of 46 is the remainder.

Since there are no additional numbers in the dividend to be divided, the quotient is 82 and the remainder, 46.

C. CHECKING THE DIVISION OF WHOLE NUMBERS

RULE FOR CHECKING DIVISION

- Multiply the quotient by the divisor.
- Add the remainder to the product. The sum is equal to the dividend when the division is correct.

NOTE: If the two quantities are not equal, first recheck the steps in the checking process. Next, if necessary, rework the original steps in division.

EXAMPLE: Check the correctness of 47)3900. The given answer is 82 plus a remainder of 46.

Step 1 Multiply the quotient by the divisor. 82 x 47 = 3,854

Step 2 Add the remainder (46). + 46

Step 3 Check the sum (3,900) with original dividend (3,900). Since both agree, the answer is correct. 3,900

ASSIGNMENT UNIT 4

A. DIVIDING WHOLE NUMBERS AND CHECKING

1. Divide each pair of numbers. Check each quotient.

A	B	C	D	E
6)126	4)120	7)147	3)135	7)182

F	G	H	I	J
11)110	12)132	27)810	53)742	92)2024

Ans.: B. 30 D. 45 F. 10 H. 30 J. 22

2. Perform the operation indicated. Where there is a remainder, mark it (Rem.). Check each answer.

   a. Divide 1,250 by 25   d. 14,091 ÷ 33
   b. Divide 1,638 by 39   e. 9,002 ÷ 45
   c. Divide 1,782 by 162   f. 80,208 ÷ 121

   Ans.: b. 42   d. 427   f. 662 + Rem. 106

B. DIVIDING WHOLE NUMBERS IN PRACTICAL PROBLEMS

1. A mason plastered an area of 425 square yards in 5 days. What was the average number of square yards plastered each day?
2. A contractor agreed to furnish and pour 27 cubic yards of concrete for $931.50. What is the cost per cubic yard? **Ans.**: $34.50
3. A plumber sets 14 water closets and uses 42 pounds of caulking compound. How much caulking compound is used on an average for each closet?
4. A tank holds 4,800 cubic inches of coolant. How many gallons of liquid are needed to fill the tank? (Each gallon contains 231 cubic inches.)
5. How many columns spaced 8′- 0″ on centers are required for a girder 72′- 0″ long? (Both ends of the girder are supported on foundation walls.) **Ans.**: 8 columns
6. Determine the rise A of each step from the drawing of the stringer.
7. Determine the run B of each step in the drawing. **Ans.**: 9″
8. A total load of 23,256 watts is distributed equally over 18 branch circuits. Find the load per circuit in watts.
9. What is the average number of feet of wire per outlet used on a job which takes 1,896 feet of BX for 82 outlets? **Ans.**: 23 ft.

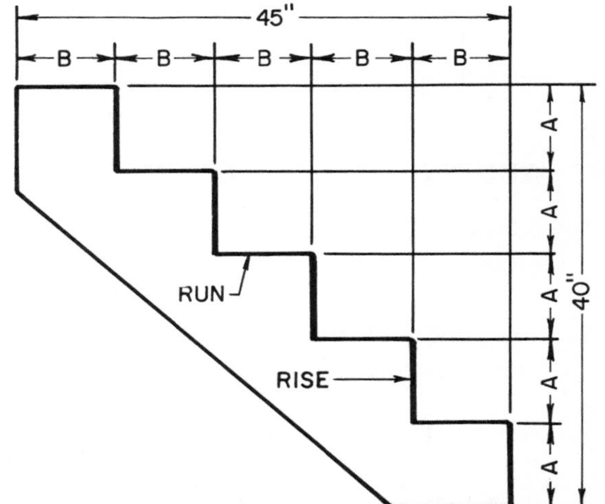

10. How much money per person can a catering service allot if there will be 350 guests at a total cost of $2100?
11. A florist has 912 flowers on hand. How many bouquets can be made if there are 6 flowers in each bouquet? **Ans.**: 152 bouquets
12. A hospital patient is allowed a total of 29,500 calories during a 20-day period. What is the patient's daily allotment?

Unit 5 ACHIEVEMENT REVIEW ON WHOLE NUMBERS

A. THE CONCEPT OF WHOLE NUMBERS

1. Write each number in expanded form.

   a. 305 b. 620 c. 735 d. 1,025 e. 7,572

2. Write each total in simplified form.

   a. 70 + 5
   b. 100 + 10
   c. 700 + 20 + 5
   d. 2,000 + 15
   e. 6,000 + 200 + 60
   f. 10,000 + 700 + 50 + 6

3. Each word or phrase in Column I expresses one of the four basic processes listed in Column II. Match each process with the correct term or phrase. Write the (A, S, M or D) symbol where it applies in Column I.

Column I			
a.	Times	f.	Product of
b.	Minus	g.	Difference between
c.	Plus	h.	Added to
d.	Divided by	i.	Sum of
e.	Increased by	j.	Quotient of

Column II
Addition (A)
Subtraction (S)
Multiplication (M)
Division (D)

B. ADDITION OF WHOLE NUMBERS

NOTE: Check all solutions to problems in addition, subtraction, multiplication and division.

1. Building materials for the repair of a barn include masonry $484, electrical $178, hardware $34, painting $112, and lumber $1,376. Find the total cost of the materials.

2. A school has sixteen electrical circuits with capacities of 2,360; 1,648; 1,235; 660; 978; 2,296; 1,586; 1,975; 462; 855; 343; 592; 2,325; 847; 2,015; and 1,238 watts respectively. Determine the total number of watts consumed when all the circuits are used to capacity.

3. Add each column of numbers two ways. Then add each row across.

201	9,716	7,061	5,012
76	253	2,562	9,109
18	2,009	4,928	6,007
35	5,265	7,465	8,160
257	374	968	5,789

C. SUBTRACTION OF WHOLE NUMBERS

1. Subtract the quantities A through F in the table. State each answer in terms of the units of measure specified in each case.

A	B	C
12,695 square miles - 2,797 square miles	9,085 tons - 6,187 tons	3,012 yards - 1,029 yards
D	**E**	**F**
4,855 board feet - 2,068 board feet	6,537 watts - 4,659 watts	28,007 barrels - 19,018 barrels

2. Determine the distance A from the outside wall to the center of the side door opening from the dimensions given on the floor plan of the two-car garage.
3. Find the width of the wall B.
4. What is dimension C at the rear of the garage?

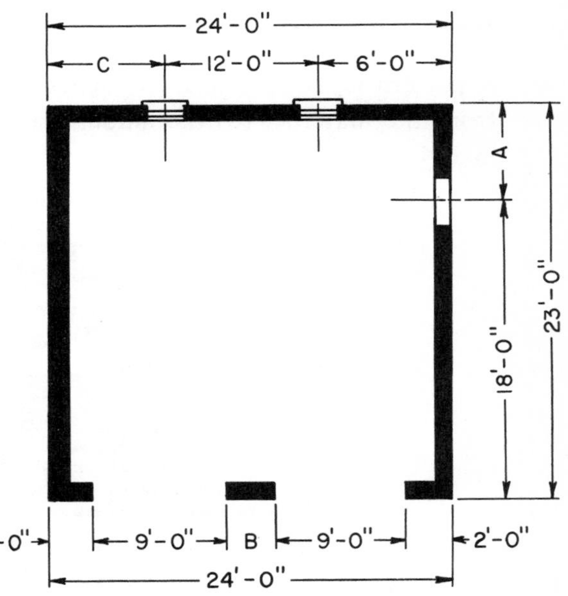

D. MULTIPLICATION OF WHOLE NUMBERS

1. Find the total cost of these materials: 65 barrels of granulated lime at a cost of $14.50 per barrel, 52 cubic yards of ready-mixed concrete at $25.20 per cubic yard, and 25 cubic yards of sand at $6.40 per cubic yard.
2. A coil magnet has 56 layers of magnet wire wound around a core. If there are 165 turns of wire per layer, how many turns of wire are there in the coil?
3. Determine the total number of watts in an electrical lighting circuit with this load: twelve 150-watt lamps, three 100-watt lamps, nine 60-watt lamps, and eleven 15-watt lamps.
4. A book contains 277 pages. The type matter on each page measures 5 inches wide and 7 inches long and there are 6 lines of type per inch. Determine how many 5-inch lines must be typeset.

E. DIVISION OF WHOLE NUMBERS

1. A total load of 22,931 watts is distributed equally over 23 branch circuits. Give the load per circuit in watts.
2. A 192-page book is to be printed. There are 1,500 copies required using a paper stock that weighs 178 pounds per thousand sheets and costs 57 cents per pound. From each sheet 32 pages can be printed. Determine the cost of paper stock.

3. In six consecutive months the following quantities of stamped metal parts were heat treated: 462,925; 378,916; 417,829; 382,885; 415,297; and 438,842 pounds. Determine the six-month hourly average per man if the department employs 16 men on a 9-hour shift, 12 on an 8-hour shift, and 4 on a 7-hour shift. In the six-month period, each man worked 130 days.

4. Find the average hourly production of parts A through E from the monthly (156 hours) production schedule.

Average Monthly (156 Hours) Production				
1,248	2,964	21,372	202,332	5,584,332
Parts Manufactured				
A	B	C	D	E

5. A pattern layout requires 51 inches of cloth. Find (a) how many garments can be cut from the material, (b) the amount of material left over, and (c) the number of yards in 324 inches. (1 yd. = 36 in.)

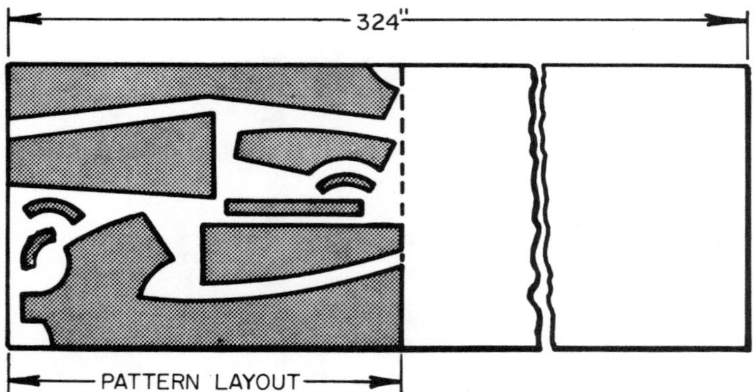

F. COMBINATIONS OF ADDITION AND SUBTRACTION OF WHOLE NUMBERS

1. Establish whether there was a profit or loss on sales A through G. Find the amount of profit (P); loss, (L).

Item	Sales	Cost of Item	Overhead Expense	Profit (P) or Loss (L)
A	$98,000	$75,000	$22,500	
B	15,750	11,429	3,000	
C	9,342	6,210	3,350	
D	56,735	38,750	17,000	
E	126,960	97,873	18,250	
F	7,942	4,975	2,635	
G	11,697	7,539	2,973	

Section 2

COMMON FRACTIONS

Unit 6 THE CONCEPT OF COMMON FRACTIONS

Craftspersons are required constantly to take measurements, do layout work, and perform hand and machine operations. These require the use of mathematics to compute missing or needed dimensions.

The use of whole numbers alone is not sufficient to obtain this information. All computations involve either whole numbers or fractions, or a combination of both. Numbers, whether they are whole or just parts of a whole, must be added, subtracted, multiplied, and divided.

A. INTERPRETING COMMON FRACTIONS

A *fraction* is a part of a whole quantity. For example, a triangle, square, or circle is divided into two equal parts. One of these parts is involved in an operation as shown by the shaded portion of each illustration. The fractional part of the whole triangle, square, or circle is one-half as shown at (A), (B), and (C).

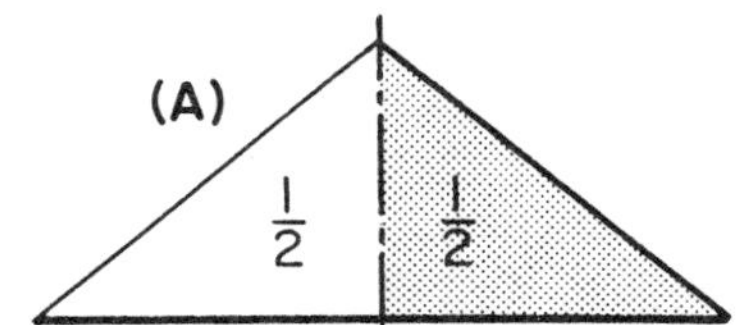

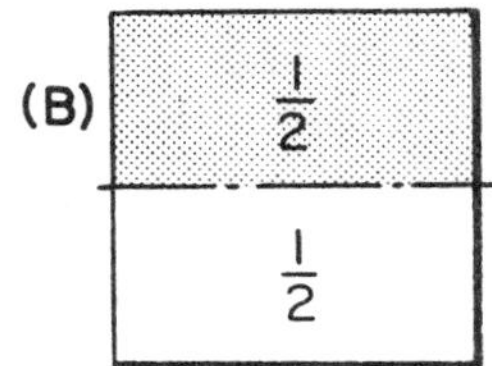

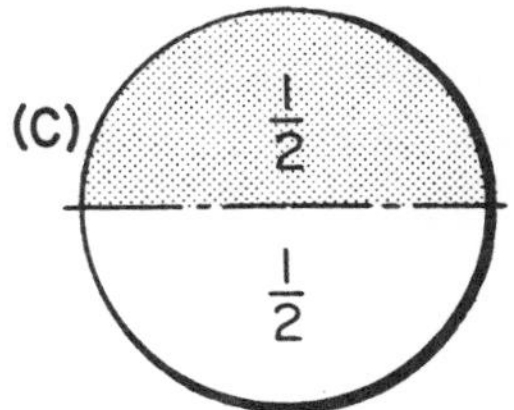

On shop prints and sketches and in mathematical computations the one-half is usually written 1/2 and is called a "common fraction." This fraction shows the number of equal parts of a unit that are taken. If the fraction 3/4 appears on a drawing, it means the unit one is divided into four equal parts and that three of the four parts are taken ⟶

Common fractions are used daily when taking measurements with line-graduated measuring tools and instruments. Rules, levels, tapes, and other measuring tools are commonly graduated in fourths, eighths, sixteenths, and thirty-seconds of an inch. For greater precision, steel rules are graduated in sixty-fourths of an inch. In the printing trades, measurements are expressed as fine as seventy-seconds of an inch.

Where the measurements are given as fractions, they indicate that the inch has been divided into an equal number of parts. The object must measure a stated number of these parts.

The steel rule, a common measuring tool, may be used to show how the inch looks when it is divided into four, eight, sixteen, thirty-two, and sixty-four equal parts.

1. The inch contains four-fourths. Each equal part is expressed as 1/4 of the whole.

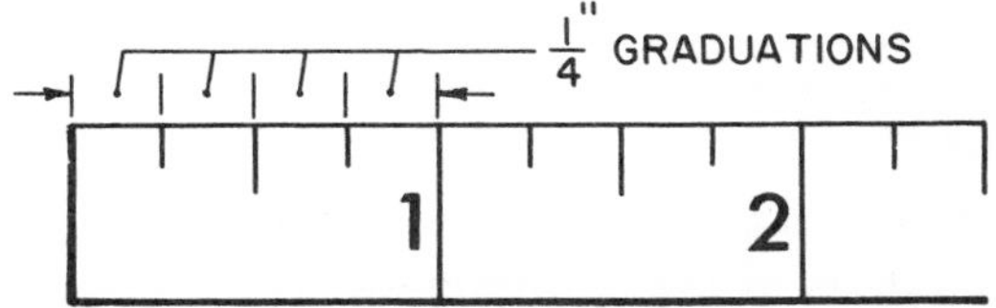

2. The inch contains eight-eighths. Each equal part is expressed as 1/8 of the whole.

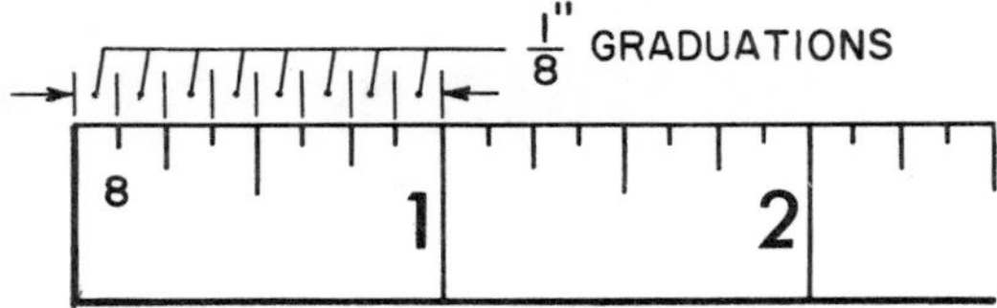

3. The inch contains sixteen-sixteenths. Each equal part is expressed as 1/16 of the whole.

4. The inch contains thirty-two-thirty-seconds. Each equal part is expressed as 1/32 of the whole.

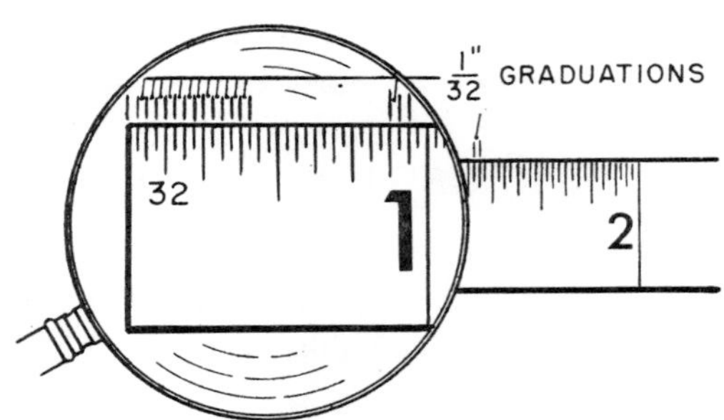

5. The inch contains sixty-four-sixty-fourths. Each equal part is expressed as 1/64 of the whole.

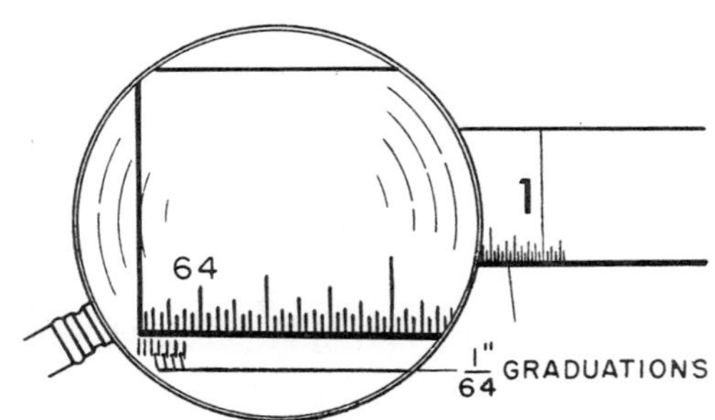

B. DEFINING PARTS OF FRACTIONS

If on the eighth scale of the steel rule, three of the eight equal parts (into which the inch is divided) are needed for a measurement, the fraction would be shown as 3/8. The terms of this fraction are a *numerator* which appears over a horizontal line and a *denominator*, under the line.

Numerator ▶ $\frac{3}{8}$ ◀ Denominator

> **RULE**
>
> - The denominator (which is always written below the line) indicates the equal number of parts into which the unit is divided.

> **RULE**
>
> - The numerator (which is always written above the line) indicates the number of equal parts of the denominator that are taken.

C. REDUCING FRACTIONS

A required measurement which is the result of adding, subtracting, multiplying, or dividing fractions is not always expressed as simply as possible. Measurements can be taken or read with greater facility when the fraction is given in its *lowest terms.*

REDUCING COMMON FRACTIONS

The mathematical expression *"proper fraction"* is used to indicate a fraction whose numerator is smaller than its denominator. Such quantities as 1/4, 3/8, 29/64, and 5/8 are examples of proper fractions.

RULE

- The value of a fraction is not changed when both the numerator and denominator are multiplied or divided by the same number.

This number, which can be used to divide both the numerator and denominator of a fraction without a remainder, is called a *common factor.*

RULE FOR REDUCING A COMMON FRACTION TO ITS LOWEST TERMS

- Divide the numerator and denominator by the same number.

  NOTE: When both the numerator and the denominator cannot be divided further by the same number, the fraction is expressed in its lowest terms.

EXAMPLE: Reduce 8/16 to its lowest terms.

Step 1 Select a number (common factor) that will divide evenly into both the numerator and denominator.

$$\frac{8}{16} = \frac{4}{8} \qquad \frac{4}{8} = \frac{2}{4} = \frac{1}{2}$$

Step 2 Continue this division until the numerator and denominator can no longer be evenly divided by the same number.

NOTE: When it is apparent that both numerator and denominator can be divided by a larger number, like 8 in the case of 8/16, the intermediate steps are omitted.

REDUCING IMPROPER FRACTIONS

A fraction whose numerator is greater than its denominator is called an *improper fraction.* Examples of improper fractions are 3/2, 25/16, and 71/32.

RULE FOR REDUCING AN IMPROPER FRACTION TO ITS LOWEST TERMS

- Divide the numerator (above the line) by the denominator (below the line).
- Reduce the resulting fraction to its lowest terms.

EXAMPLE: Reduce 20/16 to its lowest terms.

Step 1 Divide 20 by 16. $\frac{20}{16} = 1\frac{4}{16}$

Step 2 Reduce 4/16 to lowest terms. $\frac{4}{16} = \frac{1}{4}$

Step 3 Answer $\frac{20}{16} = 1\frac{1}{4}$

ASSIGNMENT UNIT 6

A. INTERPRETATION OF COMMON FRACTIONS

1. The squares and circles are divided equally into 6, 8, 16, 32, or 64 parts as indicated in each case. Visualize (by actual counting of spaces, if necessary) the part of the square or circle represented by fractions (b) to (z).

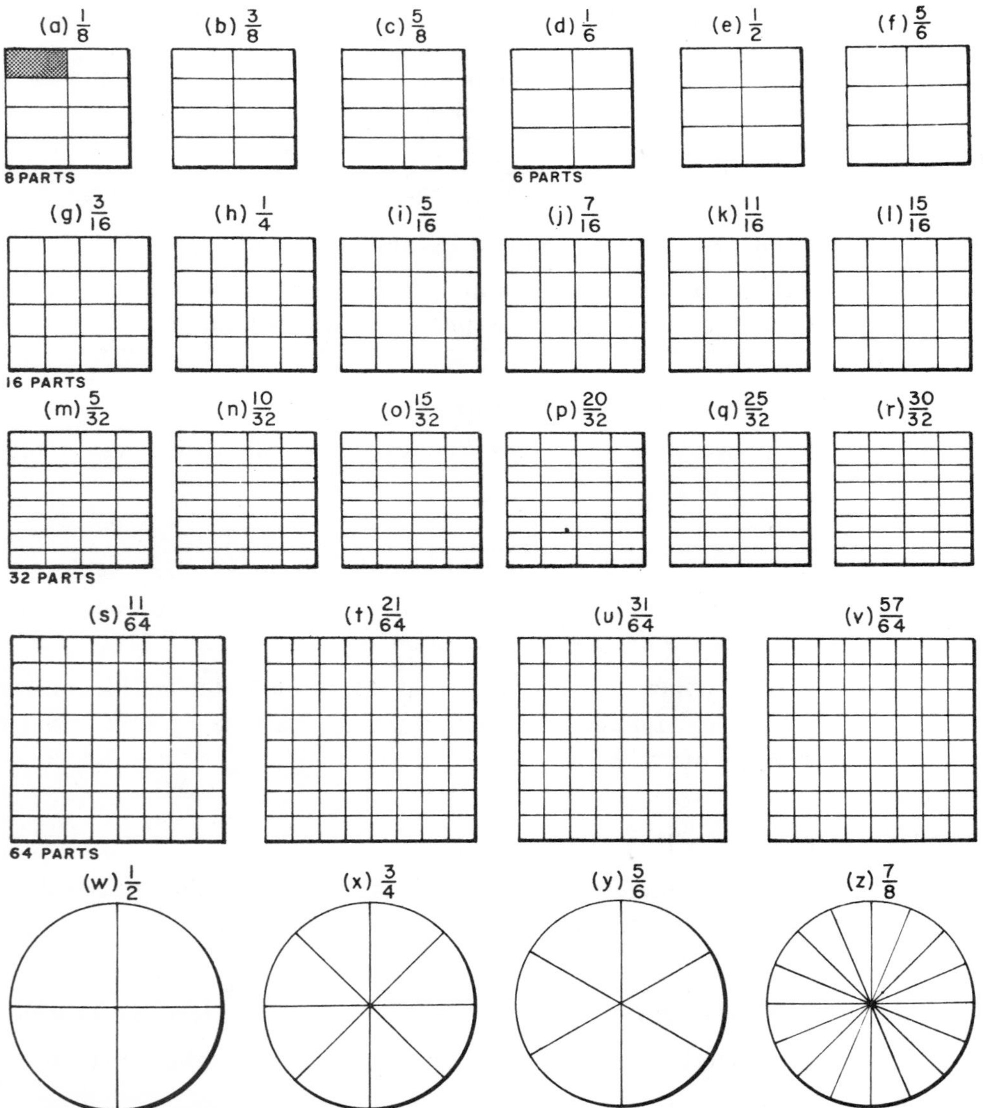

B. PRACTICAL PROBLEMS

1. Rule a table as illustrated. Include the letters in the boxes, the arrows, and all words. Arrange the following twist drills in the table in sizes ranging from the smallest to the largest.

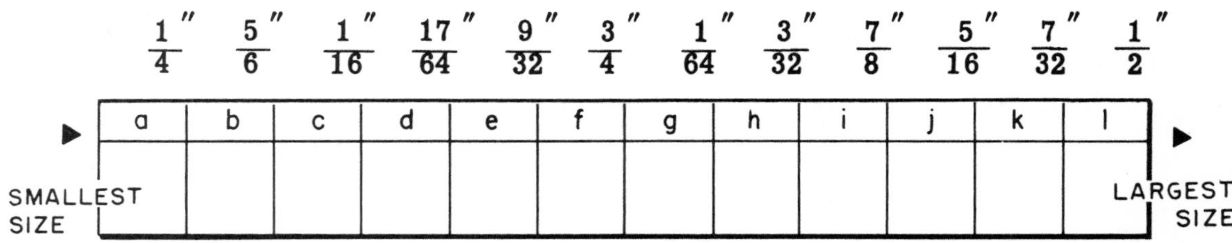

NOTE: If a rule is not available for the problems which follow, place a transparent sheet over the illustrations and trace the rules.

2. Locate the 1/4" and 3/4" graduations on a steel tape or rule.

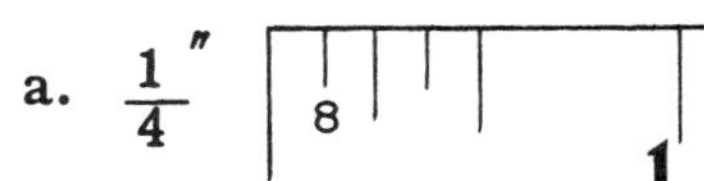

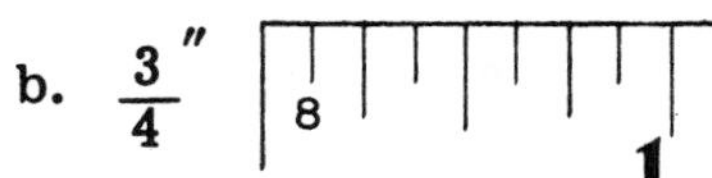

3. Locate common fractions (a) to (d) on the eighth scale of a rule.

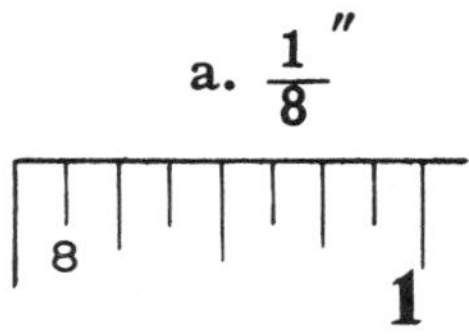

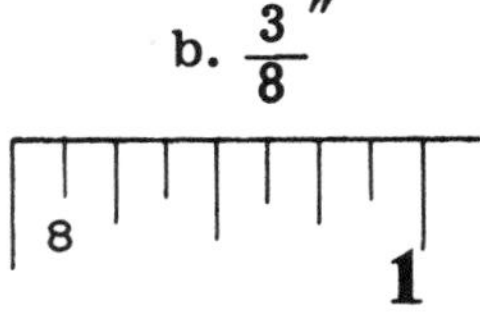

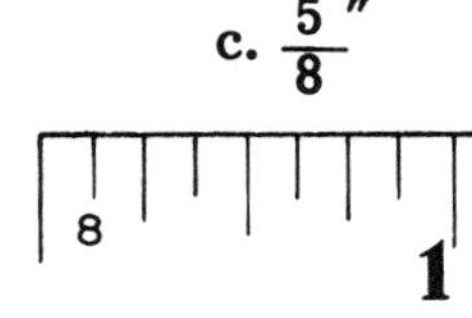

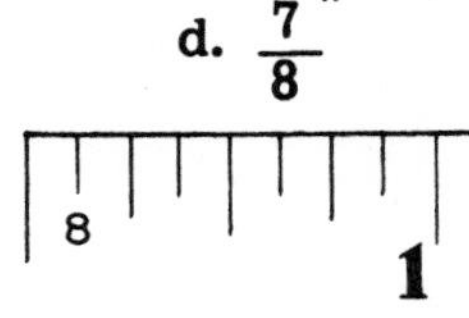

C. REDUCTION OF FRACTIONS

1. Reduce common fractions (a) to (f) to their lowest terms. Then locate each fraction on a rule.

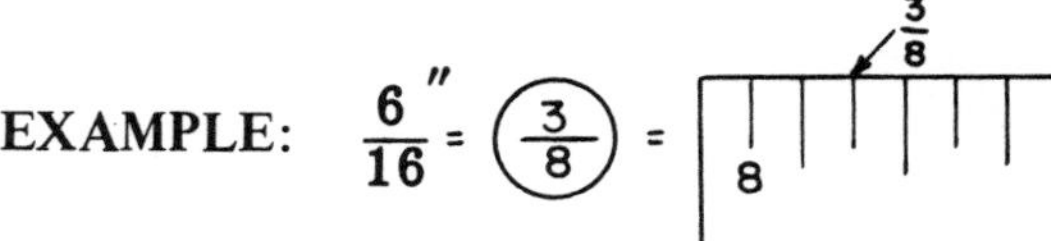

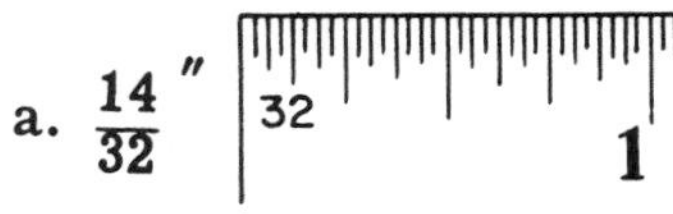

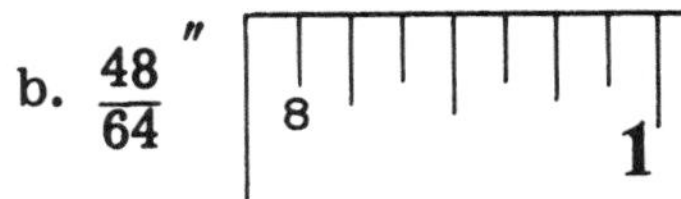

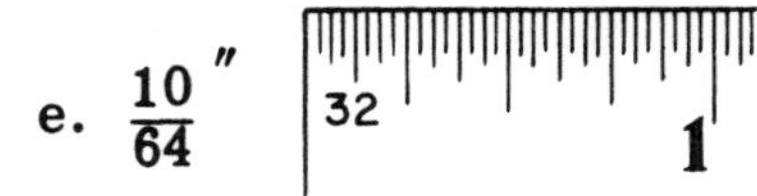

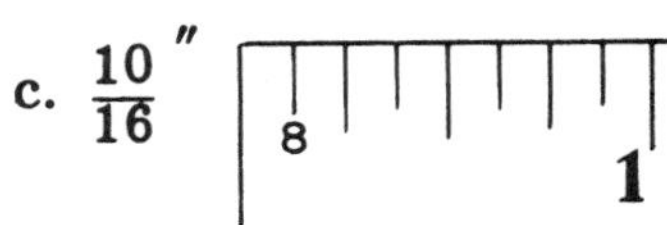

2. Reduce each improper fraction to its lowest terms and locate each measurement on a rule.

a. $\frac{5''}{2}$ b. $\frac{25''}{4}$ c. $\frac{35''}{8}$ d. $\frac{42''}{32}$ e. $\frac{85''}{64}$

3. Locate each common fraction on the sixteenth scale of a rule for problems (a) to (f).

a. $\frac{15''}{16}$ b. $\frac{13''}{16}$ c. $\frac{7''}{16}$ d. $\frac{9''}{16}$ e. $\frac{3''}{16}$ f. $\frac{11''}{16}$

4. Give each measurement as shown at A, B, C, and D on the eighth, sixteenth, and thirty-second scales.

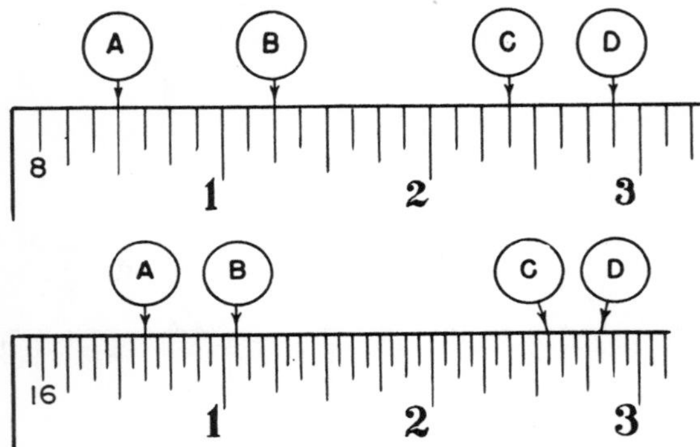

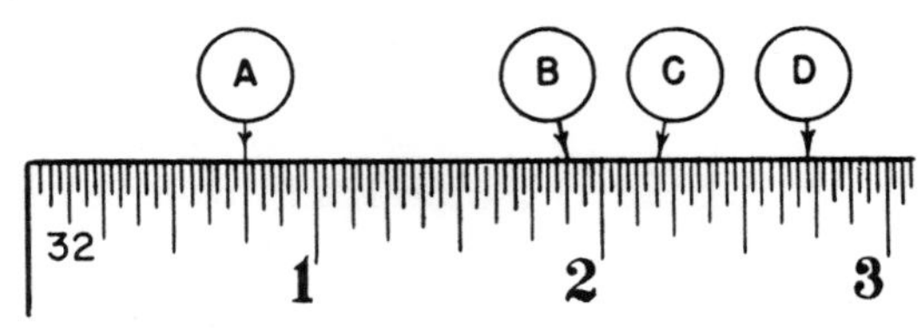

5. Draw lines to the following lengths:

a. 3″ b. $4\frac{1''}{2}$ c. $5\frac{1''}{4}$ d. $3\frac{1''}{8}$ e. $4\frac{3''}{4}$ f. $4\frac{7''}{8}$

6. Give the measurements of the stepped parts shown at A and the extensions B, C, D, and E.

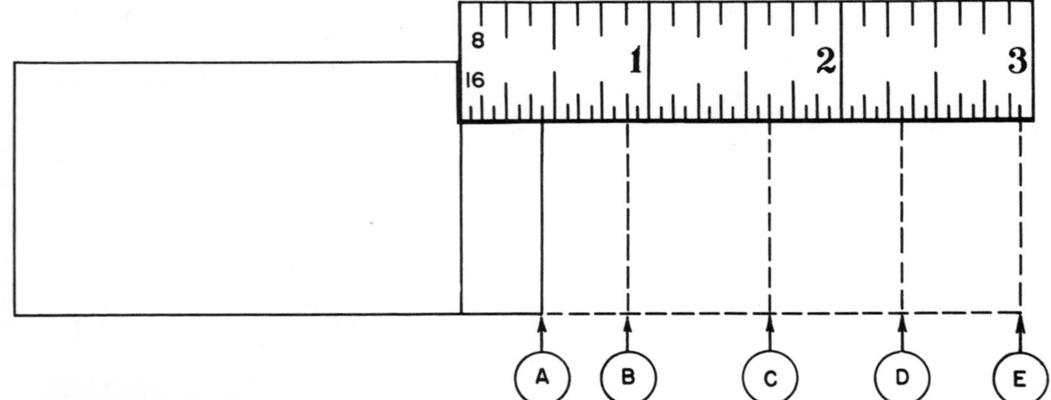

Unit 7 ADDITION OF FRACTIONS

The mechanic must often determine overall sizes by adding dimensions which are given on a drawing or written into specifications. The answers to such problems require the addition of whole numbers, common fractions, and combinations of whole numbers and fractions. Such combinations are referred to as *mixed numbers.*

To add combinations of whole numbers and fractions, the denominators of each fraction must be the same number. The smallest number that can be divided by all the denominators is called the *lowest common denominator.*

A. DETERMINING THE LOWEST COMMON DENOMINATOR (LCD)

The simplest method of determining the lowest common denominator is used when it is evident that all of the denominators divide evenly into a given number. This method is covered in this unit.

On the drawing of the special pin all of the given sizes must be added to get the overall dimension (A). Before these measurements (2, 1 31/32, 3/8, and 3/64) can be added, the lowest common denominator must be determined.

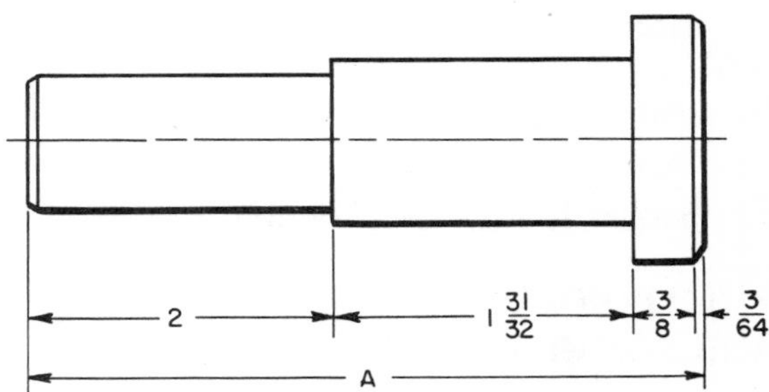

The lowest number into which each of the denominators (32, 8, and 64) will divide evenly is 64. The 64 is called the lowest common denominator.

RULE FOR REDUCING FRACTIONS TO THE LOWEST COMMON DENOMINATOR

- Divide the number selected as the lowest common denominator by the denominator of each given fraction.
- Multiply both the numerator and denominator by this quotient.

EXAMPLE: The lowest common denominator (LCD) for the pin dimension is 64.

Denominator ↓ 32)64 = 2 ← Quotient

Step 1 Divide the LCD by the denominator of first fraction.

Step 2 Multiply the numerator (31) and denominator (32) by the quotient (2).

$$\frac{31 \times 2}{32 \times 2} = \frac{62}{64}$$

Step 3 Continue the same process with the other fractions.

a. $64 \div 8 = 8$ $\frac{3 \times 8}{8 \times 8} = \frac{24}{64}$

b. $64 \div 64 = 1$ $\frac{3 \times 1}{64 \times 1} = \frac{3}{64}$

B. ADDING COMMON FRACTIONS

RULE FOR ADDING FRACTIONS

- Change to fractions having a least common denominator.
- Add the numerators.
- Write the sum over the common denominator.
- Reduce the result to its lowest terms.

EXAMPLE: Add 31/32, 3/8, and 3/64.

Step 1 Write fractions in vertical column.

Step 2 Change fractions to same denominator (64).

$$\frac{31}{32} \times \frac{2}{2} = \frac{62}{64}$$
$$\frac{3}{8} \times \frac{8}{8} = \frac{24}{64}$$
$$\frac{3}{64} \times \frac{1}{1} = \frac{3}{64}$$

Step 3 Add numerators. $62 + 24 + 3 = 89$

Step 4 Place result (89) over lowest common denominator (64). $\frac{89}{64}$

Step 5 Reduce to lowest terms. $\frac{89}{64} = 1\frac{25}{64}$ Ans.

C. ADDING WHOLE NUMBERS, COMMON FRACTIONS, AND MIXED NUMBERS

A mixed number consists of two parts: (1) a whole number and (2) a fraction. Such numbers as 1 1/2, 256 3/8, and 1927 3/5 are called "mixed numbers."

RULE FOR ADDING WHOLE NUMBERS, MIXED NUMBERS, AND COMMON FRACTIONS

- Add the whole numbers.
- Add the fractions.
- Add the two sums.
- Reduce the result to lowest terms.

EXAMPLE: Determine overall dimension A of the special shaft.

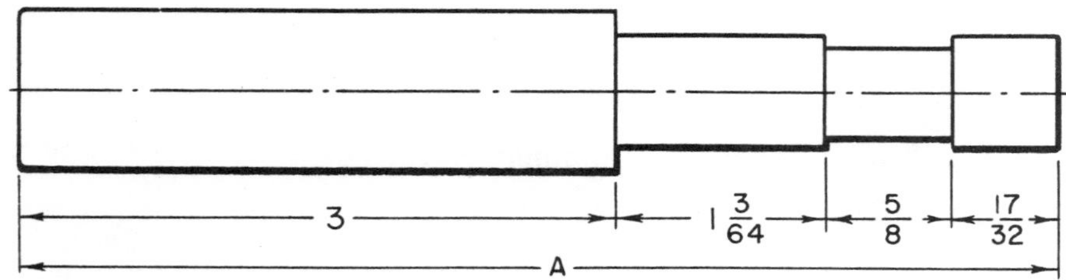

Step 1 Write all dimensions in vertical columns.

Step 2 Change fractions to same denominator (64).

$$3 = 3$$
$$1\frac{3}{64} \times \frac{1}{1} = 1\frac{3}{64}$$
$$\frac{5}{8} \times \frac{8}{8} = \frac{40}{64}$$
$$\frac{17}{32} \times \frac{2}{2} = \frac{34}{64}$$

Step 3 Add numerators. $3 + 40 + 34 = 77$

Step 4 Place result (77) over lowest common denominator (64). $\frac{77}{64}$

Step 5 Reduce 77/64 to 1 13/64.

Step 6 Add column of whole numbers. $(3 + 1 = 4)$

Step 7 Add sum of whole numbers (4) to sum of common fractions (1 13/64). $4 + 1\frac{13}{64} = 5\frac{13}{64}$ overall dimension of shaft.

ASSIGNMENT UNIT 7

A. ADDITION OF COMMON FRACTIONS

1. $\frac{1}{6} + \frac{5}{6}$
2. $\frac{1}{8} + \frac{5}{8}$
3. $\frac{1}{4} + \frac{4}{8}$
4. $\frac{1}{3} + \frac{1}{6}$
5. $\frac{1}{2} + \frac{3}{8}$
6. $\frac{1}{6} + \frac{1}{6} + \frac{5}{6}$
7. $\frac{5}{8} + \frac{3}{4} + \frac{3}{8}$
8. $\frac{1}{32} + \frac{7}{8} + \frac{3}{16} + \frac{5}{32}$
9. $\frac{61}{64} + \frac{13}{16} + \frac{5}{8} + \frac{23}{64}$

Ans.: 2. 3/4 4. 1/2 6. 1 1/6 8. 1 1/4

B. ADDITION OF COMMON FRACTIONS AND MIXED NUMBERS

1. $121 + 7\frac{5}{12}$
2. $10\frac{9}{16} + 4\frac{1}{8}$
3. $23\frac{5}{8} + 10\frac{5}{8}$
4. $1\frac{17}{64} + 1\frac{13}{64} + \frac{9}{32}$
5. $4\frac{3}{16} + 10\frac{21}{64} + 1\frac{5}{16} + \frac{3}{32}$
6. $3\frac{5}{32} + 2\frac{13}{64} + 1\frac{13}{32} + 3\frac{1}{16} + \frac{1}{4}$

Ans.: 2. 14 11/16 4. 2 3/4 6. 10 5/64

C. ADDITION OF WHOLE NUMBERS, MIXED NUMBERS, COMMON FRACTIONS

1. Determine dimensions A, B, C, D, and E (in inches).

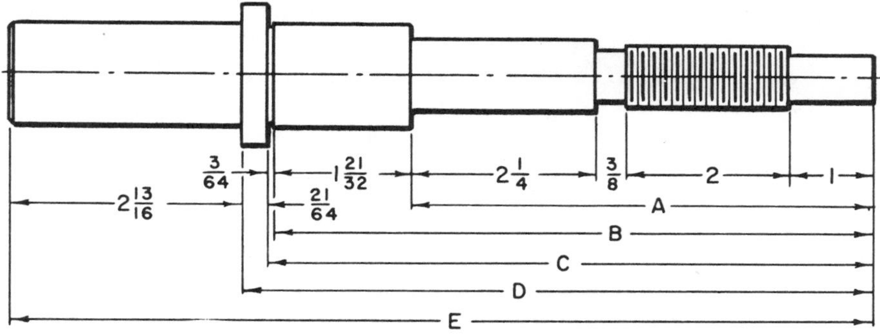

Ans.: B. 7 9/32″ D. 7 21/32″

2. Calculate dimensions A through E for the stand as illustrated.

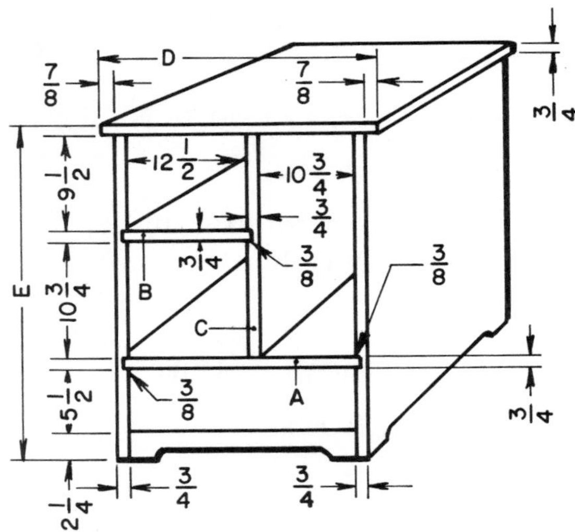

Ans.: B. 13 1/4″ D. 27 1/4″

3. Determine the overall lengths of springs A through D.

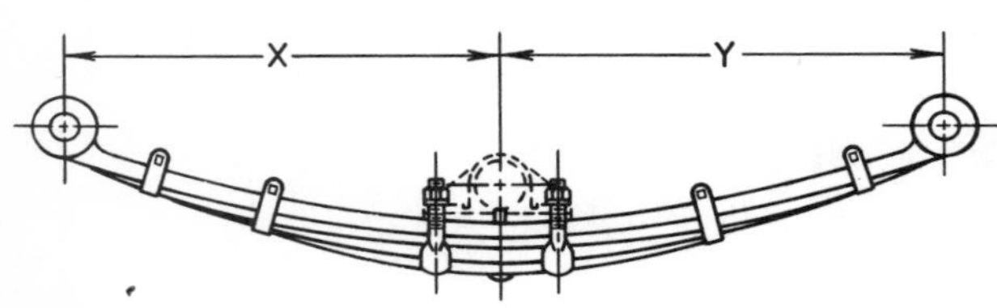

Spring	Distance		Overall Length
	X	Y	
A	17 1/2″	15 3/4″	
B	16 3/4″	15 7/8″	
C	17 3/32″	16 1/8″	
D	18 21/32″	17 3/4″	

Ans.: B. 32 5/8″ D. 36 13/32″

4. Compute the total horsepower for (a) motors 1, 2 and 3, (b) motors 4, 5 and 6 and (c) all six motors. The rated horsepower is indicated.

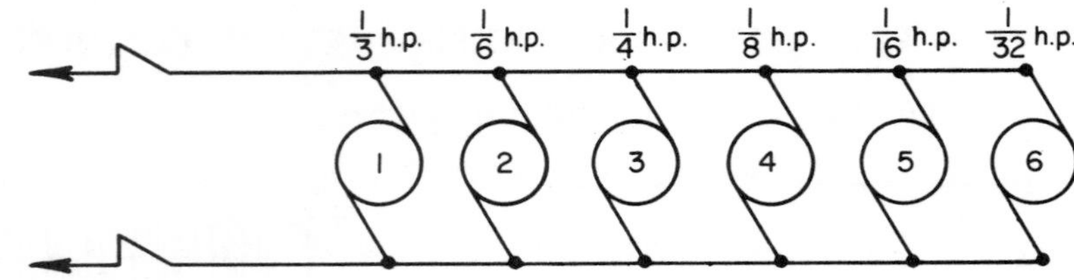

Ans.: c. 31/32 hp.

Unit 8 SUBTRACTION OF FRACTIONS

The value of a missing dimension must often be determined by subtracting whole numbers, fractions, and mixed numbers. As in addition, fractions cannot be subtracted unless they first have the same common denominator.

A. SUBTRACTING PROPER FRACTIONS

RULE FOR SUBTRACTING FRACTIONS

- Express all fractions using the lowest common denominator.
- Subtract the numerators.
- Write the difference over the lowest common denominator.
- Express the resulting fraction in lowest terms.

EXAMPLE: Subtract 7/32 from 11/16.

Step 1 Determine the lowest common denominator.

Step 2 Write the fractions in terms of lowest common denominator.

$$\frac{7}{32} = \frac{7}{32} \quad \frac{11}{16} = \frac{22}{32}$$

Step 3 Subtract numerators.

$$22 - 7 = 15$$

Step 4 Place the numerator result over the lowest common denominator.

$$\frac{15}{32}$$

B. SUBTRACTING A FRACTION FROM A WHOLE NUMBER

RULE FOR SUBTRACTING A FRACTION FROM A WHOLE NUMBER

- Take one unit from the whole number. Change it into a fraction having the same denominator as the fraction which is to be subtracted.
- Subtract the numerators of the original fraction from the one unit that was changed to its fractional value.
- Express the resulting fraction in lowest terms.
- Place the whole number next to the fraction.

EXAMPLE: Subtract 21/32 from 9.

Step 1 Take one unit from the whole number (9 – 1 = 8).

Step 2 Change the one unit to a fractional equivalent having the same denominator as the fraction to be subtracted.

$$1 = \frac{32}{32}$$

Step 3 Arrange the fractions in one column; the whole number in another.

$$\begin{array}{r} 8\,\frac{32}{32} \\ -\ \ \frac{21}{32} \\ \hline \end{array}$$

$$\frac{32}{32} - \frac{21}{32} = \frac{11}{32}$$

Step 4 Subtract the numerators (32 – 21 = 11).

$$8\,\frac{11}{32}$$

Step 5 Place the whole number (8) next to the fraction 11/32 to get the answer.

C. SUBTRACTING A MIXED NUMBER FROM A WHOLE NUMBER

RULE FOR SUBTRACTING A MIXED NUMBER FROM A WHOLE NUMBER

- Borrow one unit from the whole number and express it as a fraction which has the same denominator as the mixed number.
- Subtract the fraction part of the mixed number from the fraction part of the whole number.
- Subtract the whole numbers and reduce the resulting mixed number to its lowest terms.

EXAMPLE: Subtract 1 35/64 from 6.

Step 1 $6 = 5\frac{64}{64}$

Step 2 $1\frac{35}{64} = 1\frac{35}{64}$

Step 3 $4\frac{29}{64}$ Ans.

D. SUBTRACTING MIXED NUMBERS FROM MIXED NUMBERS

RULE FOR SUBTRACTING MIXED NUMBERS

- Express the fractional part of each mixed number using the least common denominator.
- Borrow one unit, when necessary, to make up a fraction larger than the one to be subtracted.
- Subtract the fractions first and the whole numbers next. Express the result in its lowest terms.

EXAMPLE: Subtract 2 7/16 from 5 11/32.

Step 1 $5\frac{11}{32} = 4 + \frac{32}{32} + \frac{11}{32} = 4\frac{43}{32}$

Step 2 $2\frac{7}{16} = \qquad = 2\frac{14}{32}$

Step 3 $2\frac{29}{32}$

E. COMBINING ADDITION AND SUBTRACTION OF FRACTIONS

RULE FOR ADDING AND SUBTRACTING FRACTIONS IN THE SAME PROBLEM

- Change all fractions to the least common denominator.
- Add or subtract the numerators as required.
- Express the result in lowest terms.

EXAMPLE: Add 1 9/16 + 3 5/8 + 2 1/4 and from the sum subtract 2 13/16.

$$1\frac{9}{16} + 3\frac{5}{8} + 2\frac{1}{4} - 2\frac{13}{16} =$$

Step 1 $1\frac{9}{16} + 3\frac{10}{16} + 2\frac{4}{16} - 2\frac{13}{16} =$

Step 2

$$\begin{array}{r} 1\frac{9}{16} \\ +\ 3\frac{10}{16} \\ +\ 2\frac{4}{16} \\ \hline 6\frac{23}{16} \end{array}$$

Step 3

$$\begin{array}{r} 6\frac{23}{16} \\ -\ 2\frac{13}{16} \\ \hline \end{array}$$

Step 4

$$4\frac{10}{16} = 4\frac{5}{8} \text{ Ans.}$$

ASSIGNMENT UNIT 8

A. SUBTRACTION OF PROPER FRACTIONS

Subtract:

1. $\frac{5}{8} - \frac{4}{8}$
2. $\frac{5}{6} - \frac{1}{6}$
3. $\frac{13}{16} - \frac{5}{16}$
4. $\frac{9}{32} - \frac{7}{32}$
5. $\frac{1}{2} - \frac{1}{4}$
6. 1/8 from 5/8
7. 5/32 from 9/16
8. 9/64 from 23/32
9. 3/8 + 1/8 from 9/16
10. 37/64 + 21/64 from 63/64

Ans.: 2. 2/3 4. 1/16 6. 1/2 8. 37/64 10. 5/64

B. SUBTRACTION OF FRACTIONS FROM A WHOLE NUMBER

Subtract:

1. $4 - \frac{3}{4}$
2. $7 - \frac{15}{16}$
3. $32 - \frac{13}{32}$
4. $175 - \frac{4}{5}$
5. $72 - \frac{61}{64}$

Ans.: 2. 6 1/16 4. 174 1/5

C. SUBTRACTION OF A MIXED NUMBER FROM A WHOLE NUMBER

Subtract:

1. $2 - 1\frac{1}{3}$
2. $3 - 1\frac{3}{8}$
3. $27 - 1\frac{5}{16}$
4. $142 - 6\frac{21}{32}$
5. $372 - 21\frac{5}{64}$
6. 1 21/32 from 3
7. 3 57/64 from 4
8. 3 5/32 + 1 9/32 from 5
9. 2 53/64 + 1 1/64 + 3 1/4 from 8
10. 3 7/16 + 2 25/64 + 16 17/32 from 42

Ans.: 2. 1 5/8 4. 135 11/32 6. 1 11/32 8. 9/16 10. 19 41/64

D. SUBTRACTION OF MIXED NUMBERS FROM MIXED NUMBERS

Subtract:

1. $1\frac{3}{5} - 1\frac{1}{5}$
2. $7\frac{5}{6} - 2\frac{1}{6}$
3. $18\frac{7}{8} - 9\frac{3}{8}$
4. $35\frac{5}{8} - 8\frac{1}{2}$
5. $172\frac{21}{64} - 22\frac{5}{32}$
6. 1 19/32 from 4 29/32
7. 2 31/32 from 5 15/32
8. 4 7/64 from 8 1/32
9. 2 9/16 + 1 1/8 from 5 51/64
10. 7 1/64 + 2 31/32 + 1 1/4 from 12 3/32

Ans.: 2. 5 2/3 4. 27 1/8 6. 3 5/16 8. 3 59/64 10. 55/64

E. SPECIAL PROBLEMS

1. Determine the inside diameter of each size bushing.

Outside Diameter	Single Wall Thickness
1	1/16
2 1/8	3/16
2 15/32	9/64
3 1/64	15/32
1 9/64	9/32

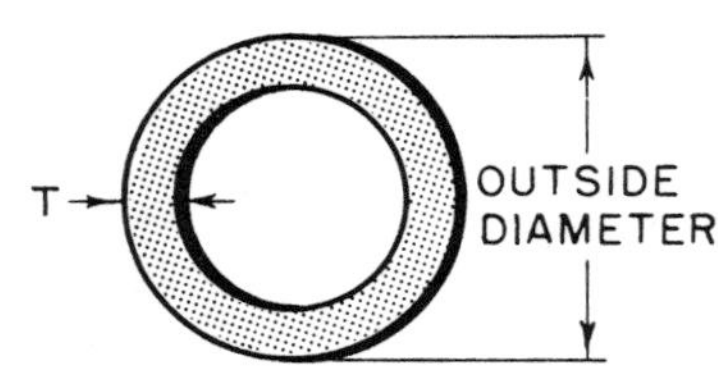

2. Determine dimensions A, B, C, D, and E.

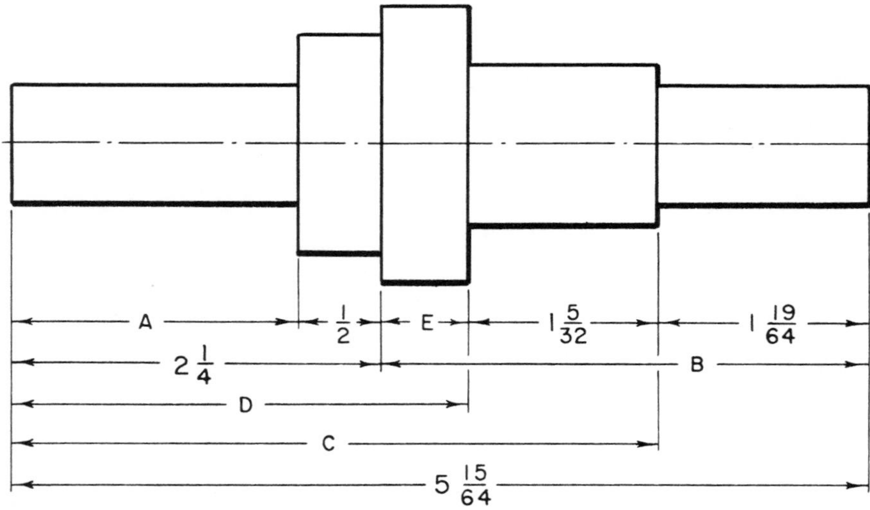

Ans.: B. 2 63/64″ D. 2 25/32″

3. How much material will be left from an 18-inch length of strip rule after four pieces are cut off in the following lengths: 2 1/2, 1 1/4, 3 1/2, and 3 3/4 inches.

4. A motor base is to be set up 4 1/2 inches from the floor. Two wooden blocks must be used. If one block is 1 5/8 inches, how thick must the second block be? **Ans.:** 2 7/8″

5. A concrete sidewalk 4 1/4 inches thick consists of a base course and a finish course. The base thickness is 3 5/8 inches. What is the thickness of the finish course?
6. Three pieces of 3-inch lead pipe are cut from a piece 35 1/2 inches long. The lengths are 7 1/4 inches, 11 3/8 inches, and 6 1/2 inches. If 3/8 inches of stock is wasted in cutting, how much pipe is left? **Ans.**: 10″
7. Four pieces are cut from a 12-foot 2 x 4. The pieces measure 3 feet 9 1/2 inches, 2 feet 6 1/4 inches, 1 foot 4 1/2 inches, and 2 feet 3 3/8 inches. If a total of 1/2 inch is allowed for the four cuts, how much of the 2 x 4 is left?
8. A piece of radiator hose is 32 1/2 inches long. Short pieces of the following lengths are cut from it: 6 1/2 inches, 5 1/4 inches, 8 13/16 inches, and 10 9/16 inches. How much hose is left? **Ans.**: 1 3/8″
9. Determine dimensions A, B, C, and D.

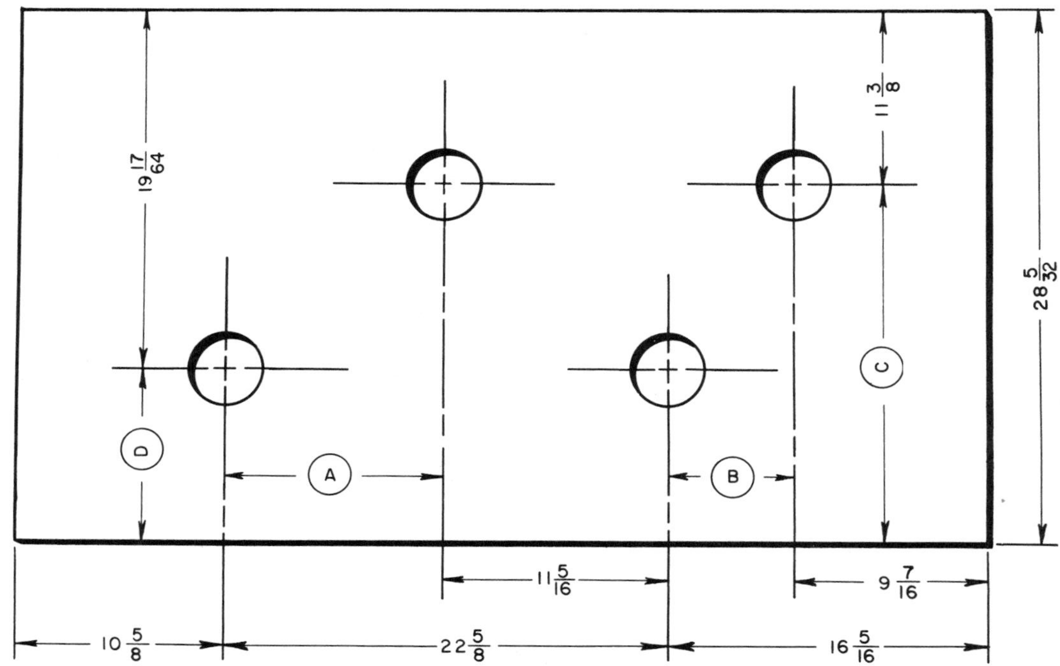

Ans.: B. 6 7/8″ D. 8 57/64″

10. Compute dimensions A, B, C, and D.

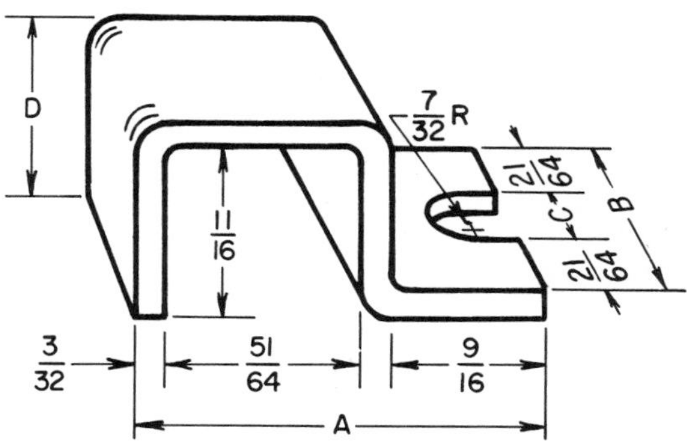

Ans.: B. 1 3/32″ D. 25/32″

11. The front and rear axle of a light truck are to be aligned. The center distance (C) measures 16′-3 5/8″ on side A. Side B measures 16′-4 7/16″. Determine how much the axles need to be changed to be aligned.

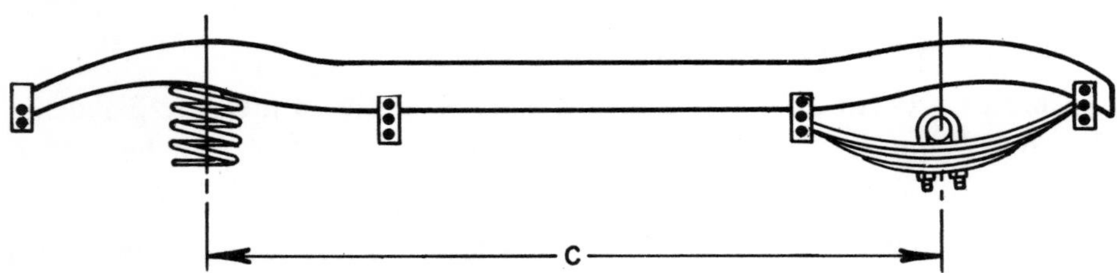

Unit 9 MULTIPLICATION OF FRACTIONS

The multiplication of fractions, like the multiplication of whole numbers, is a simplified method of addition. The multiplication of common fractions, whole numbers, and mixed numbers, typical of those used daily, are covered in this unit.

A. MULTIPLYING COMMON FRACTIONS

RULE FOR MULTIPLYING TWO OR MORE FRACTIONS

- Multiply the numerators.
- Multiply the denominators.
- Write the product of the numerators over the product of the denominators.
- Express the resulting fraction in lowest terms.

EXAMPLE: Multiply 7/8 by 3/4.

Step 1 Multiply the numerators. $(7 \times 3) = 21$

Step 2 Multiply the denominators. $(8 \times 4) = 32$

Step 3 Express as a fraction. ⟶ $\frac{21}{32}$

B. MULTIPLYING A COMMON FRACTION BY A MIXED NUMBER

RULE FOR MULTIPLYING A COMMON FRACTION BY A MIXED NUMBER

- Express the mixed number as an improper fraction where the numerator is larger than the denominator.
- Multiply the numerator of the improper fraction by the numerator of the common fraction.
- Multiply the denominators.

EXAMPLE: Multiply 4 1/2 by 1/8.

Step 1 Express the mixed number (4 1/2) as an improper fraction (9/2). $4\frac{1}{2} = \frac{4 \times 2 + 1}{2} = \frac{9}{2}$

Step 2 Multiply the numerators. $(9 \times 1) = 9$

Step 3 Multiply the denominators. $(2 \times 8) = 16$

$$4\frac{1}{2} \times \frac{1}{8} = \frac{9}{2} \times \frac{1}{8} = \frac{9}{16} \text{ Ans.}$$

C. MULTIPLYING FRACTIONS, WHOLE AND MIXED NUMBERS

RULE FOR MULTIPLYING FRACTIONS, WHOLE NUMBERS, AND MIXED NUMBERS IN ANY COMBINATION

- Express all mixed numbers as improper fractions.
- Place all whole numbers over a denominator of 1.
- Multiply all numerators.
- Multiply all denominators.
- Express resulting product in lowest terms.

EXAMPLE: Multiply 8 3/8 x 1 1/4 x 2.

Step 1 Express (8 3/8) as an improper fraction (67/8). Express (1 1/4) as an improper fraction (5/4).

$$\frac{8 \times 8 + 3}{8} = \frac{67}{8}$$

$$\frac{1 \times 4 + 1}{4} = \frac{5}{4}$$

Step 2 Place 2 over denominator of 1. $\frac{2}{1}$

Step 3 Multiply all numerators. (67 x 5 x 2)

Step 4 Multiply all denominators. (8 x 4 x 1)

$$\frac{67}{8} \times \frac{5}{4} \times \frac{2}{1} = \frac{670}{32}$$

Step 5 Express (670/32) in lowest terms.

$$\frac{670}{32} = 20\,\frac{30}{32} = 20\,\frac{15}{16}$$ Ans.

D. CANCELLING TO SIMPLIFY THE MULTIPLICATION PROCESS

RULE

- The multiplication of fractions can be simplified by "cancellation." Any numerator and any denominator is first divided by whatever number (called a factor) is common to the numerator and denominator. This process of taking out the common factor is called *cancellation.*

EXAMPLE: Multiply 72 x 3 5/8.

Step 1 Express the mixed number (3 5/8) as an improper fraction (29/8).

Step 2 Select a number which is common to any numerator and any denominator (8 in this case).

Step 3 Divide the numerator and denominator by this factor (8).

$$\frac{\overset{9}{\cancel{72}}}{1} \times \frac{29}{\underset{1}{\cancel{8}}} = 261 \text{ Ans.}$$

E. SHORTCUTS IN MULTIPLYING BY 1/2

EXAMPLE: Case 1 Find 1/2 of 7/8.

Step 1 Multiply the denominator (8) by (2).

Step 2 Use the numerator (7) as it is. The answer is 7/16.

EXAMPLE: Case 2 Find 1/2 of 2 3/4.

Step 1 Take one-half of (2). $\frac{1}{2} \times 2 = 1$

Step 2 Multiply the denominator (4) of the fraction (3/4) by (2). $4 \times 2 = 8$

Step 3 Use the same numerator (3).

Step 4 Combine the whole number (1) and the fraction (3/8). The answer is a mixed number (1 3/8). $1 + \frac{3}{8} = 1\frac{3}{8}$ Ans.

EXAMPLE: Case 3 Find 1/2 of 5 13/16.

Step 1 Take one-half of (4) (the largest number in the mixed number that will divide exactly). $\frac{1}{2}$ of $4 = 2$

Step 2 Express the remainder (1 13/16) as an improper fraction. $1\frac{13}{16} = \frac{29}{16}$

Step 3 Place the numerator (29) over twice the denominator. $\frac{29}{2 \times 16} = \frac{29}{32}$

Step 4 Combine the whole number (2) with the fraction (29/32). $2 + \frac{29}{32} = 2\frac{29}{32}$ Ans.

SPECIAL NOTE: When more than one operation is called for within a problem, multiplication and/or division operations are completed first. Other operations (addition and subtraction) are then performed. These are done in order from left to right.

ASSIGNMENT UNIT 9

A. MULTIPLICATION OF PROPER FRACTIONS

Multiply:

1. $\frac{1}{4}$ by $\frac{1}{2}$
2. $\frac{5}{9}$ by $\frac{1}{8}$
3. $\frac{1}{6}$ by $\frac{7}{12}$
4. $\frac{7}{8}$ by $\frac{1}{4}$
5. $\frac{5}{6}$ by $\frac{5}{12}$
6. $\left(\frac{21}{32} + \frac{3}{32}\right)$ by $\frac{1}{8}$
7. $\left(\frac{5}{8} + \frac{3}{16}\right)$ by $\frac{1}{2}$
8. $\left(\frac{19}{32} + \frac{1}{4}\right)$ by $\frac{3}{8}$
9. $\left(\frac{1}{64} + \frac{17}{32} - \frac{5}{64}\right)$ by $\frac{13}{16}$
10. $\left(\frac{1}{8} + \frac{19}{64} - \frac{3}{16}\right)$ by $\frac{13}{32}$

Ans.: 2. 5/72 4. 7/32 6. 3/32 8. 81/256 10. 195/2048

B. MULTIPLICATION OF COMMON FRACTIONS AND MIXED NUMBERS

Multiply:

1. $\frac{1}{6}$ by $1\frac{1}{6}$
2. $1\frac{1}{4}$ by $\frac{1}{2}$
3. $2\frac{3}{8}$ by $\frac{1}{4}$
4. $\frac{5}{8}$ by $6\frac{1}{4}$
5. $\frac{5}{6}$ by $3\frac{7}{12}$
6. $2\frac{9}{16} \times \frac{3}{8}$
7. $\frac{15}{32} \times 2\frac{1}{8}$
8. $3\frac{1}{2} + \left(1\frac{3}{4} \times \frac{7}{8}\right)$
9. $1\frac{9}{16} + \left(\frac{5}{32} \times \frac{5}{8}\right)$
10. $\left(17\frac{1}{4} + 3\frac{1}{32} - 2\frac{1}{8}\right) \times \frac{27}{64}$

Ans.: 2. 5/8 4. 3 29/32 6. 123/128 8. 5 1/32 10. 19 197/512

C. MULTIPLICATION OF MIXED NUMBERS

Multiply:

1. $1\frac{1}{3}$ by $2\frac{1}{6}$
2. $1\frac{9}{16}$ by $10\frac{3}{4}$
3. $6\frac{5}{8}$ by $2\frac{7}{32}$
4. $3\frac{5}{6} \times 1\frac{3}{4} \times 3\frac{1}{8} \times 6\frac{1}{2}$
5. $(2\frac{53}{64} - 1\frac{9}{32}) \times 2\frac{1}{2} \times 3\frac{3}{4}$

Ans.: 2. 16 51/64 4. 136 101/384

D. SHORTCUTS IN MULTIPLYING BY ONE-HALF (1/2)

Find by the shortcut method:

1. $\frac{1}{2}$ of $\frac{1}{4}$
2. $\frac{1}{2}$ of $\frac{7}{16}$
3. $\frac{1}{2}$ of $2\frac{3}{32}$
4. $\frac{1}{2}$ of $3\frac{5}{6}$

Ans.: 2. 7/32 4. 1 11/12

E. MULTIPLICATION OF WHOLE NUMBERS, FRACTIONS AND MIXED NUMBERS

1. What lengths of bar stock will be needed to machine the quantity of parts A, B, C, D, and E indicated in the table?

Parts	Quantity	Length	Allowance for Each Saw Cut
A	10	1/2″	1/16″
B	12	1 5/32″	3/32″
C	64	2 21/64″	1/8″
D	100	1 3/32″	7/64″
E	75	1 9/64″	1/8″

Ans.: B. 14 29/32″ D. 120 13/64″

2. Determine the cost of materials A, B, C, D, and E from data given in the table.

Materials	Length (ft.)	Weight (lbs./ft.)	Unit Cost (¢/lb.)
A	2	1/2	36
B	10 1/4	1/4	92
C	7 5/12	1 1/2	66 1/2
D	9 1/2	3 3/4	33 3/8
E	11 3/4	2 1/16	24 9/16

Ans.: B. $2.36 D. $11.89

3. Compute dimensions A, B, C, and D.

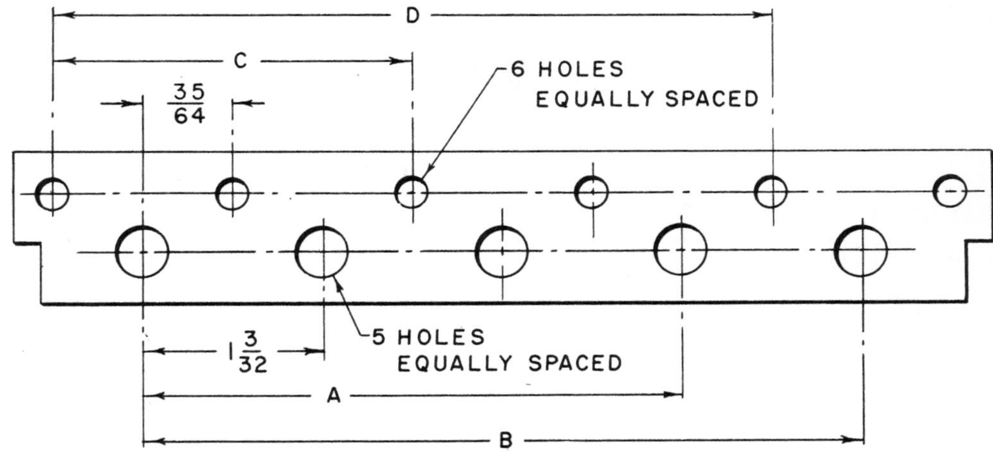

Ans.: B. 4 3/8″ D. 4 3/8″

4. Find the special pay earnings for weeks A, B, C, D, and E, and the total earnings from data given in the table. Overtime pay amounting to time and a half is paid for all hours over 40 per week.

Week	Hours per Week	Rate per Hour
A	40	87 1/2
B	44	87 1/2
C	48	87 1/2
D	43 1/4	99 1/2
E	43 3/4	99 1/2

Ans.: B. $40.25 D. $44.65

5. a. Find the daily production on parts A and B produced by methods 1, 2, and 3 for a 7 1/2-hour day.

   b. Determine the unit costs for all conditions.

Method	Part A		Part B	
	Hourly Production	Unit Cost	Hourly Production	Unit Cost
1	10	2	21	2 4/5
2	14	2 1/2	27	3 1/8
3	15	2 3/4	29 1/2	4 1/8

6. Four different foods and quantities are given in the table. Compute the cost of each food.

Ans.: B. $137.74 D. $130.73

Foods	Quantity	Cost Per Unit	Total Quantity
A	127 1/2 lbs.	$2.16/lb.	
B	29 3/4 doz.	4.63/doz.	
C	63 1/4 qts.	.87/qt.	
D	17 1/2 yds.	7.47/yd.	

Unit 10 DIVISION OF FRACTIONS

The division of fractions refers to the process of determining how many times one number is contained in another. While the division of fractions is not used as often as the other mathematical processes, the principles are applied constantly.

A. DIVIDING FRACTIONS

RULE FOR DIVIDING FRACTIONS

- Turn the dividing fraction around so the denominator becomes the numerator and the numerator, the denominator.

  NOTE: This step is often expressed as "invert the divisor."
- Change the division sign to a multiplication sign and multiply.

EXAMPLE: Divide 7/8 by 3/4.

Step 1 Invert the divisor (3/4) to become (4/3).

Step 2 Cancel the factor (4) common to both numerator and denominator. $\frac{7}{\cancel{8}_2} \times \frac{\cancel{4}^1}{3} =$

Step 3 Multiply remaining fractions. $\frac{7}{2} \times \frac{1}{3} = \frac{7}{6}$

Step 4 Express in lowest terms. $\frac{7}{6} = 1\frac{1}{6}$ Ans.

B. DIVIDING FRACTIONS AND WHOLE NUMBERS

RULE FOR DIVIDING A FRACTION AND A WHOLE NUMBER

- Express the whole number as a fraction whose denominator is (1).
- Invert the divisor.
- Proceed as in the multiplication of fractions.

EXAMPLE: Case 1 Divide 20 by 7/8.

Step 1 Express the (20) as a fraction having an equivalent value. $20 = \frac{20}{1}$

Step 2 Invert the divisor (7/8) to (8/7).

Step 3 Multiply and simplify. $\frac{20}{1} \times \frac{8}{7} = \frac{20 \times 8}{1 \times 7} = \frac{160}{7} = 22\frac{6}{7}$ Ans.

EXAMPLE: Case 2 Divide 15/32 by 6.

Step 1 Express the divisor (6) as a fraction having an equivalent value (6/1).

Step 2 Invert the divisor (6/1) to become (1/6).

Step 3 Cancel factor (3). $\frac{\cancel{15}^5}{32} \times \frac{1}{\cancel{6}_2} =$

Step 4 Multiply. $\frac{5}{32} \times \frac{1}{2} = \frac{5}{64}$ Ans.

C. DIVIDING MIXED NUMBERS

RULE FOR DIVIDING MIXED NUMBERS

- Express the mixed numbers as improper fractions.
- Invert the divisor.
- Multiply the fractions.

EXAMPLE: Divide 1 9/16 by 3 1/8.

$$1\frac{9}{16} \div 3\frac{1}{8} =$$

Step 1 Express the (1 9/16) as 25/16); the divisor (3 1/8) as (25/8).

$$\frac{25}{16} \div \frac{25}{8} =$$

$$\frac{25}{16} \times \frac{8}{25} =$$

Step 2 Invert the divisor (25/8) to (8/25).

Step 3 Cancel like factors (25) and (8).

$$\frac{\overset{1}{\cancel{25}}}{\underset{2}{\cancel{16}}} \times \frac{\overset{1}{\cancel{8}}}{\underset{1}{\cancel{25}}} =$$

Step 4 Multiply.

$$\frac{1}{2} \times \frac{1}{1} = \frac{1}{2} \text{ Ans.}$$

D. COMBINING THE MULTIPLICATION AND DIVISION OF FRACTIONS, WHOLE AND MIXED NUMBERS

RULE FOR SOLVING PROBLEMS REQUIRING THE MULTIPLICATION AND DIVISION OF FRACTIONS

- Express all mixed numbers as improper fractions.
- Invert the divisor or divisors and change the division sign or signs to multiplication.
- Cancel like factors from numerator and denominator.
- Multiply remaining fractions.
- Express product in lowest terms.

EXAMPLE: 9 1/4 ÷ 7/8 ÷ 1/32 x 1 17/32 =

Step 1 Express all mixed numbers as improper fractions.

$$9\frac{1}{4} = \frac{37}{4} \qquad 1\frac{17}{32} = \frac{49}{32}$$

Step 2 Invert the divisors (7/8) and (1/32) to (8/7) and (32/1) and change division signs to multiplication signs.

$$9\frac{1}{4} \div \frac{7}{8} \div \frac{1}{32} \times 1\frac{17}{32} =$$

$$\frac{37}{4} \times \frac{8}{7} \times \frac{32}{1} \times \frac{49}{32} =$$

Step 3 Cancel like factors (7), (4), and (32).

$$\frac{37}{\underset{1}{\cancel{4}}} \times \frac{\overset{2}{\cancel{8}}}{\underset{1}{\cancel{7}}} \times \frac{\overset{1}{\cancel{32}}}{1} \times \frac{\overset{7}{\cancel{49}}}{\underset{1}{\cancel{32}}} =$$

Step 4 Multiply remaining fractions and express result in lowest terms.

$$\frac{37}{1} \times \frac{2}{1} \times \frac{1}{1} \times \frac{7}{1} = \frac{518}{1} = 518 \text{ Ans.}$$

ASSIGNMENT UNIT 10

A. DIVISION OF COMMON FRACTIONS

Divide:

1. $\frac{3}{4}$ by $\frac{1}{4}$
2. $\frac{1}{2}$ by $\frac{1}{6}$
3. $\frac{1}{4}$ by $\frac{3}{8}$
4. $\frac{5}{8}$ by $\frac{1}{2}$
5. $\frac{3}{16}$ by $\frac{1}{4}$
6. $\frac{5}{16}$ by $\frac{11}{16}$
7. $\frac{7}{12}$ by $\frac{5}{6}$
8. $\frac{9}{64}$ by $\frac{5}{32}$
9. $\left(\frac{13}{16} \times \frac{3}{32}\right)$ by $\frac{53}{64}$
10. $\left(\frac{21}{32} \times \frac{15}{64} \times \frac{1}{4}\right)$ by $\frac{7}{16}$

Ans.: 2. 3 4. 1 1/4 6. 5/11 8. 9/10 10. 45/512

B. DIVISION OF FRACTIONS AND WHOLE NUMBERS

Divide:

1. 3 by $\frac{1}{3}$
2. 4 by $\frac{1}{2}$
3. 5 by $\frac{5}{8}$
4. $\frac{7}{16}$ by 7
5. $\frac{15}{32}$ by 30
6. $\frac{55}{64}$ by 11
7. 15 by $\frac{9}{16}$
8. 8 by $\frac{7}{16}$
9. $\left(\frac{5}{8} - \frac{1}{4} + \frac{1}{16} + \frac{1}{8}\right)$ by $\frac{3}{16}$
10. $\left(\frac{9}{32} - \frac{5}{64} \times \frac{1}{16} \times \frac{3}{32}\right)$ by $\frac{5}{8}$

Ans.: 2. 8 4. 1/16 6. 5/64 8. 18 2/7 10. 1149/4096

C. DIVISION OF MIXED NUMBERS

1. $1\frac{1}{2} \div 1\frac{1}{2}$
2. $3\frac{1}{2} \div 4\frac{1}{4}$
3. $5\frac{3}{8} \div 3\frac{1}{4}$
4. $2\frac{3}{4} \div 4\frac{3}{8}$
5. $12\frac{1}{4} \div 6\frac{5}{16}$
6. $13\frac{3}{16} \div 11\frac{3}{4}$
7. $2\frac{15}{16} \div 6\frac{3}{8}$
8. $12\frac{3}{32} \div 1\frac{7}{64}$

Ans.: 2. 14/17 4. 22/35 6. 1 23/188 8. 10 64/71

D. MULTIPLICATION AND DIVISION OF FRACTIONS, WHOLE NUMBERS, AND MIXED NUMBERS

1. $\frac{1}{2} \times \frac{1}{4} \div \frac{1}{2}$
2. $1\frac{1}{6} \times \frac{5}{12} \div \frac{1}{6}$
3. $12 \times 6\frac{3}{8} \div \frac{7}{8}$
4. $21\frac{1}{4} \times 9\frac{5}{8} \div \frac{3}{4}$
5. $2\frac{9}{32} \div 1\frac{3}{16} \times 2\frac{1}{4}$
6. $16\frac{21}{64} \times 12\frac{3}{8} \div 2\frac{1}{4} \div \frac{7}{8}$

7. $1\frac{1}{4} \times \frac{9}{16} \times \frac{5}{8} \div 3\frac{1}{32}$

8. $(17\frac{1}{2} + \frac{3}{8} + \frac{1}{4} - \frac{5}{8}) \div 12\frac{1}{8}$

Ans.: 2. 2 11/12 4. 272 17/24 6. 102 71/112 8. 1 43/97

E. PRACTICAL PROBLEMS

1. How many leads 15 picas long (2 1/2 inches) can be cut from a 20-inch strip? No waste allowance is made for trim.
2. How many pieces of stock 7/8 of an inch long can be cut from a 30-inch bar of drill rod if 1/16 of an inch is allowed on each piece for cutting? **Ans.:** 32 pieces
3. How many pieces 10 5/16 inches long may be cut from a 12-foot length of a 2 x 4? Allow 3/16 of an inch between cuts for waste.
4. How many billets of cold drawn steel 3 9/32 inches long can be cut from a bar 48 inches long? Allow 1/16 of an inch for saw cut and another 1/16 of an inch for facing. **Ans.:** 14 billets
5. Determine the number of pieces that can be blanked from a 50-yard roll of brass when each stamping is 4 1/2 inches long, and each piece requires an additional 5/32 of an inch for positioning.
6. A drafting scale of 1/4" to 1 foot is used on a drawing of a house. Compute the length of rooms A, B, C and D.

   Ans.: B. 41′ D. 57 1/4′

Room	Scale Measurement (length)	Actual Room Length
A	9 1/4"	
B	10 1/4"	
C	13 1/8"	
D	14 5/16"	

7. The I-beam lintel of a brick doorway opening is 4 1/3 feet long. It weighs 32 1/2 pounds. Find the number of pounds per foot in the I-beam.

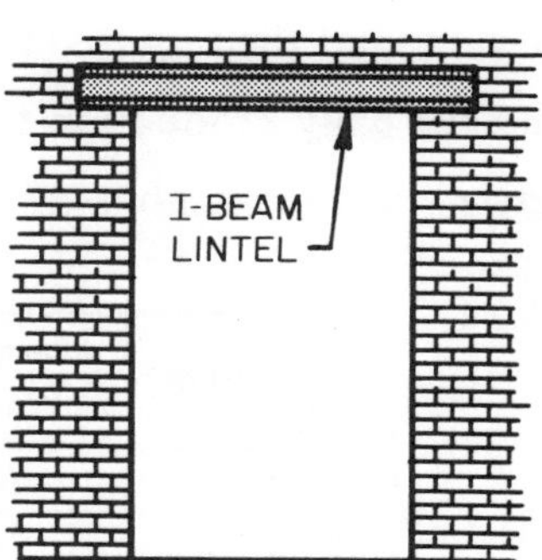

8. Determine dimensions A and B.

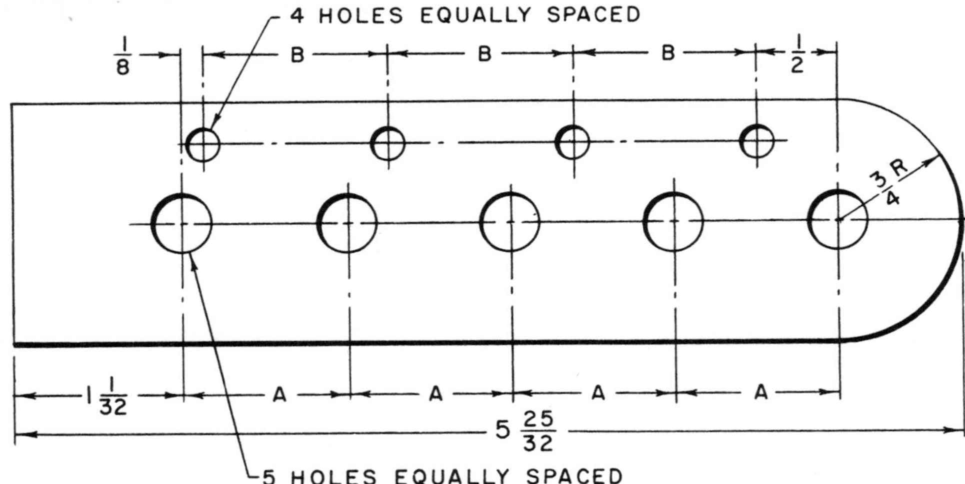

Ans.: B. 1 1/8″

9. In milling flat surfaces, the work is fed against a revolving plain milling cutter with a specified feed.

   a. Find the length of time it will take to mill pieces A, B, C, D, and E for the lengths of work and feed indicated in the table.

   b. Determine the total time for milling.

Cut	Length of Work	Feed per Minute
	(in inches)	
A	4	3/4
B	11	1 3/8
C	11 1/2	2 7/8
D	13 9/16	3 3/4
E	6 3/32	8 1/8

10. The average hourly production of a plastic part, the number of work hours per item per station, and the required production are given in the table.

   a. Find the daily production for items 1, 2, and 3.

   b. Determine the number of days required to produce the units needed of the three items.

Item	Average Hourly Production	Daily Work Hours per Station	Required Units
1	20	14	3220
2	18	15 1/2	3720
3	16 1/2	20 1/2	5158

Ans.: Item 2 a. 279 per day b. 13 1/3 days

Unit 11 ACHIEVEMENT REVIEW ON COMMON FRACTIONS

A. THE CONCEPT OF COMMON FRACTIONS – REPRESENTATION AND REDUCTION

1. What common fraction is represented by the shaded area of each square?

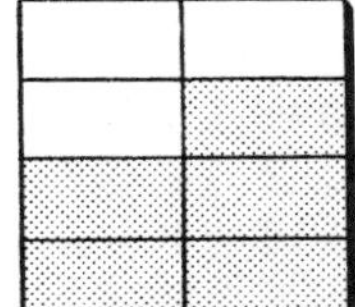 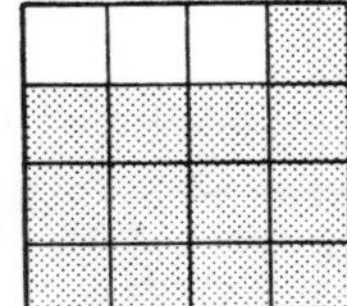 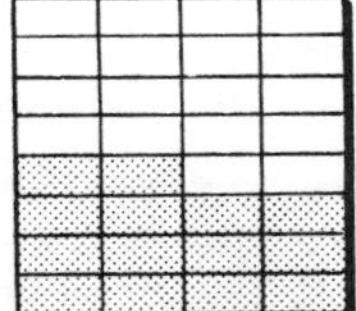 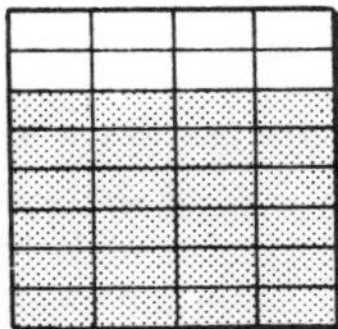 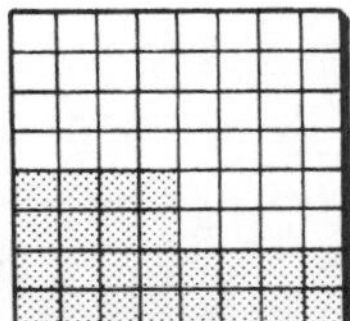 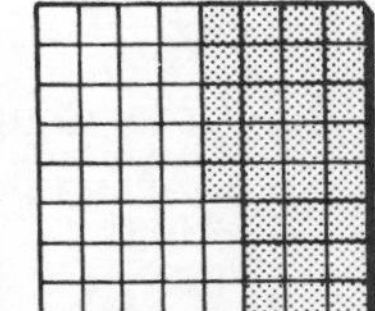

2. Reduce the fractional dimensions A, B, C, D, E, and F, given in the drawing to lowest terms. Locate each dimension on a rule.

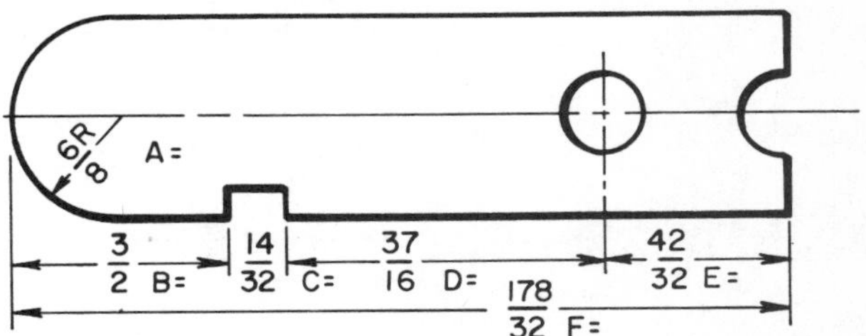

B. ADDITION OF FRACTIONS

1. Add the following fractions:

a. $\frac{1}{8} + \frac{1}{4} + \frac{3}{8}$

b. $\frac{3}{32} + \frac{5}{8} + \frac{3}{4}$

c. $\frac{27}{64} + \frac{3}{16} + \frac{3}{32}$

d. $1\frac{1}{16} + \frac{3}{64} + 4\frac{17}{32}$

e. $3\frac{23}{32} + 2\frac{1}{8} + \frac{57}{64} + \frac{1}{4} + \frac{3}{16}$

f. $\frac{1}{9} + \frac{1}{6} + 2\frac{7}{8} + 3\frac{27}{32}$

2. Determine dimensions A, B, C, D, E, and F for the stripper plate.

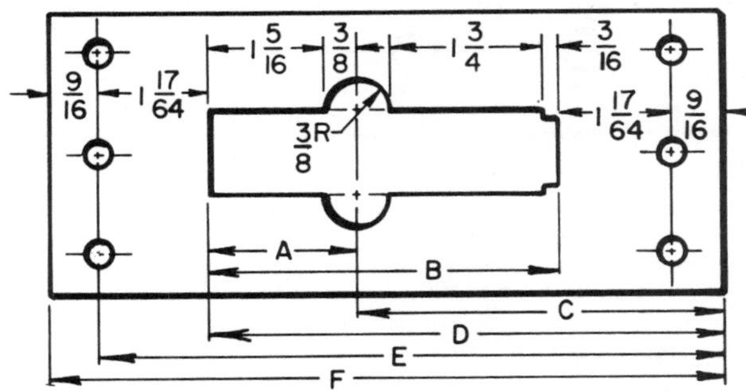

3. A pattern layout for a jacket is illustrated. Determine the length of material needed for one pattern.

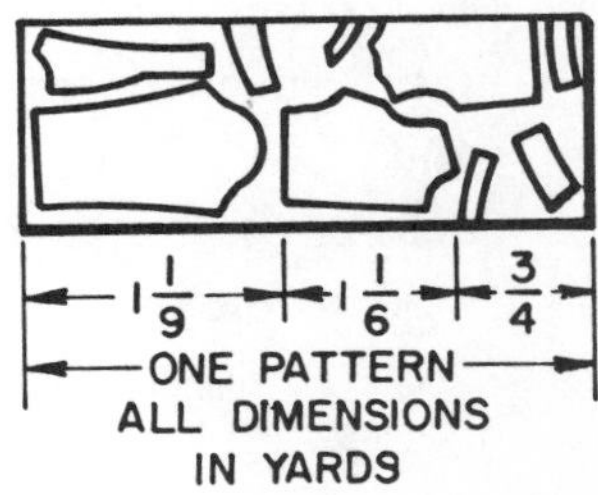

C. SUBTRACTION OF FRACTIONS

1. Subtract the following fractions:

a.	$\frac{9}{16} - \frac{3}{16}$	d.	$122 - 3\frac{3}{8}$	g.	$19 - 2\frac{25}{64}$
b.	$\frac{19}{64} - \frac{7}{32}$	e.	$17 - \frac{55}{64}$	h.	$13\frac{9}{16} - 7\frac{9}{32}$
c.	$3 - \frac{27}{32}$	f.	$203 - 6\frac{9}{16}$	i.	$5\frac{37}{64} - 2\frac{1}{4} - 1\frac{7}{64}$

2. Determine dimensions A, B, C, D, E, and F. Reduce all answers to lowest terms.

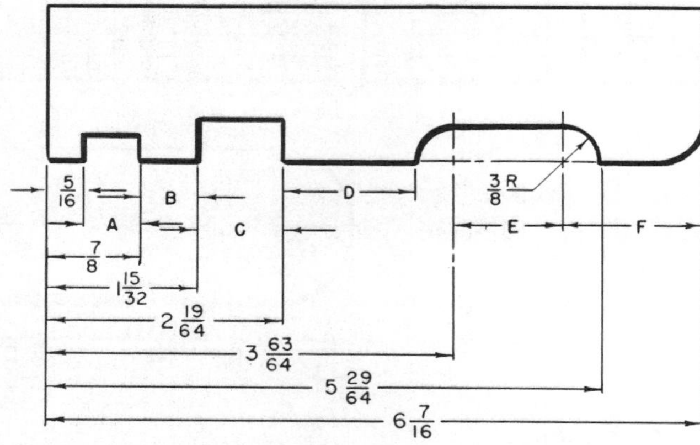

D. MULTIPLICATION OF FRACTIONS

1. Determine dimensions A, B, C, D, E, and F. Reduce all answers to lowest terms.

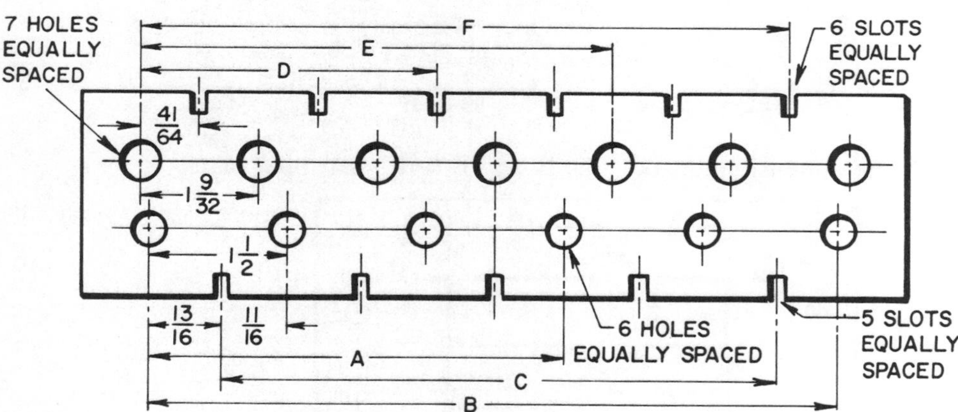

2. Determine the length of corduroy fabric needed for jackets A, B, and C. State any fractional answer in terms of the nearest next whole number.

Jacket	Material per Jacket (including selvages)	Quantity	Length of Material Needed
A	2 7/8 yds.	70	
B	3 1/4 yds.	120	
C	3 5/8 yds.	325	

E. DIVISION OF FRACTIONS

1. Divide the following fractions and reduce all answers to lowest terms.

a. $\frac{1}{8} \div \frac{3}{4}$

b. $\frac{21}{64} \div \frac{7}{16}$

c. $11 \div \frac{5}{6}$

d. $\frac{21}{32} \div 7$

e. $3\frac{3}{32} \div 1\frac{5}{64}$

f. $2\frac{3}{16} \div 1\frac{3}{64} \div 4 \div 1\frac{3}{64}$

2. Determine dimensions A, B, C, D, E, and F. Reduce all answers to lowest terms.

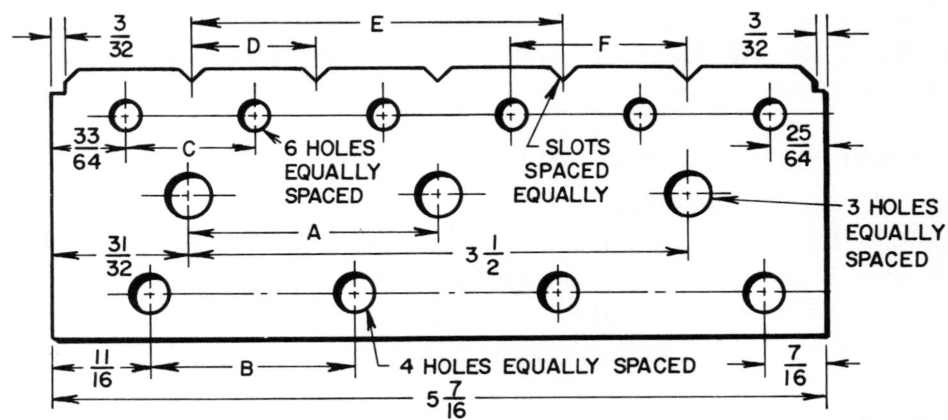

Section 3

DECIMAL FRACTIONS

Unit 12 THE CONCEPT OF DECIMAL FRACTIONS

Machine, hand, and assembly operations must often be performed to a greater degree of accuracy than a fractional part of an inch. Where this accuracy is required, as in mating or interchangeable parts, precise dimensions are given on specifications, drawings, and sketches. These dimensions are given in thousandths, ten-thousandths, and, for extremely accurate work, in hundred-thousandths and millionths of an inch.

A. INTERPRETING THE DECIMAL SYSTEM

This system which is based on (10) is known as the decimal system. It has been adopted universally throughout many industries because of the ease and accuracy with which dimensions may be measured and computed. Steel rules, micrometers, indicators, and other precision instruments are available for taking measurements based on the decimal system.

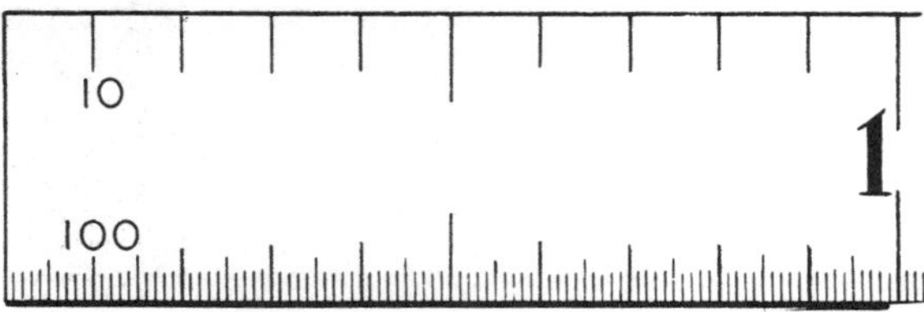

DESCRIBING A DECIMAL FRACTION

A decimal fraction is a fraction. The denominator is 10, 100, 1000, 10,000, or any other value which is obtained by multiplying (10) by itself a specified number of times. Instead of looking like a common fraction, the decimal fraction is written on one line with a period in front of it. This is possible because the denominator is always one (1) followed by zeros. By placing a period before the number which appears in the numerator, the denominator may be omitted. This period is called a decimal point. For example, the common fraction (5/10) is written as the decimal (.5), (5/100) as (.05), (5/1000) as (.005).

WRITING DECIMAL FRACTIONS

It is apparent that any whole number with a decimal point in front of it is a decimal fraction. The numerator is the number which follows (to the right of) the decimal point. The denominator is one (1) with as many zeros after it as there are places in the number to the right of the decimal point.

For example, the fraction nine-tenths (9/10) may be written as the decimal fraction (.9). This means that (9) is the numerator and the denominator is (1) plus as many zeros as there are places (or digits) in the number to the right of the decimal point. In this case, there is one so the denominator is (10). The decimal fraction (.9) is, therefore, the same as (9/10).

To illustrate further

.999 is the same as $\frac{999}{1000}$ ← (3 places or digits)

(1) + (as many zeros as there are places in the numerator)

WRITING WHOLE NUMBERS AND DECIMAL FRACTIONS

B. EXPRESSING DECIMAL VALUES

With whole numbers and fractions, the whole number is placed to the left of the decimal point. The decimal fraction appears to the right. Three examples are given to show how different quantities may be expressed.

EXAMPLES:

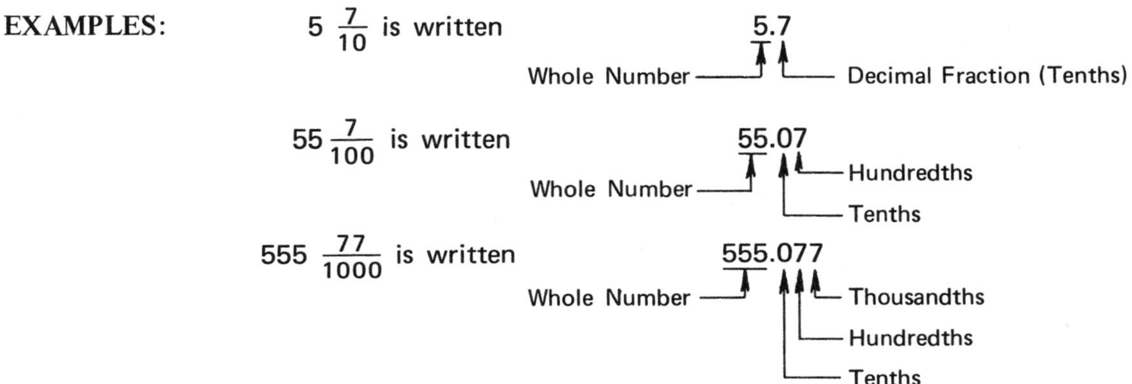

INDICATING DEGREE OF ACCURACY

Whole numbers are sometimes expressed on drawings and in computations in the decimal system with zeros following the decimal point to indicate the degree of precision to which certain dimensions must be held.

EXAMPLE: The quantity (2″) is written (2.00″) if the dimension must be accurate to the second decimal place. If accuracy to the thousandth part of an inch is required, the (2″) is written (2.000″).

A decimal fraction such as (.46) is often written (0.46). The zero which is placed before the decimal point emphasizes the fact that the decimal fraction is less than one.

C. READING DECIMALS

A decimal is read like a whole number except that the name of the last column or place to the right of the decimal point is added. The names of six of these places are illustrated.

EXAMPLES:

- .63 is read sixty-three *hundredths.*
- .136 is read one hundred thirty-six *thousandths.*
- .5625 is read five thousand six hundred twenty-five *ten-thousandths.*

- 3.5 is read three and five *tenths.*
- 2.15625 is read two and fifteen thousand six hundred twenty-five *hundred-thousandths.*
- 0.0625 is read six hundred twenty-five *ten-thousandths.* This quantity is also commonly expressed as sixty-two and a half *thousandths.*

SIMPLIFIED METHOD OF READING DECIMALS

Dimensions involving whole numbers and decimals are frequently expressed in an abbreviated form.

EXAMPLES:

- A dimension like (7.625) is spoken of as "seven point six two five."
- A dimension like (21.3125) is spoken of as "twenty-one point three one two five."

The use of decimal fractions provides an easy method of solving problems. Accurate computations may be made in addition, subtraction, multiplication, and division of fractions having a denominator of 10, 100, 1000, and the like. The units which follow deal with each one of the four fundamental mathematical operations as applied to decimal fractions.

D. ROUNDING-OFF DECIMALS

The degree of precision to which a part is to be machined or finished sometimes determines how accurately the answer to a problem is computed. Many drawings indicate an accuracy in terms of thousandths or ten-thousandths of an inch. However, in computing dimensions, the answers may be accurate to four, five, or more decimal places.

The process of expressing a decimal to the number of decimal places needed for a predetermined degree of accuracy is called "rounding-off decimals."

RULE FOR ROUNDING-OFF DECIMALS

- Check the drawing, sketch, or specifications to determine the required degree of accuracy.
- Look at that digit in the decimal place which indicates the required degree of accuracy.
- Increase that digit by (1) if the digit which follows immediately is (5) or more.
- Leave that digit as it is if the digit which follows is less than (5). Drop all other digits that follow.

EXAMPLE: The sum of a column of decimals is .739752. The part must be machined to an accuracy of only three places. Round off the decimal to three places.

Step 1	Write the computed decimal (6 places).	.739752
Step 2	Locate the digit which shows the number of .001″. The third digit (9) does this.	.739
Step 3	Look at the fourth place digit to determine whether or not the third digit should remain the same, or be increased.	.7397
Step 4	Increase the (9) by (1) because the fourth place digit (7) is greater than (5). The correct answer is .740.	.740 Ans.

All of the intermediate steps in the example are given to serve as a guide in rounding-off decimals. With actual practice, it is possible to round off a decimal to any desired degree of accuracy by just looking at it.

ASSIGNMENT UNIT 12

1. Examine each circle and square. Determine visually what fractional part of each circle or square is represented by the shaded portions (A through I).

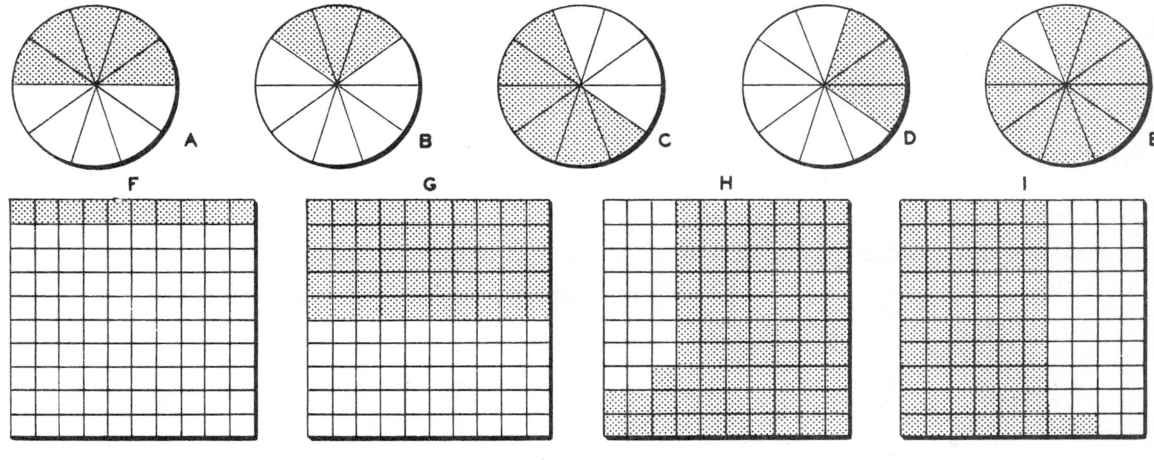

Ans.: B. .3 D. .3 F. .1 H. .77

2. Express decimals (a, b, c, d, e, and f) in words.

   a. .3
   b. .07
   c. 1.25
   d. 0.3125
   e. 5.375
   f. 27.01563

3. Write the value of each quantity (a, b, c, d, e, and f) as a decimal.

   a. Seven tenths
   b. Sixteen hundredths
   c. Fifteen thousandths
   d. Eleven ten-thousandths
   e. Two thousand one hundred fifty-two ten-thousandths
   f. Three point one eight seven five

Ans.: b. .16 d. .0011 f. 3.1875

4. Write the following fractions as decimal fractions.

a.	$\frac{1}{10}$	e.	$\frac{73}{100}$	i.	$\frac{3}{10,000}$	m.	$\frac{1,000}{10,000}$
b.	$\frac{3}{10}$	f.	$\frac{1}{1,000}$	j.	$\frac{19}{10,000}$	n.	$\frac{793}{100,000}$
c.	$\frac{9}{100}$	g.	$\frac{93}{1,000}$	k.	$\frac{205}{10,000}$	o.	$\frac{1,027}{100,000}$
d.	$\frac{29}{100}$	h.	$\frac{157}{1,000}$	l.	$\frac{1,923}{10,000}$	p.	$\frac{30,019}{100,000}$

Ans.: b. .3 d. .29 f. .001 h. .157 j. .0019
l. .1923 n. .00793 p. .30019

5. Write the following mixed numbers as decimals.

a. $1\frac{1}{10}$ c. $25\frac{91}{100}$ e. $2525\frac{21}{10,000}$

b. $3\frac{9}{100}$ d. $272\frac{67}{1,000}$ f. $362\frac{2,007}{10,000}$

Ans.: b. 3.09 d. 272.067 f. 362.2007

6. Secure a rule with a "tenth" and "hundredth" scale on it. Locate dimensions (a, b, c, d, and e) on the "tenth" scale.

a. $\frac{1}{10}$ d. 1.2

b. $\frac{3}{10}$ e. 1.5

c. $\frac{5}{10}$

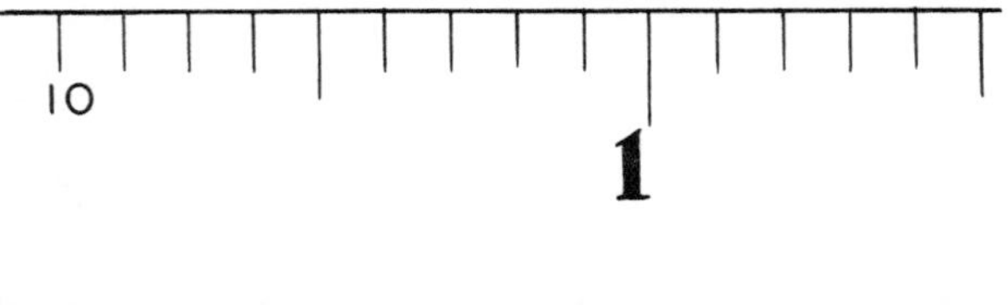

7. Locate dimensions (a, b, c, d, and e) on the "hundredth" scale.

a. $\frac{10}{100}$ d. 1.20

b. $\frac{33}{100}$ e. 1.32

c. $\frac{77}{100}$

8. Express dimensions (a) through (e) on the drawing as decimals.

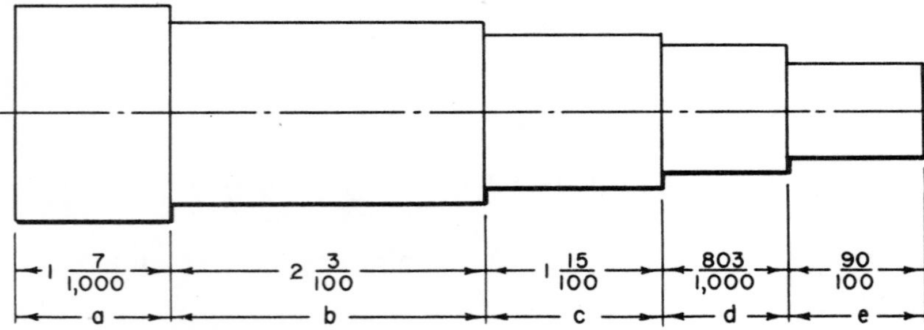

Ans.: b. 2.03 d. .803

9. Read dimensions (A) through (G) on the rules as illustrated. Express as decimal fractions and decimals.

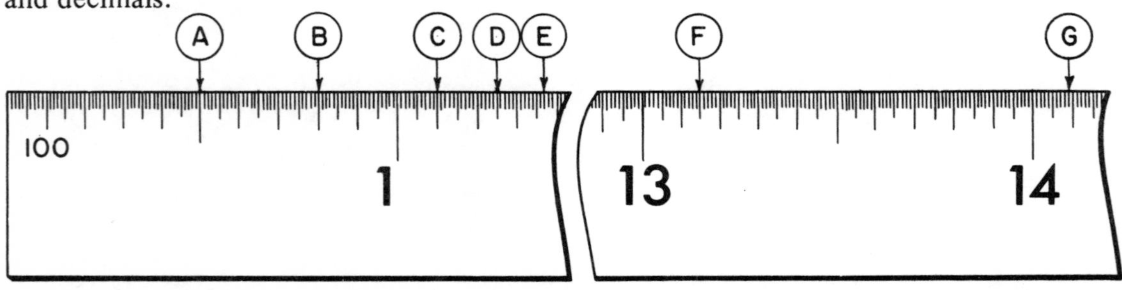

Ans.: B. .8 D. 1.25 F. 13.15

10. Round off decimal fractions (a) through (i) to two decimal places.

a. .756	d. 29.409	g. 221.7557
b. 1.952	e. 2.5644	h. 0.89673
c. 7.324	f. 18.2707	i. 20.99974

Ans.: b. 1.95 d. 29.41 f. 18.27 h. .90

Unit 13 ADDITION OF DECIMALS

On many drawings and sketches, dimensions must be computed which require the addition of two or more decimals.

A typical example is illustrated. The distance (A) on the gage may be determined by adding the decimal dimensions (2.20″), (2.76″) and (.50″). The addition of these decimals is the same as the addition of regular whole numbers. The exception is that the location of the decimal point must be given.

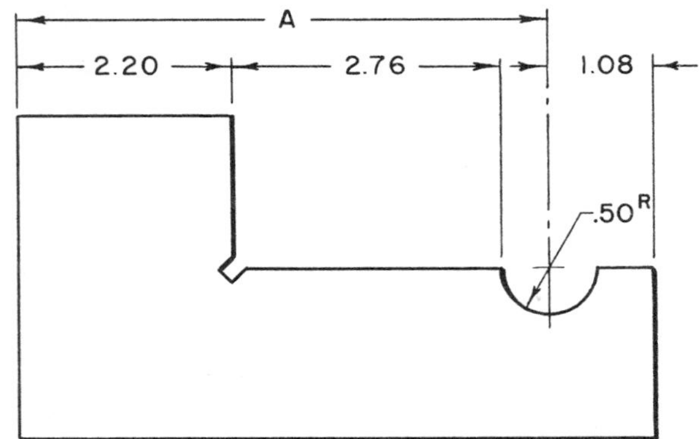

A. ADDING DECIMALS

RULE FOR ADDING DECIMALS

- Write the given numbers one under each other so that all of the decimal points are in a vertical column.
- Add each column of numbers the same as for regular whole numbers.
- Locate the decimal point in the answer by placing it in the same column in which it appears with each number.

EXAMPLE: Add .875 + 1.2 + 375.007 + 71.1357 + 735.

Step 1 Write the numbers under each other so that all of the decimal points are in a vertical line.

```
    .875
   1.2
 375.007
  71.1357
 735.
```

NOTE: Zeros are sometimes added to the numbers so that they all have an equal number of places after the decimal point. This practice may be followed to eliminate errors.

```
    .8750
   1.2000
 375.0070
  71.1357
 735.0000
```

Step 2 Add each column.

Step 3 Locate the decimal point in the answer in the same column in which it appears with the numbers being added.

```
1183.2177
```

ASSIGNMENT UNIT 13

A. ADDITION OF DECIMALS

1. Add:

a.	b.	c.	d.
.5	9.3	76.8	195.7
.6	17.7	119.32	83.02
8.3	72.4	24.6	9.006

e. .4 + .7 + .4
f. 269.1 + 201.3
g. 0.57 + 29.35 + 1.6
h. 0.872 + 1.54 + 725.093
i. 2.9834 + 0.7256 + 329.7 + 21.0006
j. 0.00850 + 0.93006 + 3225.06 + 0.0875

Ans.: b. 99.4 d. 287.726 f. 470.4 h. 727.505 j. 3226.08606

2. Add decimals (a) through (e). Then round off sum correct to three decimal places.

a.	b.
25.0097	.7895
0.9237	.6842
1.125	12.7
	231.0924

c. 11.61254 + 0.735 + 1.3 + 625.003125
d. .7 + 1.707 + 22.0625 + 3.09375 + 0.625
e. 7.251 + 0.98475 + .03125 + 25.0 + 5.105

Ans.: b. 245.266 d. 28.188

B. **SPECIAL PROBLEMS**

1. Determine dimensions A, B, C, D, and E for the Die Plate.

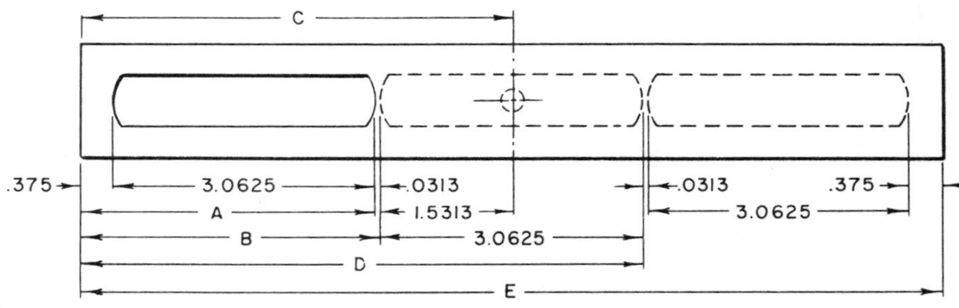

Ans.: B = 3.4688 D = 6.5313

2. Determine baseline dimensions A, B, C, D, and E.

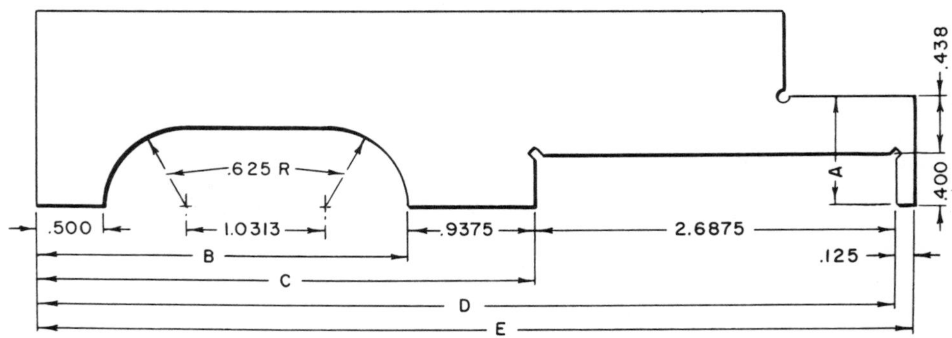

Ans.: B = 2.7813 D = 6.4063

3. Determine overall dimension A of the Template. Round off answer to three decimal places.

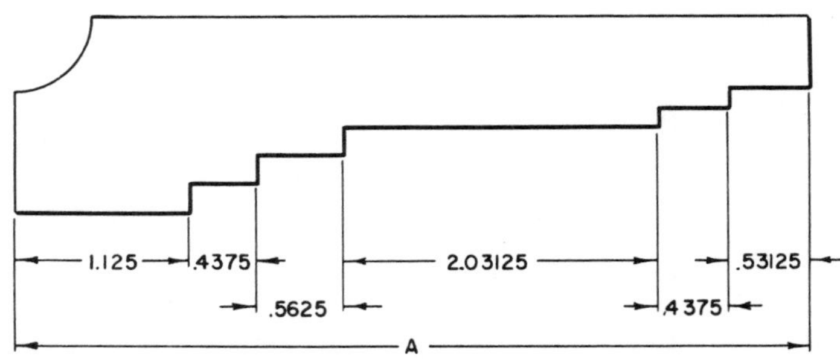

4. Find dimensions A through E. Start each computation with the dimensions given on the drawing. Round off answers to two decimal places.

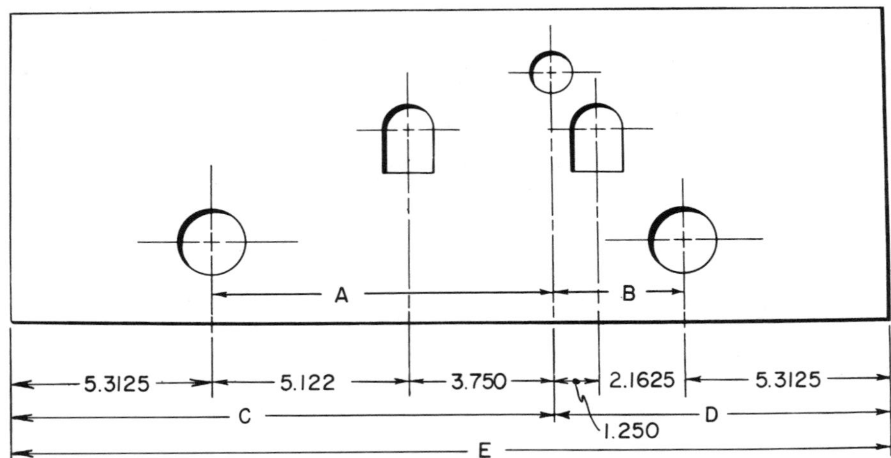

Ans.: B = 3.41″ D = 8.73″

5. A counter top is 1.725″ thick. It is covered with laminated plastic .0625″ thick. Give the total thickness of the top.
6. Find the thickness of the plywood panel as illustrated.

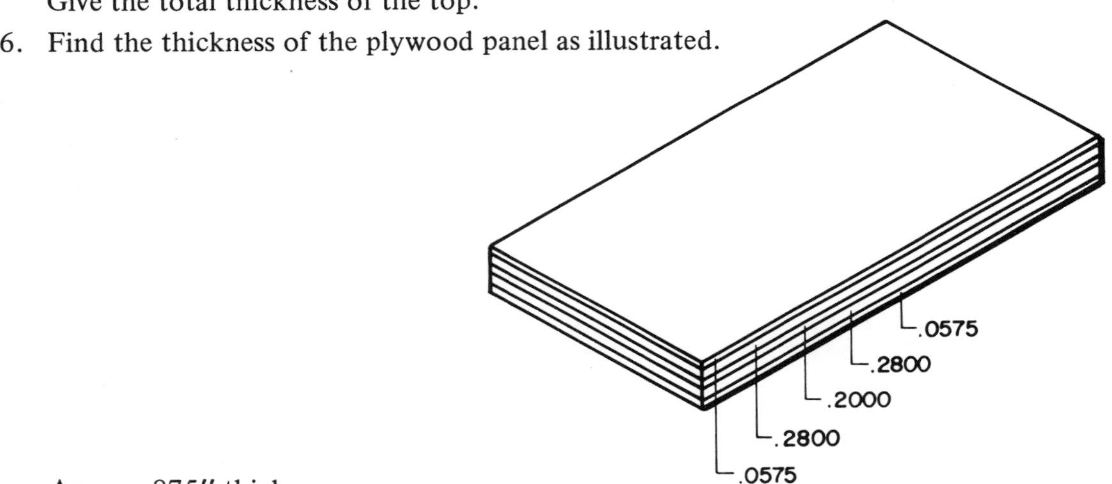

Ans.: .875″ thick

7. The total current in the circuit is measured by an ammeter (A). The total current is distributed in the four appliances. State what the reading is on the ammeter to the closest hundredth ampere.

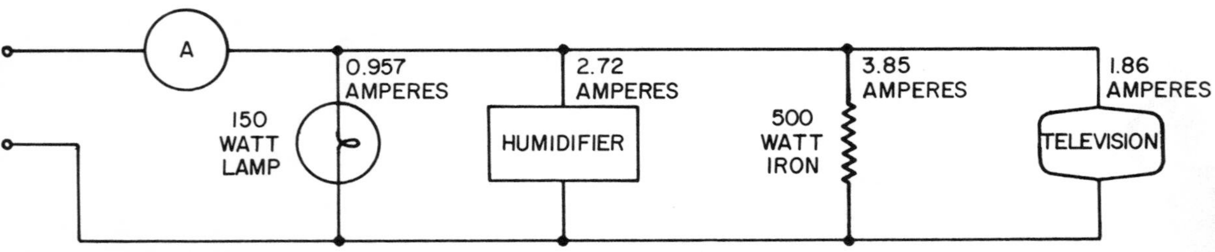

Unit 14 SUBTRACTION OF DECIMALS

The subtracting of one decimal dimension from another is common practice in the factory, store, hospital and home. As far as the mathematical operation itself is concerned, it is the same as the subtraction of whole numbers. However, there is an exception. The position of the decimal point in the answer must be considered similar to the addition of decimals.

The drawing of the tapered plug gage shows a typical method of dimensioning a taper. The difference in diameters can readily be determined by the "subtraction of decimals." The smaller diameter (1.5936″) is subtracted from the larger diameter (1.875″). The answer is referred to as the "difference."

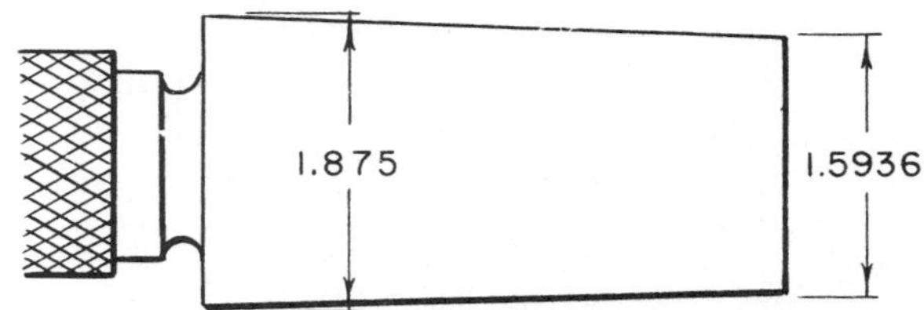

A. SUBTRACTING DECIMALS

RULE FOR SUBTRACTING DECIMALS

- Write the given numbers so that the decimal points are under each other.
- Subtract each column of numbers the same as for regular whole numbers.
- Locate the decimal point in the answer by placing it under the column where it appeared in the problem.

EXAMPLE: Determine the amount of taper of the tapered plug gage. Give the dimension to the nearest thousandth.

Step 1 Write the two dimensions (1.875″ and 1.5936″) so that the smaller is under the larger. The decimal points are in the same column.

$$\begin{array}{r} 1.875 \\ \underline{1.5936} \end{array}$$

NOTE: Zeros may be added to one of the numbers (1.875). It has fewer digits after the decimal point than the other number. The addition of zeros does not change the value.

$$\begin{array}{r} 1.8750 \\ \underline{1.5936} \end{array}$$

Step 2 Subtract the numbers by starting with the last digit on the right.

$$\begin{array}{r} 1.8750 \\ \underline{1.5936} \end{array}$$

Step 3 Locate the decimal point in the answer. 0.2814

Step 4 Round off the answer to the required number of places 0.2814″ rounded-off to three places. = 0.281

ASSIGNMENT UNIT 14

A. SUBTRACTING DECIMALS

1. Find the difference in diameters (taper) of the Taper Plugs A, B, C, D, and E.

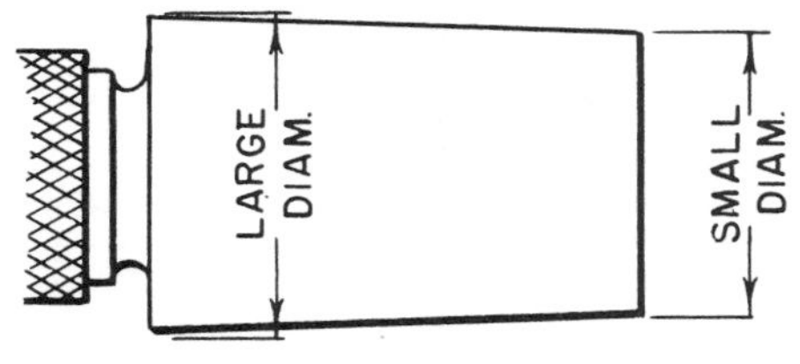

Plug	Diameter	
	Large End	Small End
A	1.750″	1.500″
B	3.0935″	2.837″
C	4.5312″	3.687″
D	10.1563″	8.3125″
E	7.0781″	5.7812″

Ans.: B. .2565″ D. 1.8438″

2. Find dimensions A, B, C, D, and E for the plate shown.

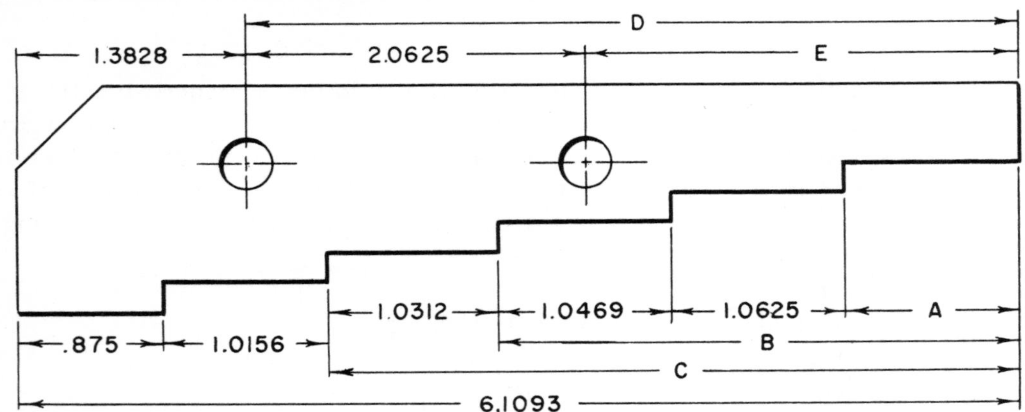

Ans.: B = 3.1875 D = 4.7265

3. Determine dimensions A, B, C, D, and E. Round off each answer to three decimal places.

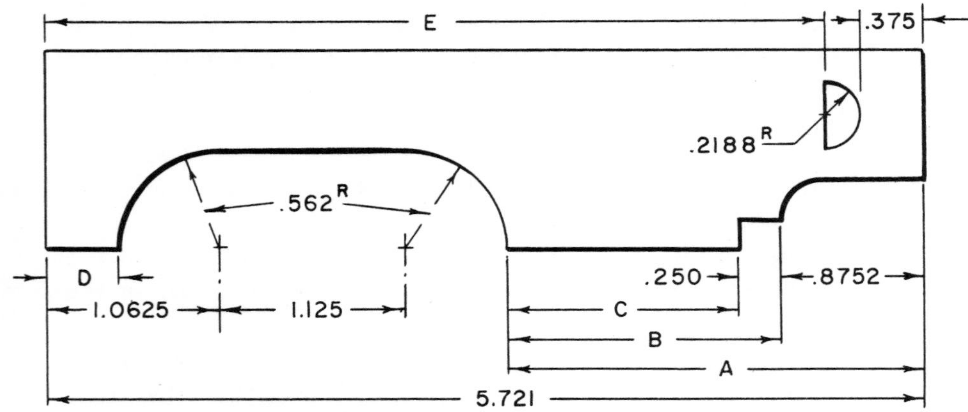

Ans.: B = 2.097 D = .500

4. Determine dimensions A, B, C, D, and E correct to two decimal places.

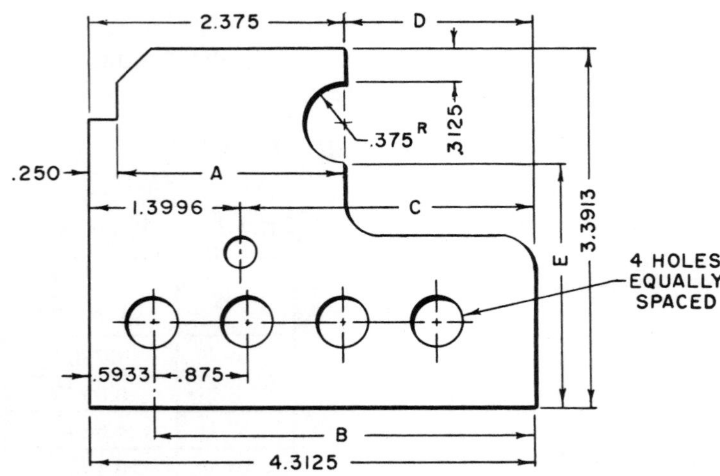

Ans.: B = 3.72 D = 1.94

5. Find dimensions A, B, C, D, and E correct to three decimal places.

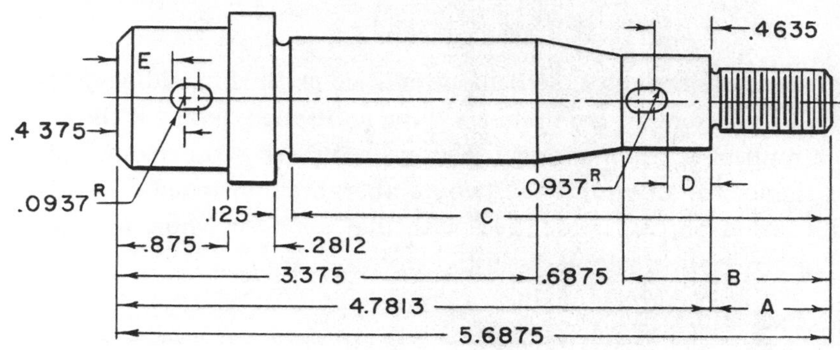

Ans.: B = 1.625 D = .370

6. The wire diameter for sizes 10 through 16 of copper conductors is given in the table. Indicate the difference in diameter between sizes.

   a. 10 and 16
   b. 10 and 11
   c. 13 and 14
   d. 15 and 16

   Ans.: b. .01116″
   d. .00625″

Wire Size	
National Gage Number	Diameter in Inches
10	0.10190
11	0.09074
12	0.08081
13	0.07196
14	0.06408
15	0.05707
16	0.05082

7. The opening between two parts is "three and a half thousandths" (0.0035″). A shim 0.00225 is available. Find the additional thickness to fill the opening.

8. A diet permits a daily intake of 1.67 quarts of liquid a day. 0.375 quart and 0.750 quart of liquid are used for two meals. Determine the remaining amount of liquid that may be taken during the day. Round off the answer to two decimal places.

Unit 15 MULTIPLICATION OF DECIMALS

Multiplying decimals is a convenient and simplified method of adding them. One method of multiplying is to take one of the numbers to be multiplied, listing it the number of times indicated by the multiplier, then adding. This procedure is cumbersome. Also, it is easier and there is less chance for an error if the two numbers are multiplied.

The multiplication process is identical with that used for whole numbers. The exception is in pointing-off the decimal places in the answer.

A. MULTIPLYING DECIMALS

RULE FOR MULTIPLYING DECIMALS

- Multiply the same as with whole numbers.
- Total the number of decimal places to the right of the decimal point in both of the numbers being multiplied.
- Locate the decimal point in the answer.

  NOTE: Start at the extreme right digit in the answer. Count off as many places to the left as there are in both the multiplier and multiplicand.

EXAMPLE: Multiply 27.935 x 7.07.

Step 1 Multiply the (27.935) by (7.07).

Step 2 Add the number of digits to the right of the decimal point in both numbers that have been multiplied.

Step 3 Start at the right in the product. Count off the five decimal places to the left. Place the decimal point here. The result then is the product of multiplying the two decimals.

```
  27.935  ◄ (3 decimal places)
    7.07  ◄ (2 decimal places)
  ------
  195545
195545
--------
197.50045
    ▲
(5 decimal places)
```

B. CONVERTING PERCENT VALUES TO DECIMALS

The term percent means comparison in terms of so many hundredths of a quantity. In most percentage problems, multiplication is the mathematical process involved. The percent value is often converted to the decimal system for ease in computing and accuracy in pointing-off the required number of decimal places. Instead of writing out the word percent each time, the symbol (%) is used.

RULE FOR CHANGING A PERCENT TO A DECIMAL

- Remove the (%) sign.
- Place a decimal point two digits to the left of the number for the given percent.

  NOTE: If the percent is a mixed number, change the fraction to a decimal and place this value after the whole number.
- Use the decimal value for the given percent the same as any other decimals to perform the required mathematical operations.

EXAMPLE: Change 12% to a decimal.

Step 1 Remove percent (%) sign. 12

Step 2 Place decimal point two digits to the left. .12

Step 3 12% = .12 Ans.

C. CONVERTING DECIMALS TO PERCENT

RULE FOR CHANGING A DECIMAL TO A PERCENT

- Move the decimal point two places to the right.
- Place the percent sign (%) after this number.

EXAMPLE: Change .055 to a percent.

Step 1 Move decimal point two places to the right. 05.5

Step 2 Place % sign after this number. 5.5%

Step 3 .055 = 5.5% Ans.

Different ways of representing common and decimal fraction and percent values of the same quantities are shown in the accompanying table.

Fraction	Decimal Equivalent	Percent Value	Expressed in Words
1/100	.01	1%	One one-hundredth
10/100	.10	10%	Ten hundredths
100/100	1.00	100%	One hundred hundredths
150/100	1.50	150%	One hundred fifty hundredths
175/1000	.175	17.5%	One hundred seventy-five thousandths

D. CHECKING

Problems in multiplication may be checked by one of two methods the same as for whole numbers.

- The multiplier and multiplicand may be interchanged.
- The multiplication process may be repeated, using the same multiplier and multiplicand.

In either case, one of the most important steps is to check the location of the decimal point in the product.

ASSIGNMENT UNIT 15

A. MULTIPLICATION OF DECIMALS

1. Multiply the whole number and decimal fractions. Check each answer.

   a. 9 by .8 b. 16 by 1.5 c. 12 by .72 d. .37 by 100

e. 1.3 x 98 g. 11.7 x 1.82 i. 92.07 x 7.392 k. 125.002 x 2.14
f. 9.5 x .76 h. 11.31 x 6.14 j. 1.0313 x 2.937 l. 10.063 x 2.030

Ans.: b. 24 d. 37 f. 7.22 h. 69.4434 j. 3.0289281 l. 20.42789

2. Multiply these decimal fractions. Check each answer. Then, round off the answers to four decimal places.

a. 10.0625 x 6.437 b. 1.0937 x 3.0313 c. 1.5 x 3.7 x 5.12

Ans.: b. 3.3153

3. Determine the cost of bar stock needed for parts A, B, C, D, and E. Give the answer in terms of dollars and cents for each part and the total cost.

Parts	Weight (Pounds per Foot)	Required Number of Feet	Cost Per Pound
A	2.5	3.5	.75
B	2.25	7.5	.63
C	1.25	7.75	.93
D	7.5	27.125	.527
E	.0125	10.25	4.375

Ans.: B. $10.63 D. $107.21

B. CONVERSION OF PERCENT VALUES

1. Determine the weight of metals A, B, C, and D which were alloyed to cast a bronze plate weighing 79.5 pounds. The composition of the bronze is indicated by percent of each alloying metal.

A	B	C	D
Copper	Tin	Zinc	Lead
81%	6.5%	7.25%	5.25%

Ans.: B. 5.1675 lbs. D.4.17375 lbs.

C. SPECIAL PROBLEMS

1. Find the lengths of insulating strip required to blank out each of the quantity of plates specified in A, B, C, D, and E. Round off all answers to one decimal place. Also, determine the total length required.

Part	Quantity	Length of Plate	Allowance for Blanking
A	100	1.5	.25
B	100	2.25	.25
C	75	2.375	.25
D	75	2.625	.125
E	75	2.8906	.0937

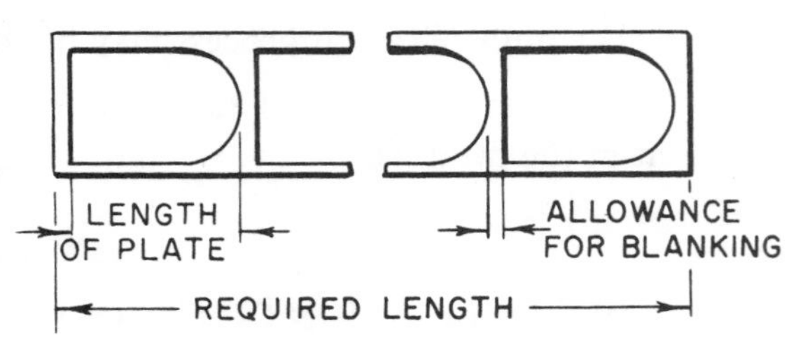

Ans.: B. 250.3 D. 206.4

2. Determine the distance in inches which a tool travels for each of five cuts A, B, C, D, and E. Each distance should be rounded-off to one decimal place. Also, determine the total distance.

Cuts	Rpm	Feed per Rev. (in inches)	Time (in minutes)
A	900	.005	1.5
B	424	.008	2.25
C	368	.015	6.75
D	336	.062	5.75
E	128	.062	25.25

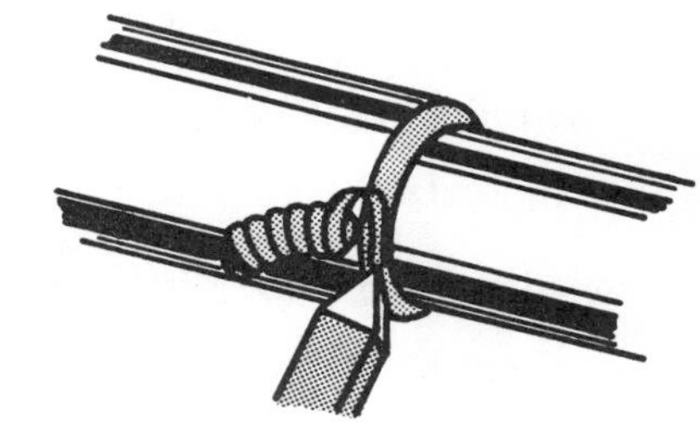

Ans.: B. 7.6″ D. 119.8″

3. The table gives the thickness, number of laminations, and meter readings of resistance for each lamination for each of three different core materials.

a. Determine the thickness of cores 1, 2, and 3.

b. Find the total resistance of the laminations in the three cores.

NOTE: Round off all answers to two decimal places.

Core Material	Thickness per Lamination	Number of Laminations	Resistance per Lamination
1	.003″	200	.1 amp
2	.012″	21	.125 amps
3	.1352″	15	.3157 amps

Ans.: 2. a. .25″ b. 2.63 amps

4. It takes an average of 3.4 hours to lay 100 square feet (one square) of finish flooring. Compute the time required to lay finish flooring in rooms A, B, and C.

Room	Floor Area (Squares)	Flooring Time
A	12.2	
B	13.75	
C	17.87	

5. The unit price for four foods, weight per container, and quantity required are given in table form. Determine the cost of each item correct to two decimal places.

Food	Cost ¢ per Ounce	Ounces per Container	Quantity	Cost
A	.043	12	24 pkgs.	
B	.039	18	12 pkgs.	
C	.03	15.75	24 cans	
D	.017	15.75	48 cans	

6. An electric (kilowatt hour) meter registers | 7 5 2 3 | on June 1. On July 1 the reading is | 7 8 6 9 |. The difference represents electrical energy used. The cost of electrical energy averages \$0.033 per kilowatt hour (kWh).

   a. Find the cost of the electrical energy.

   The bill is reduced by a rate adjustment of \$0.0025 per kWh.

   b. Indicate the amount the bill is reduced.

   A sales tax of 0.075 is levied against each adjusted utility bill.

   c. Compute the sales tax on the adjusted bill.

Unit 16 DIVISION OF DECIMALS

Division is the simplified process of computing the number of times one number is contained in another. The division of decimals, like all other mathematical operations for decimals, is essentially the same as for whole numbers. In addition, consideration must be given to the location of the decimal point in the answer.

A. DIVIDING DECIMALS

RULE FOR DIVIDING DECIMALS

- Place the number to be divided (called *dividend*) inside the division box.
- Place the *divisor* outside.
- Move the decimal point in the divisor to the extreme right. The divisor then becomes a whole number.
- Move the decimal point the same number of places to the right in the dividend.

  NOTE: Zeros are added in the dividend if it has fewer digits than the divisor.
- Mark the position of the decimal point in the *quotient.* The position is directly above the decimal point in the dividend.
- Divide as whole numbers. Place each figure in the quotient directly above the digit involved in the dividend.
- Add zeros after the decimal point in the dividend if it cannot be divided exactly by the divisor.
- Continue the division until the quotient has as many places as are required for the answer.

EXAMPLE: Case 1 Divide 25.5 by 12.75.

Step 1 Move the decimal point in the divisor to the right (2 places).

Step 2 Move the decimal point in the dividend to the right the same number of places (2).

NOTE: Since there is only one digit after the decimal, add a zero to it.

Step 3 Place the decimal point in the quotient.

Step 4 Divide as whole numbers.

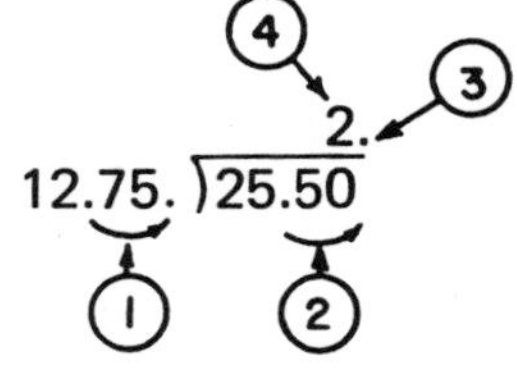

EXAMPLE: Case 2 Divide 123.573 by 137.4.

The answer must be correct to three decimal places.

NOTE: The division process is usually carried out to one more than the required number of places in the answer. The last digit may then be rounded-off for greater accuracy. In this case, the (.8993) is rounded-off to (.899).

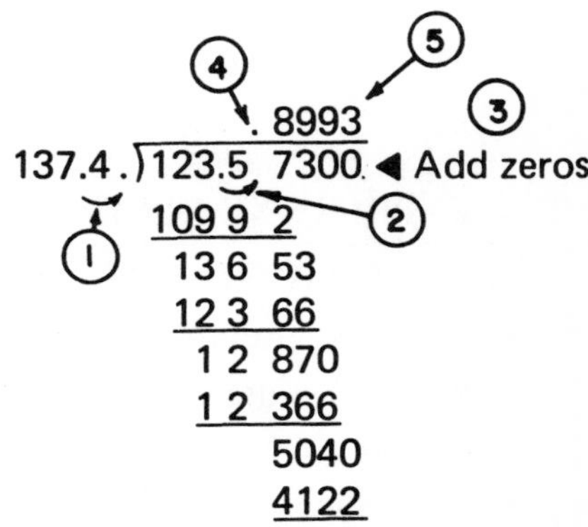

B. EXPRESSING COMMON FRACTIONS AS DECIMAL FRACTIONS

Dimensions used in machine, bench, or assembly operations are given in terms of common fractions or decimal fractions. Yet, when the actual measurements are taken, it is often necessary to either express a common fraction as a decimal fraction or a decimal fraction as a common fraction. Converting from one system to the other is comparatively easy. It involves, in most cases, the division of numbers having three or less digits.

RULE FOR EXPRESSING A COMMON FRACTION AS A DECIMAL FRACTION

- Divide the numerator by the denominator.

EXAMPLE: Express 5/16 as a decimal fraction.

Step 1 Divide the numerator (5) by the denominator (16).

Step 2 Place a decimal point after the (5).

Step 3 Locate the decimal point in the quotient.

Step 4 Add as many zeros as are needed to obtain a quotient which can be rounded-off to the required number of decimal places.

Step 5 Divide. The resulting answer (.3125) is the decimal fraction equivalent of the common fraction (5/16).

```
      .3125 Ans.
16)5.0000
   4 8
     20
     16
      40
      32
       80
       80
```

C. EXPRESSING MIXED NUMBERS AS DECIMALS

RULE FOR EXPRESSING A MIXED NUMBER AS ITS DECIMAL EQUIVALENT

- Express the mixed number as an improper fraction.
- Divide the numerator by the denominator.
- Carry out the division to the number of decimal places required for the degree of accuracy involved.

EXAMPLE: Determine the decimal equivalent of 1 3/64 correct to three decimal places.

$$1\frac{3}{64} = \frac{67}{64} =$$

```
      1.0468
64)67.0000
   64
    3 00
    2 56
      440
      384
       560
       512
        48
```

Divide the numbers to four decimal places.

The decimal equivalent of 1 3/64 correct to three places is (1.047).

D. EXPRESSING DECIMAL FRACTIONS AS COMMON FRACTIONS

RULE FOR EXPRESSING A DECIMAL FRACTION AS A COMMON FRACTION

- Write the number after the decimal point as the numerator of a common fraction.
- Write the denominator as (1) with the same number of zeros after it as there are digits to the right of the decimal point.
- Express resulting fraction in lowest terms.

EXAMPLE: Express .09375 as a common fraction.

Step 1	Write number after the decimal point as the numerator.	9375	=	9,375
Step 2	Determine denominator.	1 + 5 zeros	=	100,000
Step 3	Express fraction in lowest terms.	$\frac{9,375}{100,000}$	=	$\frac{3}{32}$

E. SIMPLIFIED METHODS OF DETERMINING DECIMAL OR FRACTIONAL EQUIVALENTS

Tables of Decimal and Fractional Equivalents are usually found in all trades, drafting rooms, production shops, and toolrooms. These tables are printed in many forms: as enlarged wall charts, as reference tables in handbooks and kits, and as handy-guide plastic cards. The tables are used extensively for determining either the decimal or fractional equivalent of a given value. The simplified use of the charts is preferred to the longhand method of dividing. The charts insure accuracy and speed up the process of computation.

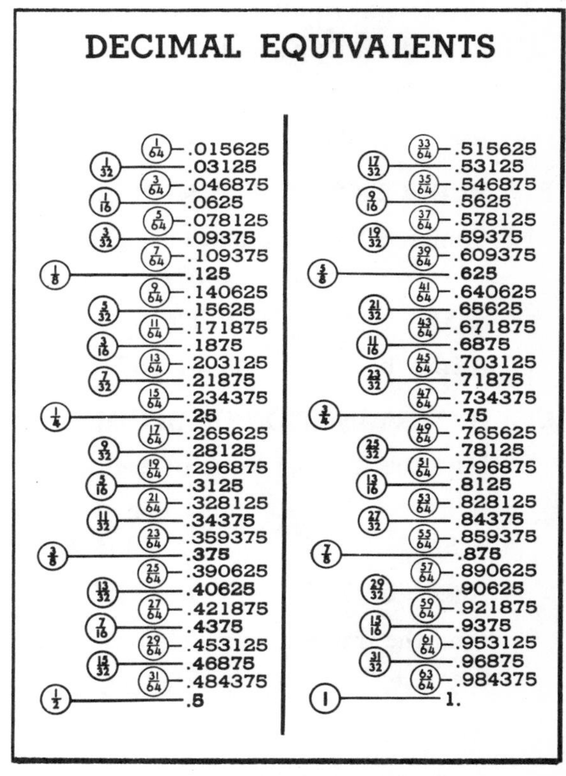

DECIMAL EQUIVALENTS
1/64 .015625
1/32 .03125
3/64 .046875
1/16 .0625
5/64 .078125
3/32 .09375
7/64 .109375
1/8 .125
9/64 .140625
5/32 .15625
11/64 .171875
3/16 .1875
13/64 .203125
7/32 .21875
15/64 .234375
1/4 .25
17/64 .265625
9/32 .28125
19/64 .296875
5/16 .3125
21/64 .328125
11/32 .34375
23/64 .359375
3/8 .375
25/64 .390625
13/32 .40625
27/64 .421875
7/16 .4375
29/64 .453125
15/32 .46875
31/64 .484375
1/2 .5
33/64 .515625
17/32 .53125
35/64 .546875
9/16 .5625
37/64 .578125
19/32 .59375
39/64 .609375
5/8 .625
41/64 .640625
21/32 .65625
43/64 .671875
11/16 .6875
45/64 .703125
23/32 .71875
47/64 .734375
3/4 .75
49/64 .765625
25/32 .78125
51/64 .796875
13/16 .8125
53/64 .828125
27/32 .84375
55/64 .859375
7/8 .875
57/64 .890625
29/32 .90625
59/64 .921875
15/16 .9375
61/64 .953125
31/32 .96875
63/64 .984375
1 1.

SELECTING DECIMAL OR FRACTIONAL VALUES

The fractions on these charts are given in steps of 1/64″ in one column with the corresponding decimal equivalents in another. Most tables are carried out to six places. Decimal fractions may be rounded-off to any desired degree of accuracy. The decimal equivalent is found by locating the given fraction in the left-hand column. The equivalent value is located in the decimal column. Reverse the practice for finding fractional equivalents of decimals.

SHOP METHOD OF DETERMINING VALUE

Even without the charts most good mechanics can quickly determine the decimal equivalents of all fractions by increments of 1/64″. In addition to knowing the decimal equivalents of eighths and quarters, many craftsmen also learn that the decimal equivalents of 1/64″ is (.015625), 1/32″ = (.03125″) and 1/16″ = (.0625″).

By thinking of the required fractions as being equal to or so much smaller or larger than a known decimal value, it is comparatively easy to determine decimal equivalents of fractions. For example, assume that the decimal equivalent of (29/32) is needed. The mechanic usually thinks of that fraction as a "thirty-second over seven-eighths." It would be equal to (.875) plus 1/32 (.03125) or (.90625). This same line of reasoning provides a shortcut in determining decimal equivalents of most fractions.

ASSIGNMENT UNIT 16

A. DIVISION OF DECIMALS

1. Divide:

a. 11.8 by 100 c. 10 by 2.5 e. 7.5 ÷ 22.5
b. 23.7 by 1,000 d. 104.26 ÷ 26 f. 26.0313 ÷ 10.25

Ans.: b. .0237 d. 4.01 f. 2.540

2. Divide and round off each answer correct to the number of decimal places indicated.

a. .875 ÷ 6.25 (one place) c. .4375 ÷ 156.25 (three places)
b. 2.234 ÷ 24.63 (three places) d. 145.26 ÷ 13.750 (two places)

Ans.: b. .091 d. 10.56

B. REDUCTION OF COMMON FRACTIONS AND MIXED NUMBERS TO DECIMALS

1. Compute the three-place decimal fraction equivalent of each of the following.

a. 3/4 c. 9/16 e. 7/72 g. 29/64
b. 5/8 d. 1/6 f. 13/32

Ans.: b. .625 d. .167 f. .406

C. DETERMINATION OF DECIMAL AND FRACTIONAL SIZES BY TABLE

1. Find the decimal value of each fractional size drill, using a Decimal Equivalents table.

a. 1/2″ c. 3/8″ e. 7/32″
b. 3/4″ d. 5/16″ f. 19/64″

Ans.: b. .75″ d. .3125″ f. .296875″

2. Find the fractional drill equivalent to each decimal. Use a table.

a. .250″ b. .875″ c. .5625″ d. .6875″ e. .71875″ f. .046875″

Ans.: b. 7/8 d. 11/16 f. 3/64

D. SPECIAL PROBLEMS

1. Determine the depth of cut for each tooth on broaches A, B, C, D, and E.

Part	Depth to be Broached (in inches)	Teeth in Broach
A	.1	10
B	.126	42
C	.255	150
D	.063	30
E	.0924	42

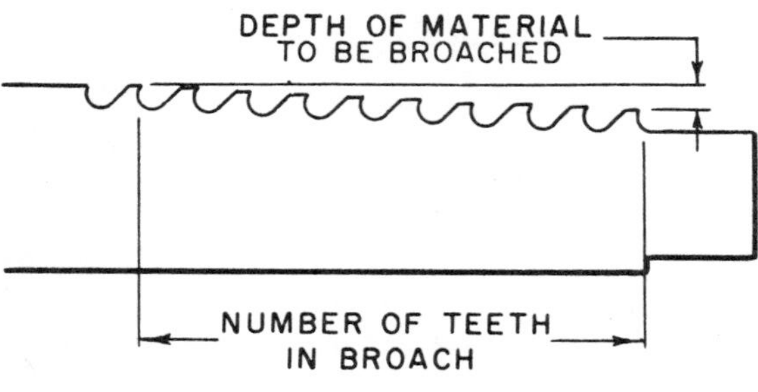

Ans.: B. .003 D. .0021

2. Determine how many spacing collars are needed for sawing operations A, B, C, D, and E. (All dimensions are given in inches.)

Operation	Thickness of Collars	Spacing Required
A	.5	4.5
B	.25	3.5
C	.125	2.375
D	.1875	1.875
E	.09375	1.125

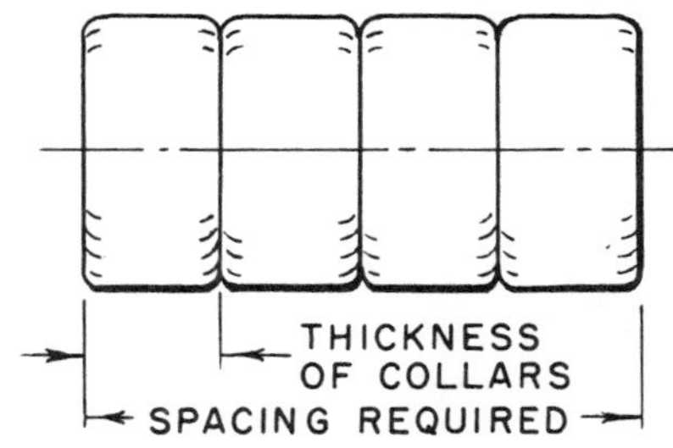

Ans.: B. 14 D. 10

3. In a production operation, pins A, B, C, D, and E are cut off to the lengths indicated. Determine the whole number of pieces that can be cut from the workable lengths of stock given. (All dimensions are given in inches.)

Pins	Workable Length	Length of Pin	All. for Cutoff and Facing
A	10	1/2	.120
B	33	3/4	.120
C	68	1 1/4	.125
D	68	2 1/8	.125
E	11	17/32	.094

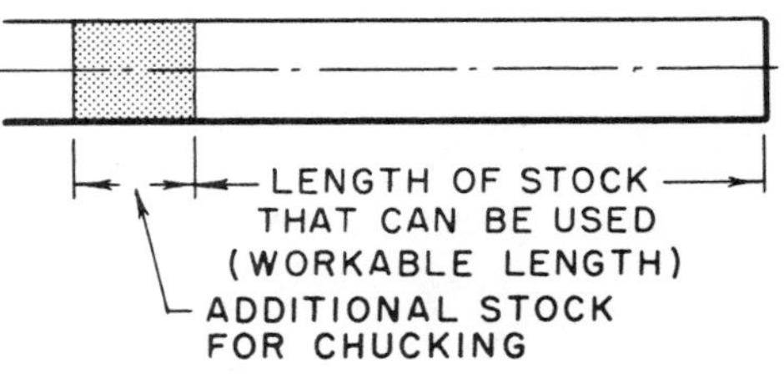

Ans.: B. 37 D. 30

4. A power sewing machine is set at eight stitches per inch of seam.
   a. Determine the length of one stitch.
   b. Calculate the number of stitches in a seam that is 20.25″ long.

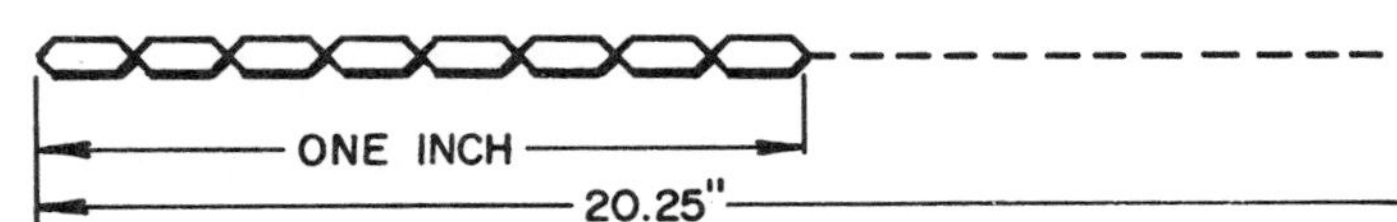

5. Express the decimal quantities of food products A, B, C, and D as the fractional equivalents.

Food Product	Contents	
	Decimal Value	Fractional Equivalent
A	14.437 oz.	
B	25.4 gr	
C	175.375 qts.	
D	9.56 lbs.	

Unit 17 ACHIEVEMENT REVIEW ON DECIMAL FRACTIONS

A. THE CONCEPT OF DECIMAL FRACTIONS

1. Write dimensions A, B, C, D, and E as decimals. Locate each dimension on a steel rule.

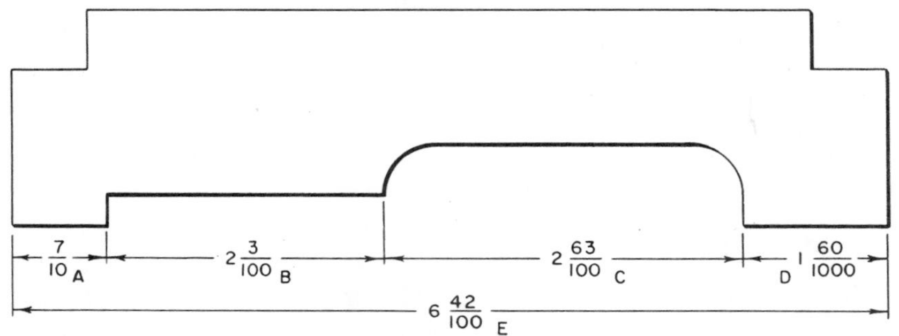

B. ADDITION OF DECIMALS

1. Determine distances A, B, C, D, and E.

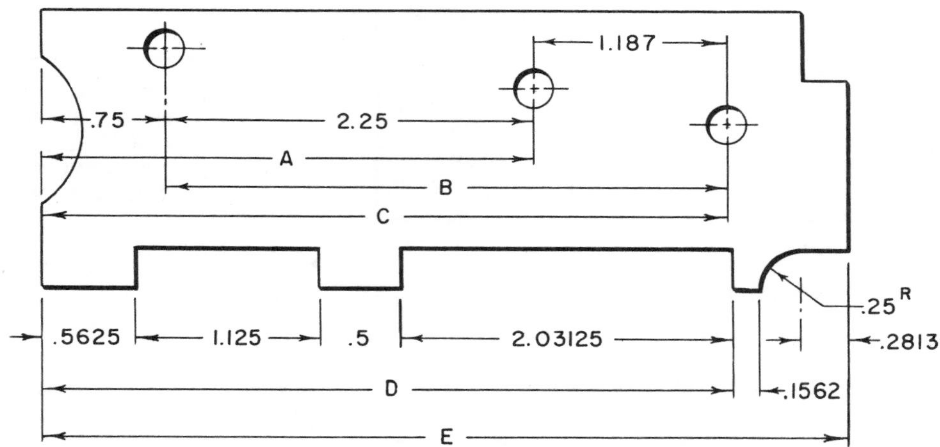

2. Prepare a table similar to the one illustrated and fill in the appropriate columns.
   a. List the values obtained for A, B, C, D, and E in the preceding problem.
   b. Round off each measurement to three decimal places.
   c. Express each decimal as a mixed number.

	Value Obtained	Rounded to Three Places	Expressed as Mixed Number
A			
B			
C			
D			
E			

3. The elevation at the top of the girder is 39.72 feet. Indicate what the elevation is on the surface of the terrazzo floor.

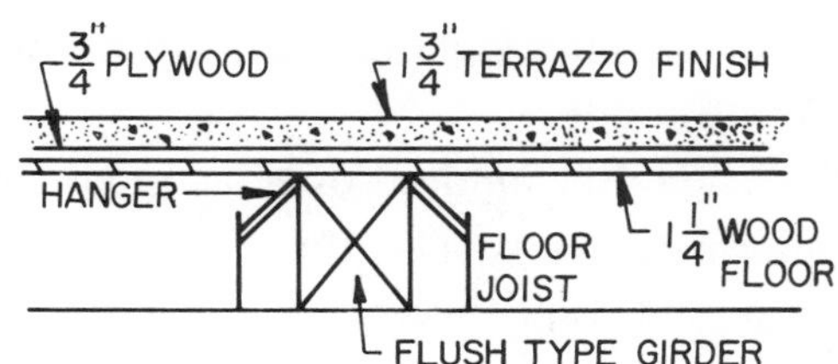

C. SUBTRACTION OF DECIMALS

1. Determine dimensions A, B, C, D, and E. Recheck the accuracy of each dimension to three places.

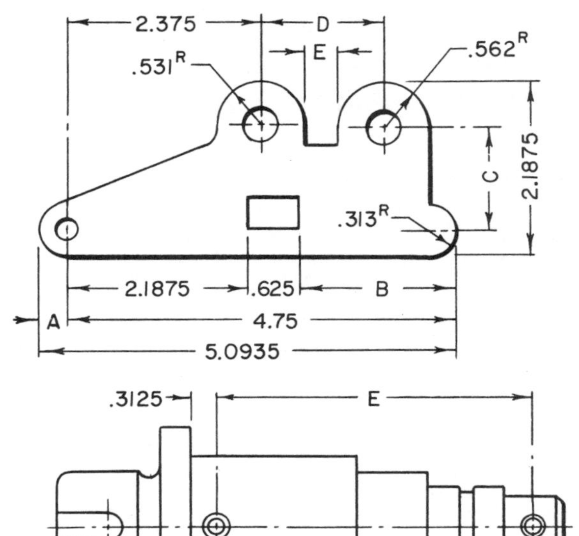

2. Determine dimensions A, B, C, D, and E correct to three decimal places.

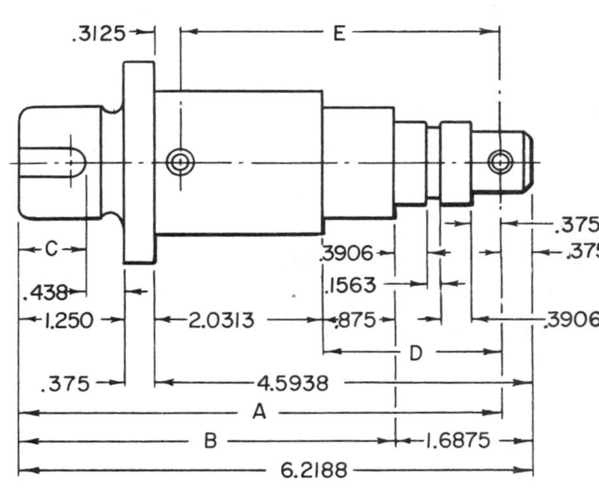

D. MULTIPLICATION OF DECIMALS

1. Determine the overall dimension of the saw and spacing collar combination for each of five setups as given in the table: A, B, C, D, and E. Dimensions must be correct to three decimal places.

Setup	Collars		Saws	
	No.	Width	No.	Width
A	4	.5	3	.1
B	8	.25	7	.1
C	7	.25	6	.06
D	10	.187	9	.03
E	12	.1875	11	.0313

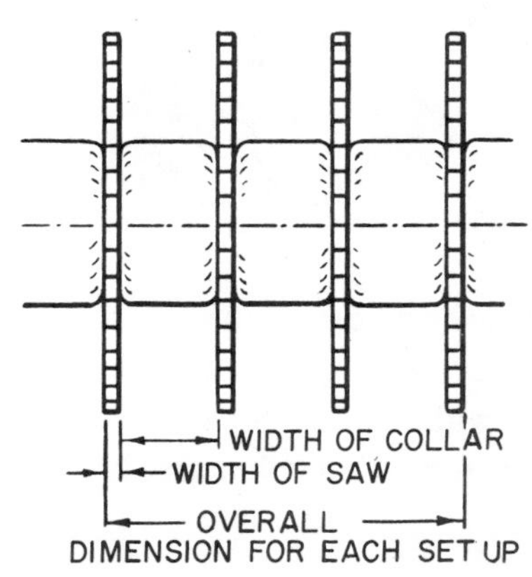

2. A bar of babbit weighing 142.5 pounds is composed of 79.5% tin, 11.25% copper, and 9.25% antimony.
   a. Determine the amount of tin, copper, and antimony in the bar.
   b. Determine the cost of the copper and tin if these metals sell for $.744 and $1.628 per pound respectively.

E. ADDITION, MULTIPLICATION, DIVISION OF DECIMALS

1. Determine the whole number of parts A, B, C, D, and E that can be machined from the workable lengths of stock given. (Each dimension is in inches.)

   NOTE: Round off the length of each part to two decimal places before determining the number of parts.

Parts	Length of Part	Allowance for Cutting Off	Allowance for Facing	Spoilage	Workable Length
A	1/2	.100	.010	1%	28
B	3/4	.100	.010	2.5%	34
C	1.25	.100	.005	4.5%	69 1/2
D	2.125	.120	.015	3 1/4%	69 1/2
E	3.187	.125	.015	5 1/2%	69 1/2

2. How many pieces can be stamped from each length of stock indicated in the table for parts A, B, C, D, and E?

Part	Length of Stock (in feet)	Length of Stamping (in inches)	Allowance on One End (in inches)
A	16	1 1/10	2/10
B	12 1/2	2.25	2/10
C	12 3/4	3.13	.25
D	25 1/4	3.187	.25
E	240 3/4	5.125	.375

3. Compute the micrometer readings for the finished diameters of cylinders A, B, and C.

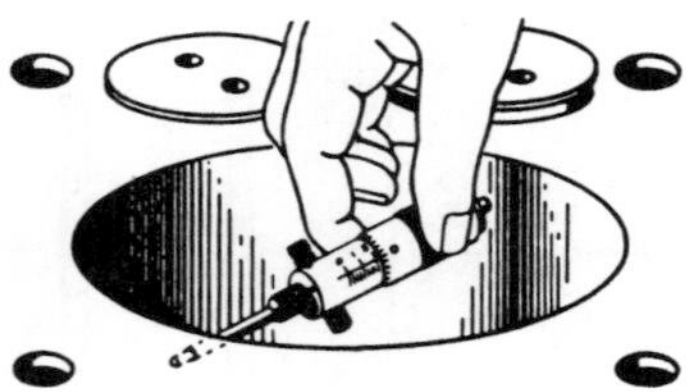

Cylinder	Diameter	Oversize Bore	Finished Diameter
A	3 1/2″	+0.040″	
B	4 1/4″	+0.0625″	
C	5 1/8″	+0.0781″	

4. A carbon brush has a 0.016″ copper plating on all sides. Find the width and thickness of the carbon brush as illustrated.

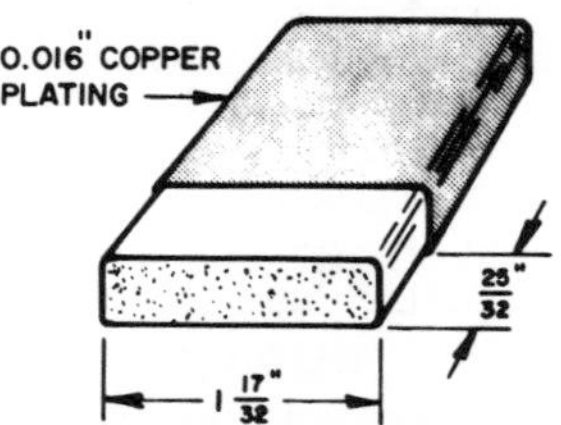

Section 4
MEASUREMENT: DIRECT AND COMPUTED: CUSTOMARY UNITS

Unit 18 PRINCIPLES OF LINEAR MEASURE

The exchange of goods and services among nations depends on communications. Though languages will differ, it is necessary that universally accepted international standards for measurements, technical terms and data be established. The current worldwide standards movement is toward metrication, using the International System of Units (SI). "Metrication" refers to any program or process of conversion to SI Metrics. This means that the continuing development of SI Metric units by the International Standards Organization must in turn be adopted by the nations of the world.

The United States is one of the few nations that continues to use a non-metric system of measurement. Following legislative adoption of SI Metrics, the system will not be mandated nor will it be the sole system of measurement. Conversion is intended to be voluntary, based on industry-by-industry decision.

The measurements with which each individual must be familiar in order to solve common mathematical problems in business, industry, agriculture, health occupations, and in the home and for other daily activities, include:

- Linear measure
- Area measure
- Circular measure
- Volume measure

These measurements are covered in this section by "Customary" units. These units are used to define the quantity of each measurement. The term "customary" refers to the American system of units based on the Imperial British System. "Conventional Metric" units and the newer SI Metrics follow in Part 2. Standardization, in terms of these three major systems, affects the life of each individual.

DIRECT AND INDIRECT MEASUREMENT

Some measurements are taken directly. When measuring tools, weights, instruments, and other line-graduated rules are used and the quantity is read directly, the term "direct measurement" applies. There are other instances where it is impractical or impossible to take direct measurements. In such cases, dimensions are computed, resulting in an "indirect or computed measurement."

A. CONDITIONS AFFECTING DEGREE OF PRECISION

The British, American, Metric, SI Metrics, and other special systems of measurement all provide for varying degrees of precision. For some applications, a value rounded-off to the closest 1/100th is adequate. In other cases, a dimensional tolerance, accurate to three or more decimal places is required. Besides dimensional accuracy, precision is also affected by surface finish. The movement of parts and mechanisms requires differing conditions of finish and measurement precision.

Precision applies equally to indirect measurements. These may relate in the fields of science to light, heat, sound, nuclear, and other energy sources. Precision relates to all industries; foods, health, construction, banking, manufacturing, service. . .these, and all others, use measurements.

MEASURING TOOLS AND INSTRUMENTS

The greater the degree of precision, the more precise the measuring instruments must be. Higher precision usually involves higher production expenses due to additional processing costs. Where a rough direct measurement within 1/16" is required, the dimension may be measured easily with a ruler. If a drawing shows a tolerance of plus or minus 1/32" or 1/64", a line-graduated steel rule is a practical measuring tool to use.

A micrometer is needed for tolerances within a plus or minus "one-thousandth" range (±0.001"). An operation, like precision grinding to a tolerance of plus or minus "one-ten-thousandth" (0.0001"), requires a micrometer having vernier graduations reading in ten-thousandths of an inch. Still other parts require that direct measurements be taken to within limits of two-millionths (0.000002") of an inch. Gage blocks are used industrially in combination with other measuring instruments to make direct measurements to this limit.

Common rules, measuring instruments and accessories are described in this section. The different measurement applications range from a precision of 1/16" to "two-millionths" (0.000002"). These experiences are intended to develop skill in applying mathematical principles to direct and computed measurements.

LINEAR MEASUREMENTS

Linear measure is the measurement of straight line distances between two points, lines or surfaces. In this Section, linear measurements are treated in terms of British linear units. These units are still the most widely used. The yard is the standard unit of length. The smallest unit of measure in the British Imperial System is the inch.

In 1856 England presented the United States with two bronze bars as a standard representation of the yard. The American system of linear measure is based on the British system. The bronze bars are kept for historical significance and not accuracy. The standard for all linear measurements was authorized by law in 1893 as the National Standard of Length.

Table of Linear Measure		
12 inches	=	1 foot
3 feet	=	1 yard
5 1/2 feet	=	1 rod
40 rods	=	1 furlong
8 furlongs	=	1 mile

Smallest unit of measure = one inch

A. APPLICATIONS OF RULES, TAPES AND LINE-GRADUATED TOOLS TO LINEAR MEASUREMENTS

Linear measurements may be made by craftspersons and technicians with solid rules, flexible steel tapes, and other line-graduated measuring instruments. Containers and other vessels are sometimes graduated to permit linear measurements to be taken directly.

Consumers generally use a ruler, yardstick, steel tape or a tape measure. When the tape measure is made of fabric, measurements should be checked for accuracy against a

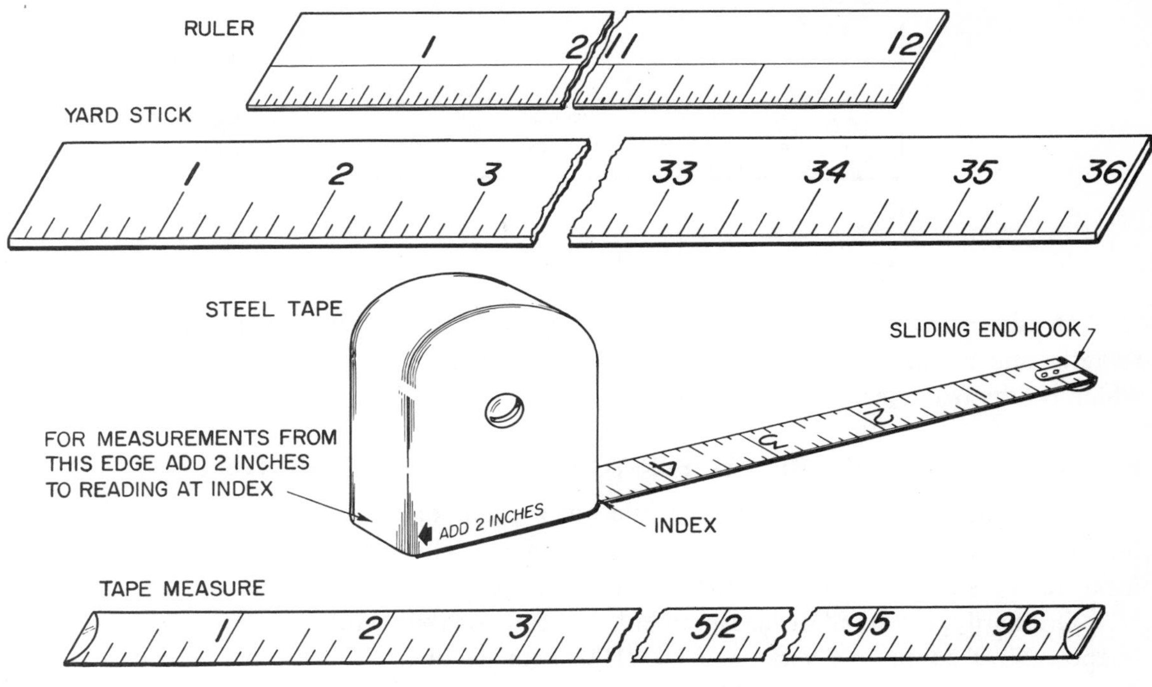

CONSUMER LINEAR MEASURING TOOLS

more precise measuring tool. Line graduations of sixteenths and eighths are common on consumer measuring tools.

STANDARD UNIT OF LINEAR MEASURE

The most commonly used unit of measure is the inch. The inch as a standard unit of linear measure in turn is subdivided into smaller fractional parts representing either common or decimal fraction equivalents.

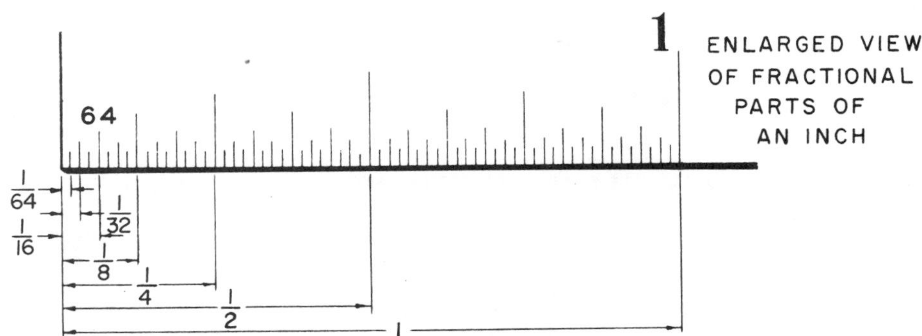

The fractional divisions of an inch which are most commonly used on rules represent halves, quarters, eighths, sixteenths, thirty-seconds, and sixty-fourths of an inch.

The decimal system is used when smaller units of measure are required. It is common practice in the shop and laboratory to express fractional parts of an inch in decimals which are called "decimal equivalents". For example, the decimal equivalent of one-fourth (1/4″) would be two hundred fifty thousandths (.250″).

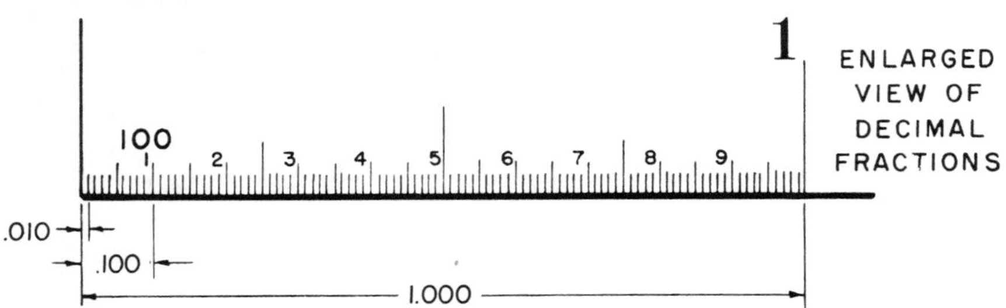

Measurements up to (1/100″) may be made direct with a steel rule graduated in fiftieths and hundredths of an inch. The use of such rules reduces the possibility of error which results from changing common fractions to decimals.

B. APPLICATION OF THE CALIPER TO LINEAR MEASUREMENTS

The outside and inside caliper, while not a graduated measuring tool, is used in combination with the rule to measure linear distances. The caliper is used to transfer linear measurements from the work to the steel rule.

Ordinarily, the smallest measurement that can be taken with a caliper and rule is (1/64″) in the case of common fractions and (1/100″) for decimal fractions. Where measurements in terms of thousandths are to be taken, the caliper size is measured with a micrometer.

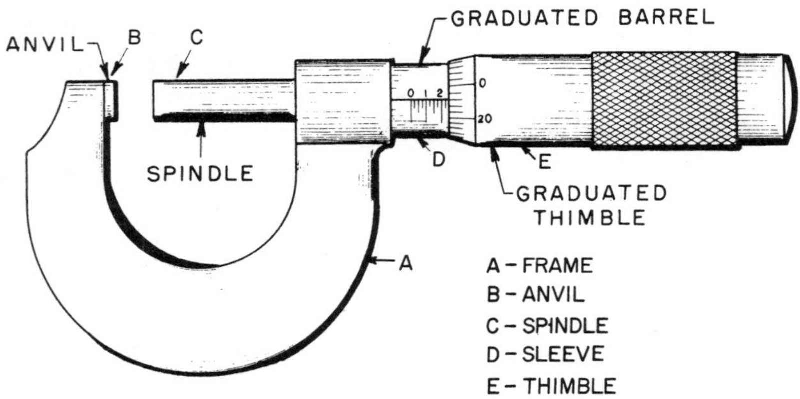

C. PRINCIPLES OF MICROMETER MEASUREMENT

The standard micrometer is used to measure parts requiring an accuracy of "one thousandth."

These readings are obtained by turning a graduated thimble on a graduated barrel. The movement of this thimble is at the rate of (1/40″) per turn. The 1/40″ is determined by the pitch of the screw threads which are concealed. As the thimble turns, the spindle moves closer to or further away from the anvil. The anvil is a stationary part of the frame.

ONE REVOLUTION
OF THIMBLE MOVES THE SPINDLE 1″/40 OR .025″

The barrel of the micrometer has 40 vertical graduations to indicate this movement of (.025″). Each fourth division on the barrel is marked for ease in reading.

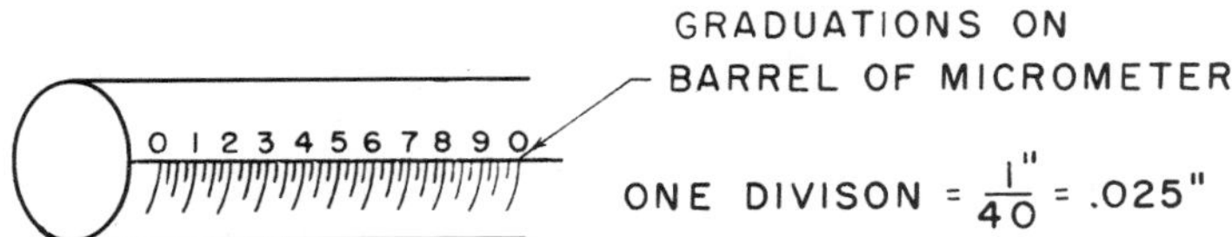

The thimble of the micrometer is divided into 25 equal parts. As each line crosses the horizontal line on the barrel, the space between the anvil and spindle is greater or smaller by (1/25) of a revolution or (.001″). Each fifth division of the spindle is numbered 5, 10, 15, 20, and 0 or 25. These numbers are in terms of thousandths: (.005″), (.010″), (.015″), (.020″), and (.025″).

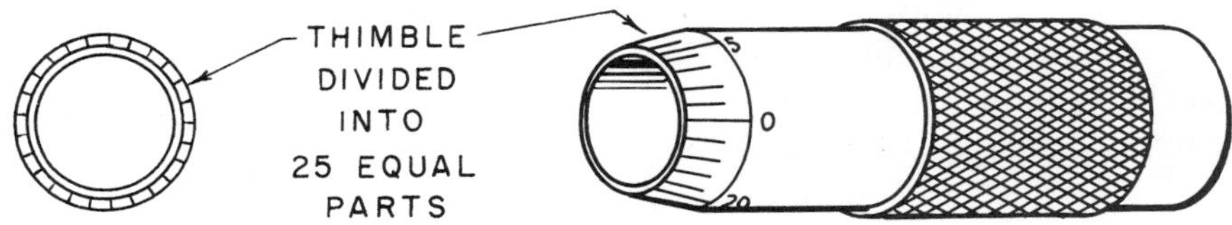

RULE FOR READING A MICROMETER

- Note the last vertical line that is visible on the barrel.
- Determine its reading with respect to a numbered graduation.
- Add to this reading the number of the line on the sleeve that crosses the horizontal line on the barrel.

EXAMPLE: Determine the following micrometer reading.

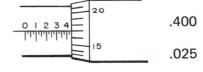

Step 1 Read last numbered vertical line on barrel. .400

Step 2 Add (.025″) for each additional line which shows (reading on barrel). .025

Step 3 Add number of graduation on sleeve (reading on sleeve). .017

Step 4 Read the required reading as the sum of all additions. Ans. .442″

Some micrometer manufacturers recommend that the number of vertical graduations on the barrel be multiplied by 25 to get the reading. Although this may be necessary at first, with practice the value of the graduations can be determined readily. It is also possible to measure accurately to the "half-thousandth" by splitting the distance between lines on the thimble.

EXAMPLE: The decimal equivalent of (9/16″) is (.5625″). The measurement would indicate a reading of (.550″) on the barrel plus (.012 1/2″) on the thimble.

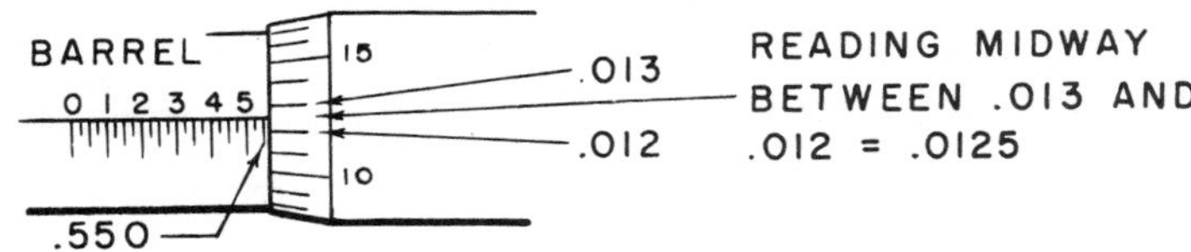

The micrometer head includes the graduated barrel, graduated sleeve and spindle, and modified frame. The micrometer head has many applications in addition to the micrometer caliper. On internal work the micrometer principle is applied in a measuring tool called an inside micrometer. Examples of other applications are the depth micrometer and height gage attachment for V-blocks.

Micrometer heads of slightly different construction are used widely for accurate machining, measuring and inspection processes. Regardless of the construction or size, the micrometer principle remains the same. The total measurement is equal to the sum of the reading on the barrel and sleeve.

D. PRINCIPLES OF VERNIER MICROMETER MEASUREMENT

In appearance and construction the vernier micrometer, with which measurements can be taken to (.0001″), is identical with the standard micrometer. The only difference is that the vernier micrometer has additional graduations running lengthwise on the barrel.

Readings in one ten-thousandths of an inch are obtained by the vernier principle. Pierre Vernier invented this device in 1631. The vernier principle is comparatively simple. There are ten graduations on the top of the barrel. These occupy the same space as nine divisions on the thimble.

The difference between the width of one of the nine spaces on the thimble and one of the ten spaces on the barrel is one-tenth of one space.

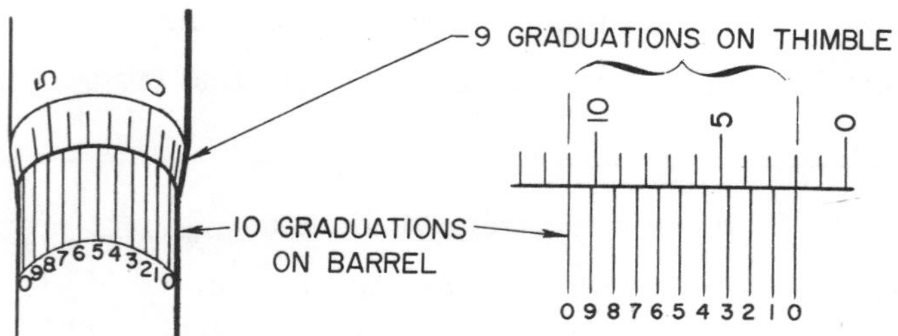

Since each space on the thimble represents one thousandth of an inch, the difference between the graduation on the thimble and barrel is one-tenth of one-thousandth or one ten-thousandth (1/10 of 1/1000 = 1/10,000 = .0001″).

RULE FOR READING A VERNIER MICROMETER

- Read as a standard micrometer graduated in thousandths.
- Add to this reading the number of the line on the vernier scale of the barrel which coincides with a line on the sleeve. This number gives the ten-thousandths to be added.

EXAMPLE: The micrometer reading in the illustration in thousandths is (.281″). Add to this reading the number of the line on the vernier scale which coincides with a line on the thimble. In this case, the first line coincides. This indicates one ten-thousandth. The second line would be two tenths of one-thousandth, the third line three-tenths. These "tenth" readings continue until the zero line on the barrel coincides with a line on the thimble. In this position the fourth place number in the reading is zero.

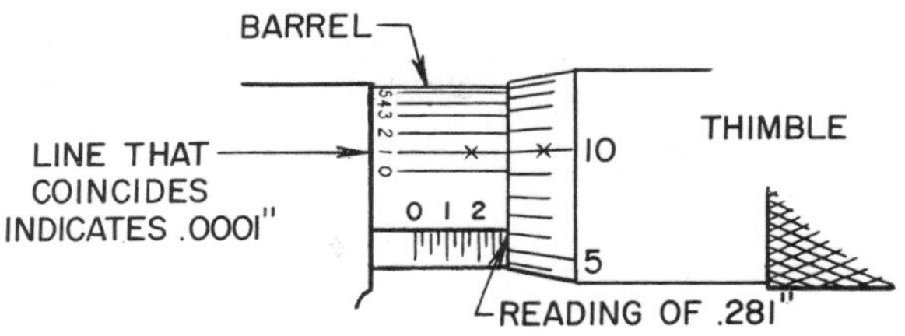

To read the vernier micrometer in the illustration, correct to four decimal places:

Step 1	Take regular reading.	.281
Step 2	Determine which lines on vernier scale coincide.	.0001
Step 3	Add regular reading to vernier reading.	Ans. .2811″

E. PRINCIPLES OF VERNIER CALIPER MEASUREMENT

The vernier caliper differs from the vernier micrometer in construction and principle of operation. The reading on the vernier caliper is not obtained by any relationship between the pitch of a screw and the movement of a thimble. Instead, the vernier caliper legs are slid into position. They are accurately adjusted for measurement by means of a fine screw which moves a sliding leg on a beam. The measurement is then determined by adding the reading on the beam and a graduation on the vernier scale.

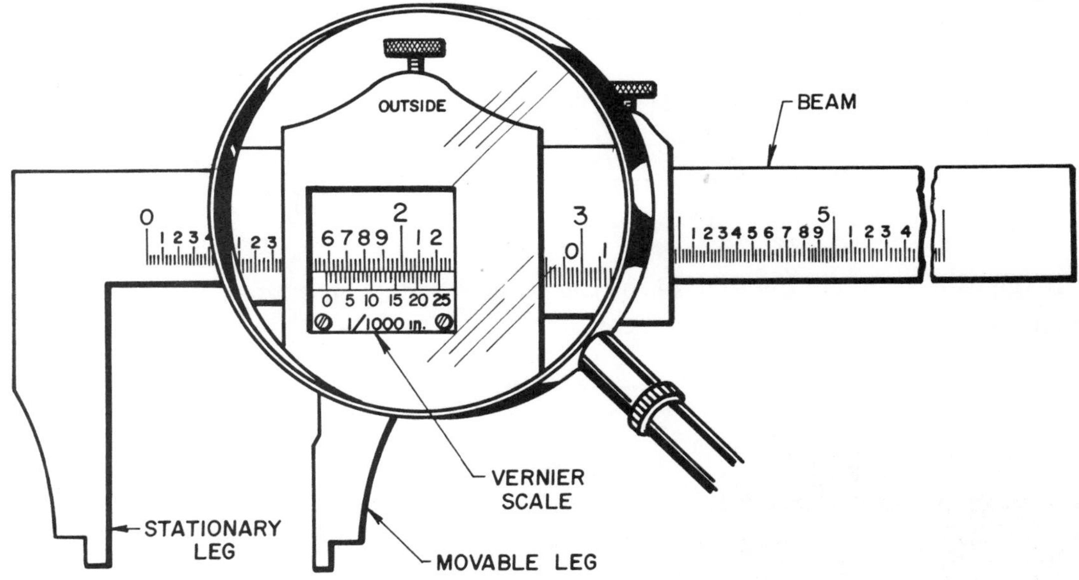

By varying the design of the stationary or solid leg, the beam can be used for other measuring needs as a height gage and depth gage. In many instances the beam is fitted to the table of a machine and the scale to a stationary part. Accurate linear measurements for machine operations may thus be taken with greater ease and less chance of error than by using the graduated collar on machines.

Each inch on the beam of a vernier caliper is divided into 40 equal parts. The distance between each graduation is (1/40″) or (.025″).

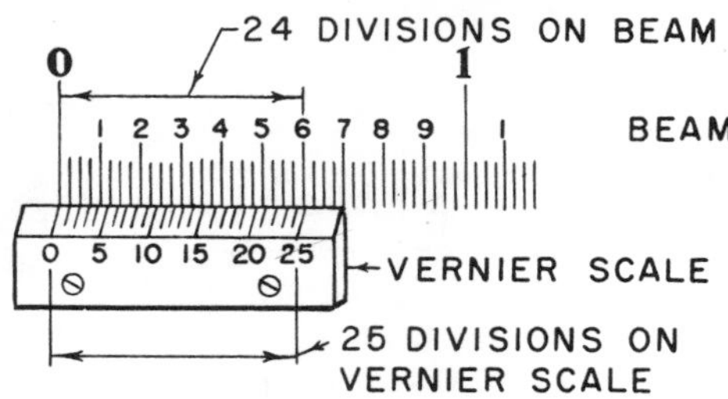

The vernier scale has 25 divisions which correspond to 24 divisions on the beam. The difference between one division on the scale and one on the beam is (1/25) of (.025″) or (.001″).

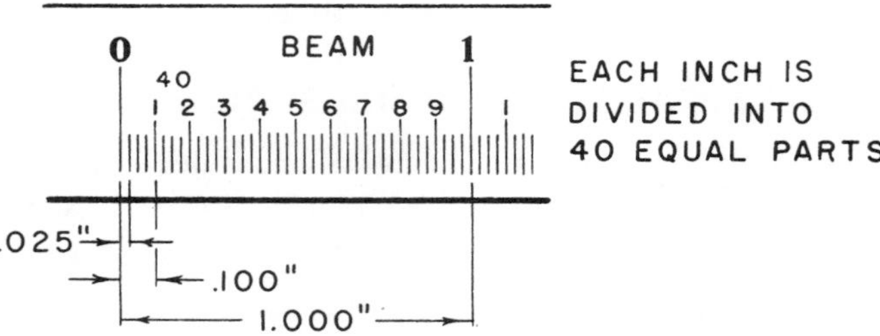

If the movable or sliding leg of the caliper (to which the vernier is attached) is moved to the right until the first line on the beam and vernier coincide, the leg will open (.001″).

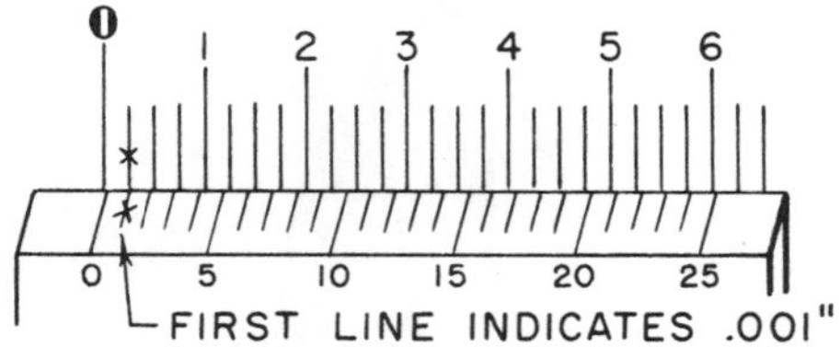

If this movement continues until the jaw is opened (.025″), the zero line on the vernier scale and the first line on the beam will coincide.

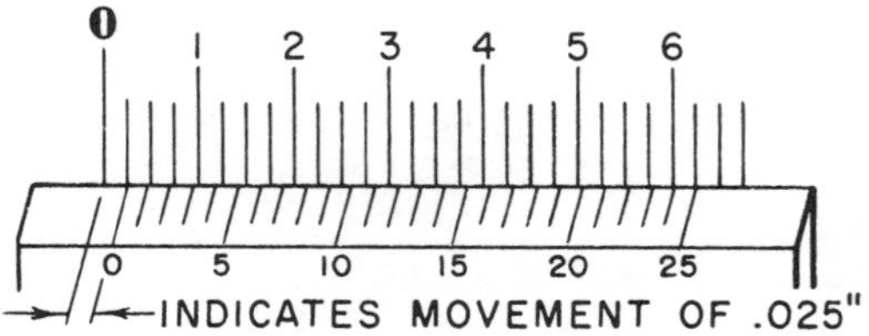

RULE FOR MEASURING WITH THE VERNIER CALIPER

- Read the graduation on the beam to the left of the zero on the vernier scale.
- Determine the number of the line on the vernier that coincides with a line on the beam.
- Add the reading on the beam to that of the vernier.

EXAMPLE: Case 1

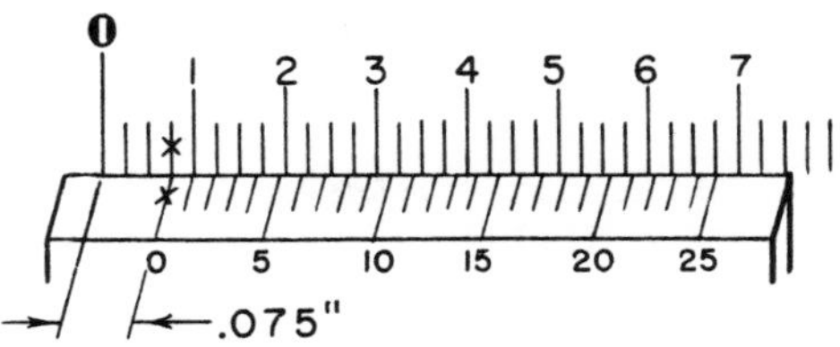

Step 1	Read graduation on beam to left of zero on vernier scale.	.075
Step 2	Determine which line on vernier scale coincides with line on beam.	<u>.000</u>
Step 3	Add beam and vernier scale readings.	Ans. .075″

EXAMPLE: Case 2

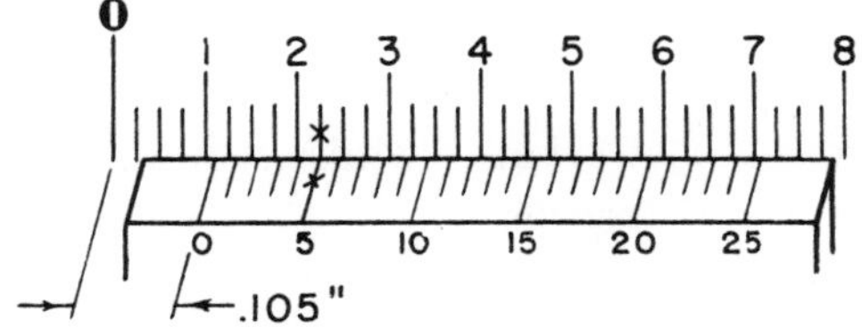

Step 1	Read graduation on beam to left of zero on vernier scale.	.100
Step 2	Determine number of line on vernier scale that coincides with line on beam.	<u>.005</u>
Step 3	Add beam and vernier scale readings.	Ans. .105″

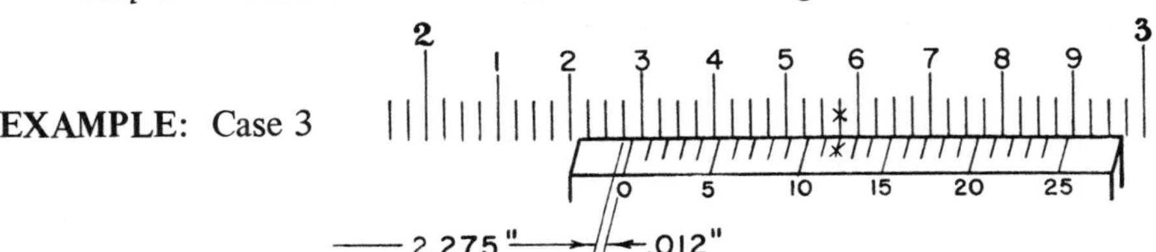

Step 1	Read graduation on the beam to left of zero on vernier scale (two inches plus .275).	2.275
Step 2	Determine number of line on vernier scale that coincides with line of beam.	<u>.012</u>
Step 3	Add beam and vernier scale readings.	Ans. 2.287″

F. PRINCIPLES OF PRECISION GAGE BLOCK MEASUREMENT

Gage blocks are hardened, smooth, rectangular-shaped blocks of steel. The blocks are machined, ground, and finished to a degree of accuracy ranging from 8 millionths (.000008″) for standard working gages to 2 millionths (.000002″) for master gages in temperature-controlled laboratories. Gage blocks are used for checking precision measuring instruments and gages, layout work, and machined surfaces where linear measurements to a high degree of accuracy are required.

Gage blocks are usually furnished in sets. The various sizes, when combined, can be used to measure linear distances in steps of (.0001″). The number of combinations possible with each set is almost limitless. For example, with a set of 35 gage blocks it is possible to obtain over 80,000 different measurements.

In practice, the combination of blocks to use for a specified dimension is determined by the addition and subtraction of decimals.

RULE FOR DETERMINING GAGE BLOCK COMBINATIONS

- Determine from the required dimension what number is in the "ten-thousandths column."
- Select the gage block from the series (.1001) to (.1009) whose fourth place number is the same as the required dimension.
- Select any gage block from the (.001) series whose third place (thousandths) dimension ends in the same number of thousandths as the required dimension.

  NOTE: Make sure that the sum of the two blocks is not greater than the required dimension.
- Select any gage block from the (.01) series whose second place dimension (hundredths) ends in the same number of hundredths as the right dimension.
- Continue to add blocks until the sum of the gages equals the required dimension.

EXAMPLE: Determine the combination of blocks needed for a measurement of (5.9325″) using the 35-piece set indicated below.

.0001 Series	.1001	.1002	.1003	.1004	.1005	.1006	.1007	.1008	.1009
.001 Series	.101	.102	.103	.104	.105	.106	.107	.108	.109
.010 Series	.110	.120	.130	.140	.150	.160	.170	.180	.190
.100 Series	.100	.200	.300	.400	.500				
1.000 Series	1.000	2.000	3.000						

Step 1	Determine number in fourth place of decimal.	(5.9325)
Step 2	Select gage block in (.0001) series which ends in (5).	.1005
Step 3	Select gage block in (.001) series which ends in same third place decimal as required dimension (5.932).	.102
Step 4	Add the two.	.2025
Step 5	Select gage block in (.010) series which ends in the same second place decimal as required dimension (5.93).	.130
Step 6	Add the three gages.	.3325
Step 7	Subtract the decimal value of the gages (.3325″) from the required dimension (5.9325″).	5.9325 .3325
Step 8	Select the smallest number of blocks in (.100) and (1.000) series to obtain this number.	5.600″
Step 9	Recheck gage block combination for accuracy. Also, determine whether or not a combination having fewer blocks may be used.	

ASSIGNMENT UNIT 18

A. DIRECT MEASUREMENT

1. Determine the reading of each measurement illustrated.

a.

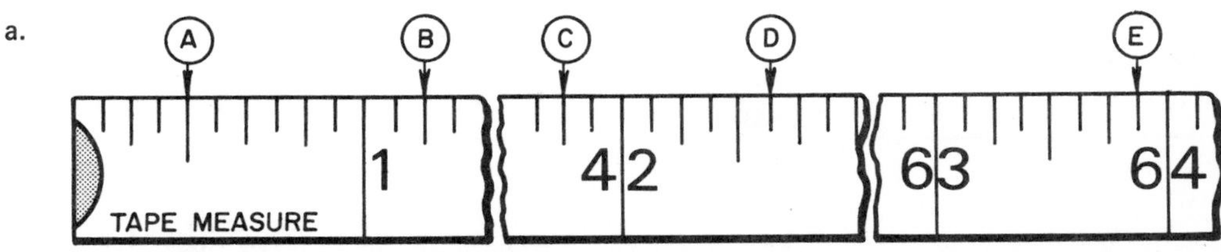

Ans.: B. 1 1/4″ D. 42 5/8″

b.

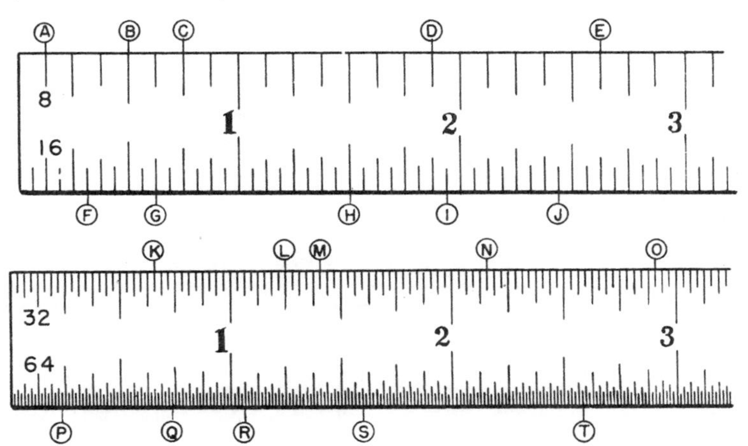

Ans.: D. 1 7/8″ J. 2 7/16″ O. 2 29/32″ S. 1 19/32″

2. Determine the reading of each measurement indicated on the rule graduated in 10ths, 50ths, and 100ths of an inch.

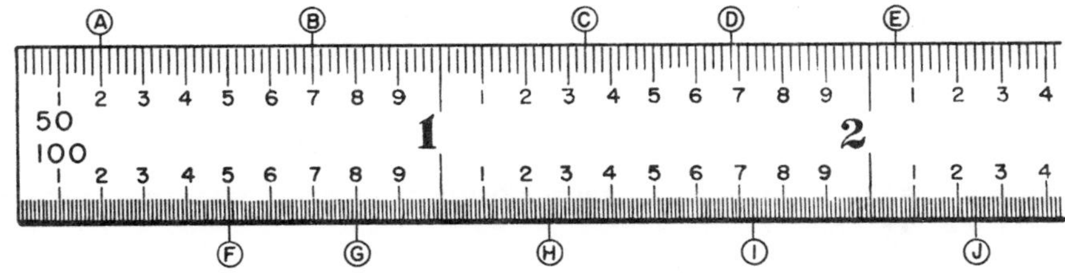

Ans.: C. 1 17/50 F. 5/10 I. 1 73/100

3. Measure the length of lines (a) through (j) to the degree of accuracy indicated in each case.

a. Nearest 1/4″

b.

c. Nearest 1/8″

d.

e. Nearest 1/16″

f.

g.

h. Nearest 1/32″

i.

j. Nearest 1/64″

Ans.: d. 3 5/8 g. 2 31/32 j. 3 7/16

4. Measure lengths A, B, C, and D and check the sum of these against the overall dimension E.

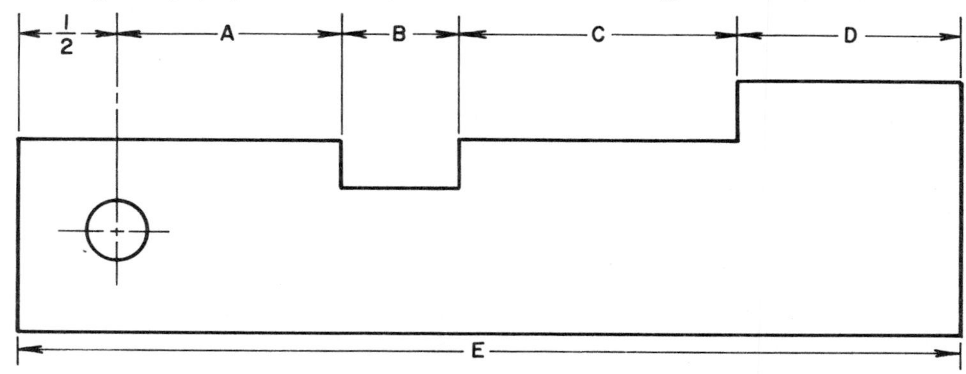

Ans.: E = 4 15/16

5. Measure lengths A, B, C, D, E, F, and G and check the sum against the overall dimension H.

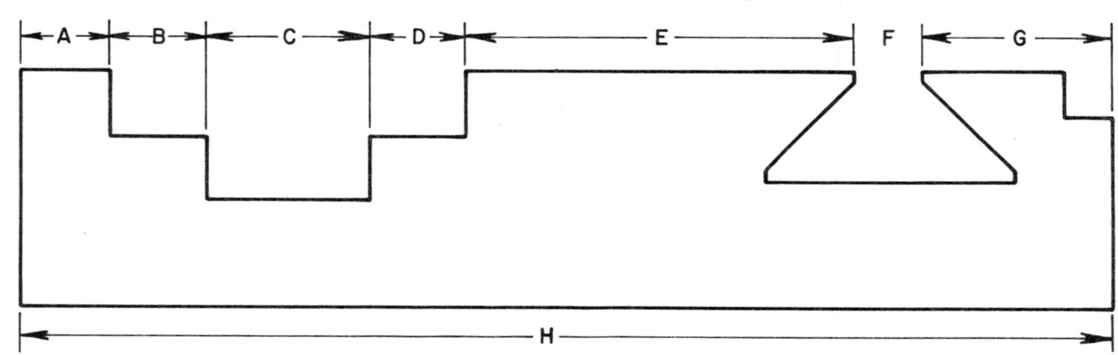

Ans.: H = 5 23/32

6. Measure the outside diameters of the metal bars A, B, C, D, and E with a caliper. Transfer the measurement to a rule and record the diameter to the nearest 1/50″.

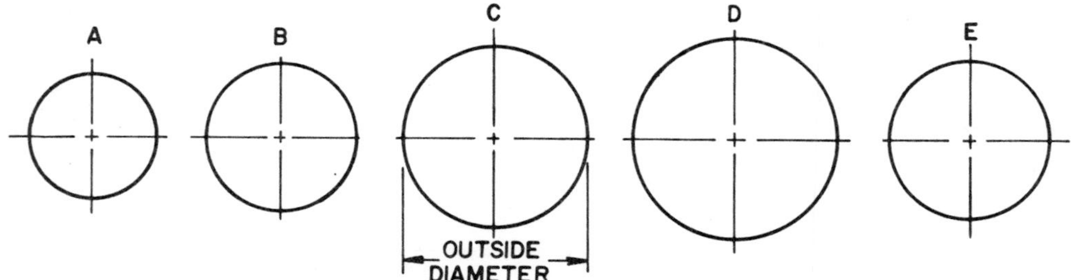

Ans.: B. 37/50″ D. 1 1/50″

7. Measure the length of lines (a) through (d) to the degree of accuracy indicated in each case.

a. ├────────────────────────────────────┤ Nearest 1/10″

b. ├──────────┤

c. ├────────────────────────────────┤ Nearest 1/50″

d. ├──────────────────────────┤

Ans.: b. 1 d. 2 33/50

8. Measure the diameter of bored holes A, B, C, D, E, and F with an inside caliper. Then transfer the measurement to a rule and record the diameter to the nearest 1/32″.

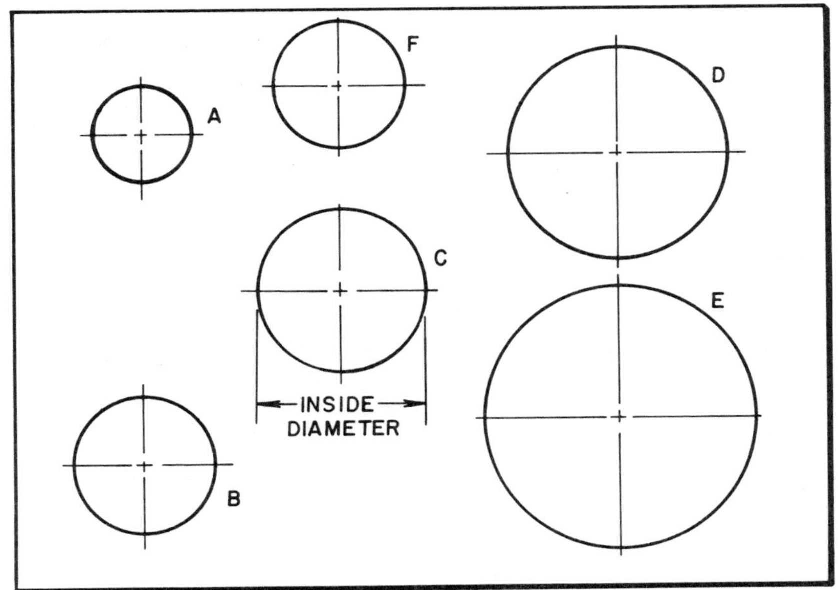

Ans.: B. 23/32 D. 1 1/8 F. 21/32

B. INDIRECT MEASUREMENT

1. Determine dimensions A, B, C, D, E, and F.

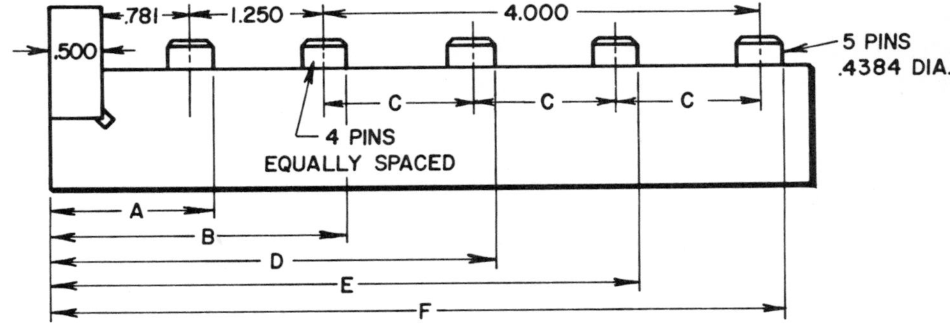

Ans.: B. 2.7502 E. 5.4168

2. Find dimensions A through J to which the shaft must be *rough turned.* Allow 1/16″ on all diameters and 1/32″ on all faces for finish machining.

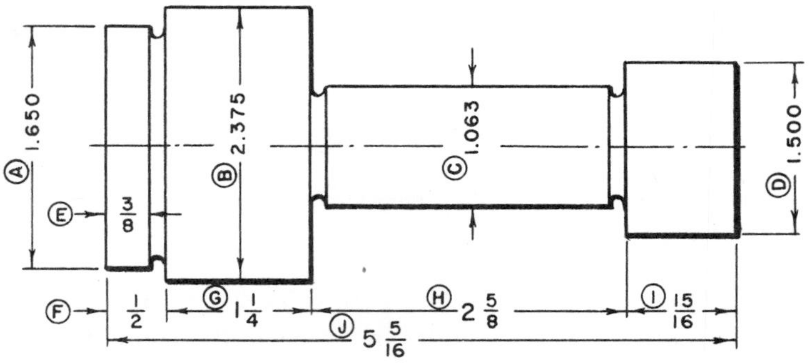

Ans.: A. 1.712″ E. 7/16″ J. 5 3/8″

3. Find dimensions A through J to which the part must be *finish turned* before grinding. Allow .010″ on all diameters and .008″ on all faces for grinding.

Ans.: B. 2.385″ D. 1.510″ I. .953″

4. Determine (a) the outside perimeter of the house and (b) the inside perimeter of each of the six rooms. The perimeter equals the sum of the linear measurements of each side of an object.

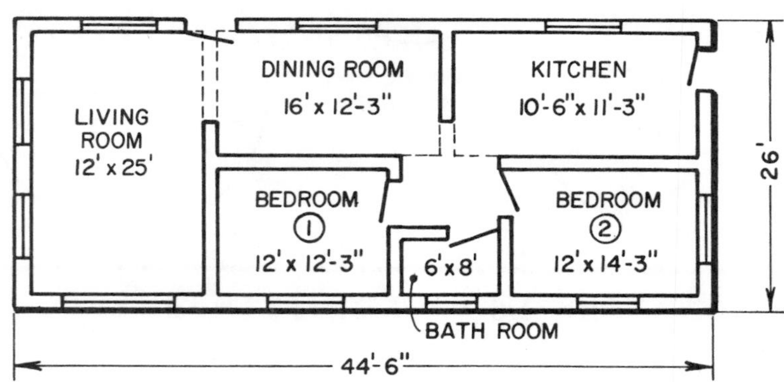

Ans.: a. 141 ft. b. Bedroom 1 is 48′-6″, Kitchen is 43′-6″

C. DIRECT MEASUREMENT – STANDARD MICROMETER

1. Determine the linear dimension indicated at A, B, C, D, E, and F on the standard micrometer.

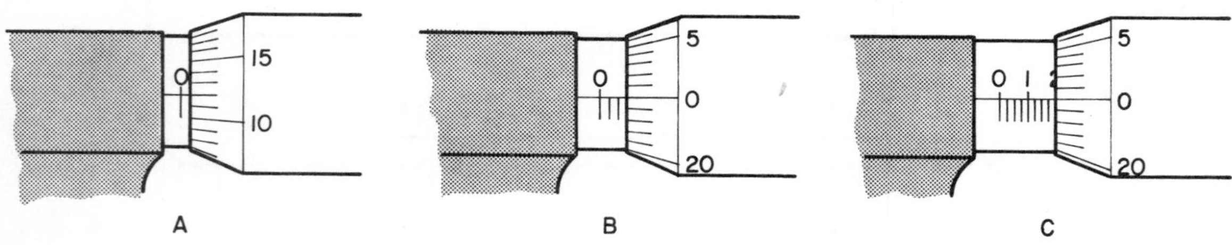

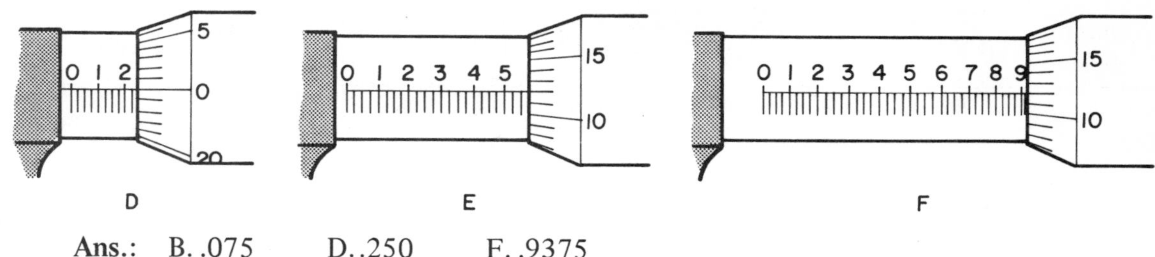

Ans.: B. .075 D..250 F. .9375

D. DIRECT MEASUREMENT – VERNIER MICROMETER

1. Determine the linear dimension on the vernier micrometer settings at A, B, and C.

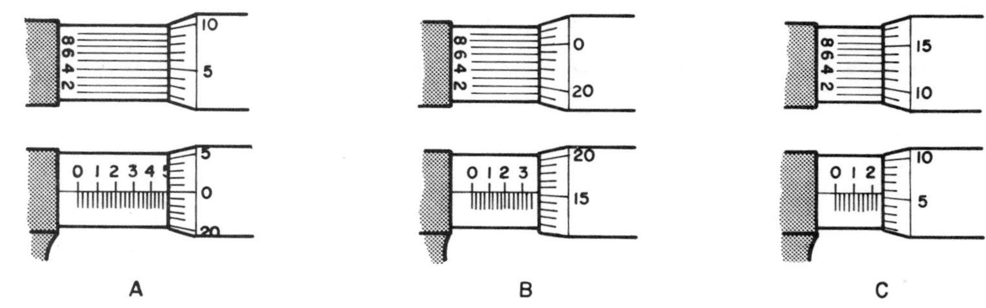

Ans.: B. .3906

E. DIRECT MEASUREMENT – VERNIER CALIPER

1. Determine the vernier caliper readings A, B, C, and D.

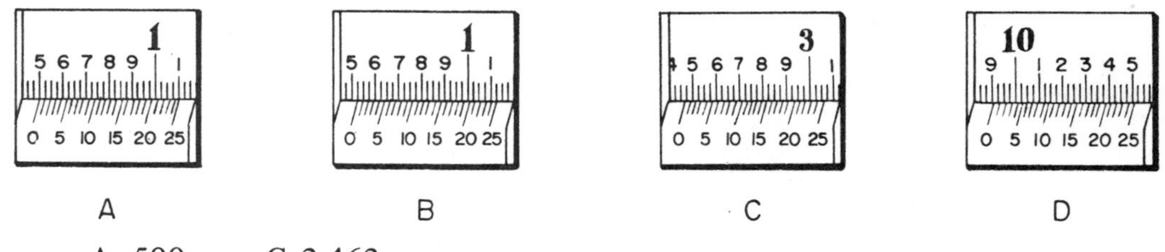

Ans.: A..500 C. 2.463

F. DIRECT AND COMPUTED MEASUREMENT – GAGE BLOCKS

The set of 81 gage blocks indicated in the table may be used to make 120,000 accurate combinations of measurements in steps of .0001″ from .200″ to over 24″.

Determine the sizes of gage blocks which, when combined, will give the required dimensions A through J.

A	.500
B	.750
C	.875
D	.265

E	.6001
F	.7507
G	1.2493

H	2.2008
I	11.0049
J	11.885

.0001 Series	.1001	.1002	.1003	.1004	.1005	.1006	.1007	.1008	.1009	
.001 Series	.101	.102	.103	.104	.105	.106	.107	.108	.109	
	.110	.111	.112	.113	.114	.115	.116	.117	.118	.119
	.120	.121	.122	.123	.124	.125	.126	.127	.128	.129
	.130	.131	.132	.133	.134	.135	.136	.137	.138	.139
	.140	.141	.142	.143	.144	.145	.146	.147	.148	.149
.050 Series	.050	.100	.150	.200	.250	.300	.350	.400	.450	
	.500	.550	.600	.650	.700	.750	.800	.850	.900	.950
1.000 Series	1.000	2.000	3.000	4.000						

Unit 19 PRINCIPLES OF ANGULAR AND CIRCULAR MEASURE

The measurement of circles, curved surfaces, cylinders, and angles takes place daily in the home, in business, and in industry. Measuring these rounded surfaces calls for an understanding of the fundamental principles relating to circular and angular measurement.

Some problems require simply the application of a principle to compute a missing value or dimension. Under actual conditions measurements are made directly on the job, using tools and instruments which will measure to the required degree of accuracy.

This unit gives step-by-step procedures for computing answers (where basic principles alone are applied) and for direct measurement with tools and instruments.

A. DEVELOPING A CONCEPT OF ANGULAR AND CIRCULAR MEASURE

DEFINING THE CIRCLE AND ITS PARTS

A circle is defined as a closed curved line on a flat surface. Every point on the closed curved line is the same distance from a fixed given point called a *center.* The distance around the circle, or periphery, is the *circumference.* This circumference is measured either in terms of the standard units of linear measure or in degrees.

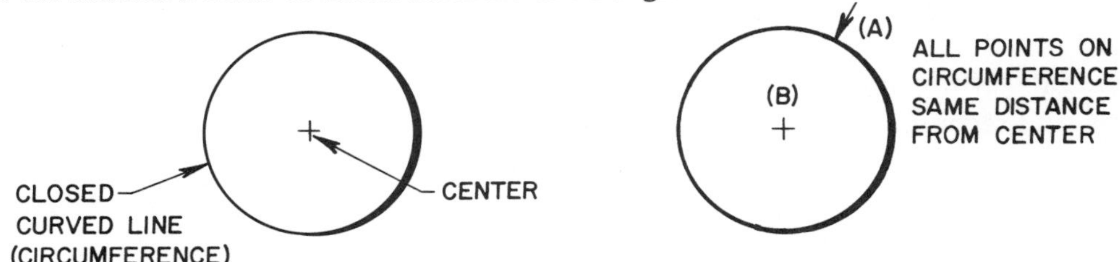

The *diameter* is the straight line through the center of the circle. Its ends terminate in the circumference. The diameter divides the circle into two equal half circles called *semicircles.* The *radius* is a straight line starting at the center of the circle and terminating in the circumference. The symbol (R) or (r) is usually used to indicate radius. The term *radial* is in common usage. A line or surface on a circular object is radial if, when extended, it cuts through the center.

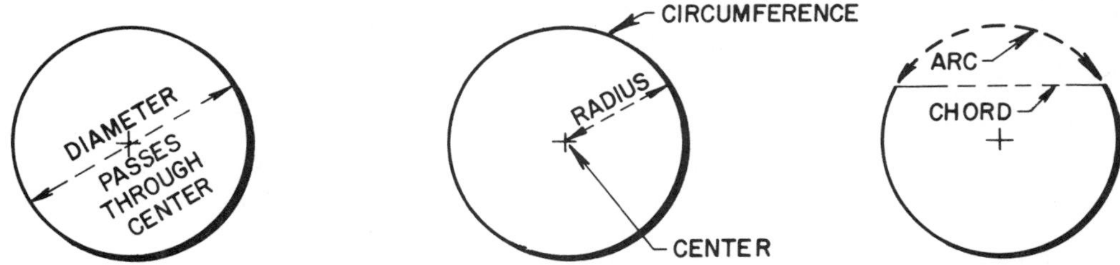

In all circles the circumference is related to the diameter in a specific way. It is approximately 3 1/7 or 3.1416 times the diameter. This value is a constant relationship between the diameter and circumference of the same circle. For convenience it is called "pi" or π. To find the circumference of a circle multiply the value of π times the diameter of the circle.

On many objects, only a *segment* of a circle is used. The segment refers to the area of that portion of the circle which is being considered. The segment consists of an *arc* on the circumference whose ends are joined by a straight line in the circle.

An *arc* is a curved part of the circumference. The straight line which extends inside the circle to join both ends of the arc is known as a *chord.*

Two other terms are widely used: *concentric circles* and *eccentric circles.* When two or more circles have a common center, they are *concentric.* Circles which are on the same flat surface and are used in the same part but do not originate from a common center, are called *eccentric* circles. On concentric circles the inner circle is sometimes designated by the letters (ID) for inside diameter; the outer circle by (OD) for outside diameter.

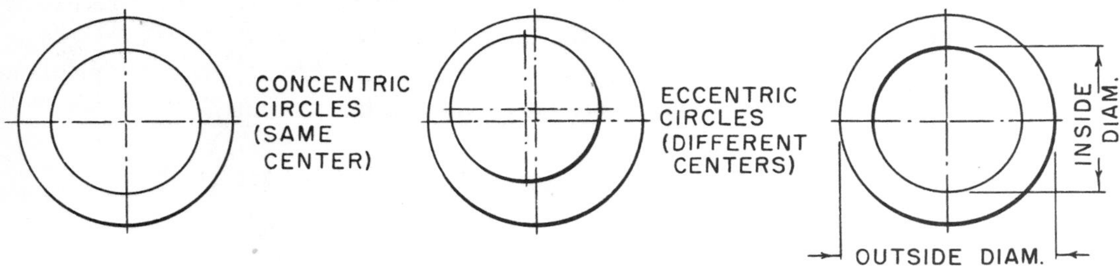

DEFINING AN ANGLE AND ITS PARTS

Most measurements of round surfaces are in linear measure. However, many dimensions are expressed in angular measure. Angular measure indicates the size of an opening formed by two lines or surfaces (intersecting lines). The lines or surfaces open as they extend from a common starting point called a *vertex.* The angles formed are measured in *degrees, minutes,* and *seconds.*

The size of an angle depends upon the space between the sides and not on the length of the sides. In speaking of an angle it may be referred to as $\angle ABC$, or $\angle 1$, or $\angle A$ and the angle is marked or lettered accordingly.

A circle is divided into 360 equal parts which are called degrees. An angle of one degree is formed by drawing two lines from the center to two consecutive division points.

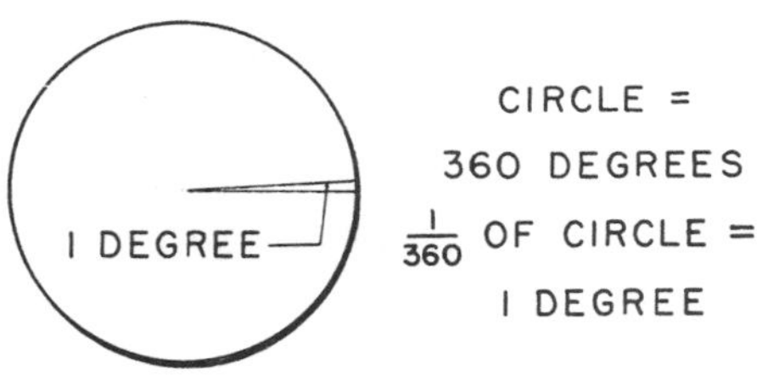

Degrees are designated by placing a small zero to the right and slightly above the number: thus, 4 degrees is 4°. Sometimes degrees are given in tenths. For example, four and three-tenths degrees is written (4.3°).

Each degree is divided into 60 equal parts, each of which is called a *minute.* A degree therefore equals 60 minutes. Minutes are indicated by placing a single line in the same relative position as the degree sign. Thus, 15 minutes is written ($15'$).

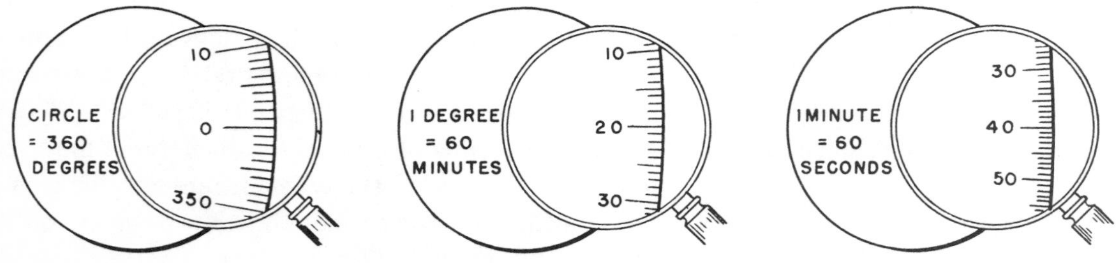

For greater accuracy, measurements are made in divisions finer than the minute. Each minute is divided into 60 equal parts, each of which is called a *second.* Seconds are written with two lines to the right and slightly above the number. An angle ending in 25 seconds is written (25″).

To summarize, angles are measured in degrees (°), minutes (′), and seconds (″). There are 360 degrees in a circle, 60 minutes in a degree, and 60 seconds in a minute. These values are given in standard table form for angular measure.

Table of Angular Measure		
1 Circumference (or circle)	=	360 degrees
1 Degree	=	60 minutes
1 Minute	=	60 seconds

The circle is very often divided into four equal parts, each of which represents an angle of 90°. The term *right angle* is used to denote such an angle. When the circle is divided into two equal parts, the 180° for each part is called a *straight angle.*

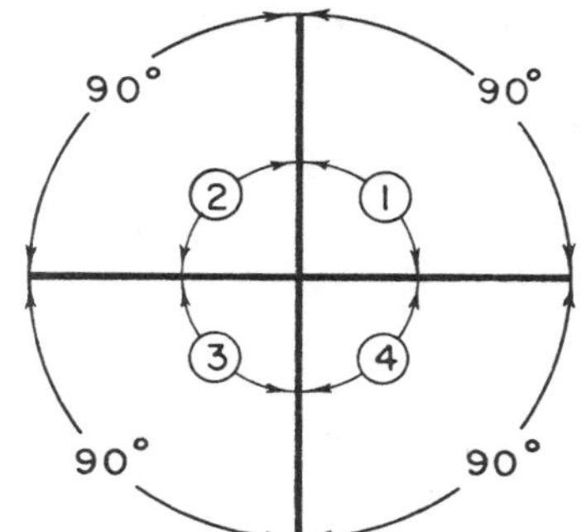

THE CIRCLE DIVIDED INTO 4 EQUAL PARTS OF 90°, OR 4 RIGHT ANGLES ① ② ③ ④

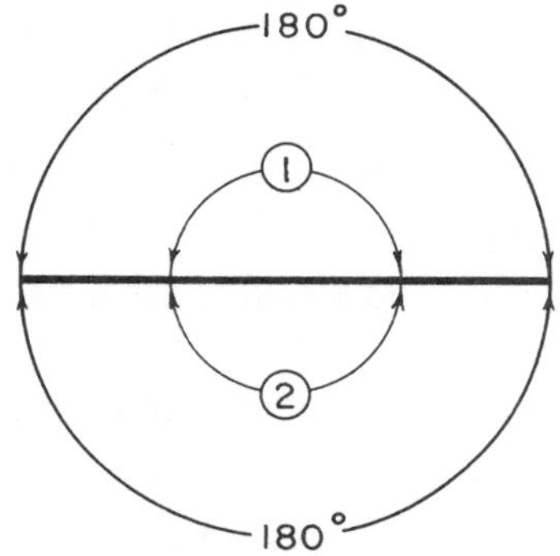

THE CIRCLE DIVIDED INTO 2 EQUAL PARTS OF 180°, OR 2 STRAIGHT ANGLES ① ②

B. COMPUTING ANGLUAR MEASURE

Problems in angular measure involve the four basic processes of addition, subtraction, multiplication, and division of angles and parts of angles. To do these operations, it is necessary to change degrees, minutes, and seconds to whichever one of the three units will expedite the mathematical processes involved. Angles given in fractional or decimal parts of a degree, minute, or second may be added, subtracted, multiplied, or divided the same as any fraction or decimal.

RULE FOR EXPRESSING DEGREES IN MINUTES

- Multiply the number of degrees by (60).
- Express the product in terms of minutes.

EXAMPLE: Express 15 degrees (15°) in minutes.

Step 1 Multiply 15 degrees (15°) by (60). $15 \times 60 = 900$

Step 2 Express answer in minutes (′). Ans. $15° = 900'$

RULE FOR EXPRESSING MINUTES IN SECONDS

- Multiply the number of minutes by (60).
- Express the product in terms of seconds.

EXAMPLE: Change 32 minutes to seconds.

Step 1	Multiply 32 minutes (32′) by (60).	32 x 60 = 1920
Step 2	Express answer in seconds (″).	Ans. 32′ = 1920″

RULE FOR EXPRESSING AN ANGLE IN DEGREES AND MINUTES AS SECONDS

- Multiply the given number of degrees by (60).
  NOTE: The product denotes minutes.
- Multiply the product by (60).
  NOTE: This product denotes seconds in the given number of degrees.
- Multiply the given number of minutes by (60).
- Add the number of seconds in the given number of degrees to the number of seconds in the given number of minutes.
- Express the answer in terms of seconds.

EXAMPLE: Case 1 Change 3° 10′ to seconds.

Step 1	Multiply (3°) by (60).	3 x 60 = 180′
Step 2	Multiply (180′) by (60).	180 x 60 = 10,800″
Step 3	Express ten minutes (10′) as seconds.	10′ x 60 = 600″
Step 4	Add values of (3°) and (10′) in seconds.	3° = 10,800″ 10′ = 600″ Ans. 11,400″

EXAMPLE: Case 2 Express 2.75° as minutes.

Step 1	Multiply (2.75°) by (60).	2.75 x 60 = 165.00
Step 2	Locate the decimal point.	Ans. 2.75° = 165′

EXAMPLE: Case 3 Express 7.12° as minutes and seconds.

Step 1	Multiply (7.12°) by (60).	7.12 x 60 = 427.20
Step 2	Point off decimal places. NOTE: The whole number of minutes is (427). The remainder (.20′) must be changed to seconds.	
Step 3	Multiply the decimal part of the minutes (.20) by (60) and locate the decimal point.	.20 x 60 = 12.00
Step 4	Combine the number of minutes and seconds.	Ans. 7.12° = 427′12″

RULE FOR EXPRESSING MINUTES AS DEGREES

- Divide the number of minutes by (60).
- Express the quotient in terms of degrees.

NOTE: Seconds are changed to minutes in the same way.

EXAMPLE: Express 45′ as degrees.

Step 1 Divide the minutes (45′) by (60).

Step 2 Express the quotient as degrees (3/4°).

NOTE: This quotient may also be written as (.75°).

$$\frac{45}{60} = \frac{3}{4}$$

C. COMPUTING CIRCULAR LENGTH

There are many cases where the length of an arc must be computed. This length is equal to the length of a portion of the circumference which is included in a given angle.

RULE FOR MEASURING THE LENGTH OF AN ARC (Circular Length)

- Determine the number of degrees in the arc.
- Determine the diameter of the circle.
- Place the number of degrees in the angle over the number of degrees in the circle (360°) to determine what part the included angle is of the whole circle.
- Multiply this quantity by the circumference of the circle.

NOTE: The circumference is equal to its diameter multiplied by (3.1416). The result is in the same dimension as the diameter.

EXAMPLE: What is the length of an arc included in an angle of 45° when the diameter of the circle is 2 inches?

Step 1 Determine size of angle (45°) and diameter of circle (2″).

Step 2 Place number of degrees in angle (45°) over the number of degrees in circle (360°).

$$\frac{45}{360} = \frac{1}{8}$$

Step 3 Compute circumference of (2″) circle.

Circumference = 2 x 3.1416 = 6.2832

Step 4 Multiply the circumference (6.2832) by the fractional part of circumference in the included angle (1/8).

$$6.2832 \times \frac{1}{8} = .7854$$

Step 5 The product is the required length of the arc in inches.

Ans. .7854″

D. APPLICATION OF THE PROTRACTOR TO ANGULAR MEASUREMENTS

Three general types of instruments, called *protractors,* are used to measure and lay out angles. The simplest type of protractor used for comparatively rough work is flat, semicircular in shape and graduated in degrees. Each tenth division is usually marked for ease in reading. The semicircular protractor finds wide application in laying out and measuring simple angles.

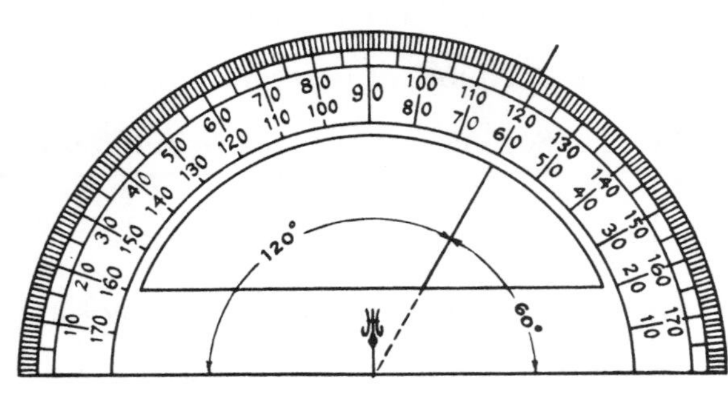

In the shop and on the job, the bevel protractor is the one most widely used. This protractor can be adjusted accurately to lay out or measure any angle from 0° to 180° by degrees. It is possible to estimate fairly accurately to a half degree, or 30′. The number of degrees is read directly from the graduations on a movable turret. The swinging blade protractor is sometimes more convenient to use because of its simplicity of construction. Here again the degrees from 0° to 180° are read at a center mark on one of the blades.

The third type of angle measuring tool is the universal vernier bevel protractor. This instrument is equipped with a vernier scale for very accurate measurement and layout of angles in terms of degrees and minutes.

ASSIGNMENT UNIT 19

A. DETERMINING EQUIVALENT VALUES OF ANGLES

1. How many degrees are there in the following parts of a circle?

   a. 1/6 b. 2/9 c. 3/8 d. 5/36 e. 7/24

   Ans.: b. 80° d. 50°

2. What part of a circle is each of the following angles?

   a. 40° b. 108° c. 9° d. 54° e. 96°

   Ans.: b. 3/10 d. 3/20

3. Change each angular measurement (a) to (h) to its equivalent value in the unit of measure indicated.

   a. 30′ to degrees
   b. 45′ to degrees
   c. 75′ to degrees
   d. 5° to minutes
   e. 7 1/2° to minutes
   f. 1.4° to minutes
   g. 5′ to seconds
   h. 5 1/2′ to seconds

   Ans.: a. 1/2 c. 1 1/4 e. 450 g. 300

B. COMPUTATION OF CIRCULAR AND ANGULAR MEASUREMENTS

1. Multiply and reduce each result to degrees, minutes and seconds, whichever combination is needed.

   a. 5° x 6
   b. 17° x 15
   c. 12 1/2° x 8
   d. 12.75′ x 6
   e. 9° 12′ x 9
   f. 23° 16′ 20″ x 4

   Ans.: a. 30° c. 100° e. 82°48′

2. Divide each angular measurement.

a. 180° ÷ 9	d. 90° 30′ ÷ 6
b. 135° ÷ 10	e. 75.8° ÷ 10
c. 120° ÷ 9	f. 144° 24′ 48″ ÷ 12

Ans.: b. 13° 30′ d. 15° 5′ f. 12° 2′ 4″

C. MEASUREMENT OF ANGLES (Direct and by Computation)

1. Read angles A through H on the semicircular protractor.

   Ans.: C. 32°
   F. 160°
   H. 20°

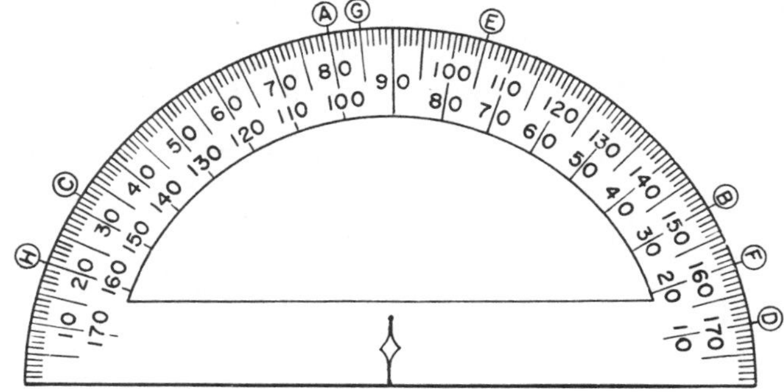

2. Measure angles A through F with a flat semicircular protractor.
   NOTE: It may be necessary to extend the sides of the angles in order to measure them.

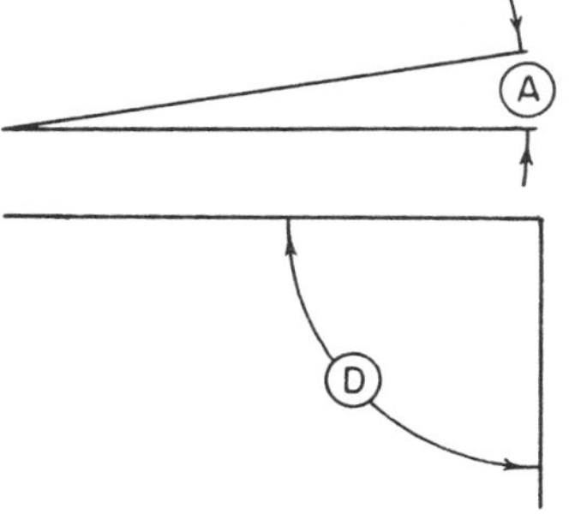

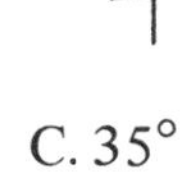
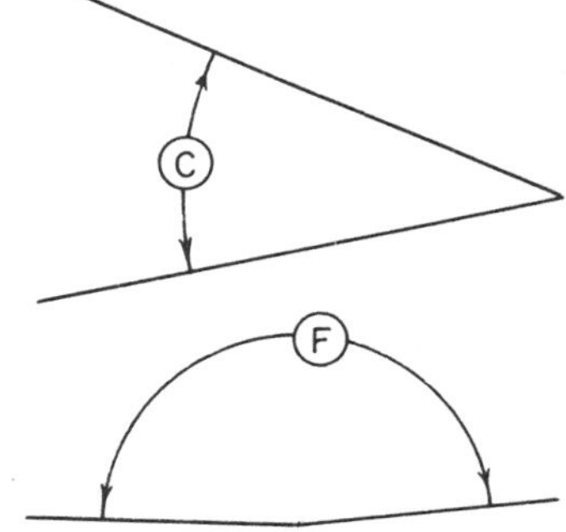

Ans.: A. 8° C. 35° E. 140°

3. Lay out angles A through D with a semicircular protractor.
   A. 10° B. 25° C. 100° D. 120°

4. The bevel protractor readings A, B, and C appear on one make of instrument; those at D, E, and F, on another. Determine the reading for each setting.

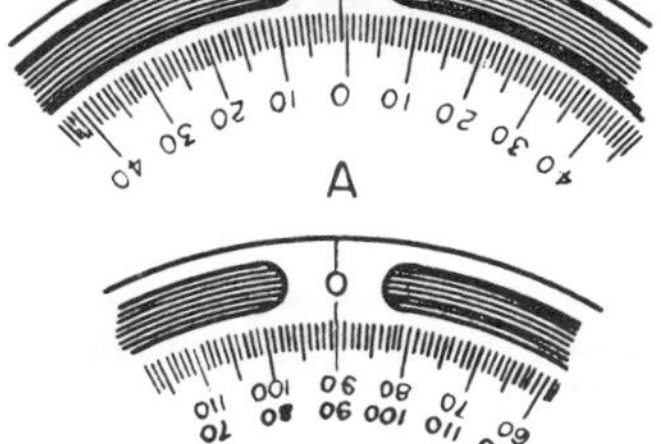

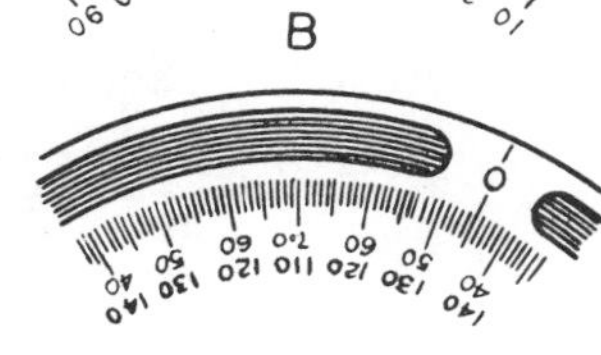

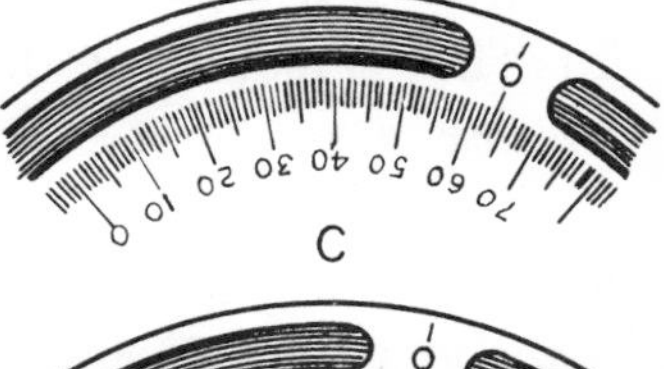

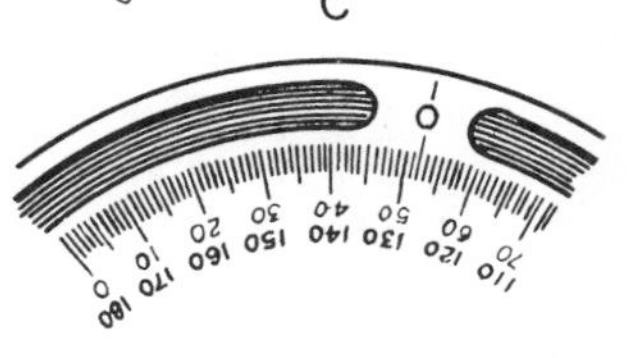

Ans.: B. 82° D. 90° F. 52°

5. The table and the illustration relate to four engine strokes. The angular valve opening/ closing and/or movement of the crankshaft are given. Compute the missing angular (X°) measurements for A, B, C and D.

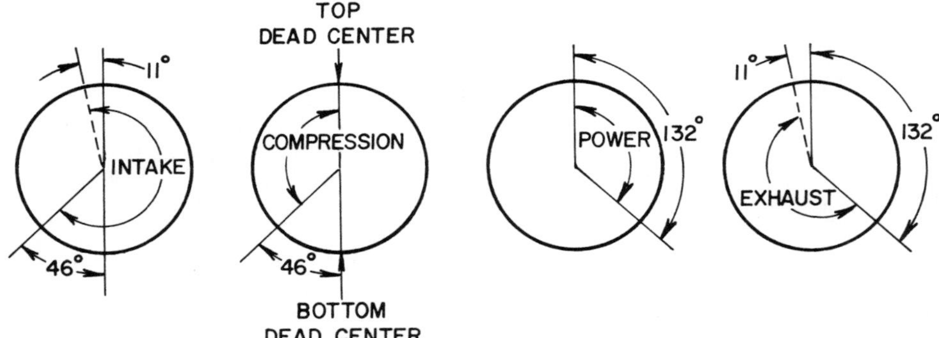

	Stroke	Exhaust Valve Opening	Exhaust Valve Closing	Angular Movement of Crankshaft
A	Intake	11° before top dead center	46° after top dead center	(X°)
B	Compression	top dead center	46° past bottom dead center	(X°)
C	Power	top dead center	(X°) before bottom dead center	132°
D	Exhaust	(X°) end of power stroke	11° before top dead center	132°

Ans.: A. 237° C. 48°

D. COMPUTATION OF CIRCULAR LENGTH

1. Compute the length of arcs A through D for the circles whose diameters are given.

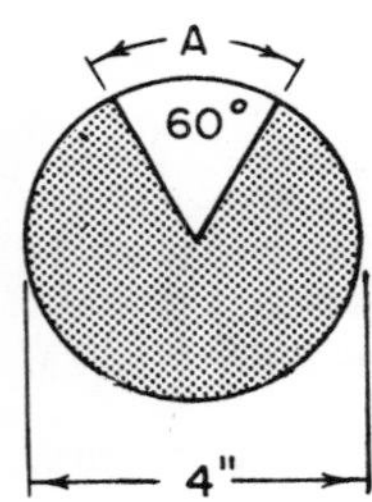

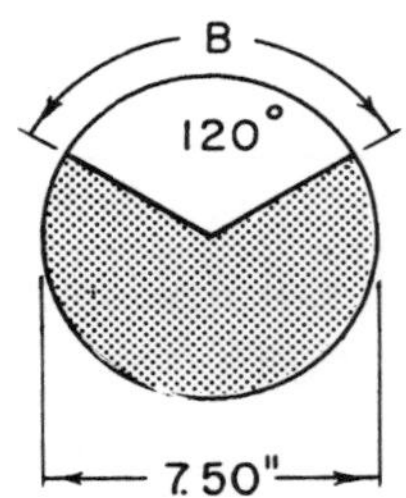

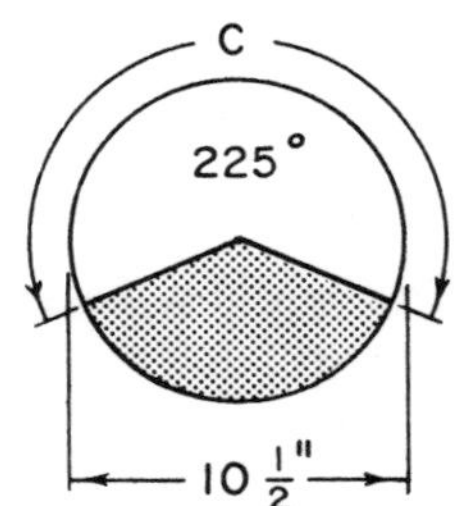

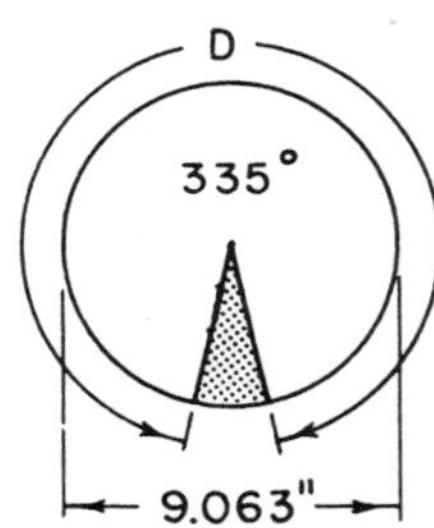

Ans.: B. 7.854′ D. 26.495″

2. The diameters of three roof plates are (a) 7′, (b) 8′-6″ and (c) 29′-1″, respectively. Use $\pi = 3.1416$. Give the length (circumference) of each circular roof plate to the nearest inch. **Ans.:** b. 26′-8″

3. Find the semicircular length of forms A, B, and C. State each length in feet and inches.

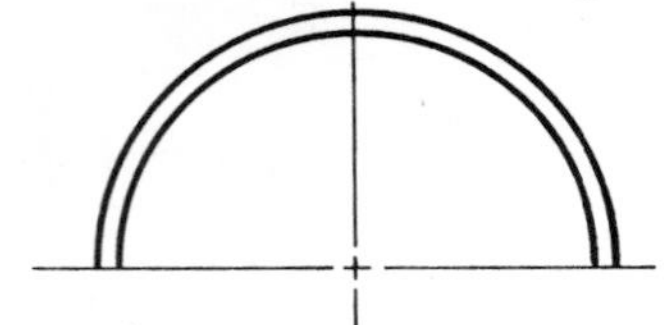

Form	Diameter	Semicircular Length
A	3′-0″	
B	4 1/3′	
C	5.25′	

Ans.: B. 6′-10″

Unit 20 PRINCIPLES OF SURFACE MEASURE

The term *surface measure* refers to the measurement of an object or part which has length and height. There are eight common objects or shapes for which each student must be able to compute the area or surface measure. The list includes surfaces that are defined by pairs of lines like the square, rectangle, and parallelogram; by four lines like the trapezoid; by three lines like the triangle; then the circle and sector; and finally, the cylinder. The characteristics by which each of these shapes is recognized and defined are covered separately in this unit.

A. DEVELOPING A CONCEPT OF SQUARE OR SURFACE MEASURE

A surface is any figure which has length and height but no thickness. To measure a surface, its length and height must be in the same unit before they are multiplied. The result of this mathematical process is called the *area* of the surface. The area is expressed in square units of the same kind as the linear units. For example, if the length and height of an object are given in inches, the area will be in square inches. In this case, the surface contains a number of square inches. One square inch is the area a square figure measures which is one linear inch long and one linear inch high.

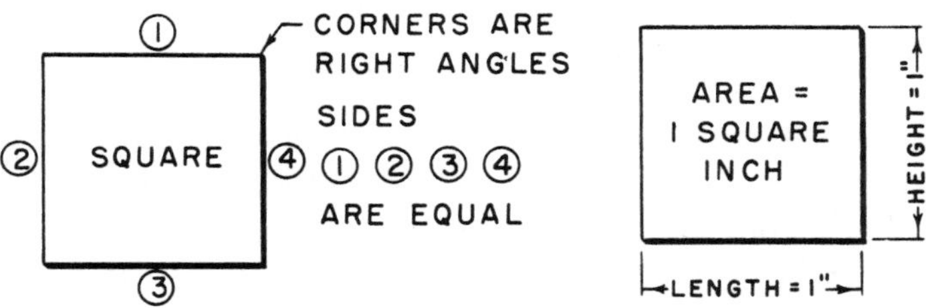

One square foot is the area a square figure measures which is 12 linear inches long and 12 linear inches high. One square yard is the area a square figure measures which is 36 linear inches long and 36 linear inches high.

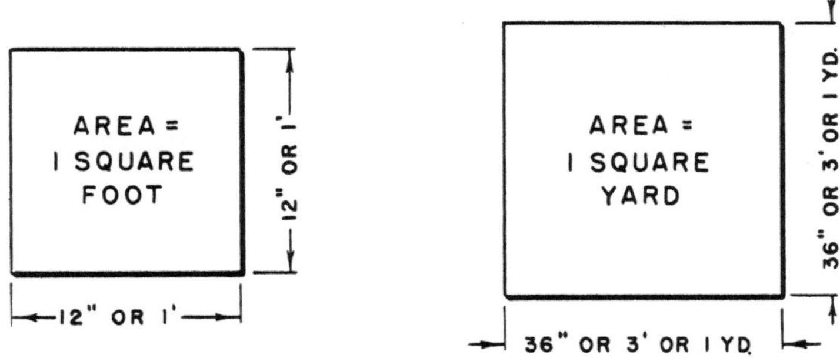

In each case the area of the square is found by multiplying the linear length by the linear height. Both dimensions must be in the same unit of measure.

By comparison, the area of a square one inch on a side is 1 square inch. The area of a square 12" on a side is 144 square inches. The area of a square 36" on a side is 1296 square inches.

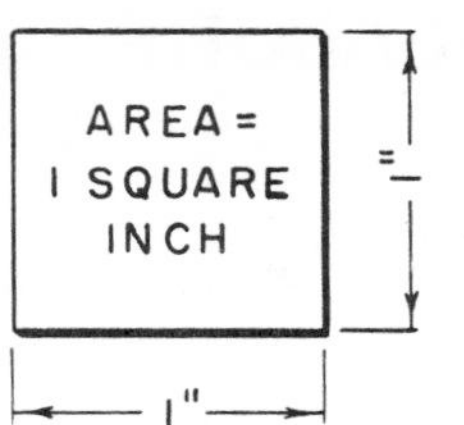

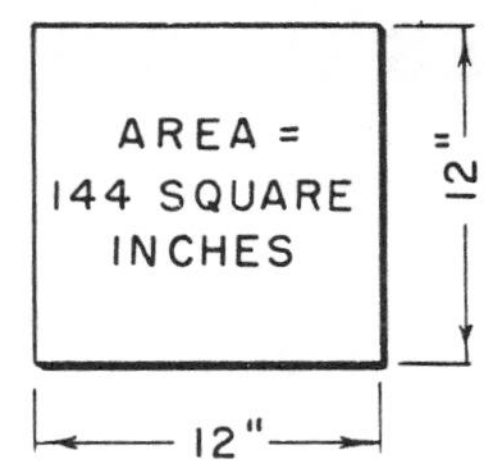

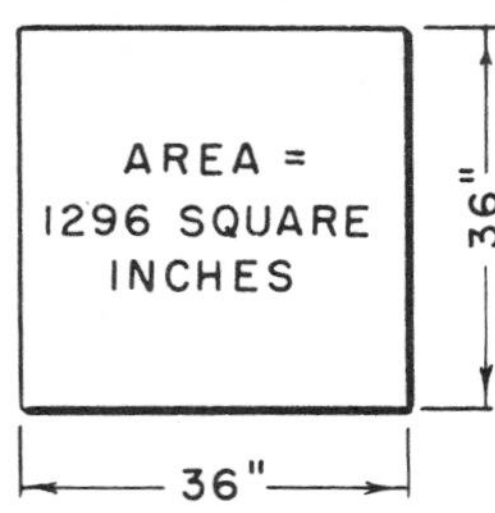

The area of the second square illustrated above is 144 square inches. Since this value is obtained by multiplying the length and height (each of which is equal to one foot), the area may be given as 1 square foot. The square foot is, therefore, equivalent to 144 square inches.

By the same reasoning, in the third square the 36 inches = 3 feet = 1 yard. The area of the square, therefore, is equal to 1296 square inches, or 9 square feet, or 1 square yard.

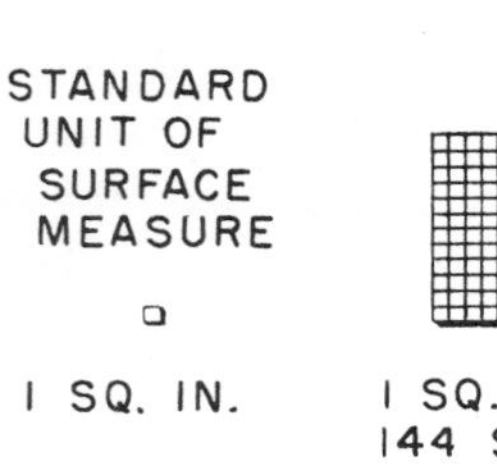

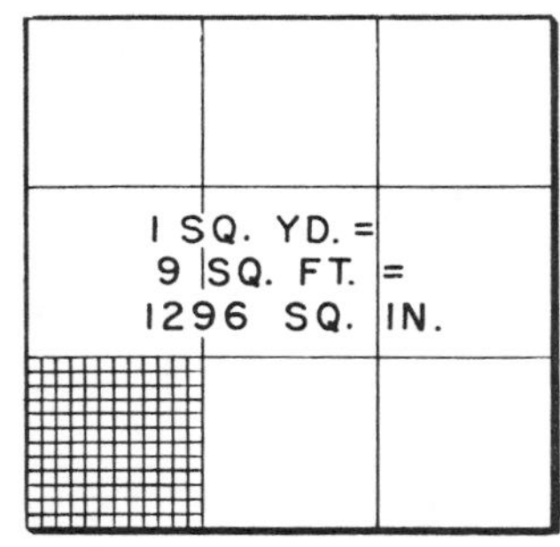

In place of continually writing the word "square" and the unit of measure, the symbol □ is used to indicate *square*. This symbol is followed by other symbols for inches (□"), feet (□'), or yards (□ yds.). Another way of writing areas is to abbreviate the word square (sq.) and the units of measure: (in.) for inches, (ft.) for feet, and (yd.) for yard. One square inch may be written 1 sq. in. or 1 □"; one square foot, 1 sq. ft. or 1 □'; and one square yard, 1 sq. yd. or 1 □ yd.

The three common units of surface measure which find daily application are the square inch, the square foot, and the square yard. The value of each of these units is shown in the accompanying table.

Table of Surface Measure		
Unit of Surface Measure	=	1 sq. in.
144 sq. in.	=	1 sq. ft.
9 sq. ft.	=	1 sq. yd.

B. CHANGING FROM ONE UNIT VALUE OF SURFACE MEASURE TO ANOTHER

A value expressed in square inches may be changed to square feet by dividing by 144 (144 sq. in. = 1 sq. ft.). By the same process, an area given in square feet may be changed to square yards by dividing by 9 (9 sq. ft. = 1 sq. yd.). If an area is given in inches, the value may be changed to square yards or a fractional part by dividing by 1296 (1296 sq. in. = 1 sq. yd.).

RULE FOR EXPRESSING A UNIT OF SURFACE MEASURE AS A LARGER UNIT

- Divide the given area by the number of square units contained in one of the required larger units.
- Express the quotient in terms of the required larger unit.

EXAMPLE: Case 1 Express 288 sq. in. in sq. ft.

Step 1	Divide given area by the number of sq. in. in a sq. ft. (144).	$\frac{288}{144} = 2$
Step 2	Express quotient (2) in terms of required unit (sq. ft.).	288 sq. in. = 2 sq. ft. Ans.

EXAMPLE: Case 2 Express 27 sq. ft. in sq. yds.

Step 1	Divide given area by the number of sq. ft. in a sq. yd. (9).	$\frac{27}{9} = 3$
Step 2	Express quotient (3) in terms of required unit (sq. yds.).	27 sq. ft. = 3 sq. yds. Ans.

EXAMPLE: Case 3 Express 2592 sq. in. in sq. yds.

Step 1	Divide the given area by the number of sq. in. in a sq. yd. (1296).	$\frac{2592}{1296} = 2$
Step 2	Express quotient (2) in terms of required unit.	2592 sq. in. = 2 sq. yds. Ans.

When the given area cannot be divided exactly, then the quotient may be expressed in more than one unit. For example, if 12 square feet is changed to square yards, the result may be given as 1 1/3 sq. yds. or as 1 sq. yd. and 3 sq. ft. In other words, the fraction (1/3) is expressed in terms of a smaller unit.

RULE FOR EXPRESSING LARGER AS SMALLER UNITS OF SURFACE MEASURE

- Multiply the given unit by the number of smaller units contained in one of the required units.
- Express the product in terms of the required smaller unit.

EXAMPLE: Case 1 Express 5 sq. ft. in sq. in.

Step 1	Multiply given unit (5) by the number of smaller units contained in one of the required units (144).	5 x 144 = 720
Step 2	Express the product (720) in terms of the required unit (sq. in.).	5 sq. ft. = 720 sq. in. Ans.

EXAMPLE: Case 2 Express 3 sq. yds. in sq. in.

Step 1	Multiply given unit (3) by the number of smaller units contained in one of the required units (1296).	3 x 1296 = 3888
Step 2	Express the product (3888) in terms of the required unit (sq. in.).	3 sq. yds. = 3888 sq. in. Ans.

An area given in terms of two or more units (2 sq. ft. 9 sq. in.) may be changed in value to a smaller unit. Only that portion of the area which is not in terms of the required unit is multiplied by the number of smaller units contained in one of the given units. The remainder of the given area is added to this product.

EXAMPLE: Express 2 sq. ft. 9 sq. in. in sq. in.

Step 1	Multiply only that portion of the given area which is not in terms of the required unit. Multiply by the number of smaller units contained in one of the given units.	2 sq. ft. = 2 x 144 (sq. in. in 1 sq. ft.) = 288
Step 2	Express the product in terms of the required unit (sq. in.).	= 288 sq. in.
Step 3	Add the remainder of the given unit (9 sq. in.).	288 + 9 = 297 sq. in. Ans.

C. APPLYING SURFACE MEASURE TO THE SQUARE AND RECTANGLE

The area of a square surface may be found by multiplying the length by the height. Since both of these dimensions are equal, the area is equal to the side multiplied by itself.

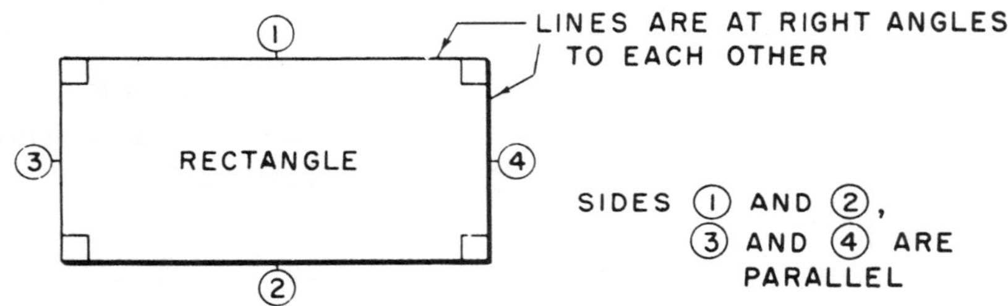

The term *rectangle* refers to a surface whose opposite sides are parallel. The adjacent sides are at right angles to each other. The area of this surface is the number of square units which it contains. In place of adding the number of square units contained in both the height and length, the process is simplified by multiplication.

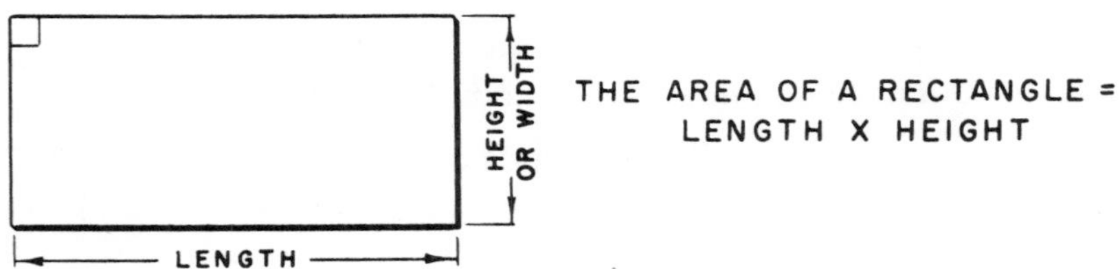

RULE FOR FINDING THE AREA OF A RECTANGLE

- Express the dimensions for length and width (sometimes called *height*) in the same linear unit of measure, when needed.
- Multiply the length by the height.
- Express the product in units of surface measure.
- Express product in lowest terms, if required.

EXAMPLE: Case 1 Determine the area of a rectangle 9″ long by 3″ high.

Step 1	Multiply length by height.	9 x 3 = 27
Step 2	Express product (27) in terms of units of surface measure.	27 sq. in. Ans.

EXAMPLE: Case 2 Determine the area of a rectangular surface 3′ long and 10″ wide.

Step 1	Express dimensions in same unit of linear measure.	3′ = 36″
Step 2	Multiply length (36″) by height (10″).	36 x 10 = 360
Step 3	Express product (360) in units of surface measure.	= 360 sq. in.
Step 4	Express (360 sq. in.) in lowest terms by dividing by (144).	$\frac{360}{144}$ = 2 sq. ft. and 72 sq. in. Ans.

D. APPLYING SURFACE MEASURE TO THE PARALLELOGRAM

A *parallelogram* has two pairs of sides which are parallel to each other. The sides are not necessarily at right angles as in the case of the rectangle. The parallelogram may be made into a rectangle, as illustrated by the shaded triangles, by cutting off the triangular surface (A) and placing it in position (B). It should be noted that the rectangle is a special kind of parallelogram in which the angles are right angles.

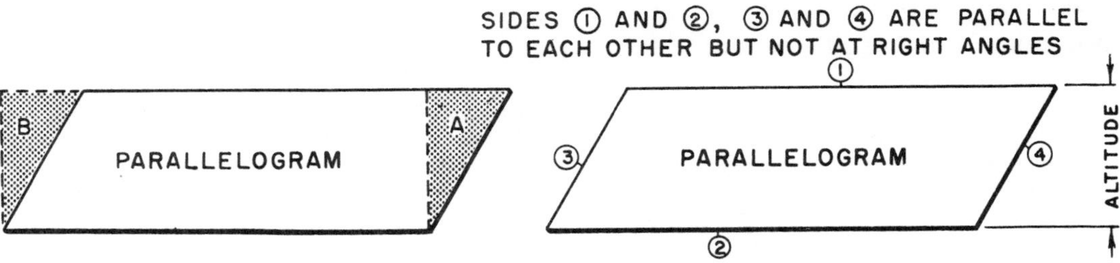

The rectangle thus formed has the same length base as the parallelogram. The height is the same as the altitude. Since the area of a rectangle is equal to the product of the length times the height, the area of a parallelogram is equal to the product of its base x altitude. The term *length* is used many times instead of *base,* and *height* for *altitude.* Regardless of which term is used, the process of finding the area is the same.

RULE FOR FINDING THE AREA OF A PARALLELOGRAM

- Express the dimensions for base and altitude in the same unit of linear measure, if needed.
- Multiply the base by the altitude.
- Express the product in units of surface measure.
- Express product, if needed, in lowest terms.

EXAMPLE: A parallelogram has a base 4 feet long and an altitude of 18 inches. Find its area.

Step 1 Express dimensions in same unit of measure. 18″ = $1\frac{1}{2}$′

Step 2 Multiply the base and altitude. $4 \times 1\frac{1}{2} = 6$

Step 3 Express product in units of surface measure. Area = 6 sq. ft. Ans.

E. APPLYING SURFACE MEASURE TO A TRAPEZOID

A *trapezoid* is a four-sided figure. Two of the trapezoid sides, called bases, are parallel.

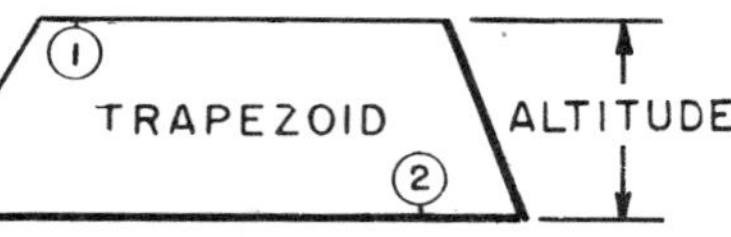

SIDES ① AND ②, CALLED BASES, ARE PARALLEL

RULE FOR FINDING THE AREA OF A TRAPEZOID

- Express the dimensions for the bases and altitude in the same unit of linear measure, if needed.
- Add the lengths of the two bases.
- Multiply the sum by one-half of the altitude.
- Express product, if needed, in lowest terms.

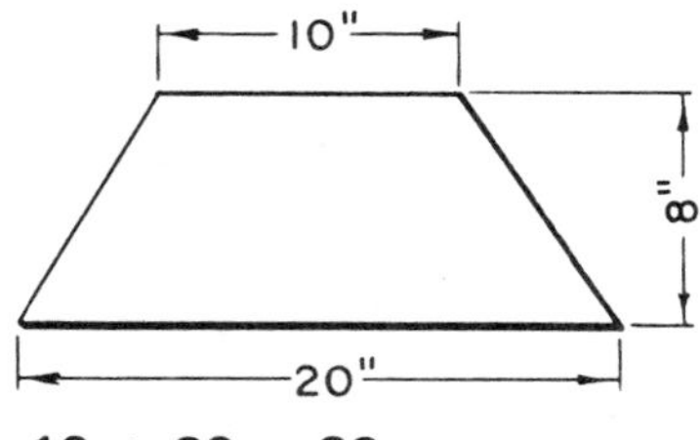

EXAMPLE: Find the area of the trapezoid.

Step 1 Add the lengths of the two bases. $10 + 20 = 30$

Step 2 Multiply the sum by (1/2) of the altitude (8). $30 \times \frac{1}{2} \times 8 =$ Area = 120 sq. in. Ans.

F. APPLYING SURFACE MEASURE TO A TRIANGLE

Two triangles of the same size and shape, when placed so that the longest side is their common side, form a parallelogram.

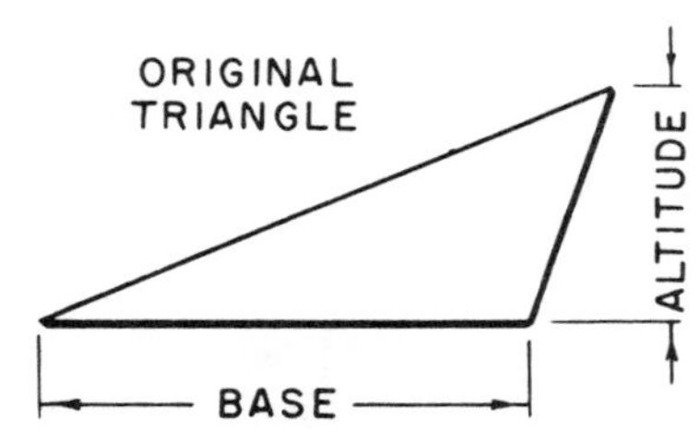

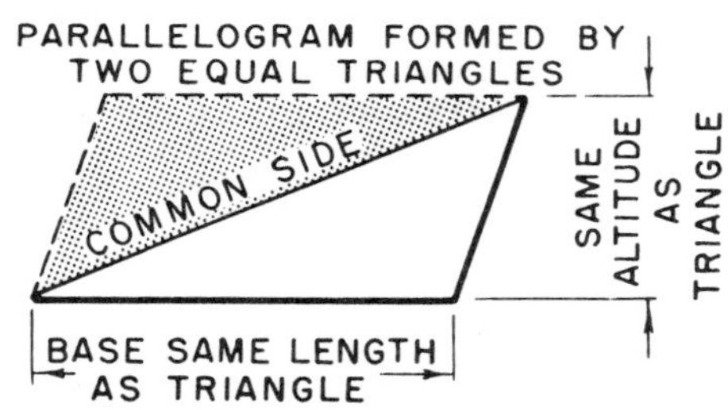

The opposite pairs of sides of this figure are parallel. The parallelogram thus formed has the same size base and altitude as the original triangle.

The area of the parallelogram is equal to the product of its base times altitude. Since the parallelogram is made up of two equal triangles, the area of each triangle is equal to one-half the area of the parallelogram. Thus, the area of a triangle may be computed directly by multiplying the base times 1/2 the altitude.

RULE FOR FINDING THE AREA OF A TRIANGLE

- Multiply the base by 1/2 the altitude.
- Express the product in units of surface measure.

EXAMPLE: Compute the area of a triangle having a 16-inch base and an altitude of 6 inches.

Step 1 Multiply the base (16) by one-half the altitude (6). $16 \times \frac{1}{2} \times 6 = 48$

Step 2 Express the product in units of surface measure. Area = 48 sq. in. Ans.

G. APPLYING SURFACE MEASURE TO A CIRCLE AND A SECTOR

1. THE CIRCLE

If a circle is divided into an equal number of parts and the sectors thus formed are stretched out along two parallel lines and these two rows of sectors are brought together, a figure approaching a rectangle is formed. As the number of sectors into which the circle is divided is increased, the length of the rectangle approaches one-half the circumference of the circle.

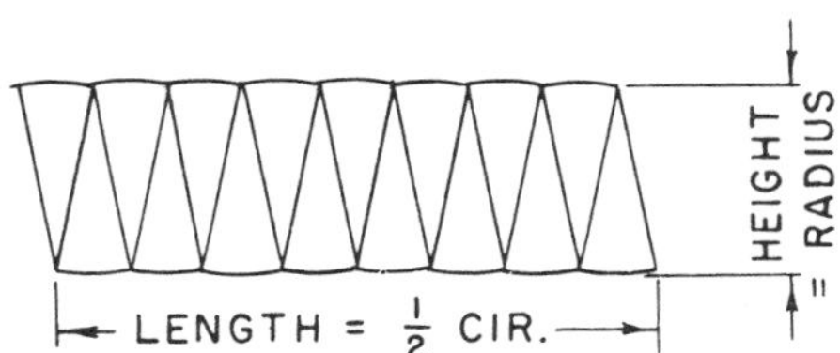

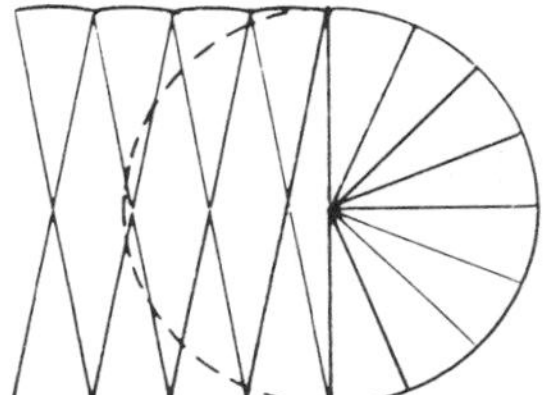

The area of the rectangle is equal to its *length x height.* The *length* is equal to 1/2 the circumference of the circle. The *height* is equal to the radius of the circle. By substituting these values, the area of the rectangle thus formed is equal to its length (1/2 the circumference) x height (radius of circle).

Area of Circle $= \frac{3.1416 \times \text{Diam. of Circle}}{2} \times \text{Radius of Circle}$

Since the diameter of the circle is twice the radius, the area of a circle in terms of its diameter

$$= \frac{3.1416 \times \text{Diam.}}{2} \times \frac{\text{Diam.}}{2} \text{ or } \frac{3.1416 \times \text{Diam.} \times \text{Diam.}}{4}$$

$$= .7854 \times \text{Diam.} \times \text{Diam.}$$

The area of a circle may be expressed in simpler terms. However, the two forms as given will be used until these values are later expressed as formulas. Where the radius of a circle is given instead of the diameter,

$$\text{Area} = \frac{3.1416 \times 2\ (\text{Radius})}{2} \times \text{Radius} = 3.1416 \times \text{Radius} \times \text{Radius}$$

In place of continually using 3.1416, the Greek letter pi (π) is used in writing a problem. The actual value is applied when working out a problem.

RULE FOR FINDING THE AREA WHEN THE DIAMETER IS GIVEN

- Multiply .7854 x Diam. x Diam.
- Express the product (area of the circle) in units of surface measure.

EXAMPLE: Find the area of a circle whose diameter is 4 inches, correct to two decimal places.

Step 1	Multiply .7854 x Diam. x Diam.	.7854 x 4 x 4 = 12.5664
Step 2	Round off product to two decimal places.	= 12.57
Step 3	Express the product in units of surface measure.	Area = 12.57 sq. in. Ans.

RULE FOR FINDING THE AREA WHEN THE RADIUS IS GIVEN

- Multiply 3.1416 x radius x radius.
- Express the product (area of the circle) in units of surface measure.

EXAMPLE: Find the area of a circle whose radius is 2.8″, correct to two decimal places.

Step 1	Multiply (π) x radius (2.8) x radius (2.8).	3.1416 x 2.8 x 2.8 = 24.630144
Step 2	Round off product to two decimal places.	= 24.63
Step 3	Express in units of surface measure.	Area = 24.63 sq. in. Ans.

2. THE SECTOR

The *sector* of a circle is the surface or area between the center and circumference. The sector is included within a given angle.

The area of a sector is equal to the area of the circle divided by the fractional part of the whole circle occupied by the sector. The angle of the sector is usually expressed as an *included angle.*

The fractional part of a circle occupied by a sector equals the number of degrees in the included angle divided by the number of degrees in a circle (360°).

RULE FOR FINDING THE AREA OF A SECTOR

- Compute the area of the circle.
- Determine the fractional part of the circle which the sector occupies by dividing the angle of the sector by 360°.
- Multiply the area of the circle by this fraction.
- Express the result (area) in square measure.

EXAMPLE: Determine the area of the sector removed from the disc.

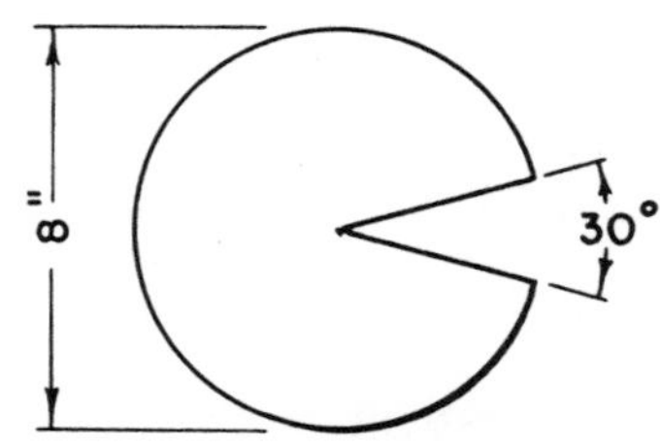

Step 1	Multiply (.7854 x Diam. x Diam.) to get the area of the circle.	$.7854 \times 8 \times 8 = 50.2656$
Step 2	Divide the number of degrees in the sector by 360°.	$\frac{30}{360} = \frac{1}{12}$
Step 3	Multiply the area of the circle (50.2656) by the fractional part occupied by the sector (1/12).	$\frac{\overset{4.1888}{\cancel{50.2656}}}{1} \times \frac{1}{\cancel{12}} = 4.1888$
Step 4	Express the product in units of surface measure.	Area = 4.1888 sq. in. Ans.

H. APPLYING SURFACE MEASURE TO THE SURFACE OF A CYLINDER

Occasionally, the area of a figure known as a *right cylinder* or a *cylinder* of *revolution* must be computed. These cylinders consist of two round bases of equal diameter and the vertical outside surface (called *lateral surface*) around the bases.

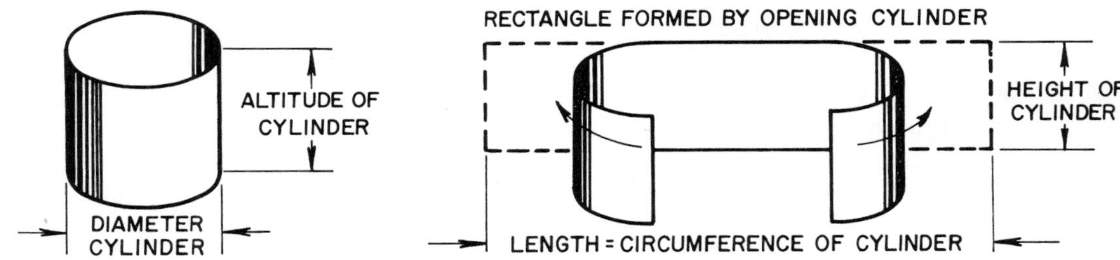

If the outside or lateral surface of the cylinder were unrolled, it would form a rectangle. The length of the rectangle is equal to the circumference of the cylinder. The rectangle height is the same as the altitude of the cylinder.

The area of this lateral surface = Circumference x Height

= (π x Diameter) x (Altitude)

RULE FOR FINDING THE AREA OF THE SURFACE OF A CYLINDER

- Find the circumference of the base.
- Multiply the circumference by the altitude of the cylinder.
- Express the area of the lateral surface in units of surface measure.

EXAMPLE: Determine the area of the lateral surface of a cylinder 2 inches in diameter and 5 inches high.

Step 1	Circumference = 3.1416 x Diam.	3.1416 x 2 = 6.2832
Step 2	Multiply circumference (6.2832) by altitude (5).	6.2832 x 5 = 31.4160
Step 3	Express area (31.416) in units of linear measure.	= 31.416 sq. in. Ans.

The *total area of a cylinder* is equal to the area of the two bases plus the area of the lateral surface.

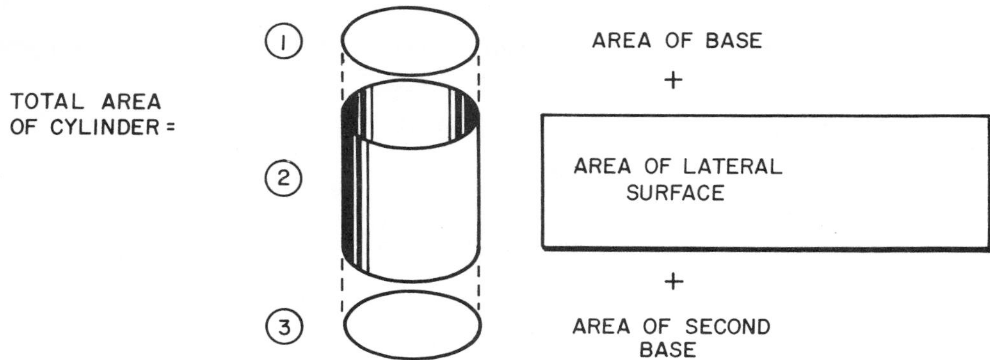

RULE FOR FINDING THE TOTAL AREA OF A CYLINDER

- Compute area of one base (.7854 x Diam. x Diam.).
- Multiply this area by (2) for two bases.
- Compute area of lateral surface (Circumference x Height).
- Add area of both bases to area of lateral surface.
- Express total area in units of surface measure.

EXAMPLE: Determine the total area of a cylinder 4 inches in diameter and 10 inches in height, correct to two decimal places.

Step 1	Compute area of base (.7854 x Diam. x Diam.).	.7854 x 4 x 4 = 12.5664
Step 2	Multiply area of one base by (2).	12.5664 x 2 = 25.1328
Step 3	Compute area of lateral surface. Multiply the circumference of base x altitude.	3.1416 x 4 x 10 = 125.6640
Step 4	Add areas of two bases ——→	25.1328
	to area of lateral surface ——→	125.6640
	Total area =	150.7968
Step 5	Round off to two decimal places.	Total area = 150.80 sq. in. Ans.

ASSIGNMENT UNIT 20

A. AREAS OF SQUARES AND RECTANGLES

1. Determine the areas of squares A, B, and C, and rectangles D, E, and F.

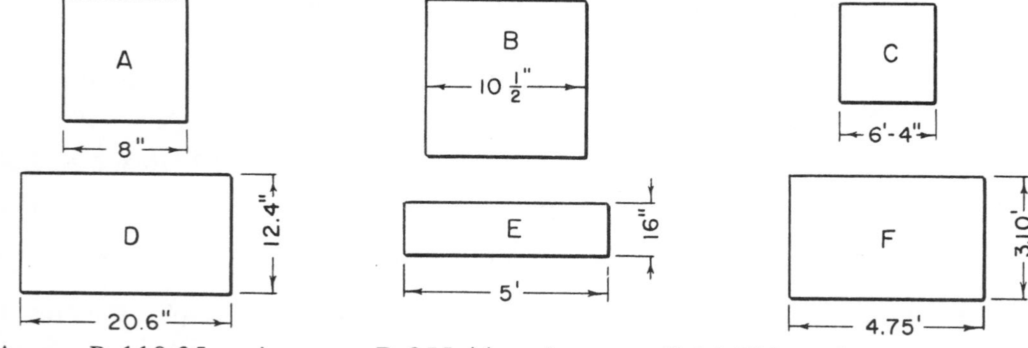

Ans.: B. 110.25 sq. in. D. 255.44 sq. in. F. 14.725 sq. ft.

2. Find the cross-sectional areas of parts A, B, and the area of the shaded portion at C. All dimensions are in inches.

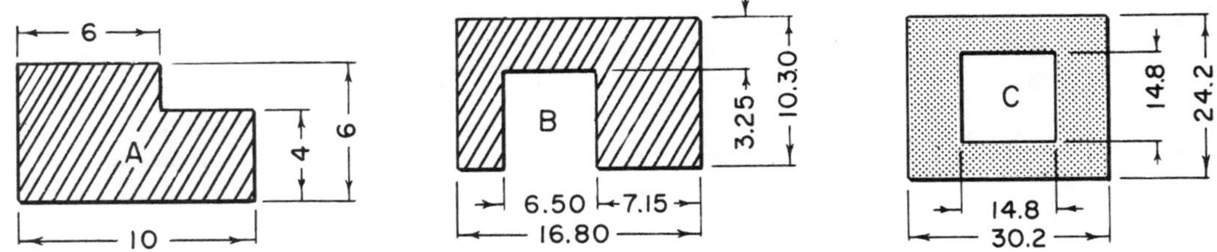

Ans.: B. 127.215 sq. in.

3. Find the total square foot area of the roof. The front portion is 46′ long x 18′ wide.

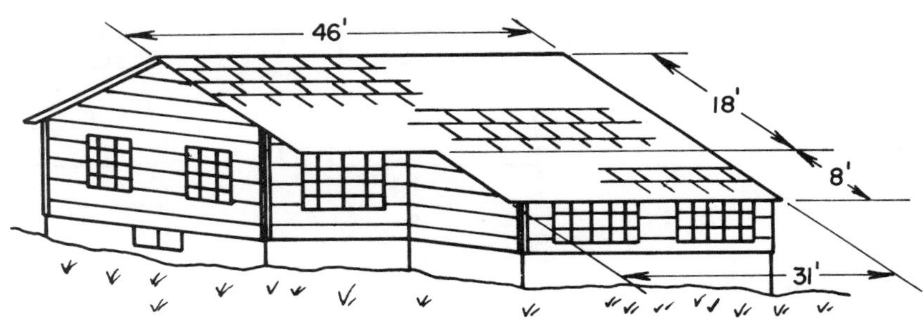

4. Assume the entire rectangular face of the carbon brush makes contact on a motor commutator. Calculate the contact surface areas of brushes A, B and C. Round off answers to two decimal places.

Brush	Dimensions		Contact Area
	Length (L)	Width (W)	
A	1 1/4″	1/2″	
B	1 1/4″	7/8″	
C	3 3/4″	1 1/8″	

W

L

Ans.: B. 1.09 sq. in.

B. AREAS OF PARALLELOGRAMS

1. Determine the areas of parallelograms A, B, and C. All dimensions are in inches.

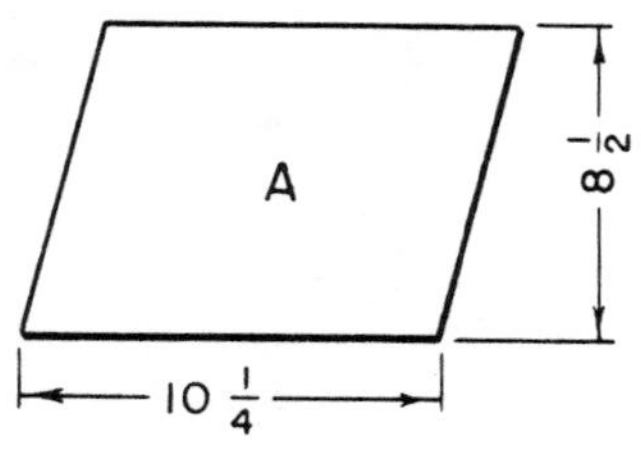

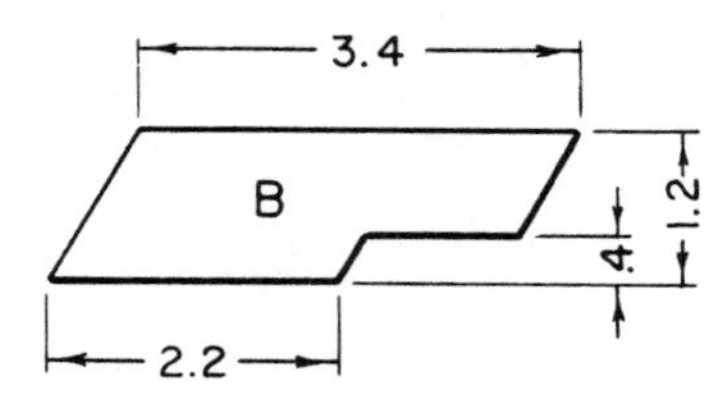

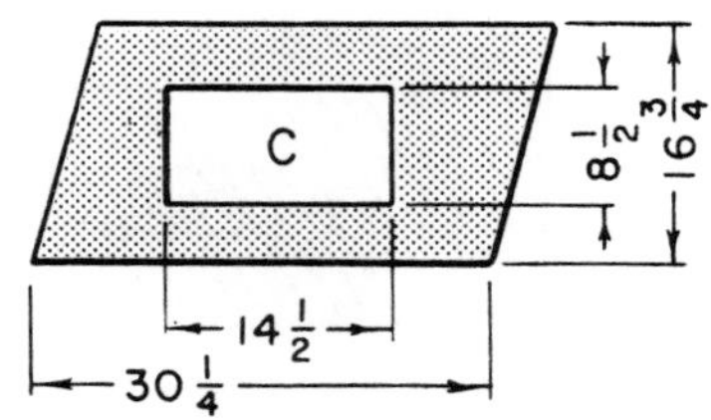

Ans.: B. 3.6 sq. in.

C. AREAS OF TRAPEZOIDS

1. Find the areas of trapezoids A, B, and C. Use the lengths of bases and altitudes given in each case. All dimensions are in inches.

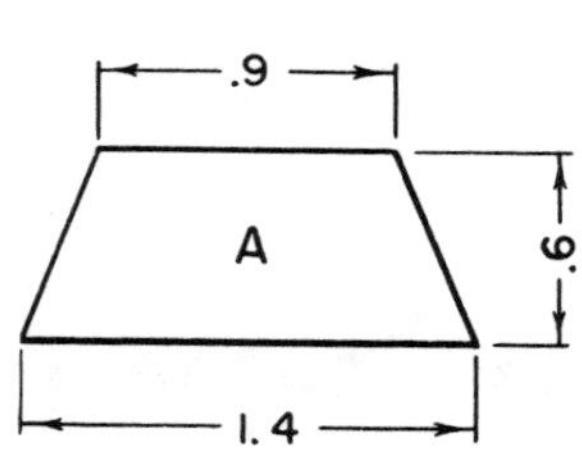

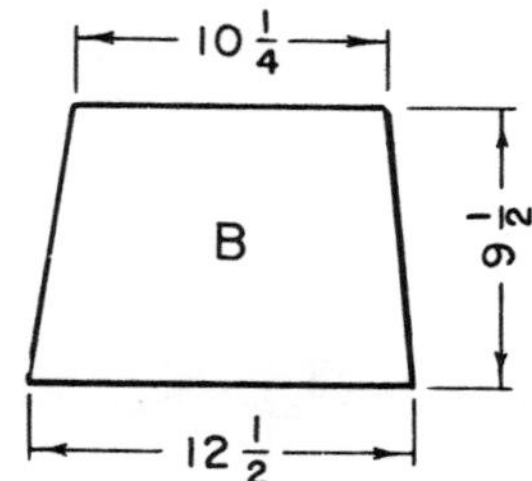

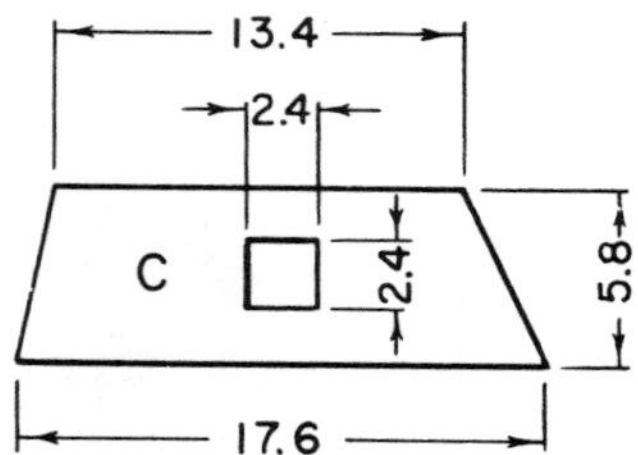

Ans.: B. 108 1/16 sq. in.

2. Determine the altitude of a trapezoid whose area is 122 square inches and bases are 12.2″ and 18.3″.

3. Compute the land area of each of the two trapezoidal-shaped lots (A and B).

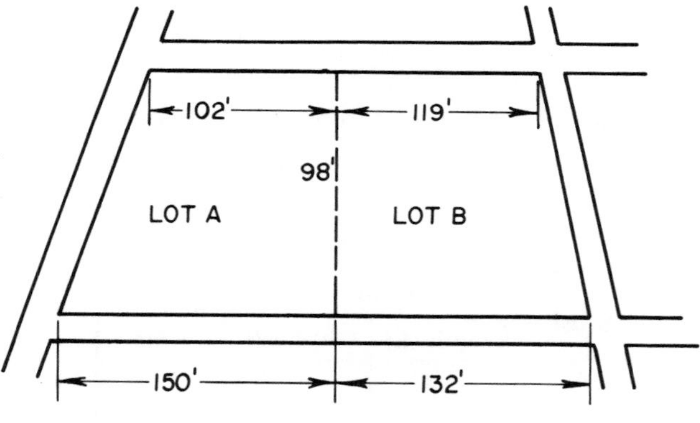

Ans.: B. 12,299 sq. ft.

4. Compute the area in square feet in the end of the concrete retaining wall as illustrated.

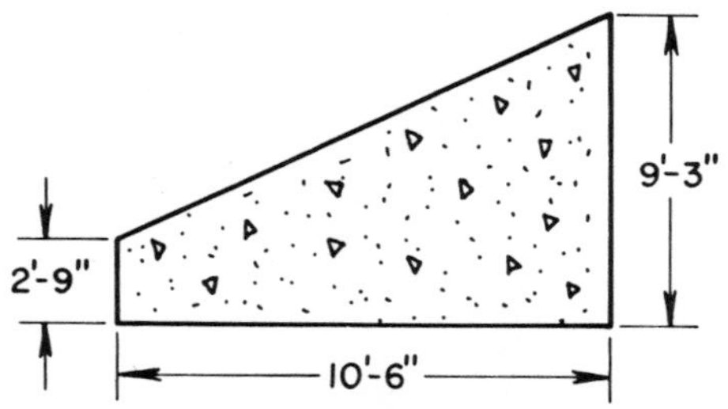

D. AREAS OF TRIANGLES

1. Find the areas of triangles A, B, and C, and triangular stamping D. All dimensions are in inches.

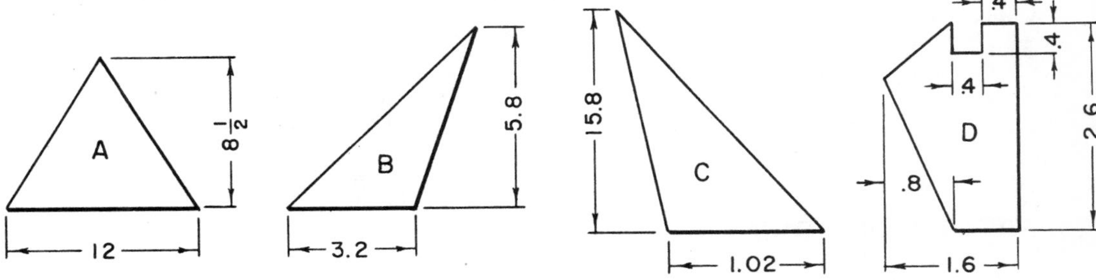

Ans.: B. 9.28 sq. in. D. 2.96 sq. in.

2. Compute the area of a triangular louver that is 4′-6″ wide x 2′-6″ high.

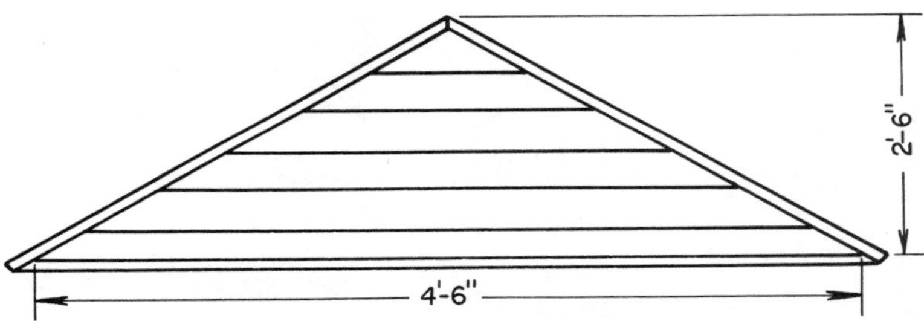

E. AREAS OF CIRCLES

1. Determine the areas of circles A through F. The diameter or radius is given in the table. Express the result in each case correct to two decimal places.

	A	B	C
Diameter	.8″	6″	5.25″

	D	E	F
Radius	.5″	2″	3.8″

Ans.: B. 28.27 sq. in. D. 12.57 sq. in.

2. Find the area of stampings A and B. All dimensions are in inches.

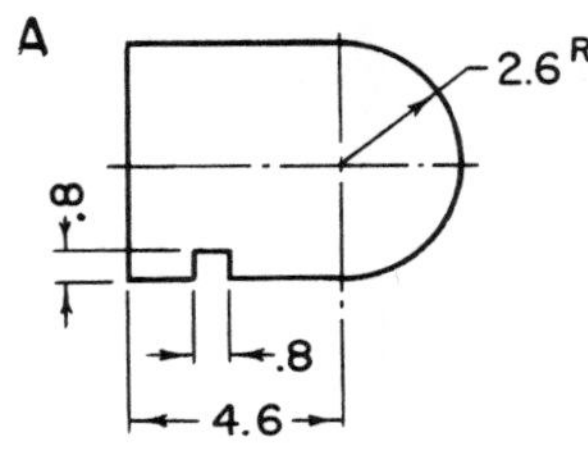

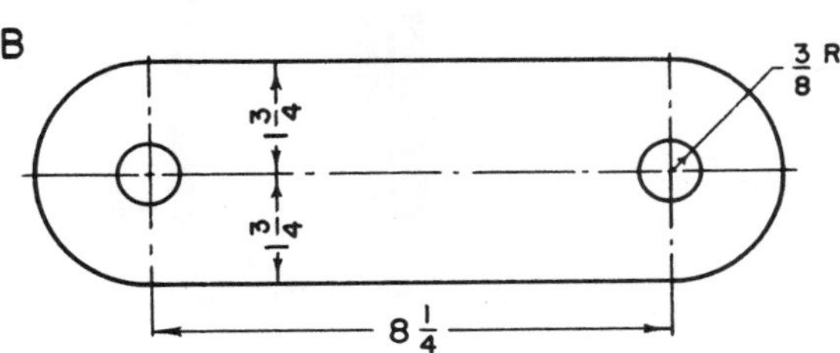

Ans.: B. 37.61 sq. in.

3. The brake lining of a magnetic disc motor brake has an outside diameter of 12″. It is 2 3/4″ wide.

   Calculate the braking area of one disc.

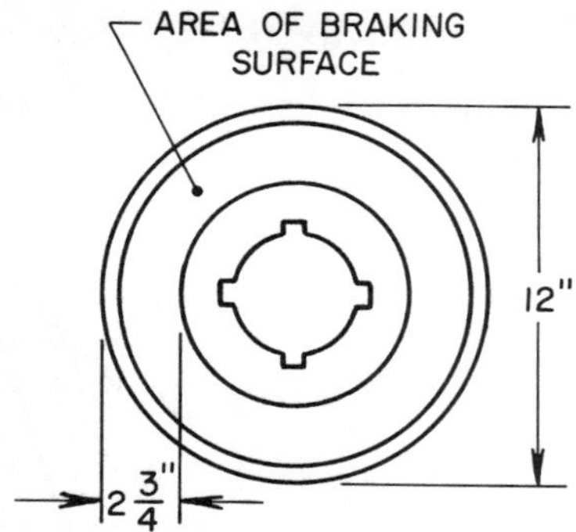

F. AREAS OF SECTORS

1. Determine the area of the shaded sectors A, B, and C, correct to three decimal places.

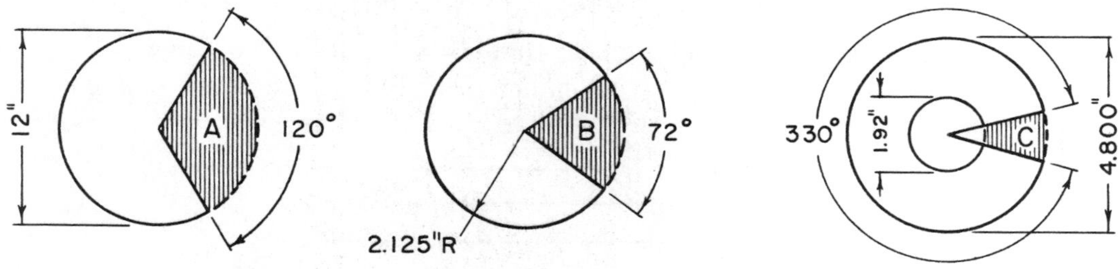

Ans.: B. 2.837 sq. in.

2. Compute the area of the garment pattern shown in the sketch. Give the answer in the nearest whole number.

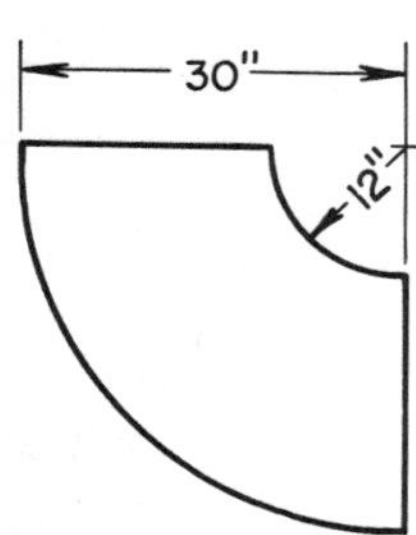

G. AREAS OF LATERAL SURFACES AND CYLINDERS

1. Determine the area of the surface of cylinder A and the total area of cylinder B. The answers should be correct to two decimal places.

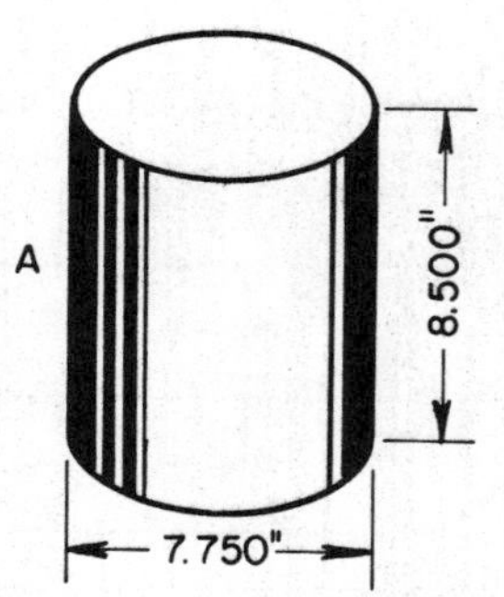

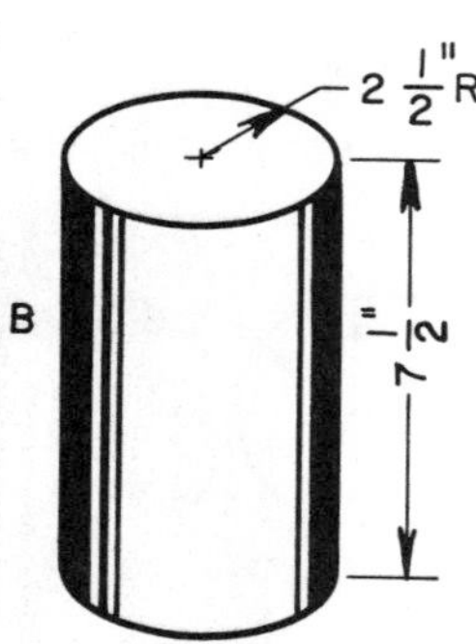

Ans.: B. 157.08 sq. in.

Unit 21 PRINCIPLES OF VOLUME MEASURE

Volume or cubic measure refers to the measurement of the space occupied by a body. Each body has three linear dimensions: length, height and depth. The principles of volume measure are applied in this unit to three common shapes and the combinations of these three shapes: (1) the cube, (2) the rectangular solid, and (3) the cylinder.

A. DEVELOPING A CONCEPT OF VOLUME MEASURE

Volume measure is the product of three linear measurements. Each measurement must be in the same linear unit before being multiplied. The product is called the *volume* of the solid or body. Volume is expressed in cubic units of the same kind as the linear units. For example, if the length, height, and depth of a solid are given in inches, the volume will be cubic inches.

The standard unit of volume or cubic measure is the cubic inch. The *cubic inch* is the space occupied by a body (called a cube). The cube is one linear inch long, one inch high, and one inch deep.

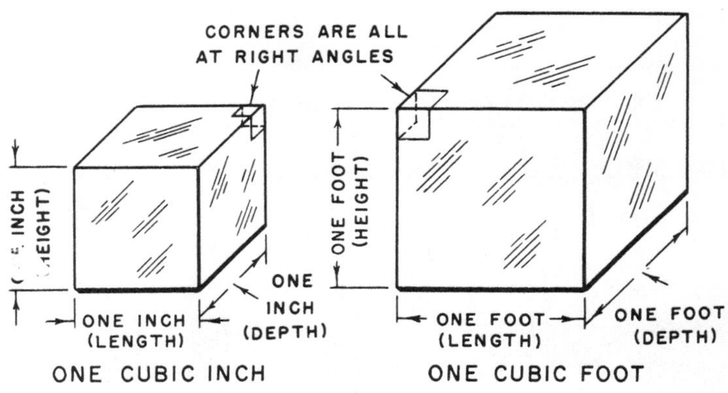

ONE CUBIC INCH ONE CUBIC FOOT

One cubic foot is the space occupied by a cubical body which is one linear foot long, one foot high, and one foot deep. If 12 inches is used as the length of each side in place of the linear foot, the volume is equal to 1728 cubic inches (12 x 12 x 12).

One cubic yard is the space occupied by a cube which is one linear yard long, one yard wide, and one yard deep. Using the equivalent value of the yard, namely, three feet, the volume is equal to 27 cubic feet (3 x 3 x 3).

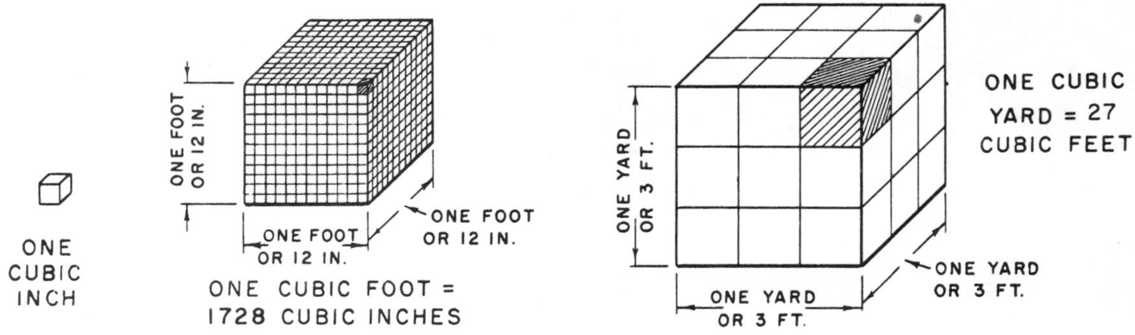

Cubic or volume measure is computed by multiplying three dimensions. By comparison with surface measure, only two dimensions are multiplied. The value of each of three standard units of volume measure may be compared. The number of cubic inches which the cubic foot and the cubic yard contain are illustrated.

The word cubic is abbreviated (cu.) for ease in writing. It is followed by the symbol for the linear unit of measure. The three units of volume measure that are used most often are the cubic inch (cu. in.), cubic foot (cu. ft.), and the cubic yard (cu. yd.).

Table of Cubic or Volume Measure		
Standard unit of measure	=	1 cu. in.
1728 cu. in.	=	1 cu. ft.
27 cu. ft.	=	1 cu. yd.

B. EXPRESSING UNITS OF VOLUME MEASURE

A volume in cubic inches may be expressed in cubic feet by dividing by 1728 (1728 cu. in. = 1 cu. ft.). Volumes given in cubic feet may be expressed in cubic yards by dividing by 27 (27 cu. ft. = 1 cu. yd.).

RULE FOR EXPRESSING A UNIT OF VOLUME MEASURE AS A LARGER UNIT

- Divide the given volume by the number of cubic units contained in the required larger units.
- Express the quotient in terms of the required larger unit.

EXAMPLE: Express 5184 cu. in. as cu. ft.

Step 1 Divide the given volume (5184) by the number of cu. in. in one cu. ft. (1728). $\frac{5184}{1728} = 3$

Step 2 Express the quotient (3) in terms of the required larger unit. Ans. 5184 cu. in. = 3 cu. ft.

NOTE: If the given volume cannot be divided exactly, the quotient may be expressed in more than one unit. A given number of cubic feet plus a stated number of cubic inches is an example.

RULE FOR EXPRESSING A LARGER UNIT OF VOLUME MEASURE AS A SMALLER UNIT

- Multiply the given unit by the number of smaller units contained in one of the required units.
- Express the product in terms of the required smaller unit.

EXAMPLE: Express 10 cu. yds. in cu. ft.

Step 1 Multiply the given unit (10) by the number of cu. ft. in one cu. yd. (27 cu. ft. = 1 cu. yd.) $10 \times 27 = 270$

Step 2 Express the product (270) in terms of the required unit (cu. ft.). Ans. 10 cu. yds. = 270 cu. ft.

RULE FOR EXPRESSING TWO OR MORE UNITS OF MEASURE

If a volume expressed in two or more units of measure is to be expressed in a smaller unit,

- Multiply those units of measure which are not in terms of the required unit by the number of smaller units equal to one given unit.
- Add the remaining units in the original given volume to this product.

EXAMPLE: Express 2 cu. yd., 10 cu. ft. as cu. ft.

Step 1	Multiply (2) cu. yds. by the number of cu. ft. in one cu. yd.	2 x 27 = 54 cu. ft.
Step 2	Add to the product (54 cu. ft.) the remainder of the given volume (10 cu. ft.).	10 cu. ft. Ans. 64 cu. ft.

C. APPLYING VOLUME MEASURE TO THE CUBE AND RECTANGULAR SOLID

In volume measure the three linear dimensions which express length, height, and depth, or their equivalents, are multiplied to determine the cubical contents of a regular solid. The product is in cubic inches if the dimensions are in inches, cubic feet when the dimensions are given in feet, and cubic yards when given in yards.

When the area of one surface is extended in a third direction, a solid is formed. The space the solid occupies is measured in terms of the number of cubic units which it contains.

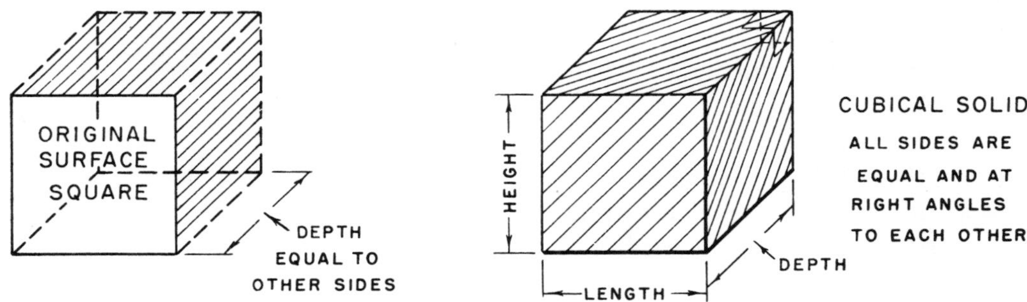

If the original surface is a square and its face is extended to add depth, the resulting figure is called a solid. When all corners of the solid are square and the linear length, height, and depth are equal, the object is called a *cube* or *cubical solid.* The volume of this cubical solid is equal to the product of its length x depth x height.

RULE FOR COMPUTING THE VOLUME OF A CUBE

- Express the dimensions for length, depth, and height in the same linear unit of measure, when needed.
- Multiply the length x depth x height.
- Express the product in terms of units of volume measure.
- Express the resulting product, if needed, in lowest terms.

EXAMPLE: Case 1 Find the volume of a cube, each side of which is 8 inches long.

Step 1	Multiply the length (8) x depth (8) x height (8).	8 x 8 x 8 = 512
Step 2	Express the product (512) in terms of volume measure.	Ans. 512 cu. in.

EXAMPLE: Case 2 Determine the volume of a cube which measures 1′ 9″ on a side.

METHOD 1

Step 1	Express 1′-9″ as 21″.	21 x 21 x 21 = 9261
Step 2	Multiply length x depth x height.	9261 cu. in.
Step 3	Express product (9261) in terms of volume measure.	$\frac{9261}{1728}$ = 5 cu. ft., 621 cu. in.
Step 4	Express as cu. ft. and cu. in.	Ans. 5 cu. ft., 621 cu. in.

METHOD 2

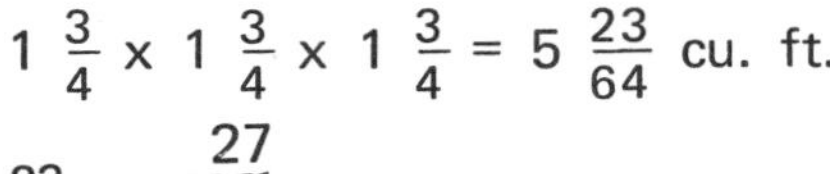

Step 1	Express 1′-9″ as 1 3/4′.	$1\frac{3}{4} \times 1\frac{3}{4} \times 1\frac{3}{4} = 5\frac{23}{64}$ cu. ft.
Step 2	Multiply length x depth x height.	
Step 3	Express (23/64) cu. ft. as cu. in. by multiplying by (1728).	$\frac{23}{\cancel{64}} \times \overset{27}{\cancel{1728}}$ = 621 cu. in.
Step 4	Add the number of cu. in. to the cu. ft. to get volume of the cube.	Ans. 5 cu. ft., 621 cu. in.

A *rectangular solid* resembles a cube except that the faces or sides are rectangular in shape. The volume of a rectangular solid is equal to the product of the length x depth x height. Sometimes the volume is expressed as the product of the area of the base (length x depth) x the height.

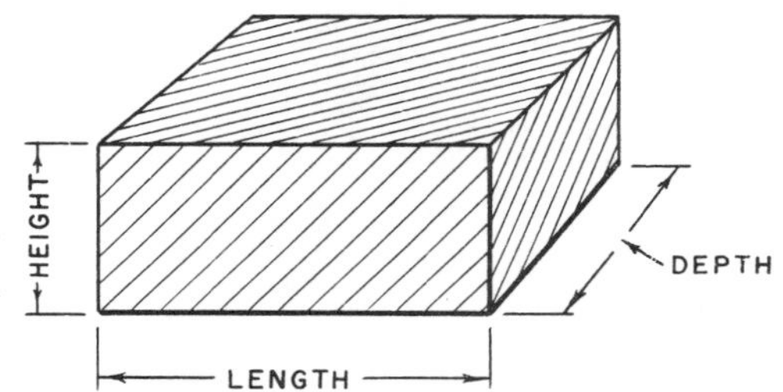

RULE FOR FINDING THE VOLUME OF A RECTANGULAR SOLID

- Express the dimensions of length, depth, and height in the same linear unit of measure if needed.
- Multiply the length x depth x height.
- Express the product in terms of units of volume measure and reduce to lowest terms, if needed.

EXAMPLE: Find the volume of the block in the accompanying sketch.

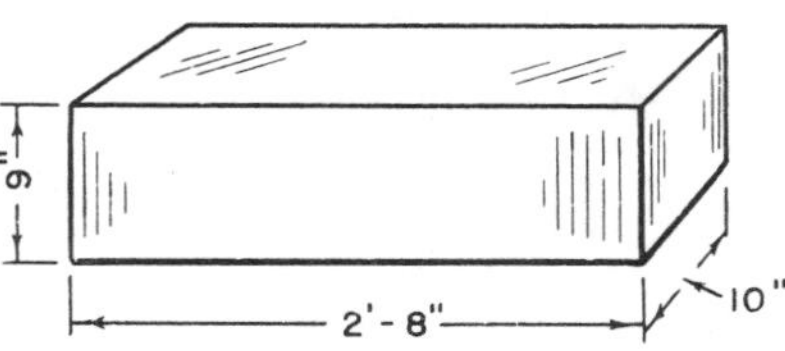

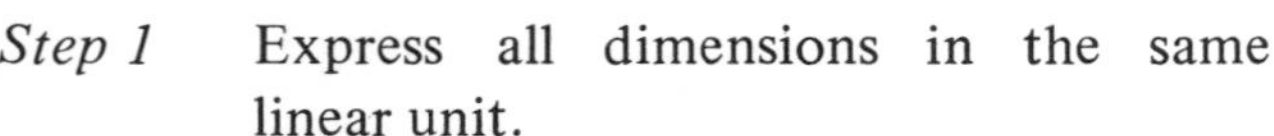

Step 1	Express all dimensions in the same linear unit.	
Step 2	Multiply length x depth x height.	10 x 32 x 9 = 2880
Step 3	Express product as units of volume measure.	2880 cu. in.
Step 4	Express in lowest terms.	Ans. $\frac{2880}{1728}$ = 1 cu. ft., 1152 cu. in.

The volume or weight of a hollow rectangular solid is computed by using the same rules and mathematical processes as for the rectangular solid. Such problems often require a double computation. One computation is required for the outer surface and one for a cored or cut-away section.

D. APPLICATION OF VOLUME MEASURE TO CYLINDERS

The volume of a cylinder is the number of cubic units of a given kind which it contains. This number is found by multiplying the area of the base by the length or height of the cylinder.

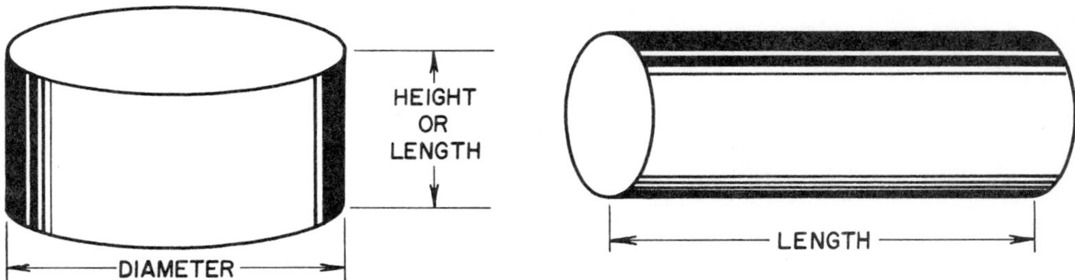

RULE FOR FINDING THE VOLUME OF A CYLINDER

- Compute the area of the base.
- Multiply this area by the height or length of the cylinder.
- Express the product (volume of cylinder) in units of volume measure.

EXAMPLE: Find the volume of a cylinder (3″) in diameter and (10″) long, correct to two decimal places.

Step 1	Compute the area of the base by multiplying (.7854 x Diam. x Diam.).	.7854 x 3 x 3 = 7.0686 sq. in.
Step 2	Multiply this area by the length of the cylinder (10″).	7.0686 x 10 = 70.686
Step 3	Express product (70.686) correct to two decimal places, in units of volume measure.	Ans. 70.69 cu. in.

E. APPLICATION OF VOLUME MEASURE TO IRREGULAR FORMS

In addition to regular solids like the cube, rectangle, and cylinder, many objects are a combination of these shapes in a modified form.

The volume of an irregular solid can be computed by dividing it into solids having regular shapes. The volume of each regular solid (or part of one) can be computed. The sum of the separate volumes equals the volume of the irregular solid.

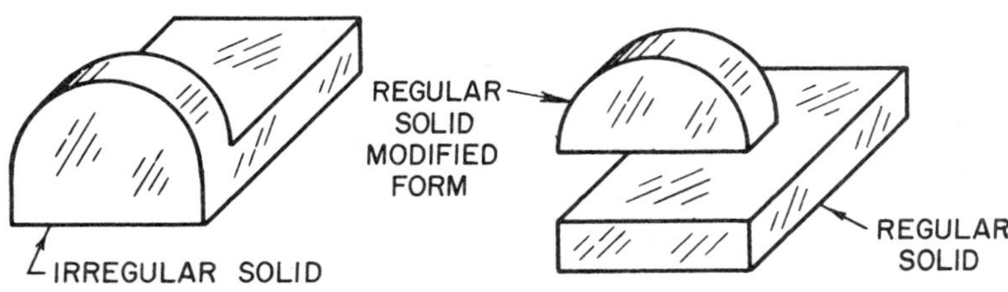

RULE FOR FINDING THE VOLUME OF AN IRREGULAR SOLID

- Divide the solid into regular forms.
- Compute the volume of each regular solid, or part of one.
- Add the separate volumes.

EXAMPLE: Determine the volume of the brass casting shown in the sketch.

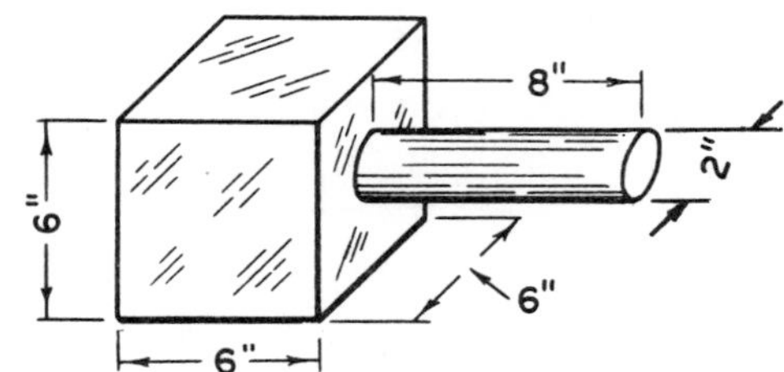

Step 1 Divide the irregular form into two regular solids (a cube and a cylinder).

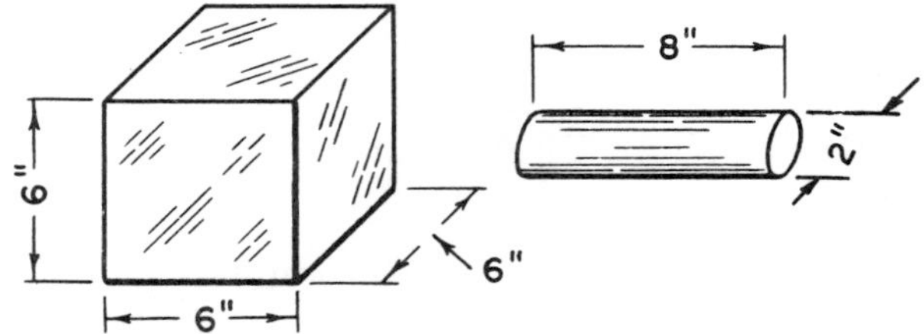

Step 2 Compute the volume of each regular solid.

a. Volume of cube = length x depth x height   6 x 6 x 6 = 216 cu. in.

b. Volume of the cylinder = area of base x height   (.7854 x 2 x 2) x 8 = 25.1328 cu. in.

Step 3 Add the separate volumes.

216 cu. in.
25.13 cu. in.

Ans. Total volume of casting = 241.13 cu. in.

F. APPLICATION OF VOLUME MEASURE TO LIQUID MEASURE

Constant reference is made in the shop to the measurement of liquids for cutting oils, oils for heat-treating metals, coolant solutions, marking fluids, cleaning agents, and lubricants. Also, an understanding of the measurement of liquids is essential in clinics and hospitals, business, merchandising, the home and in daily living.

Liquids are measured by cubical units of measure known as *liquid* measure. One common method of determining liquid capacity requires, first, the computing of the cubical contents of the object. Secondly, the resulting units of volume measure are changed to units of liquid measure.

The standard units of liquid measure are the gill, pint, quart, gallon, and barrel. These units are sometimes abbreviated for ease in writing. The pint is written (pt.), quart (qt.), gallon (gal.), and barrel (bbl.). A comparison of values for each of these units is found in the Table of Liquid Measure.

The gallon as established by law contains 231 cubic inches of liquid. With this known value, it is possible to solve problems requiring the use of liquid measure by dividing the volume, expressed in cubic inches, by 231.

Table of Liquid Measure		
4 gills	=	1 pt. (pt.)
2 pints (pts.)	=	1 quart (qt.)
4 quarts (qts.)	=	1 gallon (gal.) = 231 cu. in.
31 1/2 gallons	=	1 standard barrel (bbl.)

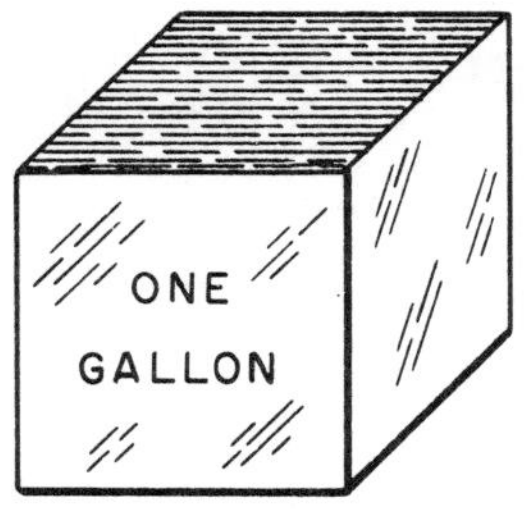

=

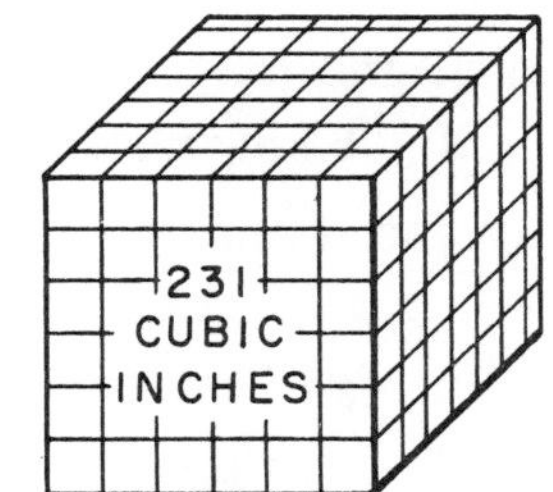

RULE FOR CHANGING UNITS OF VOLUME MEASURE TO UNITS OF LIQUID MEASURE

- Compute the volume of the object in terms of cubic inches.
- Divide this volume by 231 (231 cu. in. = 1 gallon).
- Express the quotient in terms of liquid measure (gallons).

EXAMPLE: Determine the liquid capacity of a coolant tank whose volume is 1155 cubic inches.

Step 1 Divide volume in cubic inches (1155) by the number of cubic inches (231) in one gallon. $\frac{1155}{231} = 5$

Step 2 Express the quotient (5) in terms of liquid measure. Ans. Capacity of tank = 5 gallons

RULE FOR EXPRESSING LARGER UNITS OF LIQUID MEASURE IN SMALLER UNITS (barrels to gallons to quarts to pints to gills)

- Determine the number of smaller units of liquid measure in one larger unit.
- Multiply the given units by this number.
- Express the product in terms of the required unit of measure.

EXAMPLE: Case 1 Express 4 1/2 gallons in quarts.

Step 1 Determine the number of smaller units (quarts) in one larger unit (gallons). 4 qts. = 1 gal.

Step 2 Multiply the given units (4 1/2) by this number (4). $4\frac{1}{2} \times 4 = 18$

Step 3 Express the product (18) in the required units of liquid measure (qts.). Ans. $4\frac{1}{2}$ gals. = 18 qts.

EXAMPLE: Case 2 Express 3 1/8 quarts as pints and gills.

$3\frac{1}{8}$ QUARTS = PINTS AND GILLS

Step 1 Determine the number of smaller units (pints and gills) in one larger unit (quart).

2 pts. = 1 qt., 4 gills = 1 pt.

Step 2 Multiply the given unit (3 1/8 qts.) by the number of smaller units (2 pts.) in one of the given units (1 qt.).

$3\frac{1}{8} \times 2 = 6\frac{1}{4}$ pts.

NOTE: The fractional part of a pint (1/4) may be changed to gills by multiplying by (4) the number of gills in one pint.

$\frac{1}{4} \times 4 = 1$ gill

Step 3 Combine both values (6 pints and 1 gill). The result is the equivalent of (3 1/8) quarts in terms of pints and gills.

Ans. $3\frac{1}{8}$ qts. = 6 pts., 1 gill

RULE FOR EXPRESSING SMALLER UNITS OF LIQUID MEASURE IN LARGER UNITS (gills to pints to quarts to gallons to barrels)

- Determine the number of smaller units of liquid measure in one of the required larger units.
- Divide the number of given units by this number.

NOTE: Where the result is a mixed number, the fractional part is sometimes changed to the next smaller unit. For example, 3 1/2 gallons may be written 3 gallons, 2 quarts.

EXAMPLE: Case 1 Express 24 pints in gallons.

Step 1 Determine the number of smaller units (pts.) in one of the larger required units (gals.).

8 pts. = 1 gal.

Step 2 Divide the number of given units (24) by this number (8) to get gallons.

$\frac{24}{8} = 3$

Ans. 24 pts. = 3 gals.

EXAMPLE: Case 2 Express 76 gills in gallons, quarts, and pints.

Step 1 Determine the number of smaller units of liquid measure (gills) in one of the required larger units (gallons and quarts).

8 gills = 1 qt.
32 gills = 1 gal.

Step 2 Divide the (76) gills by (32) to get the number of gallons.

$\frac{76}{32}$ = 2 gallons, 12 gills

Step 3 Express the (12) gills as quarts by dividing by (8).

$\frac{12}{8}$ = 1 quart, 4 gills

Step 4	Express the remaining (4) gills as pints by dividing by (4).	$\frac{4}{4}$ = 1 pint
Step 5	Combine all values. The result in gallons, quarts and pints is the equivalent of 76 gills.	Ans. 76 gills = 2 gallons, 1 quart, 1 pint

ASSIGNMENT UNIT 21

NOTE: Unless otherwise stated, all dimensions for all problems are expressed in inches.

A. CHANGING VALUES OF UNITS OF VOLUME MEASURE

1. Express each of the following volumes (a) through (l) in the unit of volume measure specified in each case.

a. 2 cu. ft. in cu. in.
b. 1 1/2 cu. ft. in cu. in.
c. 3 5/8 cu. ft. in cu. in.
d. 10 cu. ft., 19 cu. in. in cu. in.
e. 3456 cu. in. in cu. ft.
f. 18.144 cu. in. in cu. ft.
g. 8640 cu. in. in cu. ft.
h. 1944 cu. in. in cu. ft. and cu. in.
i. 3 cu. yds. in cu. ft.
j. 4 1/3 cu. yds. in cu. ft.
k. 5 cu. yds., 7 cu. ft. in cu. ft.
l. 7 cu. yds., 19 cu. ft. in cu. ft.

Ans.: d. 17,299 h. 1 cu. ft. 216 cu. in. l. 208 cu. ft.

B. APPLYING VOLUME MEASURE TO CUBES AND RECTANGULAR SOLIDS

1. Determine the volume of cubes A, B, and C.

Ans.: B. 614.125 cu. in.

	A	B	C
Length	6	8 1/2	1'-6"
Depth	6	8 1/2	1'-6"
Height	6	8 1/2	1'-6"

2. Compute the volume of rectangular solids A, B, and C (correct to two decimal places).

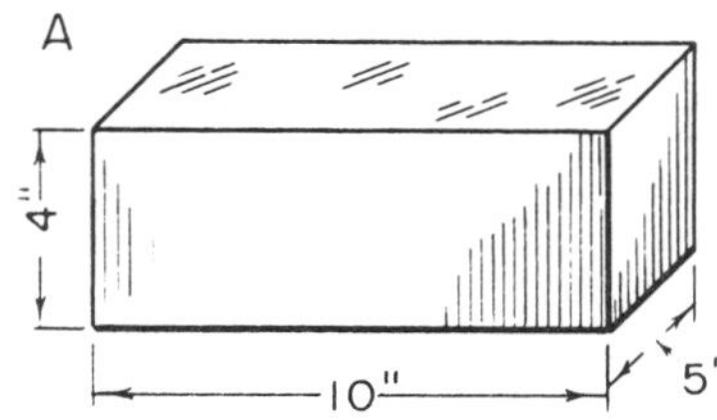

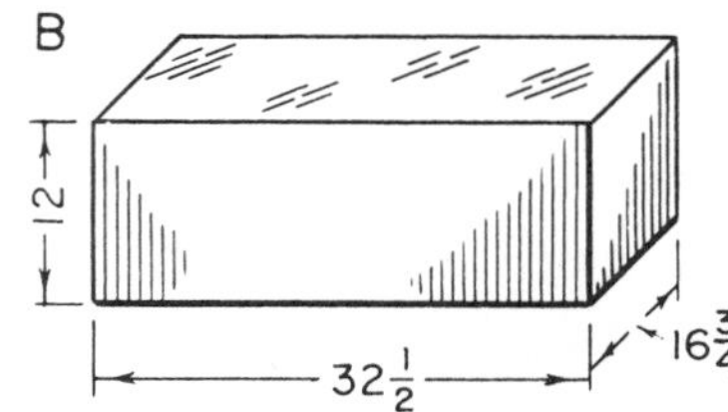

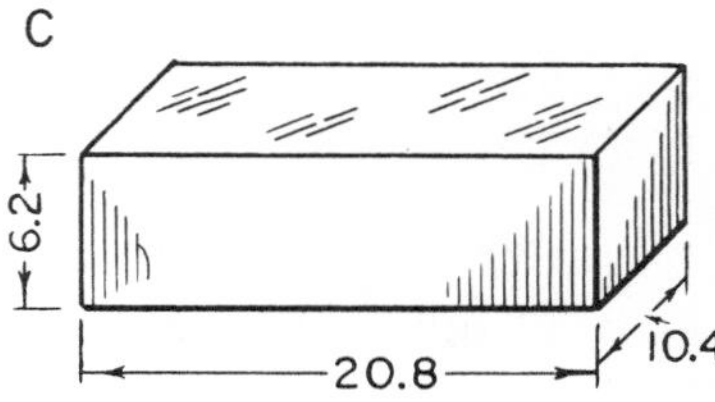

Ans.: B. 6532.5 cu. in.

3. Determine the number of cubic yards of concrete mix that is needed to pour footings A, B, and C.

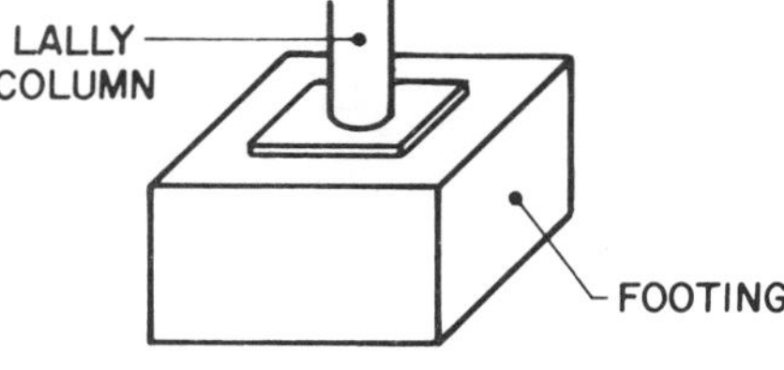

Footing	Number Required	Dimensions			Required Cubic Yards
		Width	Length	Height	
A	4	1'-6"	1'-6"	1'-6"	
B	2	1'-6"	1 yd.	9"	
C	6	1'-6"	4'-6"	1'-6"	

Ans.: B. 1/4

C. APPLYING VOLUME MEASURE TO RECTANGULAR SOLIDS

1. Compute the number of cubic yards of earth that is to be removed for a basement. The basement dimensions are 8′ deep x 36′ wide x 48′ long.

2. Determine the volume of concrete in the foundation wall. State the answer to the nearest cubic yard.

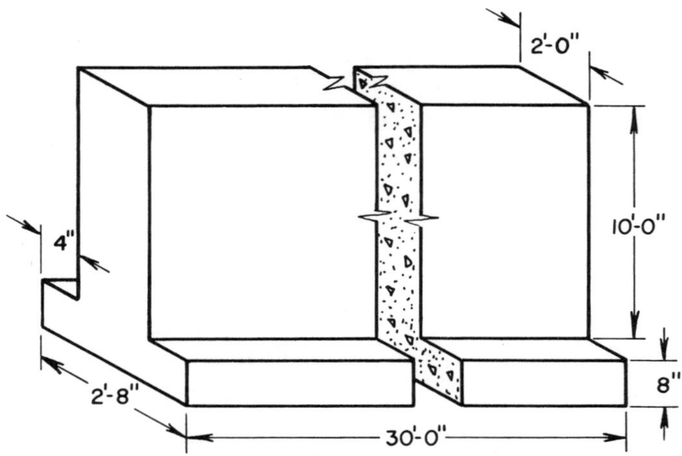

Ans.: 27 cu. yd.

3. Compute the volume of hollow rectangular solids A and B. Round off the volume of B correct to one decimal place.

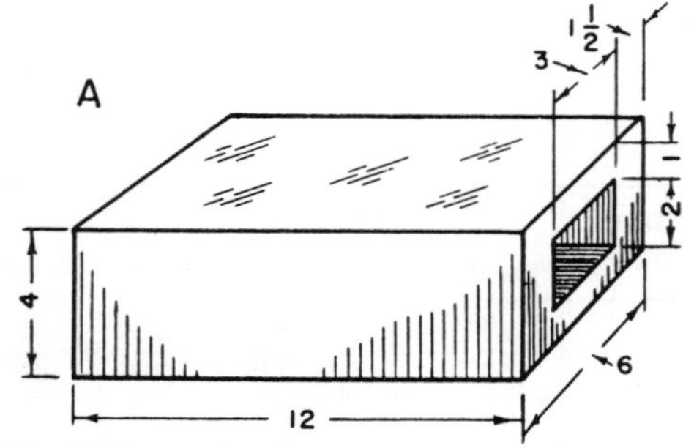

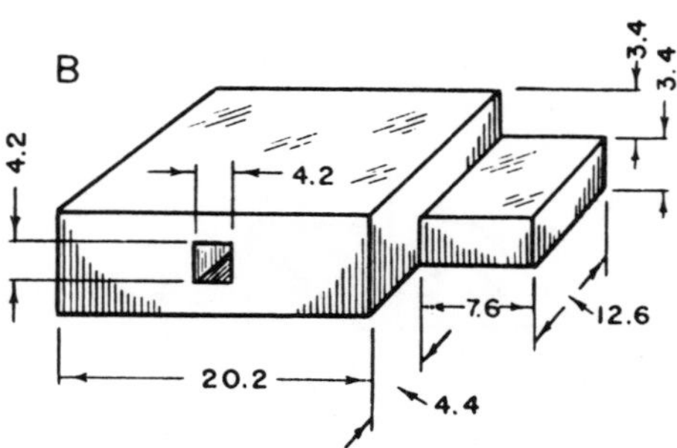

Ans.: A. 216 cu. in.

D. APPLYING VOLUME MEASURE TO CYLINDERS

1. Determine the volume of cylinders A, B, and C, correct to two decimal places.

	A	B	C
Diameter	4	12.5	
Radius			1.6
Length	10	24.5	6.4

Ans.: B. 3006.61 cu. in.

2. Compute the liquid capacity of cisterns A, B and C in gallons of water. Round off the value to one decimal place.

Ans.: B. 1425.5 gallons

Cistern	Inside Diameter	Height
A	4′-0″	6′-0″
B	5′-6″	8′-0″
C	6′-6″	8′-6″
1 cu. ft. = 7 1/2 gal.		

3. Find the volume of cored cylinders A and B, correct to one decimal place.

	A	B
Outside Diam.	5	4 1/4
Inside Diam.	2	1 1/2
Length	10	12

4. Find the weight of cored brass casting A and cored bronze casting B.

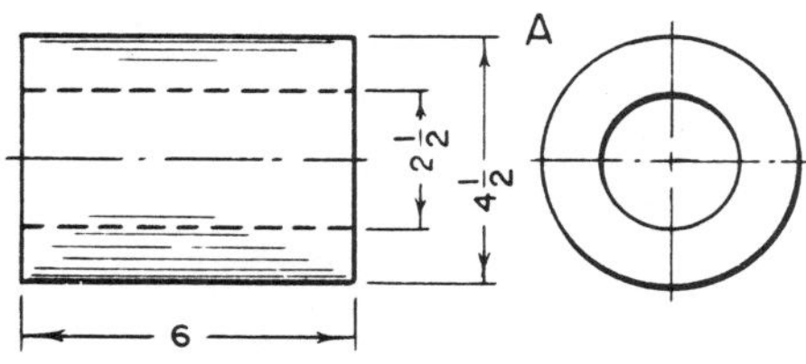

WEIGHT OF BRASS = .30 LBS. PER CU. IN.
10 REQUIRED

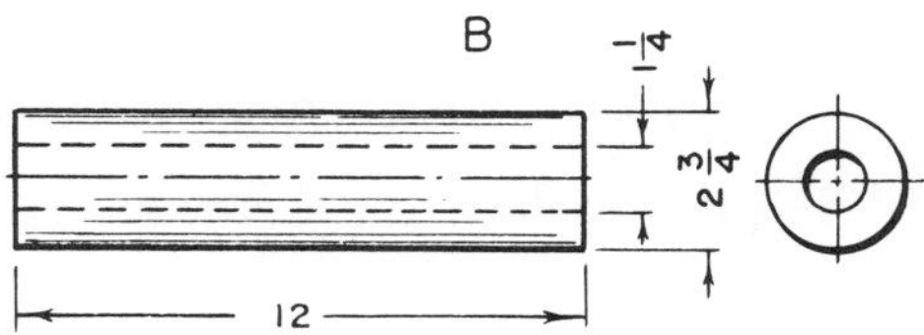

WEIGHT OF BRONZE = .32 LBS. PER CU. IN.
24 REQUIRED

Ans.: B. 434.29 lbs.

5. Determine the cost of material needed to machine 250 special pins of 3/4-inch round stock, 3 1/2 inches long. Allow 1/8 inch for cutting off each pin and an additional 107 inches of the total length for waste and stock spoilage. The material weighs 0.28 pounds per cubic inch and costs $0.42 per pound. Find the cost to the nearest dollar.

6. Determine the weight of the aluminum parts shown at A and B, correct to two decimal places. The weight of aluminum is .09 pounds per cubic inch.

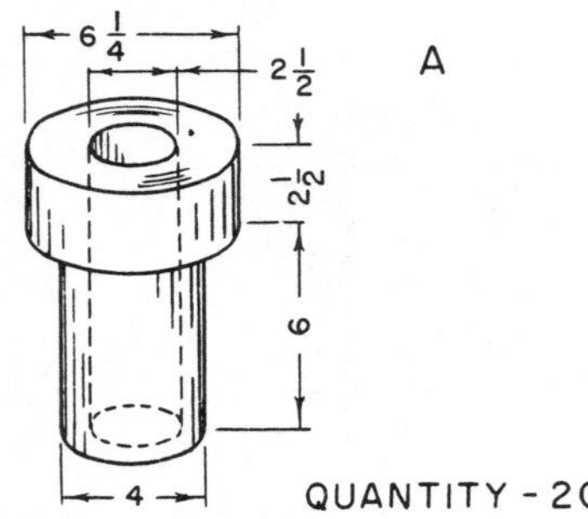

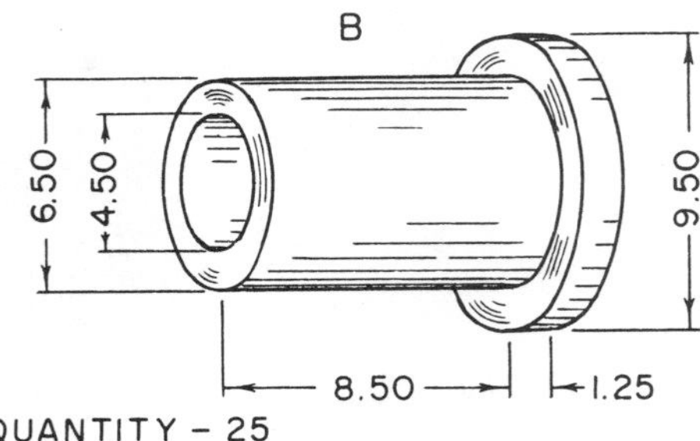

Ans.: A. 198.67 lbs.

E. APPLYING VOLUME MEASURE TO IRREGULAR SHAPES

1. Determine the weight of the rectangular cast iron blocks specified, correct to one decimal place.

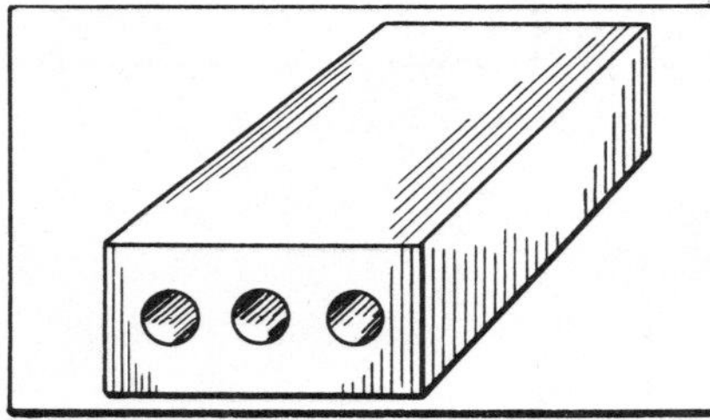

a. Width – 12″
b. Height – 6″
c. Length – 1′-4″
d. Quantity – 20
e. Diameter of cored Holes – 2″
f. Number of Cored Holes – 3
(Note: Cored holes run through entire length)
g. Weight of Cast Iron – .26 lbs. per cu. in.

2. Determine the cost of 75 steel drop forgings conforming to the specifications given. The cost should be correct to two decimal places.

Ans.: 1102.71

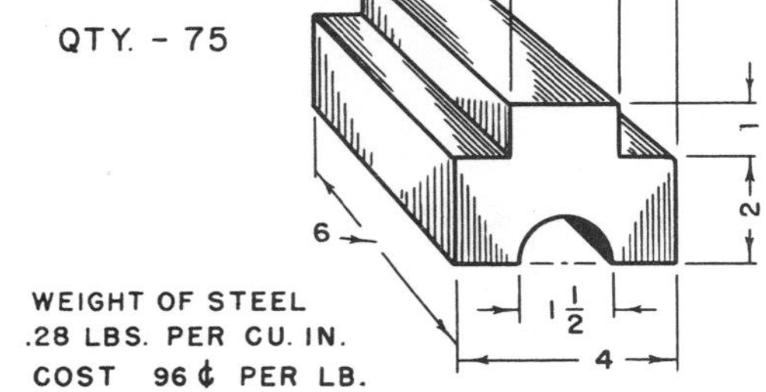

F. EXPRESSING UNITS OF MEASURE

1. Express each of the following values in the unit or units of liquid or volume measure indicated in each case.

a.	4 gallons	qts.	i.	37 qts.	gals. and qts.
b.	6 1/2 gals.	qts.	j.	63 gals.	bbls.
c.	3 3/4 gals.	qts.	k.	96 1/2 gals.	bbls. and gals.
d.	6 1/2 qts.	pts.	l.	693 cu. in.	gals. and qts.
e.	5 1/4 qts.	pts.	m.	577.5 cu. in.	gals. and qts.
f.	8 3/4 qts.	pts. and gills	n.	5 gals.	cu. in.
g.	3 7/8 qts.	pts. and gills	o.	4 gals., 3 qts.	cu. in.
h.	17 qts.	gals. and qts.			

2. Determine the liquid capacity of the rectangular coolant tank A and the circular portable container B. Compute A to nearest gallon; B to nearest quart.

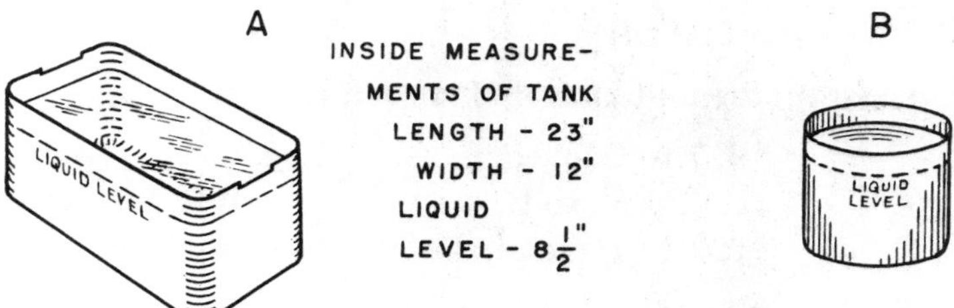

Ans.: A. 10 gallons

Unit 22 ACHIEVEMENT REVIEW ON MEASUREMENT (CUSTOMARY UNITS)

A. APPLICATION OF LINEAR MEASURE

1. Express each measurement in the unit indicated in each case.

   a. 15 ft. to yds.
   b. 8 ft. to in.
   c. 3 yds. 2 ft. to ft.
   d. 7 ft. 5 in. to in.
   e. 176 in. to ft.
   f. 12.5 ft. to in.
   g. 6 1/2 yds. to ft.
   h. 9 ft. 8 in. to in.
   i. 4 yds. 6 ft. 3 in. to in.

2. Add each series of measurement and reduce to lowest terms.

   a. 10′ + 7′ + 5′
   b. 6 yds. + 9 ft. + 6 ft.
   c. .5″ + .375″ + .125″
   d. 6.500″ + 1′-3 1/4″
   e. 10 1/2 yds. + 17 1/4 ft. + 8 in.
   f. 4 3/4 yds. + 19 ft. 6 in.

3. Perform the arithmetical process required in each case. Give result in simplest form.

   a. 3 yds. 6 ft. 9 in.
−1 yd. 4 ft. 5 in.

   c. 6 ft. 2 in.
x 28

   e. 280 in.
÷ 14 in.

   b. 9 yds. 2 ft. 4 in.
− 8 ft. 6 in.

   d. 12′ - 3.5″
x 10

   f. 9′-10″
÷ 7″

4. The diesel engine plate gage illustrated is to be machined. The part is to be rough machined, finish machined, and ground to the finished sizes given on the drawing.

   a. Allow 1/32″ on all faces and determine the rough machining dimensions for A through H.

   b. Determine the size to which dimensions A through H are to be machined before grinding if .010″ is allowed on each dimension for the grinding operation.

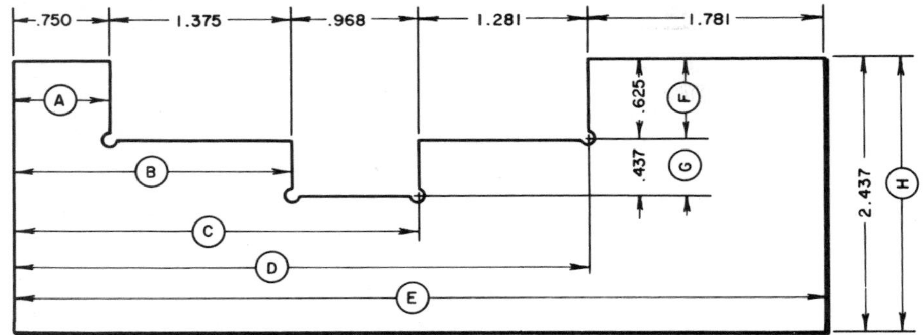

5. Determine the standard micrometer readings A, B, and C.

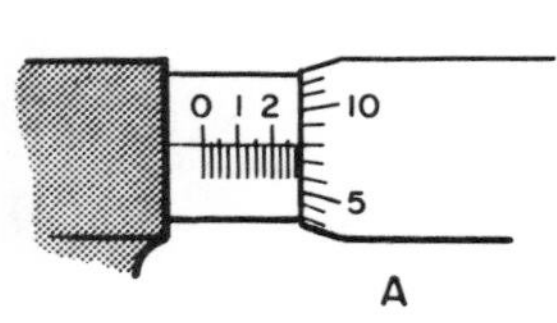

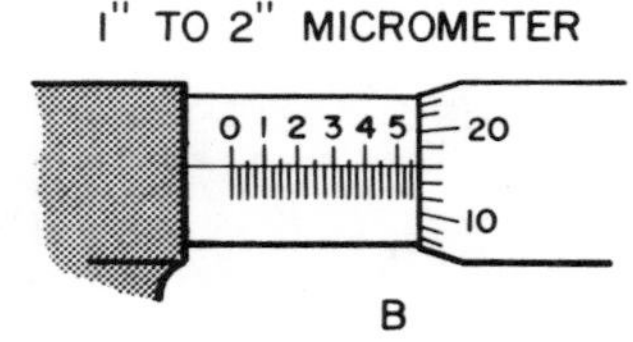

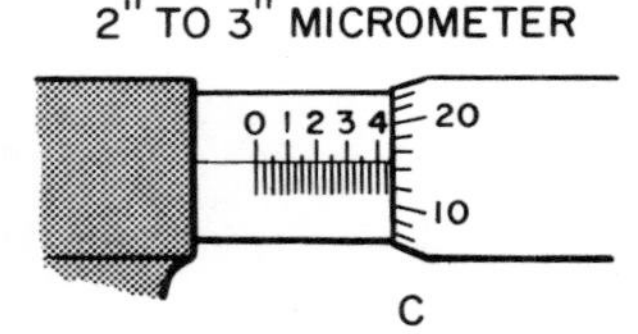

B. APPLICATION OF CIRCULAR MEASURE

1. Give the bevel protractor readings A and B.

2. Determine angles A through O for the jig plate in order to machine the required slots and drill the holes.

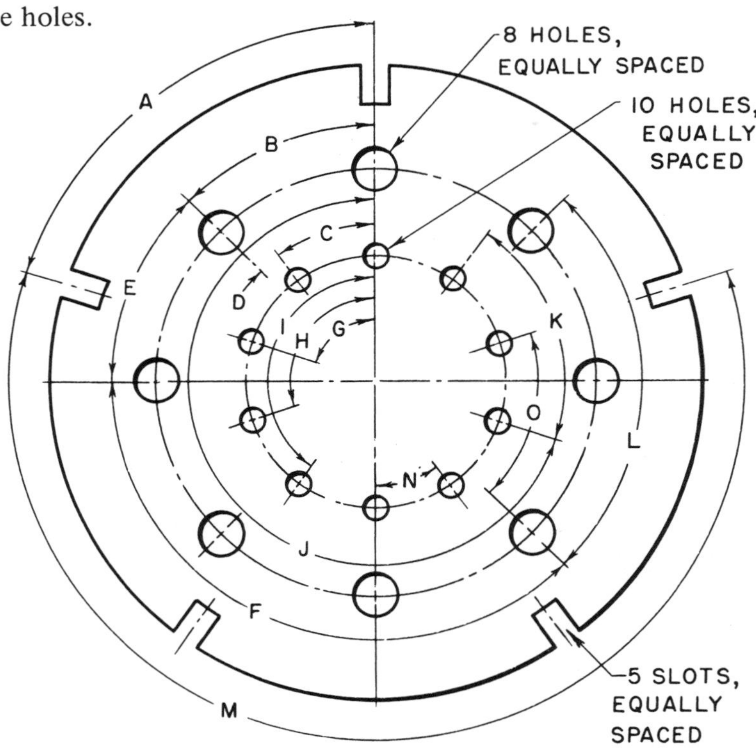

C. APPLICATION OF SURFACE MEASURE

1. Find the area of the plastic part illustrated.

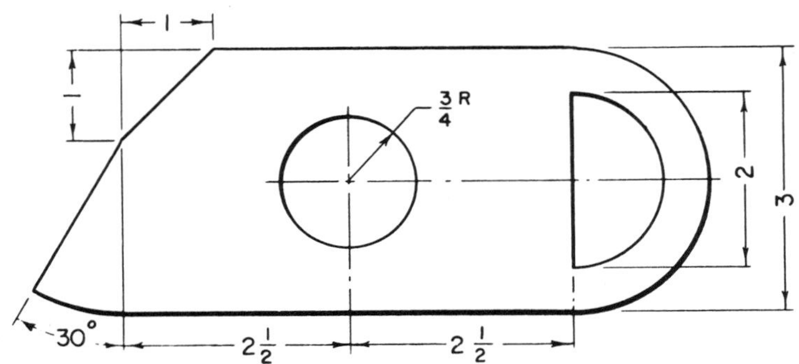

2. What is the cost of the 1-inch thick cored iron castings?

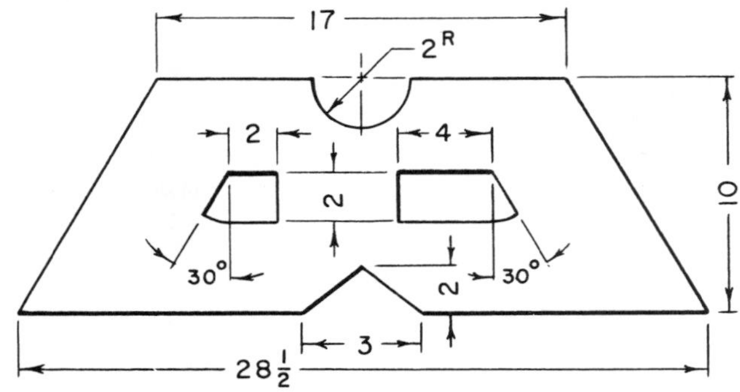

SPECIFICATIONS

① QTY. – 200 PCS.

② WT. OF C.I. = .28 lbs./cu.in.

③ COST OF C.I. = 36¢ / lb.

NOTE: All dimensions are in inches.

D. APPLICATION OF VOLUME MEASURE

1. Determine the amount of liquid held in a rectangular oil reservoir of a hydraulic machine for the liquid levels indicated in the table. Round off each answer to the nearest quart.

Gage Level	Height of Liquid
A	5″
B	5 1/2″
C	6″
D	6 1/2″
E	7″

NOTE: All dimensions are in inches.

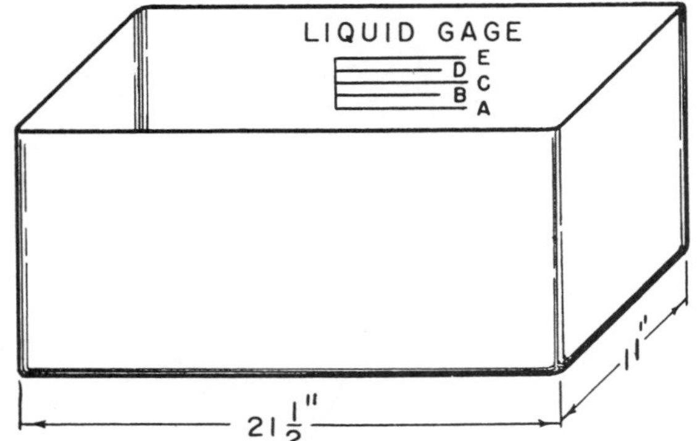

2. What is the weight of 2500 brass parts which are stamped from 1/16″ sheet brass weighing .3 pounds per cubic inch? Give the total weight to the nearest pound.

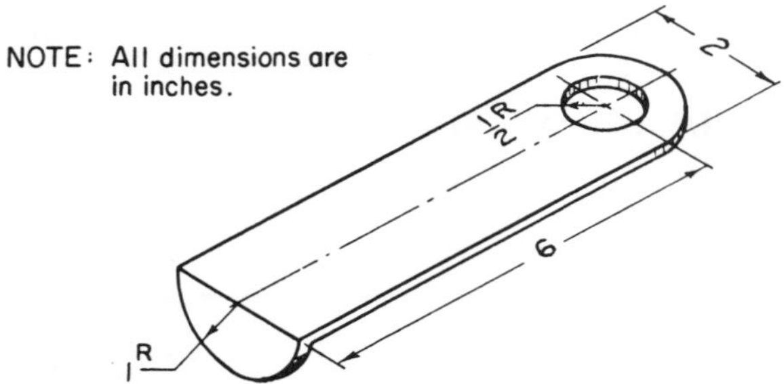

Section 5

PERCENTAGE AND AVERAGES

Unit 23 THE CONCEPTS OF PERCENT AND PERCENTAGE

Percents are given in catalogs, magazines, newspapers, handbooks for technicians, and other publications. Percents show how many parts of a total are taken out. Percents are used to make comparisons, compute wages, taxes, discounts, increases or decreases in production, and an ever-increasing number of applications of percents are found in health, business, distribution and merchandizing occupations, industry, and the home.

A. FORMS FOR EXPRESSING PERCENT

The word *percent* is a short way of saying "by the hundred or hundredths part of the whole." A percent refers to a given number of parts of the whole which is equal to 100 percent. "Fifteen percent" is the same as writing 15%.

Percent may be shown graphically by two illustrations. The square is divided into 100 equal parts. Each of the small squares is one one-hundredth of the whole (100%) or 1/100 of 100% = 1%.

100 EQUAL SQUARES = 100 %

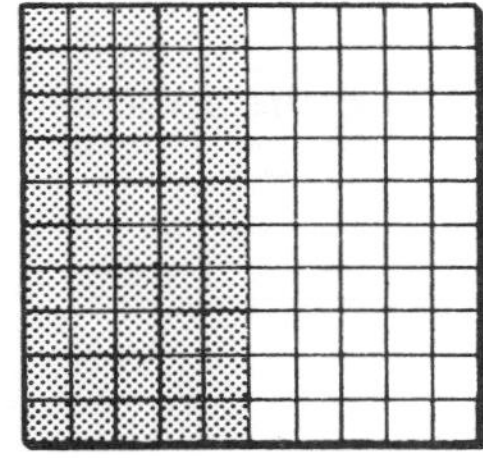

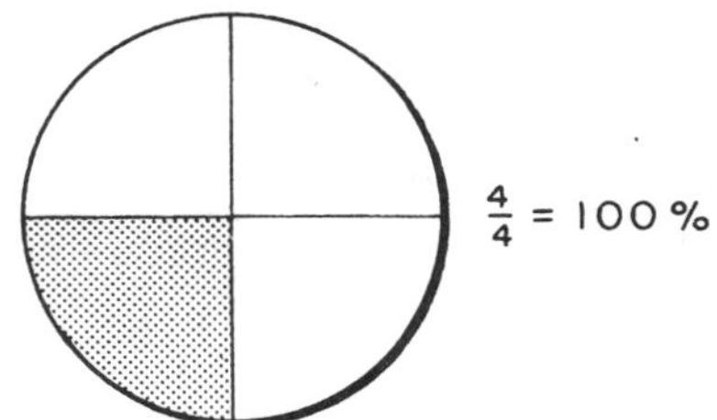

$\frac{4}{4}$ = 100 %

By the same reasoning, the 50 shaded squares are 50/100 of the total = 50/100 of 100% or 50%. In the circle, the shaded area is 1/4 of the whole circle or 1/4 of 100% or 25%.

Percent is another form of mathematical expression. A value like 50% may be represented as such. It may be given also in an equivalent form as the fraction (1/2) or as the decimal (.5). The form in which a value is given depends on the requirements of the problem.

B. DETERMINING ONE HUNDRED PERCENT OF A NUMBER

One hundred percent of a number is the same as one hundred hundredths or 1. It represents the whole number or total. Therefore 100% of a number is the number itself.

C. DETERMINING ONE PERCENT OF A NUMBER

RULE FOR FINDING ONE PERCENT OF A NUMBER

- Change one percent to an equivalent decimal and remove the percent sign. 1% = one hundredth = .01.
- Multiply the given number by the decimal equivalent of 1% (.01).
- Label the answer in the required unit of measure.

EXAMPLE: Find 1% of 275 feet.

Step 1 Multiply the given number 275 by .01.

```
 275
x.01
 275
```

Step 2 Point off, starting at the right, the same number of decimal places in the answer as there are in the multiplier and multiplicand. 2.75

Step 3 Label answer with correct unit of measure. Ans. 2.75 feet

Since 1% is the same as .01, the process may be performed mentally by just placing a decimal in the original number. For instance, 1% of 120.33 is found by just moving the decimal point two more places to the left.

1% of 120.33 = .01 x 120.33 = 1.2033 Ans.

D. DETERMINING ANY PERCENT OF A NUMBER

A percent may be converted to any equivalent mathematical form. At times, the fractional equivalent is preferred. In other cases, the decimal form is best suited to a specific problem.

RULE FOR FINDING ANY PERCENT OF A NUMBER

- Convert the percent to either a fractional or decimal equivalent.
- Multiply the given number by this equivalent.
- Point off the same number of decimal places in the product as there are in the multiplier and multiplicand.
- Label answer with appropriate unit of measure.

EXAMPLE: Find 16% of 1218 sq. yds.

Step 1 Change 16% to a decimal. 16% = .16

Step 2 Multiply the given number (1218) by the decimal (.16).

```
 1218
x .16
19488
```

Step 3 Point off two decimal places in the product. 194.88

Step 4 Label answer. Ans. 194.88 sq. yds.

These same steps are followed when the percent is a mixed number.

EXAMPLE: Find 6 1/4% of 782 hp

Step 1 Change 6 1/4% to a decimal. $6\frac{1}{4}\% = .06\frac{1}{4} = .0625$

Step 2 Multiply the given number (782) by the decimal (.0625).

```
   782
x .0625
488750
```

Step 3 Point off four decimal places in the product. 48.8750

Step 4 Label answer. Ans. 48.875 hp.

E. CHANGING PERCENTS TO DECIMALS AND FRACTIONS

A percent may be changed to its decimal equivalent. Simply move a decimal point two places to the left and take away the percent sign. The decimal value may then be changed to a fraction to get the fractional equivalent of the original percent. A few relationships between percents, decimals, and fractions are shown in table form.

Percent	Equivalent		Parts of the Whole
	Decimal	Fraction	
1%	.01	1/100	One hundredth
100%	1.00	100/100 or 1/1	One hundred hundredths
325%	3.25	3 1/4	Three hundred twenty-five hundredths
.1%	.001	1/1000	One tenth of one percent

ASSIGNMENT UNIT 23

A. THE CONCEPT OF PERCENT

1. Give the percent of the whole that the shaded area of the rectangle, triangle, and circle represents in each case.

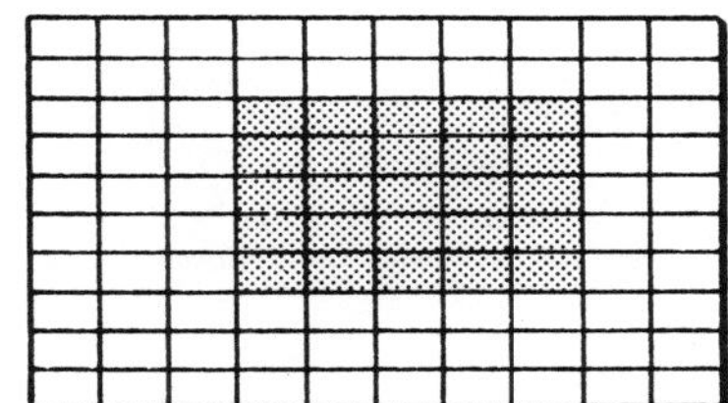
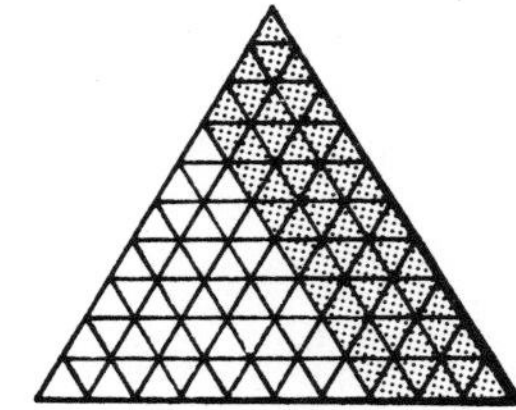
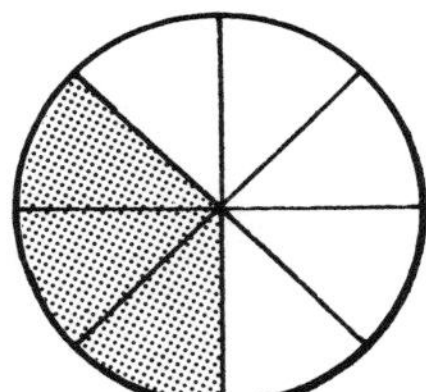

Ans.: b. 51%

2. What part of the whole square, rectangle, and circle is represented in each instance by 100%, 50%, 25%, 10%, and 1%?

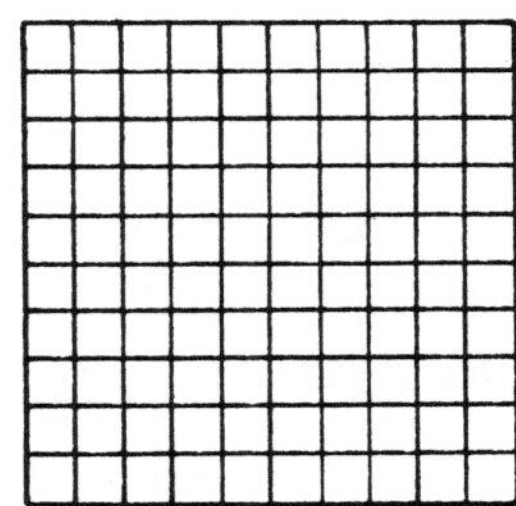
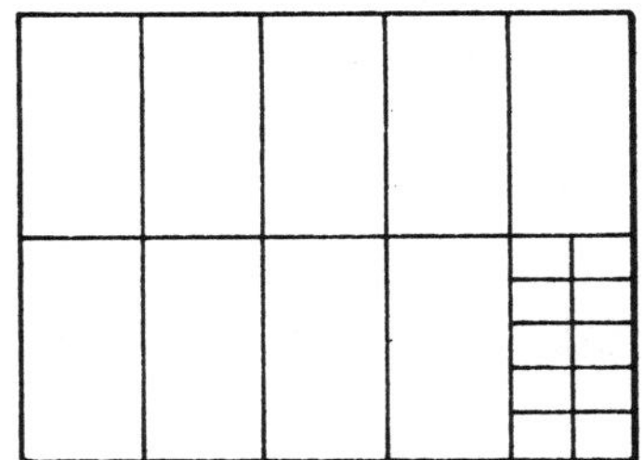
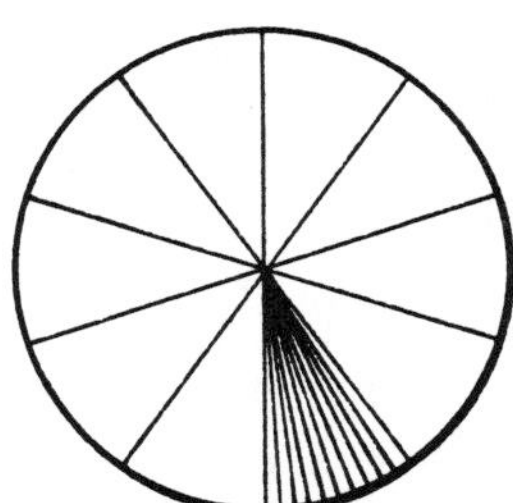

3. Write each percent using the symbol (%).

A	B	C	D	E
65 percent	6.5 percent	.6 percent	6 2/3 percent	12.25 percent

Ans.: B. 6 1/2% D. 6 2/3%

4. Draw a table similar to the one illustrated and insert the decimal equivalent of percents A through O.

	Percent	Decimal
A	50%	
B	30%	
C	25%	
D	9%	
E	1%	

	Percent	Decimal
F	125%	
G	205%	
H	312%	
I	101%	
J	250%	

	Percent	Decimal
K	.1%	
L	.25%	
M	.05%	
N	3 1/2%	
O	2 1/4%	

Ans.: A. .5 D. .09 G. 2.05 J. 2.5 M. .0005

5. Prepare a table and insert the percent equivalent of each decimal.

A	B	C	D	E	F
1.50	.75	.125	2.05	.025	.004

Ans.: B. 75% D. 205% F. .4%

B. DETERMINING 100% AND 1% OF A NUMBER

1. Find 100% of values A through E.

Ans.: B. 325 D. 125 tons

A	B	C	D	E
200	325	62.5	1.25 tons	.563 lbs.

2. Find 1% of the same values.

Ans.: B. 3.25 D. .0125 tons

C. DETERMINING ANY PERCENT OF A NUMBER

1. Find the percent indicated in each case for quantities A through F.

A	4% of $500	D	.2% of 325 cu. yds.
B	8% of 120 sheets	E	3.25% of 800 kW
C	1 1/2% of 840 acres	F	37 1/2% of 972 lbs.

Ans.: B. 9.6 sheets D. .65 cu. yds. F. 364.5 lbs.

2. The absenteeism in a large business is 1 1/2% of all employee-hours worked. If the workweek is 40 hours and there are 1750 employees, determine the total number of workdays (of 8 hours each) that are lost during each 260 workday year.

3. Find the total number of pounds of tin and lead required to make three different solder compositions.

Composition	A	50% tin 50% lead	B	90% tin 10% lead	C	60% tin 40% lead
Pounds Solder Required		212 lbs.		48 lbs.		125 lbs.

Ans.: B. 43.2 lbs. tin 4.8 lbs. lead

4. The area of a floor is 320 sq. ft. In laying this floor, there is a lumber allowance of 25% for waste and matching. Determine the amount of flooring required.

5. The power output of a motor is 58 horsepower. If 7.6% of the power is used to overcome friction and other losses, what horsepower is available under a full load?

   Ans.: 53.592 hp.

6. It takes 3.35 yards of material to make a suit. An additional 12% is required for waste and matching. Determine the total yardage that is needed to make 12 suits.

Unit 24 APPLICATION OF PERCENTAGE, BASE, AND RATE

A. DESCRIPTION OF PERCENTAGE TERMS AND RULES

Percentage refers to the value of any percent of a given number. In every percentage problem three numbers are involved. The first number is known as the *base* because a definite percent is to be taken of it. The second number, the *rate,* refers to the percent that is to be taken of the base. The third number is the *percentage.* The relationship of the base, rate, and percentage to each other may be stated in the rule: the product of the base times the rate equals the percentage.

In simplified form, percentage = base x rate

Sometimes, the letter B is used for base, R for rate, and P for percentage. Using letters instead of words, the rule may be given as, P = B x R. Wherever this rule is used, the rate must always be in decimal form.

B. DETERMINING PERCENTAGE

RULE FOR FINDING PERCENTAGE (Given: Base and Rate)

- Write the rule for percentage in simplified form (P = B x R).
- Change the given percent to its decimal equivalent.
- Substitute the given values for B and R in the rule.
- Multiply and label answer.
- Check by substituting the answer for P. Rework to see that the quantities on both sides of the = sign are equal.

EXAMPLE: Find 12 1/2% of 360″.

Step 1 Write the rule. $P = B \times R$

Step 2 Change 12 1/2% to its decimal equivalent. $12\frac{1}{2}\% = .125$

Step 3 Substitute 360″ for the base and .125 as the rate. $P = 360 \times .125$

Step 4 Multiply and label the answer. Ans. P = 45″

C. DETERMINING BASE OR RATE

It is possible to use the percentage rule to determine the base or rate when the two other terms in the rule are known.

RULE FOR FINDING BASE OR RATE (Given: Percentage and Base or Rate)

- Write the rule in simplified form. P = B x R
- Substitute the two known values in the rule.

  NOTE: If a percent is given, be certain that it is changed to its decimal equivalent.
- Divide the percentage by the base to get the rate as a decimal, or, by the rate to find the base.
- Convert the decimal or fractional value of the rate to a percent, if this is required.
- Label the answer with the appropriate unit of measure.

EXAMPLE: Case 1 200 is what percent of 500?

Step 1	Write the rule.	$P = B \times R$
Step 2	Substitute known values: the base is 500 and the percentage 200.	$200 = 500 \times R$
Step 3	Divide P by B to get R.	$\frac{\not{200}^{2}}{\not{500}_{5}} = R$
Step 4	Change 2/5 of the whole to a decimal.	$\frac{2}{5} = .4$
Step 5	Change the decimal .4 to its percent equivalent by moving the decimal two places to the right and adding the (%) symbol.	$.4 = 40\%$
Step 6	Check the values on both sides of the = sign.	$200 = 500 \times .4$ $200 = 200$

EXAMPLE: Case 2 If 56 castings are 20% of the total, what is the total number?

Step 1	Write the rule.	$P = B \times R$
Step 2	Substitute the known values: the percentage is 56, the rate is 20%.	
	NOTE: Change the 20% rate to its decimal equivalent .20 before substituting.	$56 = B \times .20$
Step 3	Divide P by R to get B.	$\frac{56}{.20} = B$
Step 4	Label answer in the appropriate unit of measure.	$280 = B$ Ans. 280 Castings

Thus, with the rule, percentage = base x rate, it is possible to solve any percentage problems when two of the three quantities are given and the rate is expressed in decimal form.

ASSIGNMENT UNIT 24

A. DETERMINING PERCENTAGE

1. Find the percentage in each problem (A through E) for each value given for the base and rate.

	A	B	C	D	E
Base	2400 tons	1875 gallons	142.6 inches	3268.5 sq. ft.	296 1/2 sheets
Rate	80%	45%	3.8%	4 1/2%	6 1/4%

Ans.: A. 1920 tons C. 5.4188 in. E. 18.531 sheets

2. A meat weighs 25.6 pounds before it is cooked and 23.2 pounds after cooking. Determine the percent of weight lost in cooking.
3. The total receipts of a merchandising store for one week total $3,800. The expenses include 40% wages, 12% rent, 9% for heating and cooling, and 27% for taxes and other overhead. Establish the (a) amount of profit and (b) the percent of profit. **Ans.:** (a) $456.

4. A car speedometer registers 52 miles per hour. The actual car speed is 55 m.p.h. State the percent of error correct to two decimal places. **Ans.:** 5.45%
5. The original cost of 1290 aluminum castings is 57.5 cents each. If 5% are scrapped as poor castings and another 7 1/2% are spoiled in machining, how many castings are used and what is the new unit cost of each good casting? **Ans.:** (a) 1128.75 castings

B. DETERMINING BASE OR RATE

1. Find the base in each problem (A through E) when the percentage and rate are given.

	A	B	C	D	E
Percentage	120 hp.	2016 cables	137.8 lbs.	78 1/2 bars	126.5 inches
Rate	90%	54%	7.2%	6 1/2%	3 1/4%

Ans.: B. 3733.33 cables D. 1207.69 bars

2. Find the rate in each problem (A through E) when the percentage and base are given.

	A	B	C	D	E
Percentage	30	360°	24″ D	8.2	92 1/2″
Base	30	30°	36″ D	19.68	294″

Ans.: B. 1200% D. 41 2/3%

3. What percent is wasted when 2.4 of every 120 sheets of metal are spoiled?
4. What percent of metal is allowed for cut-off on each 2-inch length of stock? **Ans.:** 5.88%

16
1
2
8
1/8″ FOR CUT-OFF

C. DETERMINING PERCENTAGE OR BASE OR RATE

1. One part of acid and four parts of water are mixed as an electrolyte for a storage battery. What percent is acid and what percent is water? **Ans.:** 20% acid
2. A generator rating is 42,500 kilowatts. If the output is 29,500 kilowatts, what percent of the rating is the generator delivering?
3. What is the operating spindle speed of a lathe spindle traveling at 346 rpm when 18% is lost through slippage and cutting pressure? **Ans.:** 283.7 rpm
4. The cutting speed of a milling cutter is 85 feet per minute. Friction and other cutting losses amount to 12 1/2%. Find the base cutting speed.
5. Two special bronze castings are composed of six different metals. The percent of each metal used in each casting and the casting weight are given in the table. Determine the weight (in pounds and fractional parts) of each metal.

   NOTE: Round off each decimal to one place.

Casting	Casting Weight	Composition (% by Weight)					
		Copper	Tin	Zinc	Phosphorous	Lead	Iron
A	400 lbs.	80	11	8.2	0.4	0.3	0.1
B	525 lbs.	83	8.7	7.38	0.34	0.52	0.06

Ans.: A. 44 lbs. tin, 1.6 lbs. phosphorous B. 38.8 lbs. zinc, .3 lbs. iron

Unit 25 AVERAGES AND ESTIMATES

AVERAGES

Averages are used in linear, circular, angular, temperature, weight, and all other measurements. The *average* of given quantities and values is the starting point on which many other computations and factual data are based.

A. AVERAGE QUANTITIES

The average of two or more quantities that are in the same unit of measure is found by simple addition and division.

RULE FOR AVERAGING SEVERAL QUANTITIES

- Check the units of measure in each quantity to be sure they are the same.
- Arrange the quantities in a column and add.
- Divide by the number of quantities to get the average.

EXAMPLE: What is the average of the linear dimensions given on the drawing?

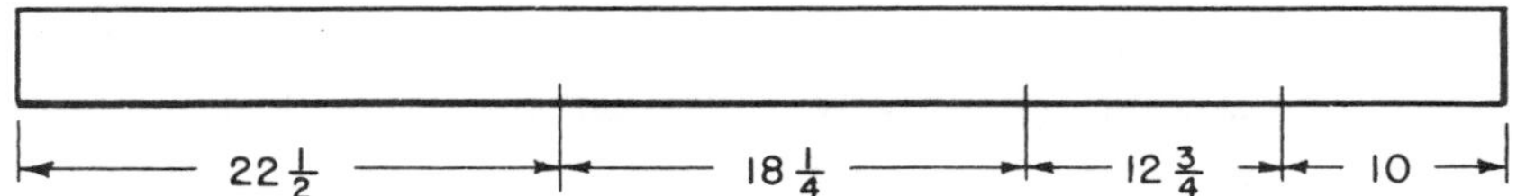

Step 1 Check each dimension and change, if necessary, to the same unit of measure.

Step 2 Arrange in a column and add.

NOTE: The mathematical processes may be simplified by expressing fractional values as decimals before averaging.

22 1/2	=	22.50
18 1/4	=	18.25
12 3/4	=	12.75
10	=	10.00
		63.50

Step 3 Divide the sum (63.50) by the number of quantities (4).

$$4\overline{)63.50}\quad 15.875$$

Step 4 Express the decimal value (.875) as a fraction (7/8), if necessary. The average of the four dimensions is 15 7/8.

15.875 = 15 7/8 Ans.

B. DETERMINING VALUES FROM AVERAGES

An unknown value may be computed when the average and all quantities but the unknown are given.

RULE FOR FINDING AN UNKNOWN VALUE

- Multiply the average by the number of quantities.
- Add the given quantities.
- Subtract this sum from the product. The difference is the missing value.
- Check by adding all quantities and dividing by the number of quantities. The numbers are correct when the given average equals the computed average in the check.

EXAMPLE: The average of four temperature readings is 1672°. Three of the actual readings are 1525°, 1683°, and 1726°. Give the fourth reading.

Step 1 Multiply the average (1672) by the number of readings (4).

$$\begin{array}{r} 1672 \\ \times \quad 4 \\ \hline 6688 \end{array}$$

Step 2 Add the three given readings.

$$1525 + 1683 + 1726 = 4934$$

Step 3 Subtract this sum (4934) from the product of the average (6688).

$$\begin{array}{r} 6688 \\ -4934 \\ \hline 1754 \end{array}$$

NOTE: The difference of 1754° is the fourth temperature reading.

Ans. 1754°

Step 4 Check the average of the four numbers with the given average.

$$\frac{1525 + 1683 + 1726 + 1754}{4} = 1672 \qquad \frac{6688}{4} = 1672$$

ESTIMATING

Estimating has a two-fold meaning. Estimating may refer to a shortcut mathematical process of determining a range against which an actual answer may be compared for accuracy. Estimating, in another instance, may require actual computations to determine cost, time, material, and other essential data. The estimate is as accurate as variations in materials, working conditions, and the like, permit.

Estimating is valuable in checking computations and in arriving at quantities and values which vary as the basic conditions change.

C. ESTIMATING AS A MATHEMATICAL CHECK

Where estimating is used to check the accuracy of a solution to a problem, certain simple steps may be used.

RULE FOR ESTIMATING MATHEMATICAL ACCURACY

- Work the problem in the conventional way.
- Reread the original problem and determine what numbers may be rounded-off.
- Use these numbers and perform the operations as required.
- Pay special attention to counting-off decimal places in the answer, as most errors occur at this point.
- Check the computed value by comparing the original answer with the estimated value.
  NOTE: If both values are close, the answer is accurate in most instances.

EXAMPLE: What is 24 1/2% of 996?

Step 1 Compute answer in the conventional way.

$$\begin{array}{r} 996 \\ \times\ .245 \\ \hline 244.02 \end{array}$$

Step 2 Estimate the answer.

Round off 24 1/2% to 25% or 1/4.
Round off 996 to 1000.
Take 1/4 of 1000 = 250.

Step 3 Compare the estimated value (250) with the computed value (244.02).

NOTE: Since the 25% and the 1000 are larger than either of the original quantities, the computed value must be smaller than the estimate. If the answer were larger, the problem would require reworking.

D. ESTIMATING AS A BASE FOR ADDITIONAL COMPUTATION

Where there are a number of variable factors in given data, an estimate may provide the only sound basis for determining costs, appropriations, employee-hours, and the like. On jobs where new materials are used, or all conditions are not known at any given time, the estimate furnishes about the best working information that is obtainable.

While estimates are determined in a number of ways, there are many steps that are common to all estimating.

Step 1 Determine the data that must be computed.

Step 2 Analyze the available information further to see what is given.

Step 3 Select (if available) or compute averages where needed.

Step 4 Perform the required mathematical operations and combine like quantities to get an accurate estimate.

NOTE: Take sufficient space for each part of an estimate. Label all answers for greater accuracy and speed.

Step 5 Total all computations. Check by reworking to see that all items are included.

Step 6 Estimate by rounding-off quantities and amounts. Then perform the mathematical operations to get an estimated answer.

Step 7 Check the accurate estimate against the rounded-off estimate to see that the final result is within an acceptable range.

Step 8 Rework the original accurate estimate if the variation is too great.

Step 9 Label all answers with the appropriate units of measure.

ASSIGNMENT UNIT 25

A. AVERAGING QUANTITIES AND ESTIMATING ACCURACY

Solve each problem. Then check each solution by estimating.

1. Find the average length of the five rods illustrated.

NOTE: All dimensions are in inches.

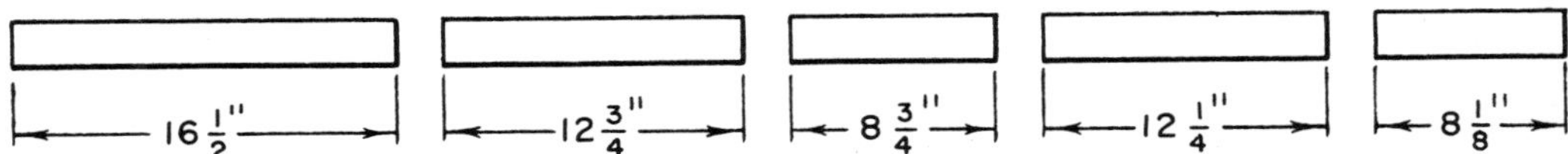

2. What is the average weight of five castings which weigh 17 1/4 pounds, 12 7/8 pounds, 9 1/4 pounds, 4 pounds, and 8 1/2 pounds? **Ans.**: 10 3/8 lbs.

3. Micrometer measurements, taken at five places on a metal part, are recorded in a table Determine the average thickness of the part.

Measurements in Inches				
A	B	C	D	E
1.252	1.249	1.249	1.248	1.251

4. Five variations in temperature are recorded on a graph for a heat-treating operation. Find the average temperature.

Reading	A	B	C	D	E
Temperature	2272°	2346°	2147°	2286°	2304°

Ans.: 2271°

B. DETERMINING MISSING VALUES WITH KNOWN AVERAGES

1. The weekly production of a mechanism averages 1235 units. The number of units produced in each of four days is 212, 224, 232, and 275. How many units must be produced the fifth day to meet the required average?

2. The space available on three floors of a loft building is 900 sq. ft., 1475 sq. ft., and 1350 sq. ft. If 140 production machines averaging 32 sq. ft. of space apiece are to be installed, how much additional space is required? **Ans.**: 755 sq. ft.

Unit 26 ACHIEVEMENT REVIEW ON PERCENTAGE AND AVERAGES

A. THE CONCEPT OF PERCENT

1. Give the percent of the whole that the shaded area represents in each case.

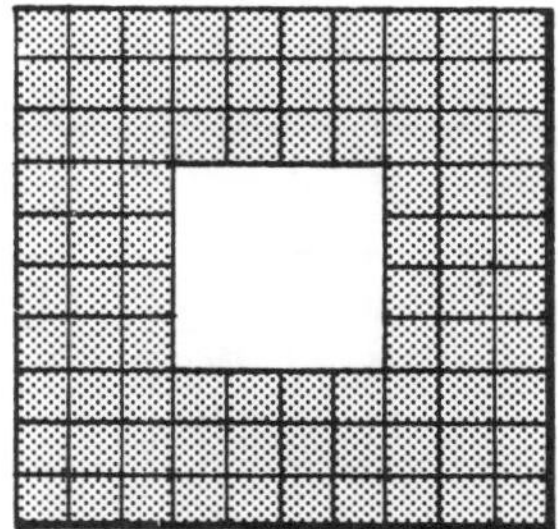

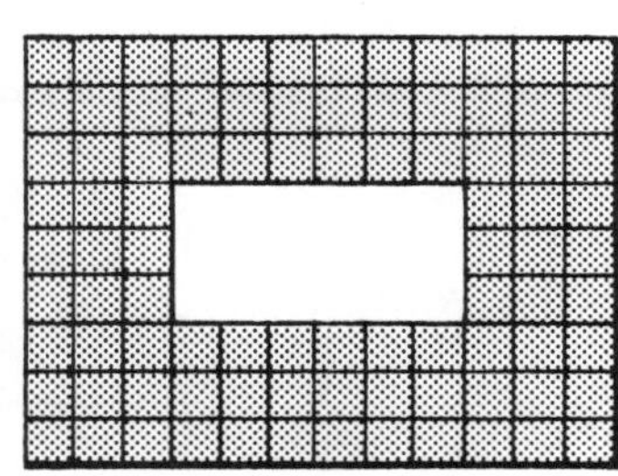

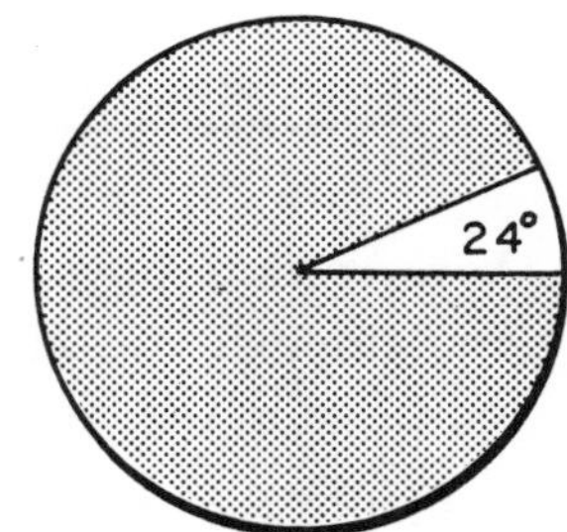

2. Prepare a table similar to the one shown and insert the missing decimal, fractional, and/or percent equivalent.

	Percent	Decimal	Fraction
A	16.5%		
B	3.5%		
C		.5	
D			1/40
E		.0025	

B. DETERMINING PERCENTAGE OR BASE OR RATE

1. A $191.10 charge for a set of forgings represents 22.5% of the total cost. Find what the job costs.
2. Determine the percent by which the area of each square or round bar is increased or decreased for each size change given in the tables.

	Square Stock	
	Original Dimension of Side	Increased or Decreased
A	2″	4″
B	2.5″	4″
C	.75″	.50″
D	1 1/4″	3/4″

	Round Stock	
	Original Diameter	Increased or Decreased
E	2″	4″
F	2″	3″
G	1.500″	.750″
H	2 1/4″	1 1/4″

3. The revolutions per minute of a milling machine spindle are reduced by friction and cutting pressure the percents indicated at A through E. Determine in each instance the rpm that the cutter actually turns.

	A	B	C	D	E
Rpm	80	150	225	335	465
Speed Losses	10%	12.5%	16 1/2%	12 1/4%	9 1/4%

4. A restaurant buys three sides of beef. The original weight and trim waste are indicated in the table.

   Compute (a) the percent of trim losses and (b) the average percent of losses for the three sides.

Sides of Beef	**Original Weight (lbs.)**	**Trim Losses**	
		Weight (lbs.)	**Percent (a)**
A	106.54	38.35	
B	148.91	49.14	
C	173.44	60.7	

C. AVERAGING QUANTITIES AND CHECKING BY ESTIMATING

Solve each problem, then check by estimating.

1. Twenty-four castings weigh 272.5 pounds and cost $1.125 per pound. Determine the average weight of one casting and its cost.

2. Find the average weight of six sheets of metal that weigh 16 1/2 pounds, 12 3/4 pounds, 12 pounds, 12 1/4 pounds, 11 1/2 pounds, and 12 1/4 pounds.

3. Find the average length of rods measuring 2′-3″, 3′-2″, 2′-8″, and 2′-6″.

D. DETERMINING MISSING VALUES WITH KNOWN AVERAGES

1. At what temperature during the last hour must a piece of metal be held in a furnace to average 1128°? Hourly readings for the first four hours were 1062°, 1110°, 1174°, and 1158°.

2. During the first four days of a workweek, the total daily output reached 276, 320, 342, and 386 parts. The rejects each day of these totals were 5%, 4 1/2%, 6%, and 5%, respectively. The weekly quota to meet a contract is 325 perfect parts per day. How many parts must be produced the fifth day to meet the schedule? (Assume that the spoilage on the fifth day is the average percent of the four other days.)

Section 6

FINANCE

Unit 27 MONEY AND TIME CALCULATIONS

A. CONCEPT OF THE MONEY SYSTEM

Money transactions are made daily in all branches of business, industry, and the home. The money system in the United States is based on the dollar as a unit. All fractional parts of the dollar are expressed in the decimal system. Thus, all amounts from one cent to ninety-nine cents may be written as decimals.

Two symbols, the dollar ($) and the cent (¢) signs are used with money. In writing a sum like ten dollars, the $ sign is placed in front of the number as, $10 or $10.00. An amount like twenty-five cents may be written with the symbol (¢) as 25¢ or as the decimal ($.25). Neither the ($) sign nor the decimal point is used with the cent sign (¢).

The decimal point separates the dollar values from the fractional parts of the dollar. The value of a few common digits in money calculations is illustrated.

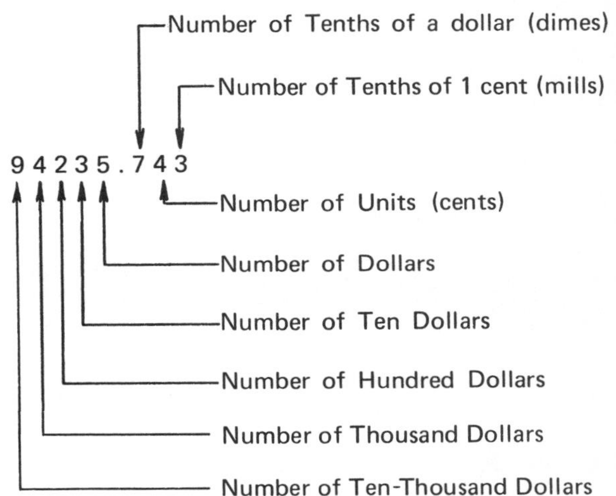

B. CALCULATIONS INVOLVING ADDITION, SUBTRACTION, MULTIPLICATION, AND DIVISION OF MONEY

Since the money system is a decimal one, it is possible to add, subtract, multiply, and divide the numbers representing different amounts in the same way as any other decimal. Care must be taken to keep the units in each number in columns, one under another, to point off the correct number of places in an answer, and to check each step.

C. CONCEPT OF THE TIME SYSTEM

Most workers are interested in time calculations as they enter into production and wages, both as a producer and a consumer. The table of time on which calculations are based is given here.

The units of time measure may be added, subtracted, multiplied, or divided, and may be used as mixed numbers or decimals.

Table of Time		
60 seconds (sec)	=	1 minute (min)
60 minutes (min)	=	1 hour (hr)
24 hours (hr)	=	1 day (da)
7 days (da)	=	1 week (wk)
365 days (da)	=	1 year (yr)
52 weeks (wk)	=	1 year (yr)

RULE FOR EXPRESSING A LARGER UNIT OF TIME AS A SMALLER UNIT

- Express the larger unit as a decimal, where practical.
- Multiply the larger unit by the number of smaller units in one of the larger ones. Count off decimal places in the product, if decimals are used.
- Add to the product any smaller units contained in the original number.
- Label the answer with the smaller unit of time measure.

EXAMPLE: Express 7 hours, 20 minutes in minutes.

Step 1 Multiply the 7 hours by the number of minutes (60) in one hour.

$$\begin{array}{r} 7 \\ \underline{\times 60} \\ 420 \text{ min.} \end{array}$$

Step 2 Add the remaining units and label the answer.

$$\begin{array}{r} \underline{+20} \\ 440 \text{ min.} \end{array}$$

This same problem may also be worked with the original time as the fraction 7 1/3 (7 hrs. 20 min. = 7 2ø/6ø or 1/3) or as the decimal 7.33 multiplied by 60.

RULE FOR EXPRESSING A SMALLER UNIT OF TIME AS A LARGER UNIT

- Divide the smaller unit by the number of smaller units contained in one larger unit.
- Label the answer with the larger unit of measure.

EXAMPLE: Express 4200 seconds in minutes.

Step 1 Determine how many smaller units make one larger unit. 60 sec. = 1 min.

Step 2 Divide the given number of smaller units (4200) by this number (60). $\frac{4200}{60} = 70$

Step 3 Label the answer in the required unit of measure. Ans. 70 min.

ASSIGNMENT UNIT 27

A. CONCEPT OF THE MONEY SYSTEM

1. Write the amounts A to G in words.

A	B	C	D	E	F	G
\$1.12	\$20.07	\$2,692.75	\$0.02	37¢	\$2.37 1/2	46 1/4¢

2. Check each amount and indicate those that are incorrectly written.

A	B	C	D	E
.29¢	\$0.17¢	\$124.04¢	\$6,292.16	57¢

B. ADDITION, SUBTRACTION, MULTIPLICATION, AND DIVISION OF MONEY

1. Find the cost of three lengths of steel as shown on the sketch.

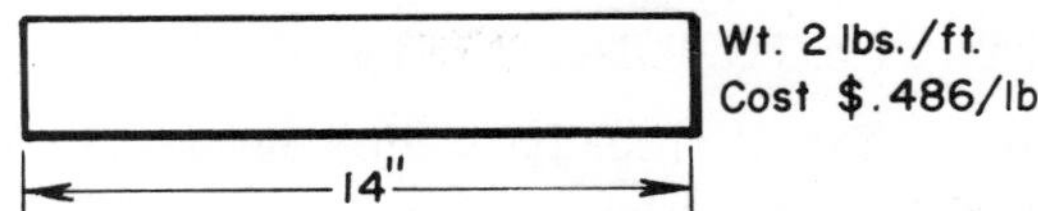

2. Twenty castings cost $17.35. If the cost per pound is 65¢, how much does each casting weigh and cost? Round the weight to two decimal places. **Ans.**: b) 87¢ per casting

3. How much coolant is required and what is the cost to fill a machine reservoir 3/4 full of a ready-mix preparation that sells for $5.50 per gallon? The reservoir measures 2′ wide x 3′ long x 8′ deep.

4. The labor and material costs for a job total $675.28. The labor costs are 68 1/2% of this amount; the material, 31 1/2%. Determine what the materials cost and what charges were made for labor. **Ans.**: $462.57 for labor $212.71 for material

C. CONCEPT OF THE TIME SYSTEM

1. Express the units of time measure as indicated in the table.

Change	A	B	C	D	E	F
From	6 hrs.	76 hrs.	12 min.	8 1/2 hrs.	100 sec.	1400 min.
To	min.	days	sec.	min.	min.	hrs.-min.

Ans.: B. 3 1/6 days D. 510 min. F. 23 hrs. 20 min.

2. Three plastic parts require the time per operation and the number of operations indicated in the table.

   a. Find the total time (days, hours, minutes, and seconds) required to produce the quantities of parts 1, 2, and 3, separately.

   b. Determine the total time required to produce the three parts. (Reduce to lowest terms).

Part	Time per Operation	Number of Operations	Quantity Needed
1	13 seconds	3	10
2	3 minutes and 30 seconds	4	19
3	12 minutes and 20 seconds	5	134

Ans.: b. Total 5 days 22 hours 15 min. 50 sec.

Unit 28 MANUFACTURING COSTS AND DISCOUNTS

A. DETERMINING MANUFACTURING COSTS

Manufacturing costs consist of three basic elements: (1) raw materials costs, (2) labor costs to convert raw materials into marketable products, and (3) overhead costs such as rent, light, power, equipment depreciation, and maintenance.

In arriving at manufacturing costs, simple addition, subtraction, multiplication, and division are used. Also, percentages and averages are needed for comparison purposes. The manufacturing cost is equal to the cost of raw materials, direct labor, and overhead.

RULE FOR DETERMINING MANUFACTURING COSTS AND PERCENTAGES

- Total the cost of all materials.
- Total all labor charges.
- Determine what items of overhead to include.
- Check by subtracting from the manufacturing costs any one of the three cost figures. The difference is the sum of the other two costs.

EXAMPLE: Determine the manufacturing costs and the percent of each item. The raw materials cost \$245, the labor charges are \$1535, and the overhead costs are \$450.

Step 1 Add raw materials and labor and overhead costs.

$$\begin{array}{r} \$\ 245 \\ 1535 \\ \underline{450} \end{array}$$

Manufacturing cost = \$2230

Step 2 Divide raw materials cost by manufacturing cost to get percent of total. $\frac{245}{2230} = 11\%$

Step 3 Divide the labor cost by the manufacturing cost for percent. $\frac{1535}{2230} = 69\%$

Step 4 Divide overhead costs by manufacturing costs for percent. $\frac{450}{2230} = 20\%$

Step 5 Check percent by adding to see if the total is 100%.

$$\begin{array}{r} 11\% \\ 69\% \\ \underline{20\%} \\ 100\% \end{array}$$

B. APPLYING SINGLE AND MULTIPLE DISCOUNTS

The *list price* is equal to the manufacturing cost and profit. As an incentive to sell or to have a product paid for faster and because production costs usually decrease with greater quantities, the manufacturer offers discounts.

A *discount* is a reduction in the list price of a part or mechanism. Discounts may be *single* like a 10% discount, or *multiple* as 10%, 10%, and 5%. With multiple discounts, each successive discount is taken on the remainder.

RULE FOR TAKING A SINGLE DISCOUNT

- Change the percent discount to a decimal.
- Multiply the list price by the discount.
- Point off the decimal places in the answer. The product then represents the discount.

EXAMPLE: Find the net cost of an instrument that lists at \$630 and discounts at 12%.

Step 1	Change the 12% to its decimal equivalent.	12% = .12
Step 2	Multiply the list price (630) by the discount (.12).	\$ 630 x .12 \$75.60
Step 3	Subtract the discount (\$75) from the list price (\$630) to get the net price of \$555.	\$630 - 75 \$555 Ans.

RULE FOR TAKING MULTIPLE DISCOUNTS

- Take the first of the series of discounts as a single discount.
- Subtract the discount from the list price to get a net price.
- Multiply the net price by the decimal equivalent of the second discount.
- Subtract the second discount from the net price.
- Continue these same steps for each discount. The last difference represents the actual cost to the consumer.

EXAMPLE: Determine the cost of 4200 pounds of metal at 45¢ per pound less 15%, 10%, and 5% discounts.

Step 1	Change the percents to decimal equivalents.	4200
Step 2	Multiply the 4200 pounds by 45¢ to get the gross cost.	x .45 \$1890.00
Step 3	Take the first discount of 15% on \$1890.00.	\$1890.00 x .15 \$283.50
Step 4	Subtract the first discount from \$1890.00.	\$1890.00 - 283.00 \$1606.50
Step 5	Take the second discount of 10% on the remaining \$1606.50.	1606.50 x .10 = 160.65
Step 6	Subtract the second discount from the \$1606.50.	\$1606.50 - 160.65 \$1445.85
Step 7	Repeat the last two steps with the third discount of 5%.	1445.85 x .05 = 72.29
	NOTE: The \$1373.56 is the actual cost of the metal.	1445.85 - 72.29 = \$1373.56 Ans.

ASSIGNMENT UNIT 28

A. DETERMINING MANUFACTURING COSTS

1. Determine the manufacturing costs according to the charges given in the table for jobs A to E.

   Ans.: B. $623.00
   D. $723.90

	Material Costs	Labor Costs	Overhead
A	$ 75.00	$232.00	$ 74.00
B	96.00	384.50	142.50
C	84.46	295.23	216.24
D	165.29	347.63	210.98
E	220.06	400.97	309.58

2. Compute the amounts spent for materials, labor, and overhead for parts A to E. Use the manufacturing costs and percents shown in the table.

   Ans.: C. $165.36, $964.60, $248.04

	Mfg. Costs	Materials	Labor	Overhead
A	$1000	50%	30%	20%
B	2428	25%	60%	15%
C	1378	12%	70%	18%
D	2532	18.5%	72.5%	9%
E	1864	22%	57 1/2%	20 1/2%

3. The cost of manufacturing 1000 parts is $792.00. Of this, 35% is spent for materials 62% for labor, and the remainder for overhead.

   a. Determine the cost for materials.

   b. Find the cost for labor.

   c. Find the overhead costs.

   d. During the next quarterly period, the materials increased 10% in price, the labor costs rose 5%, and the overhead increased 5%. Determine the new cost for materials, labor, and overhead.

   e. What is the new cost for 1000 parts?

   Ans.: a. $277.20 c. $23.76 e. $845.46

B. APPLICATION OF SINGLE AND MULTIPLE DISCOUNTS

1. Carbon steel twist drills of a certain size list at $19.50 a dozen less a trade discount of 22%. Determine the cost of each drill to the nearest cent.

   Ans.: $1.27

2. The materials cost of making the machine guard illustrated is 18%, labor 75%, and overhead 7%. Fifty guards are sold for $1050 less a discount of 10%, 8%, and 2% for cash. Determine

   a. The cost of each guard.

   b. The materials, labor, and overhead costs for the lot, based on discounted price.

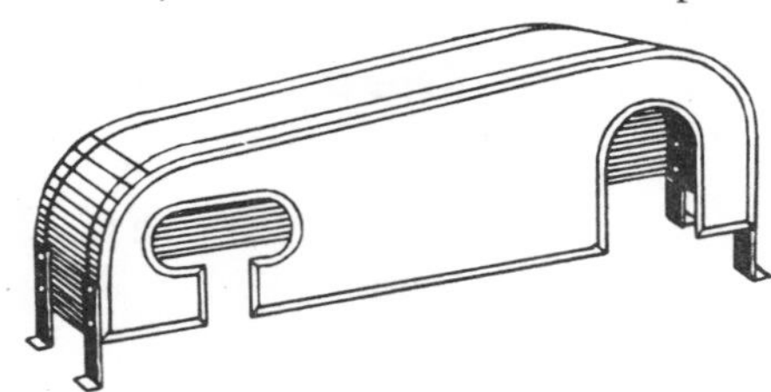

   Ans.: materials $153.36; overhead $59.64

3. Three textile manufacturers offer the same grade of fabric at the same list price of $324.00. The distributor discounts are given in the table.

Distributor	Multiple Discounts
A	18% and 17%
B	20% and 15%
C	12%, 18%, and 5%

   a. Establish which distributor offers the best total discount.

   b. Compute the net cost of the fabric from the distributor providing the best discount.

   Ans.: b. $220.32

4. Compute (a) the total discount and (b) the net cost for equipment items A through D, using (1) the single discount and (2) the successive discount rates given in the table.

		Single Discount			Successive Discounts				
Equipment	List Price	Discount %	Total Discount	Net Cost	First	Second	Third	Total Discount	Net Cost
A	$ 750	18%			12%	6%	X		
B	$ 975	16 2/3%			10%	7%	X		
C	$1440	37 1/2%			20%	10%	7 1/2%		
D	$3945	1/3 off			15%	15%	5%		
		Grand Total					Grand Total		

5. Add the separate discounts and costs and determine (a) the grand total of the discounts and (b) the net cost of the equipment (problem 4), applying the (1) single discount and (2) successive discounts.

6. Compare the single discount and the total successive discount rates for each equipment item with the net costs in each case (problems 4 and 5). State the importance of computing and comparing the net costs of equipment items A through D.

Unit 29 PAYROLLS AND TAXES

Each worker applies the four principles of addition, subtraction, multiplication, and division of decimals to keep accurate records. These deal with time worked, checking the accuracy of computations made for social security and income taxes, disability and other benefits, and bond deductions. As the number of items to be considered increases, payrolls become more complex.

A. COMPUTING PAYROLLS AND WAGES

One important payroll entry is the number of hours worked each week. In this connection, three terms are used: straight time, overtime, double time. *Straight time* is normally credited to a worker for the standard workweek.

Overtime is usually paid for hours worked in excess of the standard number of hours. The *overtime rate* is straight time or the regular hourly rate times 1 1/2. The *double time* rate applies to hours worked on Sundays, legal holidays, and for all time over a stated number of overtime hours.

RULE FOR COMPUTING WAGES (Based on hourly, overtime, and double time rates)

- Multiply the straight time each day by 1.
- Multiply the overtime by 1.5.
- Multiply the double time by 2.

EXAMPLE: Compute the total working time according to the daily hours entered in the table.

Day	Mon.	Tues.	Wed.	Thurs.	Fri.	Sat.	Sun.
Time in Hours	8	9	9	9	9	4	8

Step 1 Multiply the straight time each day by 1 and add to get the total.

M 8 x 1 = 8
T 8 x 1 = 8
W 8 x 1 = 8
Th 8 x 1 = 8
F 8 x 1 = 8
Straight time = 40 hrs.

Step 2 Multiply the overtime hours by 1.5 and add to find the total.

T 1 x 1.5 = 1.5
W 1 x 1.5 = 1.5
Th 1 x 1.5 = 1.5
F 1 x 1.5 = 1.5
S 4 x 1.5 = 6
Overtime = 12 hrs.

Step 3 Multiply the double time hours by 2.

Sun. 8 x 2 = 16 hrs.

Step 4 Add the straight time (40), overtime (12), and double time (16).

40 + 12 + 16 = 68 hours

Step 5 Multiply the total number of hours (68) by the hourly rate to get wages due.

An added incentive to improve quality and to get greater production is to increase the hourly rate by a bonus after a quota is reached. Bonus plans are given to individuals working alone, to groups, and to departments. The bonus for additional production or quota is added either to the weekly wage or given over longer periods of time.

B. COMPUTING PAYROLL TAXES

The words *take-home pay* denote the actual money which the worker receives after all deductions are made. While the deductions may include welfare funds, civic contributions, union dues, and others, only income tax and Social Security are considered in this unit.

SOCIAL SECURITY PAYMENTS

Social Security contributions are paid by an employee and/or an employer at a certain percent of a defined maximum amount of yearly income. Each employee (including special groups of self-employed persons) has a permanent, lifetime account number. All payments by the individual and/or employer are credited to the Social Security account.

At this point, Social Security taxes are treated in terms of contributions (payments) into the system. In Part eight, applications are made of mathematics related to consumer needs. Further information on the benefits and individual protection from different provisions of the system are discussed in detail at that time.

RULE FOR CALCULATING SOCIAL SECURITY TAXES

- Multiply the weekly earnings by the prevailing tax rate. The product represents the weekly Social Security deduction.

  NOTE: Social Security deductions withheld by an employer stop each year when the prescribed base yearly income is reached.

- Add the employer's contribution.

  NOTE: The total represents the amount credited to the worker's Social Security account.

EXAMPLE: A worker earns $198 a week. Determine the amount withheld from the employee for Social Security, using a 6% tax rate.

Step 1 Check the earned income for the year to determine whether it is within the prescribed base amount. Social Security taxes are deductible on this amount only.

Step 2 Multiply the weekly earning ($198) by the Social Security rate. The decimal equivalent (.06) of 6% is used.

Step 3 Point off two decimal places. The result ($11.88) is the Social Security tax to be withheld.

$$\begin{array}{r} \$\ 198 \\ \underline{\times\ .06} \\ \$11.88 \end{array}$$

INCOME TAXES

Practically all persons who receive payment for work are required to pay an income tax. These taxes help to finance the cost of Federal government operations. Each employer is required by Federal law to withhold a percentage of salary from each employee. In turn, at regular periods, the employer turns the money withheld over to the Director of Internal Revenue.

The amount withheld for income taxes depends on the number of dependents and other allowable contributions and deductions. These are either itemized in a *long form* tax return or an average is taken on a *short form*. An example of an exemption allowance table is illustrated. Withholding tax computations are based on similar tables which are adjusted periodically.

Payroll Period	One Withholding Exemption
Daily or Misc.	1.80
Weekly	13.00
Biweekly	26.00
Semimonthly	28.00

Payroll Period	One Withholding Exemption
Monthly	56.00
Quarterly	167.00
Semiannually	333.00
Annually	667.00

The employer may follow five simple steps to determine the amount to withhold for income taxes.

RULE FOR COMPUTING WITHHOLDING TAX

- Round off employee's earnings to the nearest dollar.
- Determine the exemptions claimed.
- Multiply the one withholding exemption in the table for the payroll period by the number claimed.
- Subtract this exemption amount from the rounded-off earnings.
- Multiply the difference by 20%, or the prevailing withholding tax rate. Use the decimal equivalent (.20) to get the tax.

EXAMPLE: Determine the income withholding tax on a worker earning $198.41 weekly and claiming two dependents.

Step 1 Round off earned wage from $198.41 to $198.00.

Step 2 Multiply the one withholding exemption amount ($13.00) in the table for a weekly payroll period by two exemptions (2).

$13.00
x 2
$26.00

Step 3 Subtract the exemption amount ($26.00) from the rounded-off wage ($198.00).

$198.00
\- 26.00
$172.00

Step 4 Multiply the difference ($172.00) by 20% (.20). The product ($34.40) is the income tax deduction.

$172.00
x .20
$ 34.40

C. COMPUTING TAKE-HOME PAY

While only samples of Social Security and income taxes are covered in this unit, all other deductions are computed in a similar manner. The total is subtracted from the wages earned to determine the take-home pay.

RULE FOR COMPUTING TAKE-HOME PAY

- Determine the total number of hours worked in the payroll period.
- Multiply hours worked by the hourly rate and add any amount due from a bonus plan to get the wages due.
- Compute the Social Security, income tax, and any other taxes or deductions.
- Total any payment deductions for health, accident, or similar expenses taken directly out of wages.
- Add all deductions to be paid by the employee. Subtract the total of deductions from wages due. The difference is the take-home pay.

ASSIGNMENT UNIT 29

A. COMPUTING PAYROLLS AND WAGES

1. Determine from the time sheet the total hours worked and the amount due each worker. The overtime rate applies over 40 hours.

Worker	Hours Worked						Hourly Rate
	M	T	W	T	F	S	
A	9	9	9	9	9	4	$9.30
B	8	8	8	9	9	4	9.30
C	8	8	8	8	8	4	5.80
D	8	0	8	8	8	4	5.50
E	9	9	9	9	9	6	2.75
F	8	8	8	8	8	0	2.25

Ans.: B. $455.70 D. $198.00 F. $90.00

B. COMPUTING PAYROLL TAXES

1. Compute the deductions taken from wages earned for Social Security. Use the 6% rate. Overtime based on a 40-hour workweek is 1 1/2 times the hourly rate, up to 48 hours.

Worker	A	B	C	D	E
Hours Worked	44	42	48	40	32
Hourly Rate	$11.44	$8.28	$5.00	$3.20	$2.58

Ans.: A. $71.60 C. $65.40 E. $10.60

2. Figure the income tax deduction for each worker shown on the payroll sheet. Round off each wage to the nearest dollar. Use a weekly exemption allowance of $13 each and an income tax deduction of 20%.

Worker	A	B	C	D	E
Amount Earned	$397.38	$277.92	$378.57	$121.78	$78.75
Exemption Claimed	3	1	4	3	2

Ans.: B. $53.00 D. $16.60

C. COMPUTING TAKE-HOME PAY

1. Prepare a payroll sheet similar to the one shown. Use a standard workweek of 40 hours, overtime equal to time and a half, and double time for emergency Sunday work. Complete the information for all columns: total hours, weekly earnings, exemption allowance, tax A, and tax B on total earning and take-home pay.

Worker	Hours Worked							Reg. Hours Worked	Overtime		Hourly Rate	Weekly Earning	Exemption		Tax A 20%	Tax B 2%	Take-Home Pay
	M	T	W	T	F	S	S		Hours Worked	Hours Pay			at $13	Allowance			
A	8	8	8	8	8	6	6				8.70		4				
B	9	9	9	9	9	4	0				8.70		3				
C	8	8	0	9	9	0	0				9.80		3				
D	9	9	9	9	9	8	4				5.24		4				
E	8	8	7	7	7	0	0				2.52		2				

2. Find the gross weekly salary for each of the five salespersons.

Salesperson	Salary and/or Commission Plan	Sales	Gross Salary
A	6% of all sales	$4,560	
B	5.75% of all sales	$5,325	
C	8 1/4% of all sales	$2,698	
D	$110 salary, plus 2% of all sales	$2,342	
E	$118 salary, plus 3.5% of all sales over $1,500	$4,786	

Ans.: B. $306.19 D. $156.84

Unit 30 ACHIEVEMENT REVIEW ON FINANCE

A. MATHEMATICAL PROCESSES APPLIED TO MONEY

The average budget items and percents are given in the accompanying table for a family of two, three, and four people.

Note: Figures following items are percentages of total monthly income.	Monthly Income					
	$500			$840		
	Exemptions					
Items	2	3	4	2	3	4
Food	30	35	38	24	28	32
Rent, Light, Fuel	25	25	26	22	23	23
Clothing	10	12	14	12	13	14
Church, Associations	2	2	2	3	3	3
Medical – Recreation	3	3	3	4	4	4
Auto – Transportation	7	7	7	8	8	8
Education	2	2	2	2	2	2
Savings – Insurance	9	6	4	10	7	5
Social Security – Taxes	12	8	4	15	12	9

1. Compute the amount spent monthly for each item for an income of $500 and a family of three.
2. Make the same calculations for an income of $840 and four exemptions.
3. Find the difference between the same items for the $500 and $840 incomes with three and four dependents respectively.

B. APPLICATION OF MANUFACTURING COSTS AND DISCOUNTS

1. Use the information in the table for articles A through E and determine the cost of materials, labor, and overhead.

	Quantity Produced	Total Mfg. Cost	Materials Cost (%)	Labor Cost (%)	Overhead (%)	Mark-up for List Price (%)	Discounts (%)
A	1000	$2400	30	65	5	20	10
B	750	3250	25	68	7	25	6
C	10 gross	2750	16 1/2	77 1/2	6	37 1/2	15
D	15 doz.	675	12.5	82.7	4.8	45	12 and 8
E	78 bbl.	1982	8 1/2	79 1/4	12 1/4	62 1/2	20, 10, 2

C. COMPUTING PAYROLLS, TAXES, AND TAKE-HOME PAY

1. Prepare a payroll form similar to the one illustrated. Compute the missing information in each column for each worker. Use a standard workweek of 40 hours, overtime equal to time and a quarter (1 1/4) and double time for all hours over 54. Tax B applies to weekly earnings.

Worker	Hours Worked						Reg. Hours Worked	Overtime		Hourly Rate	Weekly Earning	Exemptions		Tax A 20%	Tax B 2%	Take-Home Pay
	M	T	W	T	F	S		Hours Worked	Hours Pay			at $13	Allowance			
A	10	10	10	10	10	10				$8.46		3				
B	10	10	9	9	9	9				5.28		4				
C	8	8	9	9	9	9				3.69		2				

2. Determine the actual cash each worker in problem 1 has left after additional taxes are paid out of the take-home pay. Assume the local tax of 3% and another state tax of 5 1/4% must be paid on everyday purchases.

Section 7

GRAPHS AND STATISTICS

Unit 31 DEVELOPMENT AND INTERPRETATION OF BAR GRAPHS

Statistical data and other factual information are often represented in graphic form. In this way it is possible to compare one set of data with another. Equally important, values may be determined on the graph itself for various conditions.

TYPES AND CHARACTERISTICS OF GRAPHS

While there are many types of graphs used in all reading materials, reports, and handbooks, the greatest number fall into one of four classifications: picture graphs, bar graphs, circle graphs, and line graphs.

Each type has certain advantages as well as disadvantages. The type of graph to use depends on the nature of the data to be presented and the skill of the person to portray information graphically. The picture graph, sometimes called *pictogram,* is the easiest graph to read, but difficult to draw. In this unit, the steps required to produce and to read a *bar graph* are given.

Graph papers, obtainable with different spacings for varying conditions, simplify the representation and interpretation of factual data. Graph papers often have scales printed on them. A 10 x 10 graph sheet indicates the number of equal spaces in a given area. In this instance, the 10 x 10 means 10 equal spaces vertically and 10 spaces horizontally.

Wherever practical, graphs should be planned so that the units to be interpreted are read horizontally from left to right. Information presented in this manner is more easily readable than vertical presentation.

A. DEVELOPING BAR GRAPHS

The term bar graph merely signifies that solid lines or heavy bars of a definite length represent given quantities. Usually, graphs contain two *scales,* a *vertical scale* and a *horizontal scale.* The scale indicates the value of each ruled line or lines. These specific values depend on the information to be presented.

RULE FOR DEVELOPING A BAR GRAPH

- Determine what information is to be presented and whether or not a bar graph is the best type to use.
- Range the data from smallest to largest or in some other logical sequence.
- Select a horizontal scale which makes it possible to represent the full range of data on the sheet.
- Select a vertical scale in the same manner.
- Determine the place on the sheet where both scales come together and mark this point (0).

- Write the vertical scale. Start at zero and add values at each major division in the graph paper.

  NOTE: The starting point does not necessarily have to be zero because in many instances only higher values are needed.

- Repeat the same process for marking the horizontal scale on the graph paper.

  NOTE: Plan the spacing on both vertical and horizontal scales so the graph is balanced.

- Plot the values from an original table or compilation on the horizontal and/or vertical scale.
- Draw the bars as solid lines to furnish the required data.
- Label the scales and give the chart a descriptive title.

EXAMPLE: Develop a bar graph to show the variation in production for a one-year period from the tabular data.

Month	Jan.	Feb.	Mar.	April	May	June	July	Aug.	Sept.	Oct.	Nov.	Dec.
Prod'n Units	500	800	1200	1350	1450	1550	1300	900	850	800	750	1150

Step 1 Study the information in the chart and determine the high and low ranges in production units. These are 1550 and 500.

NOTE: The months are arranged in a logical sequence as they will appear on the graph.

Step 2 Select a graph sheet with spaces ruled to meet the job requirements.

NOTE: If no printed form is available, rule a sheet with light lines drawn to a predetermined scale.

Step 3 Determine whether to represent the months on the vertical or horizontal scale and the production units on the adjacent scale. In this case, represent the months on the horizontal scale.

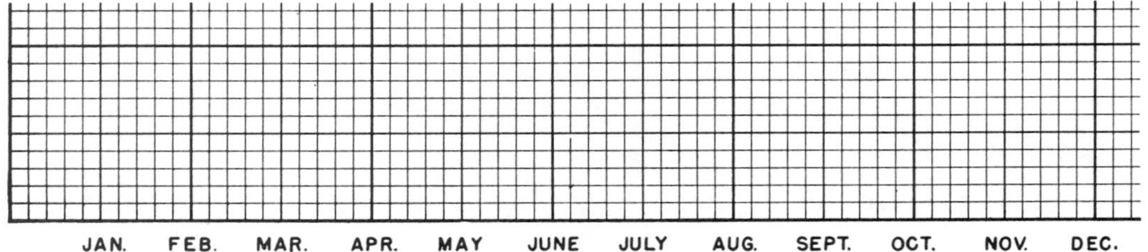

Step 4 Mark the major divisions or units on the vertical scale. Since the graph paper available is 10 x 10, each major vertical line is marked in intervals of 250 production units, starting at zero. Also, write what the scale represents.

NOTE: This scale is selected because, if a smaller one is used, the information will not fit the graph paper.

Step 5 Plot the height of the solid lines, starting with January. In this month, 500 units were produced. This value on the vertical scale is, as indicated, at the 500 point.

Step 6 Continue to plot the production units for the remaining months and recheck for accuracy.

Step 7 Label the graph so the short descriptive title gives meaning to the facts.

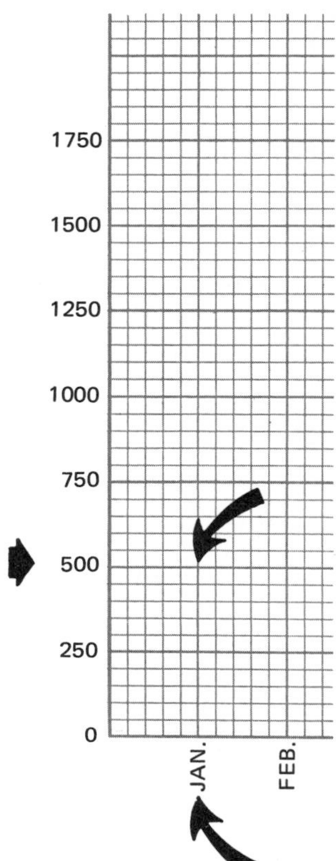

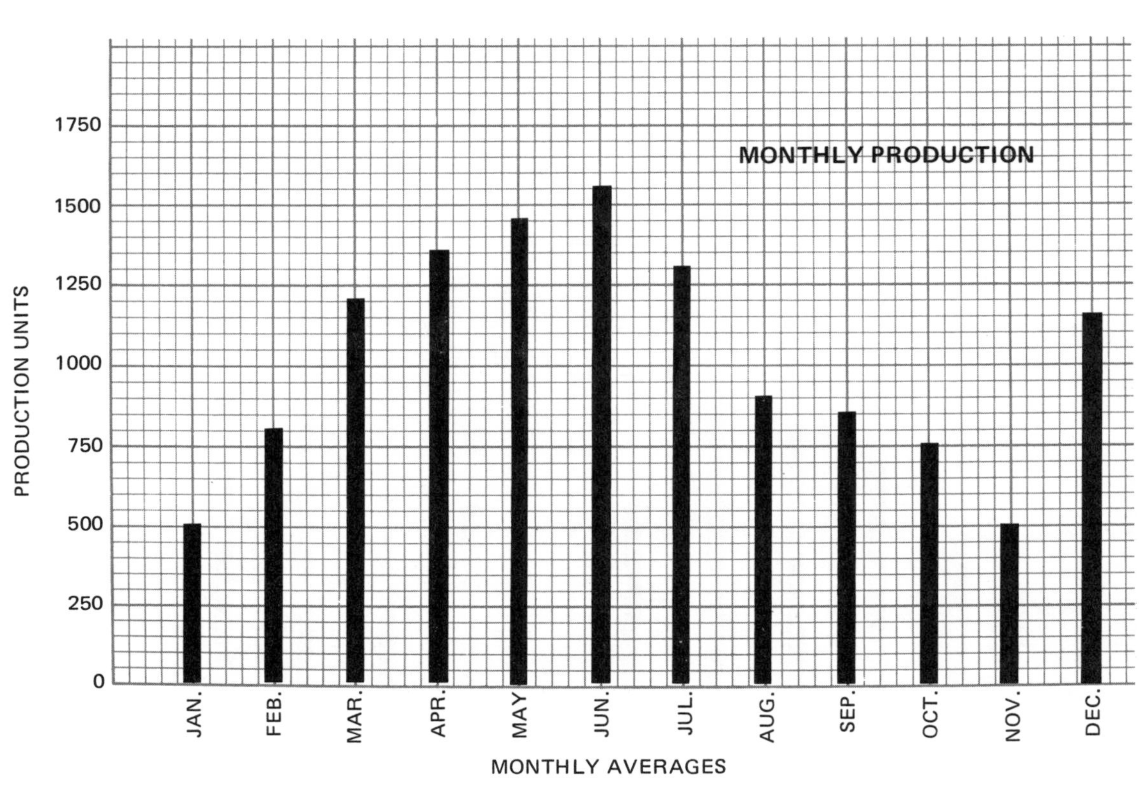

B. INTERPRETING BAR GRAPHS

The need for interpreting factual data from graphs already prepared makes the reading of graphs important. Regardless of the type of graph to be read, there are certain basic steps to be followed.

RULE FOR READING GRAPHS

- Study the problem to determine what information is given and what values must be determined from the graph.
- Read the title of the graph as a key to its organization and purpose.
- Determine the value which each major unit on the vertical scale represents.
- Read the horizontal scale for the value of each unit.
- Locate the given value or data on the horizontal scale.
- Follow an imaginary vertical line from this point to the end of the bar.
- Locate the length of the bar on the vertical scale.
- Continue to read other required values in the same manner.

Often the length of a bar does not fall on an even graduation. The extent to which a bar is above or below a graduated line may be estimated close enough for most practical purposes.

The same steps may be followed if the given values are on the vertical scale and the required value is represented somewhere on the horizontal scale.

EXAMPLE: Determine from the bar graph the number of pounds of brass plate used in manufacturing during the peak month and the lowest month.

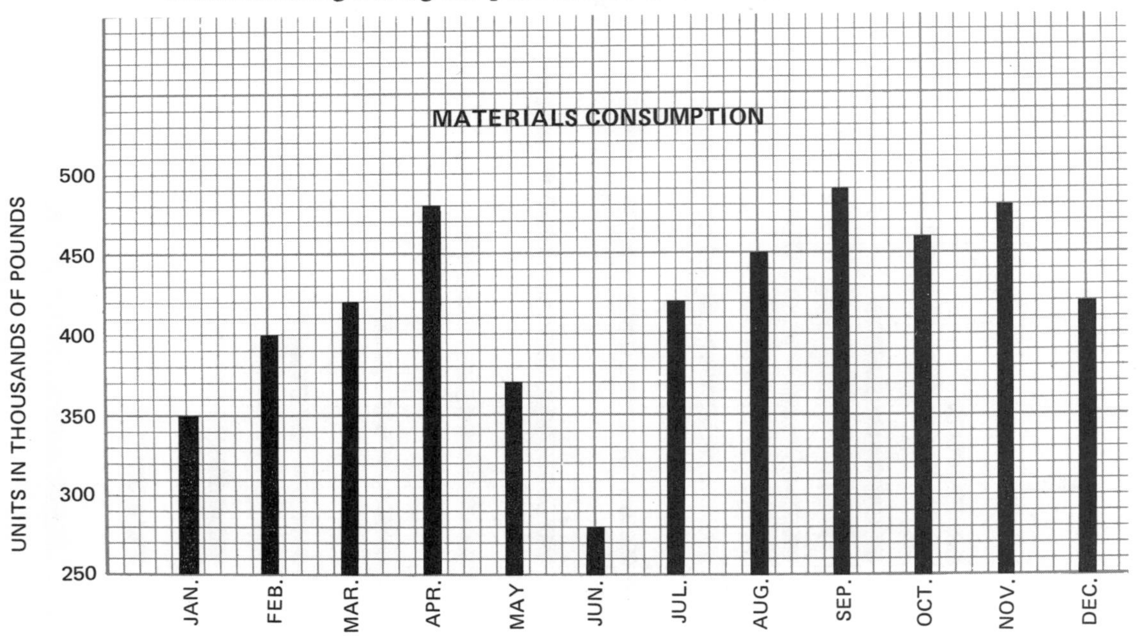

Step 1	Determine which bar and month represents the peak.	(Sept.)
Step 2	Read the value of each unit and subdivision on the vertical scale.	
	NOTE: The vertical scale reading = the unit reading (490 x 1000).	490,000
Step 3	Determine the shortest bar length.	(June)
Step 4	Read the value of this bar on the vertical scale (280) and multiply by 1000.	280,000
Step 5	State results in specific units of measure. The greatest production month was Sept. when 490,000 pounds of brass plate were used. The lowest production month was June with 280,000 pounds of brass plate.	
Step 6	Continue to read the production for other months in the same manner.	

ASSIGNMENT UNIT 31

A. DEVELOPMENT OF BAR GRAPHS

1. Make and label a bar graph to show how lumber is used according to the following average percents.

   Fuel 15% Building 50% Paper Products 9%
   Fires and Disease 11% Miscellaneous 15%

2. Show the phenomenal motor car growth for period A through J, according to the data given.

Period	Car Production
A	10,475,000
B	12,240,000
C	13,000,000
D	15,250,000
E	17,200,000

Period	Car Production
F	19,280,000
G	21,300,000
H	25,400,000
I	26,500,000
J	27,690,000

B. INTERPRETATION OF BAR GRAPHS

1. Study the horizontal bar graph.

   a. Select the greatest production year.

   b. Select the year with the smallest production.

   c. Determine the percent of increase in production between 1973 and 1976.

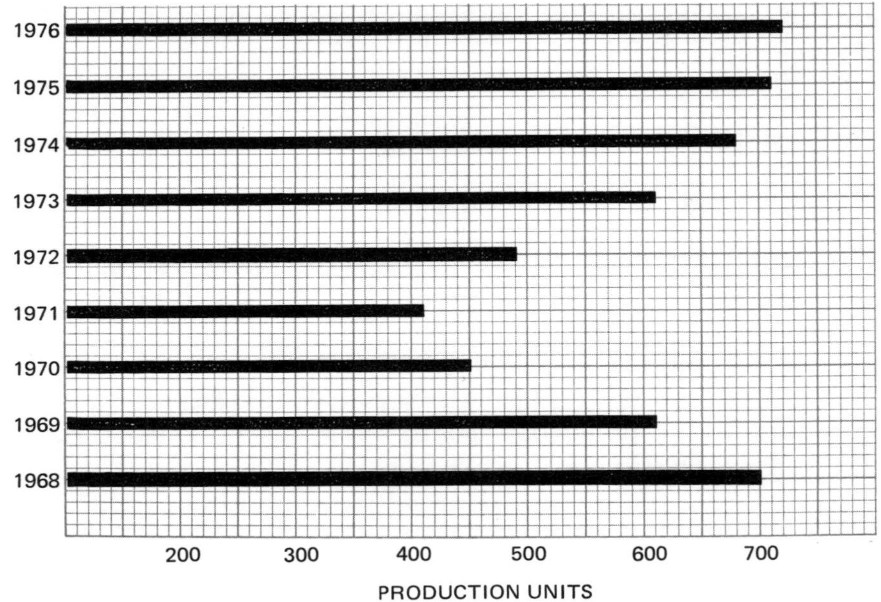

Ans.: a. 1976 c. 18%

2. Study the bar graph of productivity.
   a. Select the three years of greatest productivity.
   b. Determine the average productivity for these three years.
   c. Select the two years of lowest productivity.
   d. Determine the average productivity for these two years.
   e. Find the percent of increase in productivity between the average of the three highest years and the average of the three lowest years. (Round off answer to the nearest whole percent.)

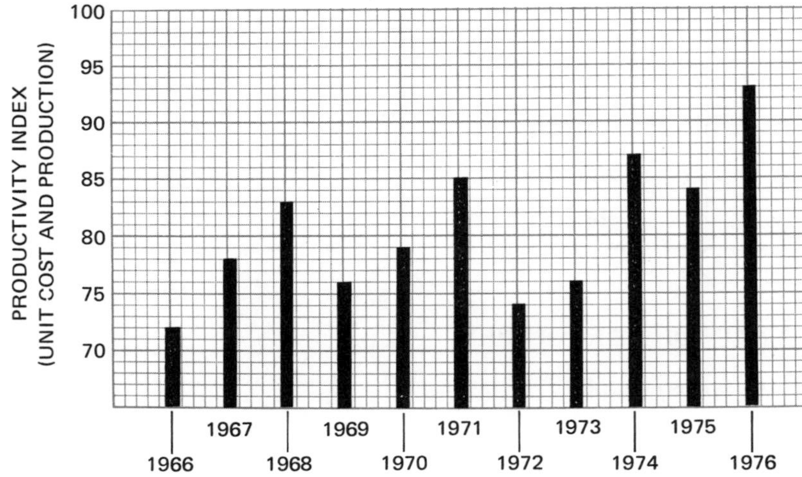

Ans.: b. 88 1/3 d. 74

Unit 32 DEVELOPMENT AND INTERPRETATION OF LINE GRAPHS

The *line graph* is the most widely used graph. It is easy to make, presents facts clearly, and is simple to interpret. Line graphs are of three general types: straight-line, curved-line, and broken-line.

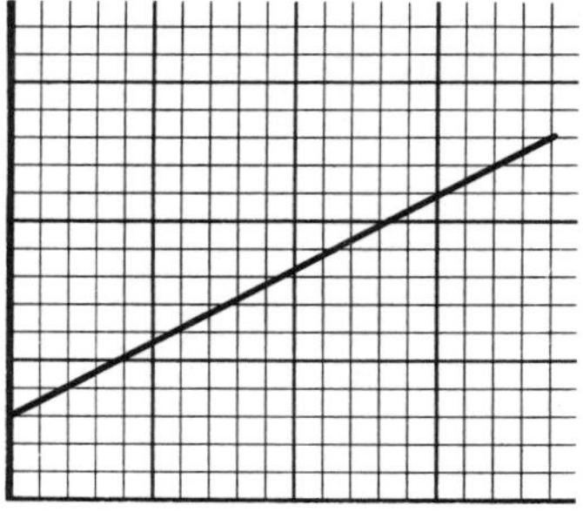

STRAIGHT-LINE GRAPH

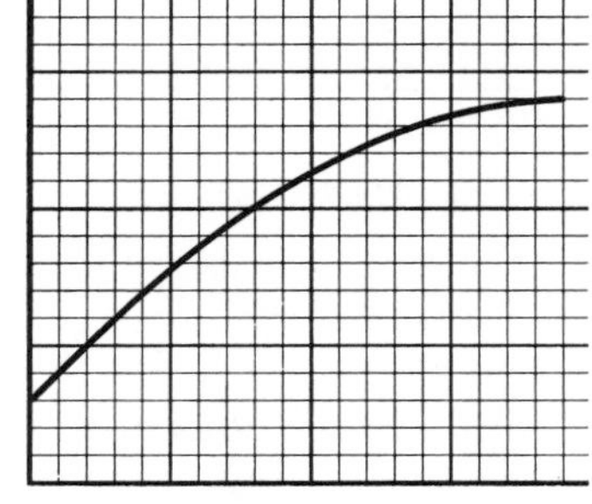

CURVED-LINE GRAPH

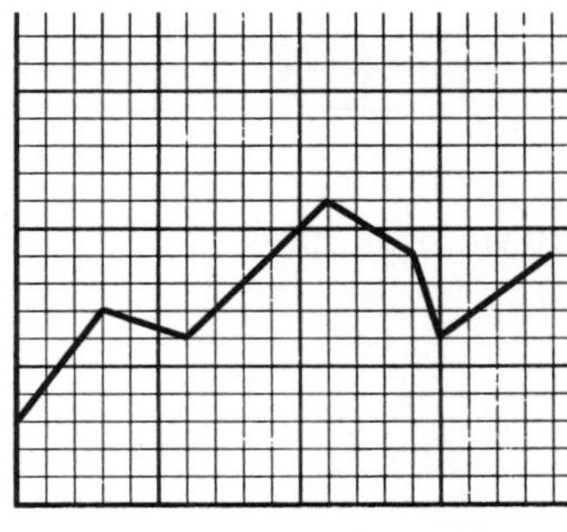

BROKEN-LINE GRAPH

A. DEVELOPING LINE GRAPHS

The straight-line graph is used for related facts where there is some regularity in changes that take place. By contrast, the broken-line graph represents unrelated data where changes are irregular. The curved-line graph presents related information. In each instance, the graph is prepared from data which is either computed or available. One advantage of a graph is that once it is made, other values may be determined without additional computation.

RULE FOR DEVELOPING A LINE GRAPH

- Select appropriate horizontal and vertical scales so the facts may be presented clearly.
- Lay out the major graduations on graph paper for the vertical and horizontal scales and label each scale.
- Arrange the data in the same sequence as it will appear on the graph.

  NOTE: Sometimes these values must be computed from other given facts, using formulas.
- Plot the pairs of numbers on the horizontal and vertical scales. Place a dot or other identifying mark on the paper.
- Connect the points with either a straightedge or curve.

  NOTE: The line may be straight, broken, curved or a combination, depending on the relationship of data.

EXAMPLE: Make a line graph showing the variation in temperature from ground level to 8000 feet.

Altitude in Feet	Ground Level	1000	2000	3000	4000	5000	6000	7000	8000
Air Temp. (°F)	85°	84°	79°	74°	64°	60°	47°	33°	10°

Step 1 Select suitable horizontal and vertical scales and label the graph.

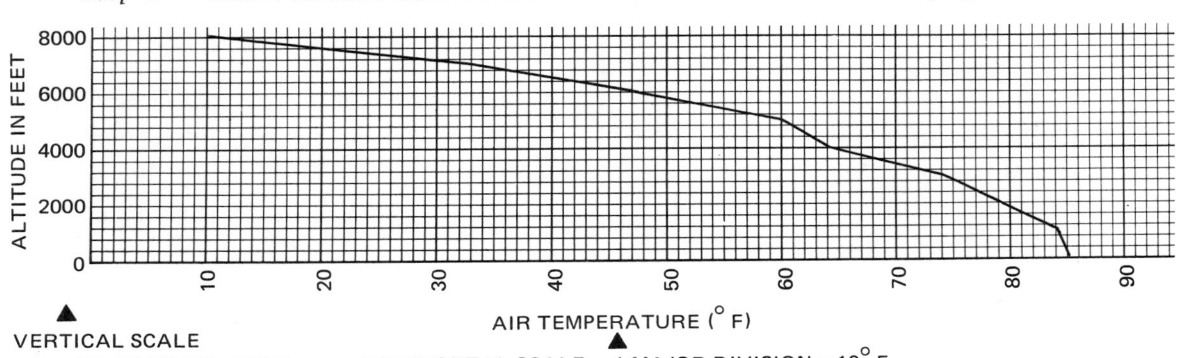

Step 2 Plot the points on the graph at which the pairs of numbers meet.

Step 3 Connect the points with a continuous line.

Step 4 Check the graph by taking an altitude of 2500 feet and 6500 feet, computing the air temperature, and plotting these values on the graph.

Step 5 Recheck the original computations and plotting if the values being checked fall outside the graph line.

B. INTERPRETING LINE GRAPHS

The line graph furnishes information for comparisons of values without further computation. The results are, in most instances, accurate approximations, as it is impractical to represent data to too large a scale. The reading of a line graph is similar to that of a bar graph except that more data may be obtained.

RULE FOR READING A LINE GRAPH

- Determine what information is required.
- Locate the given value on either the horizontal or vertical scale.
- Visualize a horizontal or vertical line which passes through the given value and intersects the graph line.
- Determine the value of this point on the adjacent vertical or horizontal scale, as the case may be.
- Label the answer with an appropriate term.

EXAMPLE: Determine the air temperatures at altitudes of 7500, 6500, 5500, 4500, and 3500 feet from the graph.

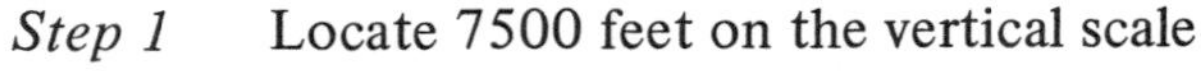
Step 1 Locate 7500 feet on the vertical scale.

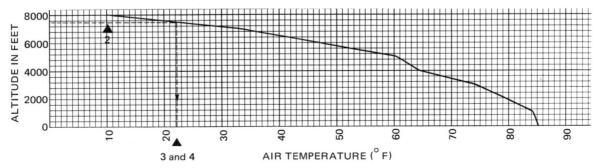

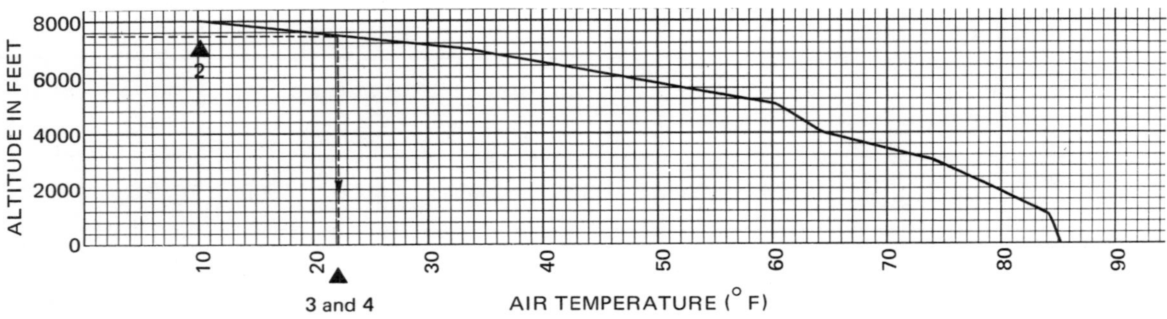

Step 2 Draw an imaginary horizontal line at 7500 feet until it intersects the graph line.

Step 3 Drop another imaginary vertical line from the intersecting point to the horizontal scale.

Step 4 Read the air temperature on the scale.

Step 5 Repeat these steps for the remaining altitudes.

Step 6 Label all answers and recheck.

ASSIGNMENT UNIT 32

A. DEVELOPMENT OF LINE GRAPHS

1. Plot a line graph which shows how the specific gravity of a battery changes as the voltage is decreased.

Voltage	2.00	1.98	1.96	1.92	1.88	1.84	1.80	1.72	1.50
Specific Gravity	1.300	1.295	1.285	1.280	1.275	1.270	1.265	1.253	1.250

2. Show by a curved line graph the number of British thermal units (heat units) required to produce a temperature range of 10° F. to 140° F.

Temperature (°F)	10°	50°	80°	110°	130°	140°
Btu	500	1000	1500	2000	3500	5000

B. DEVELOPMENT AND INTERPRETATIONS OF LINE GRAPHS

1. Make a line graph of the surface speeds of grinding wheels. The diameters range from 8 inches to 16 inches inclusive. Increments in diameter are 1 inch. The constant speed is 2500 revolutions per minute.

   a. Use the formula, Surface Speed = $\frac{\pi \text{ x D x rpm}}{12}$

   b. Round off surface speed values to the nearest 50 feet per minute.

2. Locate on the line graph the surface speeds of wheels worn to diameters of 8 1/2, 9 1/2, 10 1/2, and 11 1/2 inches.

   NOTE: Give answer to closest 50 feet per minute.

3. Make a line graph which shows the relationship of the cross-sectional area of a square pipe to its length. Use the dimensions in the table to establish the cross-section area and length of side.

Lengths of Side (in inches)	4	5	6	7	8	9	10

4. Locate on the graph in number 3, the cross-sectional area of square pipes 4 1/2, 6 1/2, 8 1/2, and 9 1/4 inches on a side.

   a. Check the area of each measurement by computation.

5. The straight-line graph shows the relationship between the diameter of a driving pulley and the surface speed of a belt (in feet per minute – '/min.). The driving pulley revolves at 300 rpm.

   a. Determine the surface speed (in '/min.) of the belt for the following drive pulley sizes (diameters): (1) 3 1/2, (2) 7, and (3) 10 1/2 inches.

   b. Locate the driver pulley diameter sizes required to produce surface speeds of (1) 475 '/min., (2) 750 '/min., and (3) 875 '/min. (Approximate to the nearest 1/4-inch diameter.)

Ans.: a. (3) 840 '/min.
b. (2) 9 1/2"

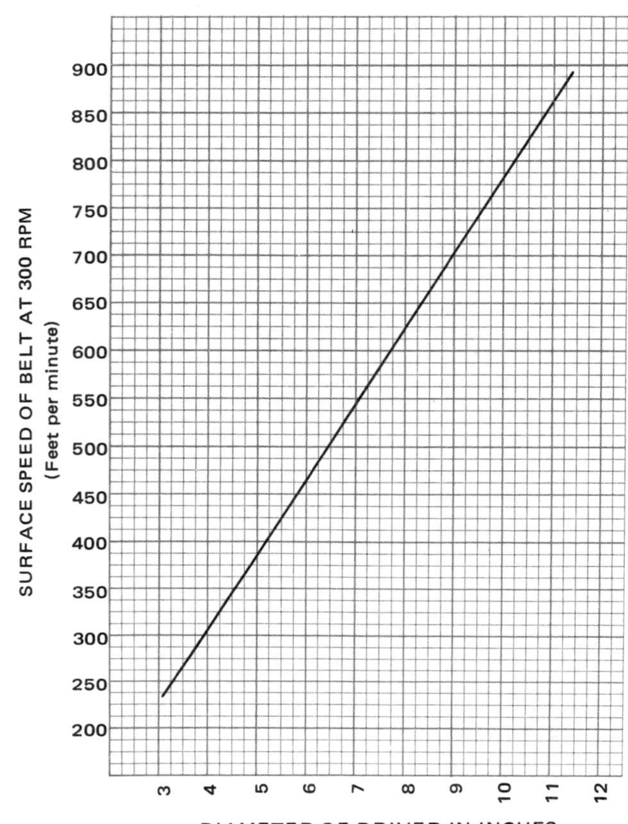

6. The curved (hyperbola) line graph represents the volume in cm^3 of certain materials. The volume is related to the density in grams per cubic centimeter (g/cm^3).

   Estimate the density of materials A, B, C and D.

	Material	Volume (cm^3)	Density (g/cm^3)
A	balsa	850	
B	cork	400	
C	maple	175	
D	ice	110	

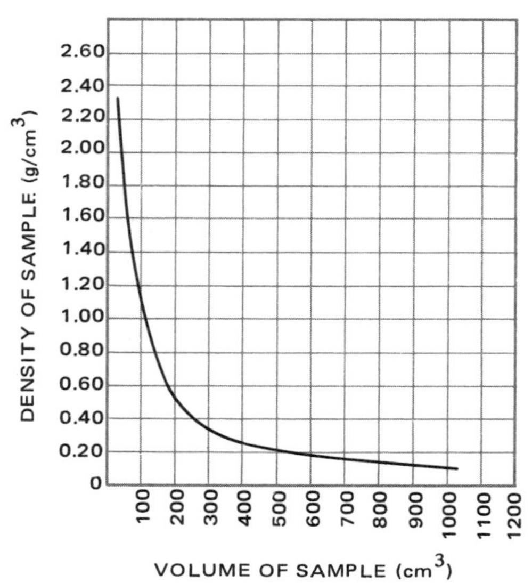

Unit 33 DEVELOPMENT AND APPLICATION OF CIRCLE GRAPHS

A *circle graph,* as the name implies, is a combination of a circle and the division of the circle into a given number of parts. The circle graph (sometimes called a *pie graph*) is especially useful in showing how one part is related to another part and to the total.

The circle graph differs from either the bar graph or the line graph in that it is used primarily for comparative purposes. It is impractical to determine other numerical values from the graph itself.

RULE FOR DEVELOPING CIRCLE GRAPHS

- Add together all of the items to be included on the graph. This sum is equal to 100%.
- Make a series of fractions of the data. The numerator represents one of the parts; the denominator, the total.
- Multiply the quotient of each fraction by 100 to get the percent equivalent each part is to the total.
- Multiply the quotient again, but this time by 360°, to get the equivalent angle of each part.
- Draw a circle large enough to divide easily into the required number of parts so that the graph may be read easily.
- Divide the circle into the number of degrees in each part.
- Label each part and the chart itself with a descriptive caption and the percent which that part represents.
- Determine the relationship of each part to the total. Then compare one part with another.

As an example, one of the best ways to make quarterly comparisons graphically is to use a circle graph.

EXAMPLE: Develop a circle graph to show quarterly production according to the information given in the table.

Quarter	First	Second	Third	Fourth
Production Units	12,500	25,000	31,250	18,750

Step 1 Total the production units.

Step 2 Determine the fractional part of the total each quarter represents.

$$\begin{array}{r} 12{,}500 \\ 25{,}000 \\ 31{,}250 \\ \underline{18{,}750} \\ 87{,}500 \end{array}$$

First	Second	Third	Fourth
$\frac{12{,}500}{87{,}500} = \frac{1}{7}$	$\frac{25{,}000}{87{,}500} = \frac{2}{7}$	$\frac{31{,}250}{87{,}500} = \frac{5}{14}$	$\frac{18{,}750}{87{,}500} = \frac{3}{14}$

Step 3 Determine the percent of the total that each quarterly production represents.

First	Second	Third	Fourth
$\frac{1}{7} = 14\frac{1}{3}\%$	$\frac{2}{7} = 28\frac{2}{3}\%$	$\frac{5}{14} = 35\frac{5}{6}\%$	$\frac{3}{14} = 21\frac{1}{6}\%$

Step 4 Draw a circle and divide it into 14 parts. Then lay out each fractional part of the total.

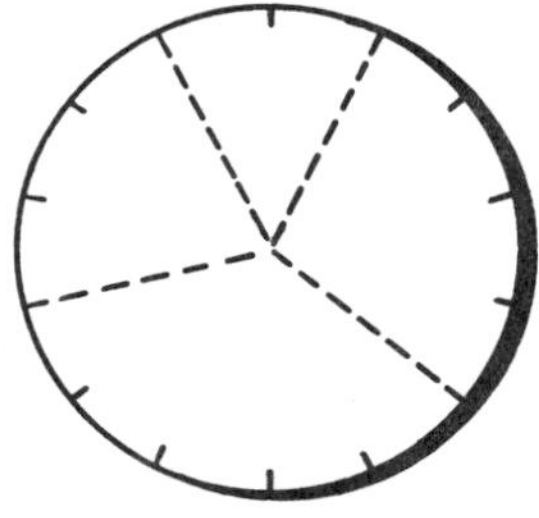

Step 5 Label the chart with a descriptive title and the percent production each quarter.

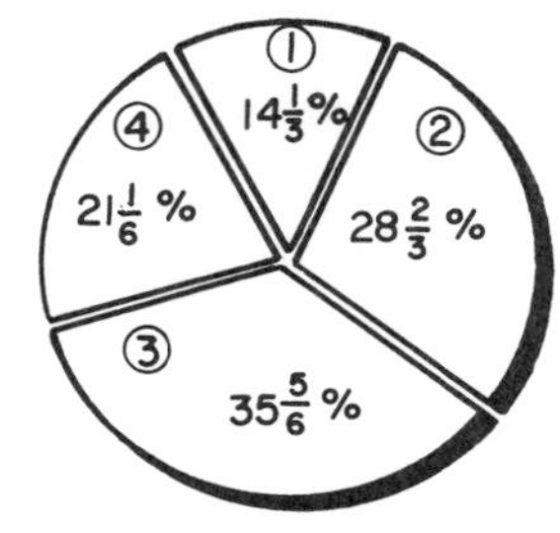

Step 6 Compare the data from the chart as may be required.

There are many ways of designating the parts of a circle graph. Another simple method is illustrated. Colors or screens may be used to emphasize and to add interest. The technique depends on the purpose and persons who are to translate the information.

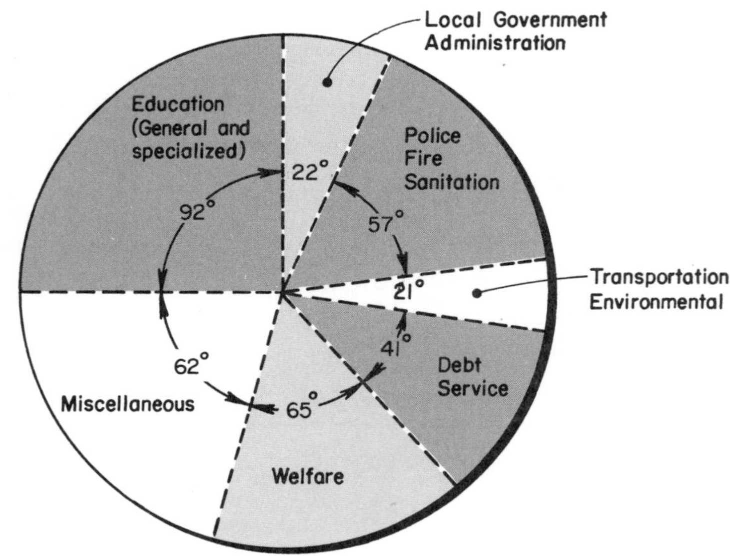

ASSIGNMENT UNIT 33

A. DEVELOPMENT OF CIRCLE GRAPHS

1. Prepare a circle graph to show the relationship between the number of men and women employed in a plant where there are 1300 men and 300 women.

2. Make a circle graph to illustrate how each dollar is spent in a particular industry.

Item	Expenditure
Adm. and Eng'g.	$100,000
Development	250,000
Tooling	180,000
Production	160,000
Sales and Service	90,000
Taxes	220,000

B. DEVELOPMENT AND INTERPRETATION OF CIRCLE GRAPHS

1. Study the circle graph.

   a. Determine total labor force in one industry of an area labor market.

   b. What percent of the total number employed are men? Women?

   c. How many men are in the 18-35 and 36-55 year age groups? How many women?

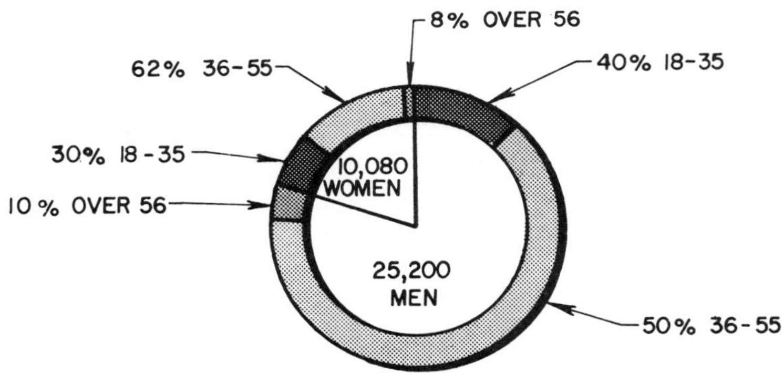

Ans.: b. 71% men; 29% women

2. The following amounts were paid for raw materials: plastics $7500, steel castings $17,500, brass castings $14,000, paints $2500, and lumber $8500.

   a. Prepare a circle graph to show the relationship of costs.

   b. Determine the percent of total spent on each material.

Ans.: b. steel castings, 35%; paints, 5%

Unit 34 ACHIEVEMENT REVIEW ON GRAPHS AND STATISTICS

A. DEVELOPMENT AND INTERPRETATION OF BAR GRAPHS

1. Compute the Celsius melting points of metals A through E.

   NOTE: Find each Celsius reading by multiplying the Fahrenheit reading minus 32, by 5/9; (C = (F – 32) x 5/9).

	Metals	Fahrenheit	Celsius
A	Chromium	2740°	
B	Cast Iron	2300°	
C	Copper	1940°	
D	Aluminum	1200°	
E	Lead	620°	

2. Prepare a bar graph to show the melting point temperatures on both the Fahrenheit and Celsius scales for all metals in the table.

   NOTE: Use a solid bar for the Celsius readings and a dotted outline for Fahrenheit.

3. Determine from the graph what the differences are in Celsius readings between chromium and lead, cast iron and aluminum, and copper and lead.

B. DEVELOPMENT AND INTERPRETATION OF LINE GRAPHS

1. Statistics compiled on the exhaust temperatures of low, medium, and high compression ratio engines, running at different rpm, are given in table form. Translate these facts into a line graph.

   NOTE: Use solid line for medium compression, dotted line (-‑-) for low compression, and an alternate solid-dash line (—-) for high compression.

Compression Ratio	Exhaust Temperature (°F)					
Low	780	870	950	1030	1100	1160
Medium	825	920	1000	1080	1150	1220
High	880	970	1060	1130	1210	1275
Rpm	1000	1500	2000	2500	3000	3500

2. What is the average difference in exhaust temperature between a medium- and a low-compression ratio engine as shown on the graph?

3. Locate on the graph the exhaust temperature of a high-compression ratio engine whose rpm is 1750, 2250, 2750, 3250, and 3750.

4. Determine from the graph what the rpm of a low-compression engine is for these exhaust temperatures: 950°, 1050°, 1150°, and 1250°.
5. What is the difference in exhaust temperatures between a high- and a low-compression engine turning at 3250 rpm?

C. DEVELOPMENT AND INTERPRETATION OF CIRCLE GRAPHS

1. Draw a circle graph to compare the productive capacity of each country to manufacture a specific product.

Country	Productive Capacity
United States	175,000
France	90,000
Great Britain	125,000
Canada	100,000
All others	60,000

2. Give the percent which each country produces of the total.
3. Determine the percent of the total that is produced by the two largest producers (to the nearest two decimal places).
4. Show by a circle graph the percent of total produced by the two largest, two smaller, and all other producers.

Section 8

METRICATION: ORGANIZATION AND SYSTEMS

Unit 35 STANDARDIZATION OF UNITS OF MEASURE

The metric system is not new in the United States. It is used in such industries as medical, pharmaceutical, optometric, and the scientific. It has also been adopted over many years to machine and metals manufacturing, space mission instrumentation and equipment, and other applications. The metric system is recognized as being simpler than the customary system in terms of calculations. Certainly, there is greater possibility of accuracy. The conventional metric system was recognized by Congress over 100 years ago. Metric units and the metric system have been used since then.

All nations depend on the foreign sale and exchange of goods and services. Many nations are moving into SI Metrics for weights and measurements. The movement is away from "customary" adaptations of British Imperial Standards, the "conventional metrics" (which is a combination of many metric systems) and some special industries' standards.

Out of these many systems, SI Metrics has evolved as a compromise system. While SI Metrics is identified as a system with specific characteristics, care must be exercised in interpreting the system. When a new term or base unit is considered by the International body and is included in its papers, this does not mean that the term or unit of measure is adopted and incorporated into the system. This action results after appropriate specialized groups study the implications and assess the value. After the item is resolved by committee action, it is brought up for adoption by the International body. Then, its adoption by the member nations is a matter which each nation decides.

Another fact must be understood. All nations have built their standards around the British and/or the old standards of metric systems. Thus, each nation will, for many years, be adjusting its system of weights and measures. Further, the design, development, production and utilization of materials, products and services need to be built upon SI Metrics. It is for this reason that this textbook treats the British, "customary" American, "conventional" metric, and SI Metric systems.

This section is organized in three units. This first unit starts with a brief historical perspective on units of measurement. Organizational relationships are analyzed to show groups and agencies who are playing key roles in metrication. Advantages of SI Metrics, the scientific notation system and a style guide are then presented.

The second unit explains in a very simple way the terms, values and foundations of the conventional metric system. These are applied to the most common units of measure for linear, surface and volume measurements. As stated, the transitional period to SI Metrics will continue for many years. Conversions of dimensions and quantities among the different systems require daily decisions. Thus, rules of conversion are included as practical and expedient.

The evolving SI Metrics is treated in a third unit. The seven units of measure are identified. Supportive supplementary and derived units of measure are also covered. Conversion factors and processes provide practical techniques for computations in the three prime measurement systems.

This combination of experiences with metric systems and metrication, and a working knowledge of basic arithmetic and advanced mathematical processes, provide essential content and methods. These, together with practical applications, are needed by workers and consumers.

A. HISTORICAL PERSPECTIVE ON STANDARDS AND UNITS OF MEASURE

For over 100 years there has been an international body known as the "General Conference on Weights and Measures" (Conference Général des Poids et Mesures, CGPM). This "Conference" is the controlling body of the International Bureau of Weights and Measures. The Bureau is responsible for preserving metric standards and comparing the standards of different nations with the metric system. The Bureau also conducts research and develops new standards of measurement. The member nations participate in research, assess findings and recommendations, and vote for international adoption by the "Conference." The matter of acceptance and implementation by the individual member nations rests with responsible groups in each nation. The National Bureau of Standards is the United States' representative to the CGPM.

The original metric system of the eighteenth century contained the meter as the keystone. All other elements in the metric system were derived from the meter, a unit of length. The kilogram was later added as a unit of mass. With these two base units, other units were "derived" for the measurement of length, area, volume, capacity, and mass. The system became the "centimeter-gram" system. The base unit of time (the second) was added in 1881. The metric system was then expanded to the "cgs" or "centimeter-gram-second" system. These base units were in contrast with the nonmetric British and "customary" American base units.

IMPACT OF TECHNOLOGY AFTER 1900

Standards for measurement respond to needs. Some result from accelerated developments in industry, agriculture, health, scientific and other major economic growth areas. Other standards are brought about by increasing consumer needs. Progress usually creates a need for new base units and other derived units of measure. For example, by the turn of the century (1900) a "meter-kilogram-second" system was adopted. This "MKS" system of measurement was found to be more practical than "cgs."

New developments and demands within the electrical and electromagnetic fields required the adoption of the "ampere" as a base unit of measure. When it was accepted in 1950 by the tenth CGPM, the system was changed to the "MKSA" system. Four years later (1954), the "candela" (cd) was recognized as the unit of light intensity and the "degree Kelvin" (°K) as the base unit of temperature. These base units, together with the "second," were redefined and revised at the 12th and 13th (1964 and 1967) CGPM. In 1964 the liter was adopted as the synonym for cubic decimeter (dm^3). At the same time, the use of the name liter was discouraged for precision measurements.

The "mole" (mol) is the seventh base unit in SI Metrics. It was added during the 14th CGPM in 1971. Other descriptive measurement terms like "pascal," "siemens," and "newton" were also accepted. It is important to note the period over which SI Metrics has been evolving. A number of years elapses between recognition of need, research, recommendations, acceptance, and adoption by CGPM. Added to this time is the interval required by responsible groups within each nation to determine its own system of measurement. Currently a widespread adoption by most nations to accept SI Metrics as the universal standard is taking place.

B. ADVANTAGES OF SI METRICS

SI Metrics is recognized as an international system of accurately measuring and quantitatively defining all measurable objects. "SI" was universally adopted as the abbreviation of the International System of Units at the 1960 CGPM. "SI" is also referred to as "SI Metrics," the term used in this book. Terms and certain units are spelled according to accepted American standards. The following are some of the most important advantages of SI Metrics.

- Seven base units are used in the measurement of every known physical quantity. These seven include the meter (length), kilogram (mass), second (time), kelvin (temperature), ampere (electric current), candela (light intensity), and the mole (substance of a system). In addition, there are two supplementary units ("radian" and "steradian"), and a number of derived units.
- A well-defined set of symbols and abbreviations are established. These are adequate to define all conditions and phenomena.
- Mathematically, a set of prefixes, multiples and submultiples is used to simplify computations involving large values or numbers of digits.
- SI is a "coherent system." The product or quotient of any two unit quantities in the system is a unit of the resulting quantity. For example, in a coherent system, multiplying unit length by unit length produces unit area.
- SI base units are precisely defined and are reproducible in laboratories in each country. The one exception is the kilogram (mass) standard. This is still preserved in the International Bureau of Weights and Measures.
- The SI system may be related by powers of ten to other units that are not a part of the system.
- SI provides for a single international standards system which affects the interchangeability of parts, processes, components and systems.

C. METRICATION: GOVERNMENT AND PRIVATE SECTOR RESPONSIBILITIES

Three important groups and organizations play predominant roles in metrication in the United States. Two of these, the American National Standards Institute (ANSI) and the American National Metric Council (ANMC), represent private enterprise.

The third organization is the National Bureau of Standards of the government. This bureau is the United States representative to the CGPM. Since legislation has finally been passed and implemented (for SI to be one of the systems of measurement in the United States), the National Metric Conversion Board has been formed.

RESPONSIBILITIES OF THE AMERICAN NATIONAL STANDARDS INSTITUTE (ANSI)

- This organization is a voluntary one. ANSI operates under the principle of "nonlegislated consensus." Members have the freedom to accept and to establish the degree of acceptance of SI Metrics. ANSI is an advisory body.
- ANSI is a coordinating body involved in compromises required to develop international standards of weights and measures.
- ANSI is a planning body to stimulate the conversion to SI Metrics. It coordinates activities to achieve this goal.
- ANSI is the United States' representative to the International Standards Organization.

FUNCTIONS AND ORGANIZATION OF THE AMERICAN NATIONAL METRIC COUNCIL (ANMC)

The ANMC was created by the ANSI. ANMC came into being in the absence of federal legislation on metrication and the establishment of the National Metric Conversion Board. There are five major functions of the American National Metric Council.

1. Promoting metrication.
2. Determining SI metric needs among standards-making industries and professional bodies.
3. Establishing priorities for recommending the development of essential measurement standards.
4. Coordinating private business needs and activities in standard setting with a National Metric Conversion Board, when established.
5. Translating the expertise developed by the United Kingdom and Commonwealth Nations in their movement to SI Metrics. This effort is directed toward resolving transitional problems in the United States.

The organization of the ANMC is shown graphically. Its functions are grouped to serve all interests and segments of society affected by metrication. Note that there are "operations committees," "coordinating committees" and "sector committees." These committees relate primarily to the industrial sector of society and deal with energy, raw materials, processes, products and services.

The ANMC efforts are complemented by other standard-setting organizations. These relate to scientific, medical, agricultural, and other major economic sectors.

THE NATIONAL BUREAU OF STANDARDS AND GOVERNMENT RESPONSIBILITIES

Metrication is an evolving process. The technological supremacy of the United States is built, principally, around customary units of weights and measures. The British system of

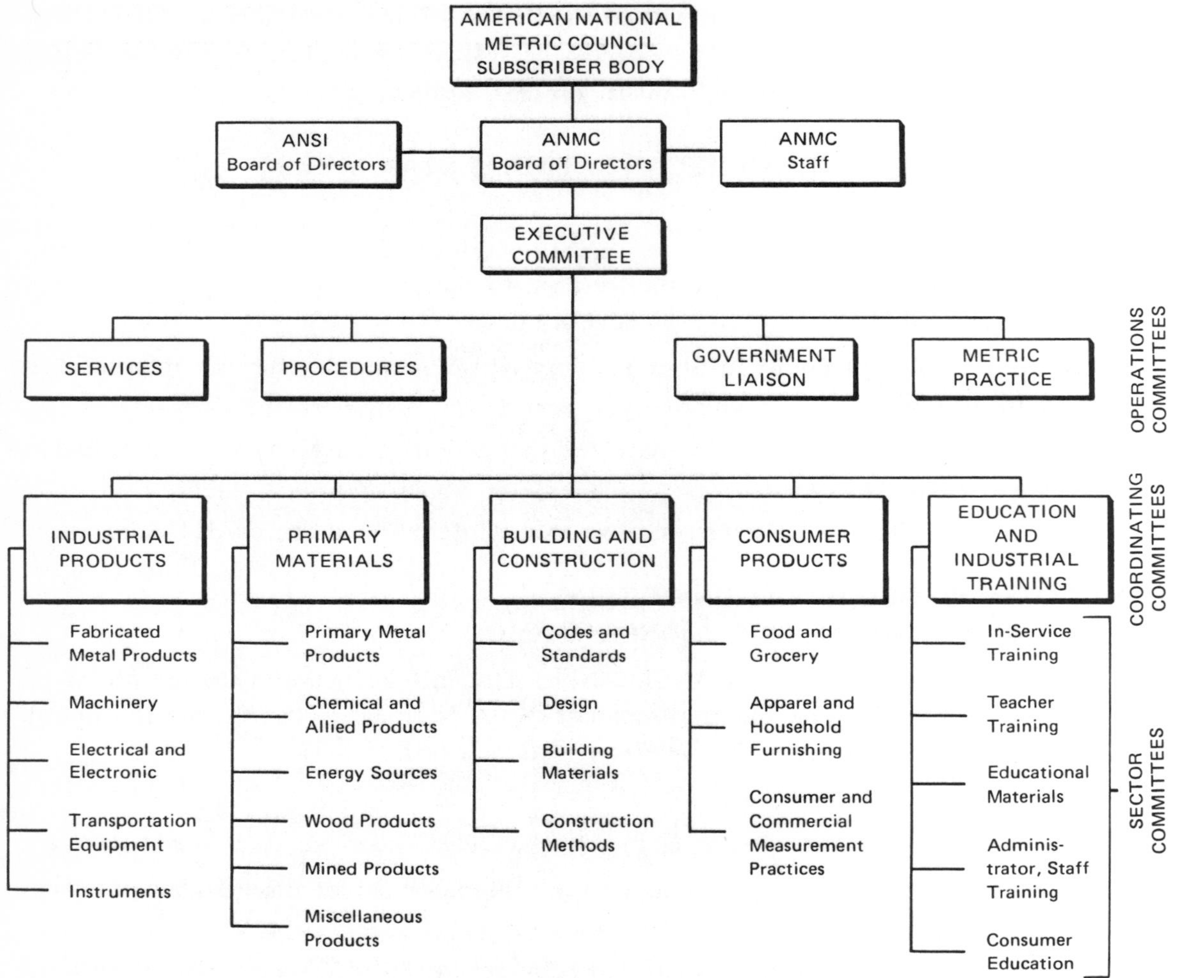

Fig. 35-1

measurement was used primarily for the development of standards for: screw threads, fasteners, parts, components, machines, instruments; manufacturing and inspection practices; and tolerance limits and other significant formulas, proportions and values.

It is possible to redefine all the measurements and standards associated with the nation's products and services. For example, a bolt size such as 1/2" can be redefined and converted to 12.7 millimeters. The problem is that in going to SI Metrics the American 1/2" bolt specifications must be redesigned metrically. The bolt will be either a 12 or 13 mm bolt. In this instance the metric bolt will not be congruent (all dimensions, angles, and relationships identical) with the American National Standard.

This example is multiplied thousands upon thousands of times to cover all standards. This is a major task of metrication.

The National Bureau of Standards (NBS) will be the responsible agency of government for metrication. When legislation is implemented, NBS is to serve four prime functions:

1. Provide technical assistance to the nation and to the formal National Metric Conversion Board, when it is formed.
2. Provide coordinating materials and other outputs which the NBS obtained during the extensive National Metric Study.
3. Provide consultant services and establish principles on which metrication should be based.
4. Promote states' efforts to change weights and measures to SI Metric units. The control of weights and measures is still the responsibility of each state.

D. SCIENTIFIC NOTATION SYSTEM

Quantities are measured and computed in the SI Metric System according to the "Scientific Notation System." This system has many advantages. Mathematical processes involving long multi-digit values are simplified. Errors in calculation are reduced. Quantities are easier to write and to read. These are a few of the obvious advantages.

The quantity 10 is used as the foundation of the scientific notation system. The writing of quantities and mathematical computations are simplified by using what are called "power of ten multiple and submultiple" values. A number of the powers are further identified by a "prefix" or a symbol for the prefix.

SELECTED SI PREFIXES, SYMBOLS AND POWER OF NONMULTIPLES AND SUBMULTIPLE VALUES

The (A) section of the table shows decimal multiple values of SI units. Note the simplified way of writing 1 million as 10^6. The 10^6 is the same as the value obtained by multiplying 1 by 10 for 6 times. The designation for 1 000 000 is "mega." "Mega" (M) is called a prefix.

Every measurement is stated in terms of a quantity and a unit of measure. An answer of 10.2×10^6 states a quantity. However, it must be more descriptive and relate, also, to a specific unit of measure. If it deals with waveforms that are measured by cycles (or frequency), the unit of measure is "hertz" (hz). Thus, the answer is stated as 10.2 MHz (megahertz). This quantity quickly defines 10 200 000 hertz.

The (B) section shows decimal "submultiple" values of SI units. Note that there is a different set of prefixes and symbols. In either instance, a prefix and its symbol is followed by a particular unit of measure. The many mathematical processes and practical applications which are performed with this scientific notation system are covered in detail in succeeding units.

E. WRITING STYLE FOR SI METRICS

As a coherent system, SI Metrics requires a uniform set of rules for communication. Numerical and "literal" (letter) quantities are identified with specific SI units of measure. The use of SI Metric units follows prescribed guidelines.

- Specific measurements (quantities) are given in terms of base units, derived units, supplementary units, and combinations of these.

SELECTED SI PREFIXES, SYMBOLS AND POWER OF TEN MULTIPLE AND SUBMULTIPLE VALUES

Prefix	Symbol	Value as Power of Ten	Multiplication Factor
(A) Power of Ten Multiple Values			
deka-	da	10	10
hecto-	h	10^2	100
kilo-	k	10^3	1 000
mega-	M	10^6	1 000 000
giga-	G	10^9	1 000 000 000
tera-.	T	10^{12}	1 000 000 000 000
(B) Power of Ten Submultiple Values			
deci-	d	10^{-1}	0.1
centi-	c	10^{-2}	0.01
milli-	m	10^{-3}	0.001
micro-	μ	10^{-6}	0.000 001
nano-	n	10^{-9}	0.000 000 001
pico-	p	10^{-12}	0.000 000 000 001
femto-	f	10^{-15}	0.000 000 000 000 001
atto-	a	10^{-18}	0.000 000 000 000 000 001

Fig. 35-2

- Digits and decimals, in excess of a required degree of precise measurement, are eliminated.
- Multiple and submultiple power of ten quantities are used in computations.
- Prefixes express the "order of magnitude" of a quantity. For example, 200 kg and 24.26 MV define precisely a 200 kilogram mass and a 24.26 megavolt circuit, respectively.
- A prefix is considered to be combined to the symbols to which it is attached.

  Example: $1\ cm^3 = (10^{-2}\ m)^3 = 10^{-6}\ m^3$
- Prefix values of 1 000 are preferred over lesser or greater values. For example, milli- (m, 10^{-3}), micro- (μ, 10^{-6}) and pico-(p, 10^{-12}) are used in expressing submultiple values. The most common and preferred power of ten multiples are the kilo- (k, 10^3), mega- (M, 10^6) and giga- (G, 10^9).
- Units of measure that are derived from proper names are capitalized; for example, volts (V), siemens (S) and henry (H).
- Numerical prefixes of mega-, giga-, and tera- are capitalized: (M), (G) and (T), respectively.
- SI Metric symbols of units of measure are written in singular form. For example, 125 megavolts is written as 125 MV; 12.7 kilometers as 12.7 km.
- Numerical quantities are written in groups of three digits. Commas are omitted. A quantity like 96243.8275 pascals of pressure is written 96 243.827 5 Pa.

It should be noted that the SI system is used in this unit and the unit on SI Metrics. Otherwise, common designations of quantities are followed in this book, using British, customary American, and conventional metric measurements.

ASSIGNMENT UNIT 35

1. State four systems of measurement currently being used in the United States.
2. Describe three functions of the General Conference of Weights and Measures (CGPM).
3. Cite three responsibilities of the International Bureau of Standards.
4. List (a) three base units of measure or combinations, (b) the period of time when each was introduced into the metric system, and (c) the name of the system at the time.

	Base Unit(s)	Period Introduced	Name of Metric System
A			
B			
C			

5. State how SI Metrics cover the "measuring and quantitative definition" of all measurable objects.
6. a. Name one private organization and one government agency that represents the United States in either the International Bureau or the General Conference on Weights and Measures (CGPM).

   b. Identify two responsibilities of each of the two United States groups in metrication.

Match each term in column I with its appropriate value in column II.

Column I Term	Column II Value	
7. Multiple power of ten	a. 10 (power of −1 or less)	f. 10 (power of 1 or more)
8. Submultiple power of ten	b. 0.000 1	g. 100
9. M (mega)	c. 0.000 000 01	h. 10^3
10. k (kilo)	d. 10^{-1}	i. 10^6
11. deci- (d)	e. 10^{-6}	j. 1 billion
12. micro- (μ)		

13. Take each of the four computed quantities in the table.

    a. Write each one as an SI Metric quantity.

    b. Round off each value to the indicated degree of accuracy. State this new quantity.

	Computed Quantity	Written as an SI Metric Quantity	Required Accuracy (Decimals)	Rounded-off SI Metric Quantity
A	7624.2796		2	
B	1729685.499		0	
C	300002.9768392		4	
D	1753.0501		1	

Unit 36 CONVENTIONAL SYSTEM OF METRIC MEASUREMENT

A. CONCEPT OF THE CONVENTIONAL METRIC SYSTEM

The British Imperial System of linear, surface, and volume measurement is still widely used in the United States. This system is the foundation for the customary American system. In this transition period, this country and many other nations have parts, mechanisms, production plants and processes that were designed and built in customary units of measure. Similar objects, components, industries and materials were also produced according to units of measure that are related to other systems of measurement.

The second basic system has been evolving for over two centuries. It is known as the Metric System of Measurement. Out of the metric system has grown a series of systems that differ from each other. The term "conventional" metric is used in this book. It identifies the system as adapted to the needs of the United States and other nations. Standards were developed and accepted in conventional metric. These, as just stated, have been used in scientific exploration, engineering design and development, in laboratories and shops, throughout many different types of industries and for export/import business, to name a few widespread uses.

The *meter* is the base unit of measure in the metric system. More than 200 years ago, the meter was defined as a specific fraction of the earth's circumference. The Paris Academy of Sciences constructed a metric measurement system. The meter was the foundation of all other elements of the system.

Today, the basic unit of length is still the meter. However, it is now defined so that the measurement may be precisely duplicated by scientists, engineers and technologists anywhere in the world. The meter, stated scientifically, refers to "a length." The length is equal to 1 650 763.73 wavelengths in a vacuum of the radiation between two energy levels of the gas atom, Krypton.

The other units of the metric system are multiples of the meter. As previously stated, prefixes like deka-, hecto- and kilo- represent positive multiples of ten. Prefixes like deci-, centi- and milli- are minus or submultiple values. For instance,

milli-	=	$\frac{1}{1000}$	=	one-thousandth
centi-	=	$\frac{1}{100}$	=	one-hundredth
deci-	=	$\frac{1}{10}$	=	one-tenth

deka-	=	10	=	ten
hecto-	=	100	=	hundred
kilo-	=	1000	=	thousand

Values of different units of measure that are commonly used in the conventional metric system are treated in this unit. Units of linear, surface and volume measure in the metric system are related to British units. Comparisons are made and rules are applied for computing and converting metric measurements.

B. APPLYING THE CONVENTIONAL METRIC SYSTEM OF LINEAR MEASURE

The standard units of linear measure in the metric system are given in the accompanying table. Unit values in relation to the meter and in terms of an equivalent in the British system are shown.

Values of Metric Units of Linear Measure		
Metric System		British System
Common Linear Units	Value of Unit in Terms of the Meter	Value in British Units
1 meter	Standard Unit of Length	39.37″
1 decimeter	0.1 meter	3.937″
1 centimeter	0.01 meter	0.394″
1 millimeter	0.001 meter	0.039″
1 dekameter	10. meters	32.80 ft.
1 hectometer	100. meters	328.00 ft.
1 kilometer	1000. meters	0.6214 mi.

The writing of linear units is simplified by the symbols shown in the table.

Unit	Symbol
meter	m
decimeter	dm
centimeter	cm
millimeter	mm
dekameter	dkm
hectometer	hm
kilometer	km

Where dimensions in the metric system are expressed in more than one kind of unit in a system of measure, the different kinds may be combined to simplify the mathematical processes. For example, a dimension 3 decimeters 4 centimeters 6 millimeters long (3 dm 4 cm 6 mm) may be expressed as 3.46 decimeters. This value is based on the fact that 10 cm = 1 dm and 100 mm = 1 dm. The 4 cm is equivalent to 4/10 and the 6 mm to 6/100 of a decimeter. The dimension then is equal to 3 + 4/10 + 6/100 decimeters. Expressed as a decimal, this value is 3.46 dm.

Dimensions in the metric system which are given as units of linear, surface, or volume measure may be simplified in the same way.

C. DIRECT LINEAR MEASUREMENTS IN THE METRIC SYSTEM

Metric measurements may be computed or taken directly. Measuring tools and precision instruments are similar to those used for customary units. However, the measurements are different. To repeat, whole and fractional part values in the customary system are related to the inch as the base unit. Metric measurements are in terms of the meter as the base unit.

Comparatively rough measurements may be taken directly with meter sticks and rulers graduated in centimeters and fractional parts. More accurate measurements are made with other line-graduated measuring tools. Metric triangular and flat scales, drafting machine scales, and metal rules are examples. Some of these tools are graduated for measurements which range from one millimeter to one-half millimeter (mm).

Still higher levels of precision are obtained with hand and bench micrometers. Some are graduated to read to accuracies of 0.002 mm. Vernier calipers and other vernier graduated

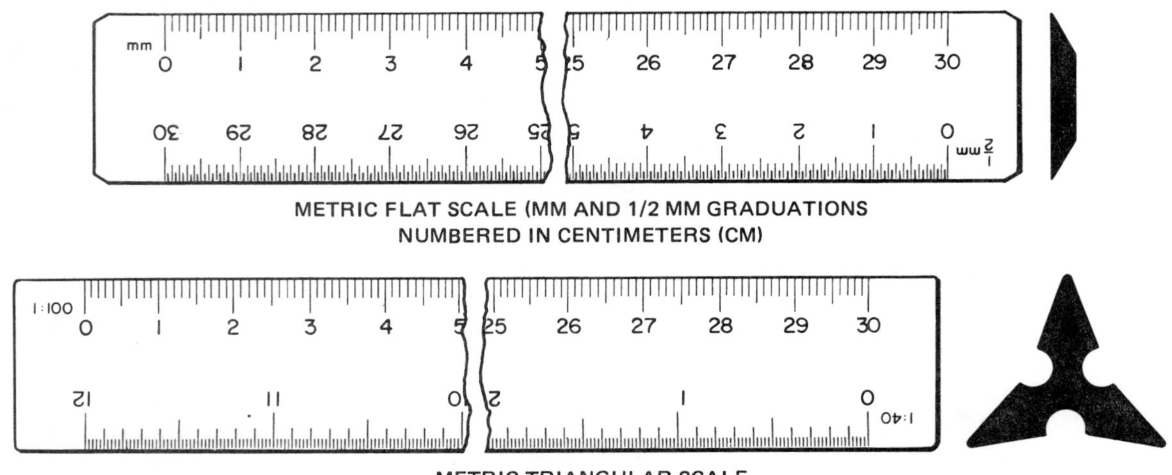

METRIC FLAT SCALE (MM AND 1/2 MM GRADUATIONS
NUMBERED IN CENTIMETERS (CM)
METRIC TRIANGULAR SCALE
SHOWING 1:100 AND 1:40 DRAWING SCALES

Fig. 36-1

height and depth gages measure to a precision of 0.02 mm. Metric gage blocks are also made in sets to measure within precise limits of 0.000 01 mm.

Micrometer heads are available for inside, outside, depth, thread, gear tooth measurements and other special applications. Dial indicators are graduated to measure to 0.002 mm. Engineering levels are available for precise off-level measurements of 0.09 mm in 300 mm. This is the equivalent of 0.0035″ per foot.

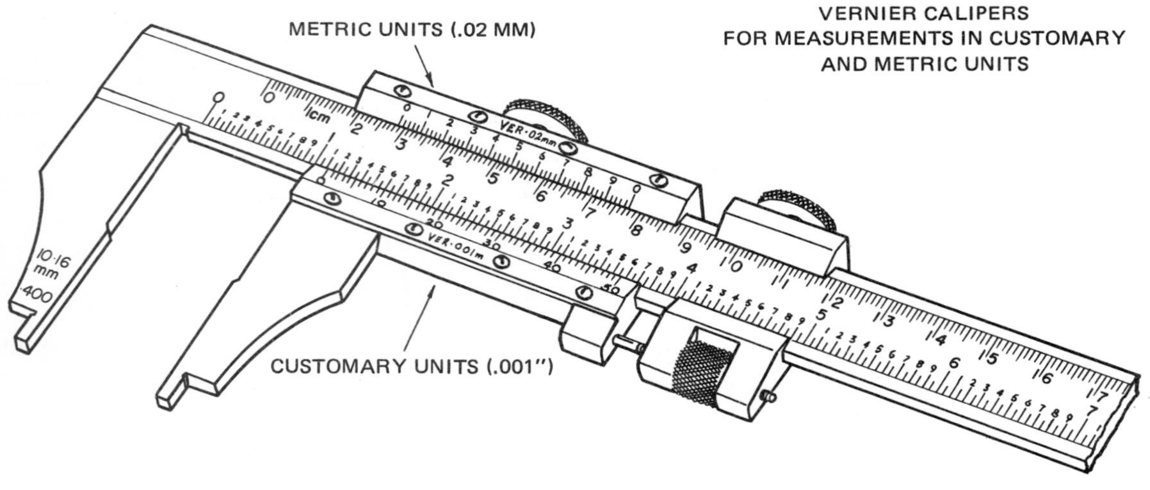

Fig. 36-2

The principles of reading measuring rules, micrometers, and vernier gages for linear measurements are the same, regardless of the system. The standard metric micrometer has line graduations along the sleeve at intervals of 0.5 millimeter. The graduations indicate the distance the thimble and spindle move each complete revolution (1/2 mm or 0.5 mm).

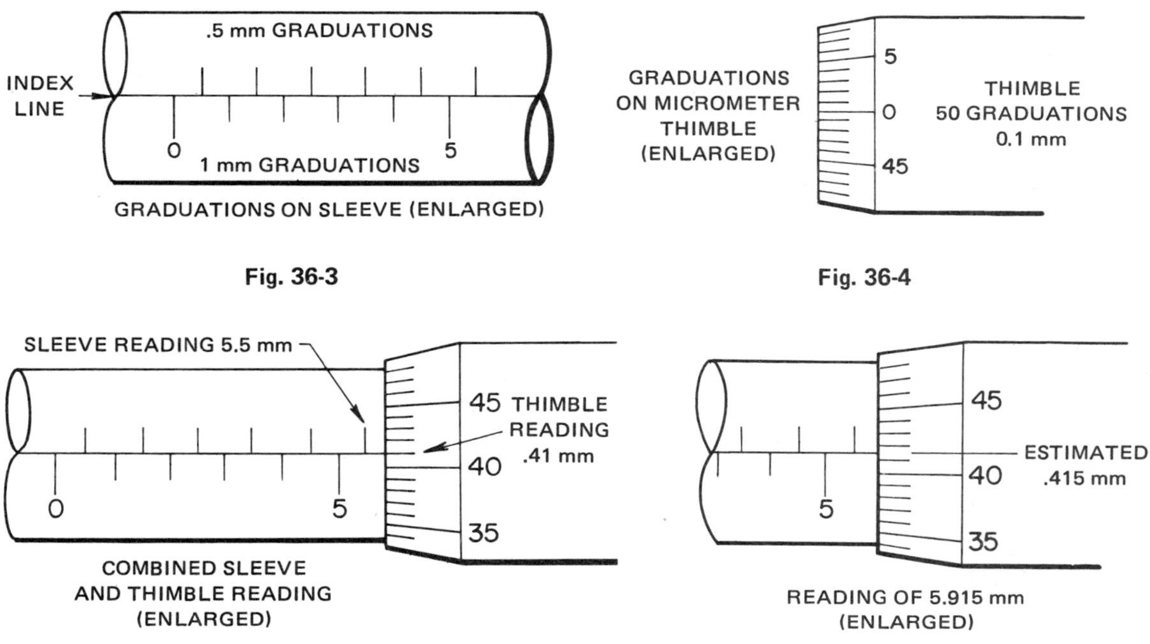

Fig. 36-3

Fig. 36-4

Fig. 36-5

Fig. 36-6

Each graduation below the line represents a measurement of 1 mm. The thimble has 50 graduations cut into the beveled edge. Each graduation represents 1/50 of 0.5 mm, or 0.01 mm.

The linear measurement is read directly by combining the sleeve and barrel readings. The line drawings show a reading of 5.5 mm on the sleeve and another 41 graduations on the thimble. The micrometer reading is 5.91 mm. (Fig. 36-5)

It is possible to estimate to a fraction of a division. A judgment is made about the additional distance between two graduations on the barrel and the index line. The illustration (Fig. 36-6) shows a reading of 5.915 mm. The additional precision of 0.005 mm is the estimated quantity.

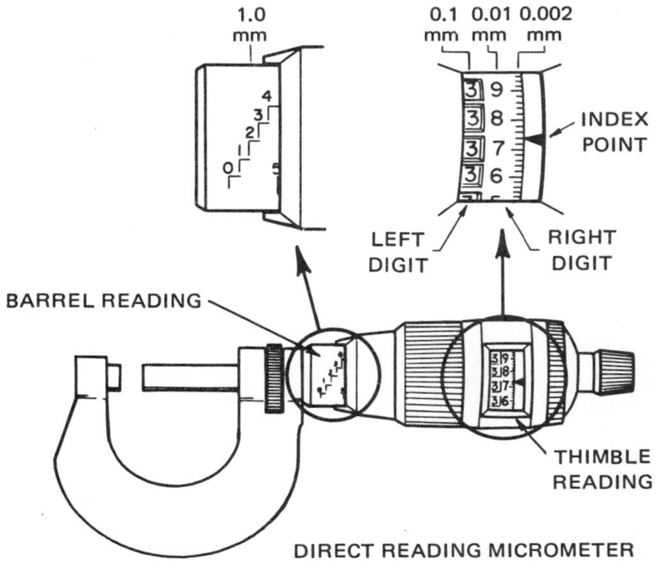

Fig. 36-7

Micrometers are designed, also, for direct reading of the numerical value. Such a micrometer, showing sections of the barrel and thimble, is illustrated. (Fig. 36-7) Each graduation shown on the barrel represents readings of 1.0 mm. Note that the barrel reading shows 5 + mm. A mechanism in the thimble moves the numerals which show the additional fractional parts of a millimeter in the measurement. The numeral in the left digit of the thimble represents 0.10 mm units. The right digit shows 0.01 mm units. Further, each 0.01 mm graduation is divided into five parts for readings of 0.002 mm.

The direct reading of the last exposed numeral on the barrel and the numerals and fractional part read on the thimble is the linear measurement of the part. In the illustration, the total reading is 5.374 mm. This three-place millimeter reading carries the same degree of precision in measurement as a micrometer graduated in customary units of 0.000 1″.

BARREL 1.0 mm		THIMBLE (mm) 0.10	0.01	0.002
5	.	3	7	4

Fig. 36-8

D. CHANGING UNITS OF MEASURE FROM ONE SYSTEM TO ANOTHER

No uniform relationship exists between the units of measure in the British and metric systems. In changing values from one system to the other it is necessary to know what the equivalent of one unit is in terms of the other system. The desired unit may then be computed by either multiplying or dividing.

Units that are commonly used to convert a measurement from the British to the metric system are given in the table.

Comparison of British and Metric Units of Linear Measure

British Units	Equivalent in Metric Units (Approximate)
One Inch	2.54 centimeters (cm) or 25.4 millimeters (mm)
One Foot	0.304 8 meter (m)
One Yard	0.914 4 meter (m)

RULE FOR CHANGING BRITISH UNITS OF MEASURE TO METRIC UNITS (inches, feet, and yards to meters, centimeters, decimeters, and millimeters)

- Determine the equivalent value of one metric unit in the British system.
- Divide the given British unit by the metric equivalent of one unit.
- Express the result in the required metric unit.

NOTE: The same result is obtained if the number of metric units in one British unit is determined and the given number is multiplied by the metric units. This second method is also illustrated.

EXAMPLE: Change 9″ to centimeters (cm).

METHOD 1

Step 1	Determine the value of one centimeter in terms of inches.	1 cm = 0.393 7″
Step 2	Divide the given unit (9) by this number (0.3937).	$\frac{9}{0.393\,7} = 22.86$
Step 3	Express the result (22.86) in terms of the required unit of metric measure (cm).	Ans. 9″ = 22.86 cm

METHOD 2

Step 1	Determine the number of metric units (cm) in one given unit (1″).	1″ = 2.54 cm
Step 2	Multiply the given unit (9) by this number (2.54).	9 x 2.54 = 22.86
Step 3	Express the product 22.86 in terms of the required unit (cm).	Ans. 9″ = 22.86 cm

The mathematical processes required to change units of measure from one system to the other are the same. This condition applies regardless of whether the unit is expressed in terms of square or volume measure.

RULE FOR CHANGING METRIC UNITS OF MEASURE TO BRITISH UNITS (millimeters, decimeters, centimeters, meters to inches, feet, or yards)

- Determine the number of equivalent metric units in one of the required units.
- Divide the given metric unit by this number.
- Express the result in terms of the required British unit.

EXAMPLE: Change 228.6 millimeters (mm) to inches.

Step 1	Determine the number of metric units (mm) in one required unit (1″).	1″ = 25.4 mm
Step 2	Divide the given metric unit (228.6) by (25.4) mm.	$\frac{228.6}{25.4} = 9$
Step 3	Express the result (9) in terms of the required British unit (inches).	Ans. 228.6 mm = 9″

E. COMPUTING SQUARE MEASURE IN THE CONVENTIONAL METRIC SYSTEM

The principles of surface measure which are used with the British units are applied in the same manner with the metric units of measure. However, the names of the units and the value of each differ in both systems.

The area of a surface in the metric system is the number of square metric units which it contains. The three metric units most commonly used for small areas are the square meter, square centimeter, and square decimeter.

One square meter represents the area of a square figure which is one meter long and one meter high. The linear meter in turn is equal to 10 decimeters or 100 centimeters. By

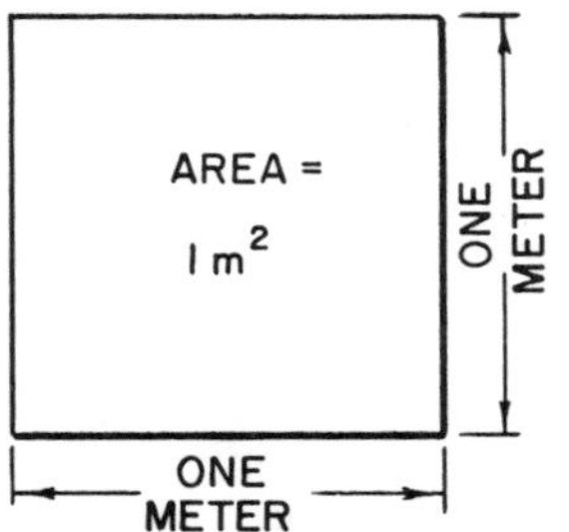

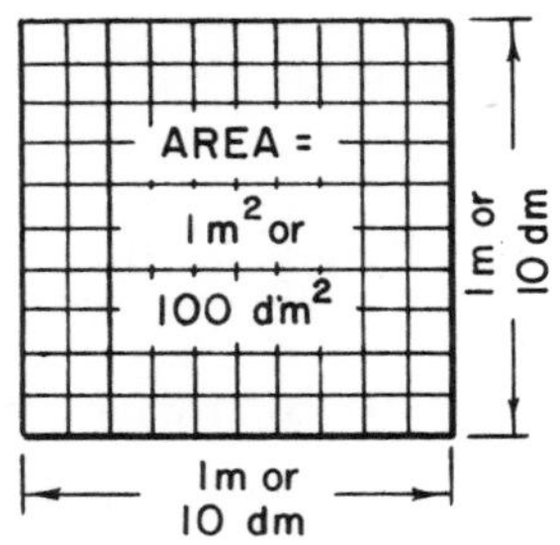

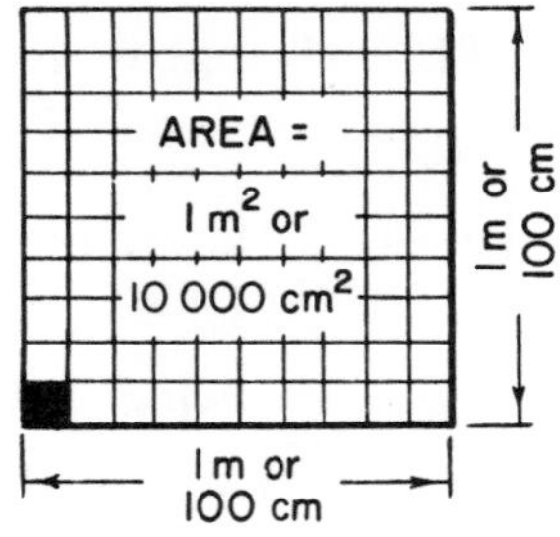

substituting these values for the meter, the area of a square 10 decimeters on a side is 100 square decimeters. The area of a square 100 centimeters on a side is 10,000 square centimeters. Thus, the value of the square meter, which is the standard unit in terms of decimeters and centimeters, is 100 square decimeters or the equivalent, 10,000 square centimeters.

The three common metric units of square measure and the value of each unit in the metric and British systems are given in table form. The second table gives the metric value of three basic units of square measure in the British system.

Values of Metric Units of Square Measure		
Metric Unit of Surface Measure	**Value of Unit in Metric System**	**Equivalent Value in British System**
1 square meter (m^2)	Standard Unit of Measure	1550 sq. in.
1 sq. decimeter (dm^2)	0.01 square meter (sq. m)	15.50 sq. in.
1 sq. centimeter (cm^2)	0.000 1 sq. m	0.155 sq. in.
1 sq. millimeter (mm^2)	0.000 001 sq. m	0.001 55 sq. in.

Comparison of British and Metric Units of Surface Measure	
British Units	**Equivalent in Metric Units (Approximate)**
1 sq. in.	6.452 sq. cm
1 sq. ft.	0.092 9 sq. m
1 sq. yd.	0.836 sq. m

RULE FOR CHANGING METRIC UNITS OF SURFACE MEASURE TO BRITISH UNITS (sq. m, sq. dm, sq. cm to sq. in., sq. ft., or sq. yds.)

- Determine the number of metric units of surface measure in one of the required British units.
- Divide the given metric units by this number.
- Express the quotient in terms of the required British unit.

EXAMPLE: The area of a sheet of brass is 11.148 square meters. Express this value in British units of surface measure (sq. ft.).

Step 1 Determine the number of metric units of surface measure (m^2) in one of the required British units (sq. ft.). $0.092\,9\ m^2 = 1$ sq. ft.

Step 2 Divide the given number of metric units (11.148) by the number of square meters in 1 sq. ft. (0.0929). $\frac{11.148}{0.092\,9} = 120$

Step 3 Express the quotient (120) in terms of the required British unit (sq. ft.). Ans. $11.148\ m^2 =$ 120 sq. ft.

The principles of surface measure which apply to the area measurement of squares, rectangles, parallelograms, trapezoids, triangles, circles, sectors of a circle, and cylinders in British units are the same for the metric system. The only difference is in the name of the unit and its size. The same rules for determining the area of a surface apply for both the British and metric systems.

F. DETERMINING VOLUME MEASURE IN THE CONVENTIONAL METRIC SYSTEM

The volume of a body is the measurement of its cubical contents. These are expressed in cubic units of the same kind as the linear units. When the linear dimensions are given as metric units, the volume is the number of cubic metric units which the body contains. The common metric units are the meter, decimeter, centimeter, and millimeter. The volume is computed as so many cubic meters (m^3), cubic decimeters (dm^3), cubic centimeters (cm^3), or cubic millimeters (mm^3).

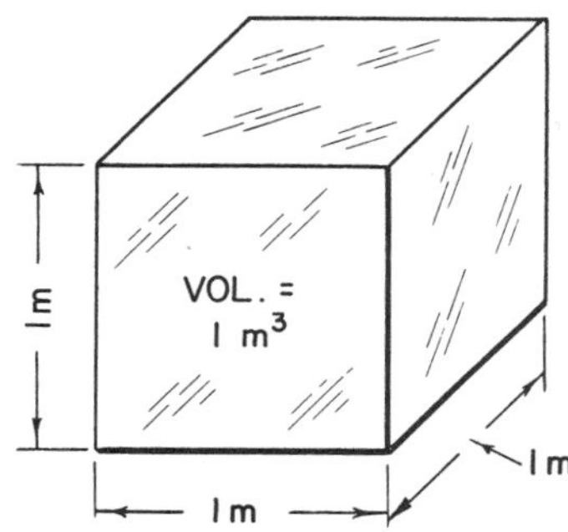

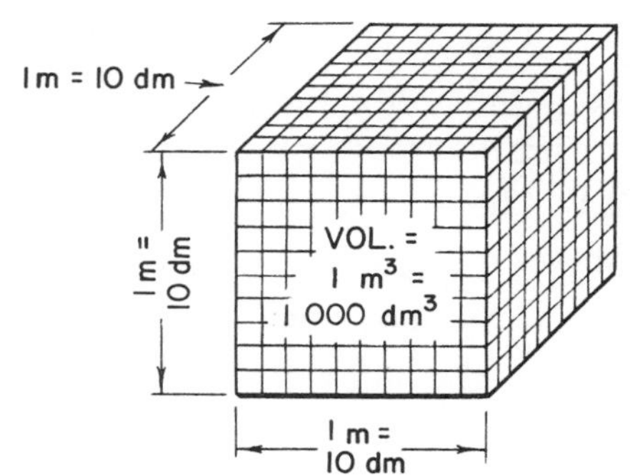

Since 1 meter = 10 decimeters, the volume of a cube 10 decimeters on a side is 1 000 cubic decimeters (dm^3), which is equivalent to 1 cubic meter (m^3).

One cubic decimeter is the volume of a cube one decimeter long, one decimeter high, and one decimeter deep. One cubic decimeter is equivalent also to the volume of a cube which measures 10 centimeters on a side (10 cm = 1 dm) or 1 000 cubic centimeters.

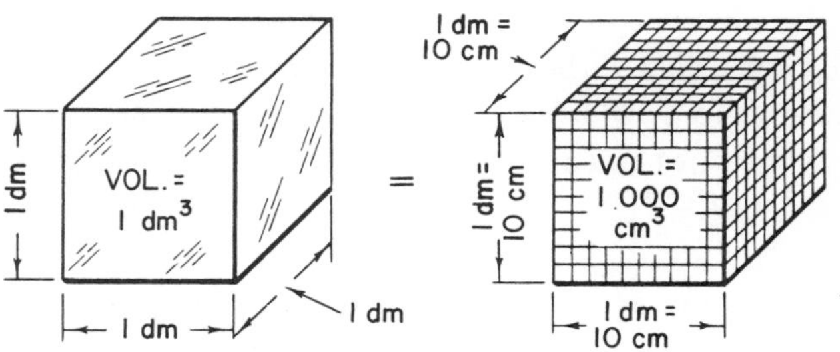

One cubic centimeter is the volume of a cube one centimeter long, one centimeter high, and one centimeter deep. Since the centimeter is equal to 10 millimeters, one cubic centimeter is equal to the volume of a cube 10 millimeters on a side, or 1 000 cubic millimeters. Values in the metric and British systems are given in the table which follows for the cubic meter, cubic decimeter, and cubic centimeter.

Values of Metric Units of Volume Measure

Metric Unit of Volume Measure	Value of Unit in Metric System	Equivalent Value in British System (Approximate)
1 cu. meter (m^3)	1 000 cu. decimeters (dm^3)	35.314 cu. ft. or 1.308 cu. yd.
1 cu. decimeter (dm^3)	1 000 cu. centimeters (cm^3)	61.023 cu. in.
1 cu. centimeter (cm^3)	1 000 cu. millimeters (mm^3)	0.061 cu. in.

The measurement of the cubical contents of squares, rectangular solids, and cylinders is the same for both the British and metric systems of volume measure. The volume of a solid is always computed in the same manner regardless of the system in which the linear dimensions are expressed.

Comparison of British and Metric Units of Volume Measure	
British Units	Equivalent in Metric Units (Approximate)
1 cu. in.	16.387 cm^3
1 cu. ft.	0.028 3 m^3
1 cu. yd.	0.764 6 m^3

RULE FOR CHANGING METRIC UNITS OF VOLUME MEASURE TO BRITISH UNITS (m^3, cm^3, dm^3 to cu. in., cu. ft., or cu. yds.)

- Determine the number of British units of volume measure in one given metric unit.
- Multiply the given metric unit by this number.
- Express the product in terms of the required British unit of volume measure.

EXAMPLE: Change 17.3 cm^3 to cu. in.

Step 1	Determine the number of British units (cu. in.) in one given metric unit (cm^3).	1 cm^3 = 0.061 cu. in.
Step 2	Multiply given metric unit (17.3 cm^3) by this value .061.	17.3 x 0.061 = 1.055
Step 3	Express the product in terms of the required British units.	Ans. 17.3 cm^3 = 1.055 cu. in.

British units of volume measure may be changed to metric units by multiplying the given unit by the number of metric units in one British unit. For example, to change 3.2 cubic feet to cubic meters, simply multiply by (0.028 3), the metric unit equivalent of one cubic foot. The product (0.090 56) is in terms of metric units (m^3). Thus, 3.2 cu. ft. = 0.090 6 m^3.

G. PRINCIPLES OF VOLUME MEASURE APPLIED TO LIQUID MEASURE (METRIC SYSTEM)

The standard unit of liquid measure in the metric system is the liter. This unit, as defined by law, is equivalent to a volume of 1 000 cubic centimeters or 1 cubic decimeter.

	Value of the Liter	
Metric Unit of Liquid Measure	Value of Unit in Metric System	Equivalent Value in British System (Approximate)
1 liter	Standard Unit of Liquid Measure	1.057 qts.
	1 000 cm^3 1 dm^3	61.023 cu. in.

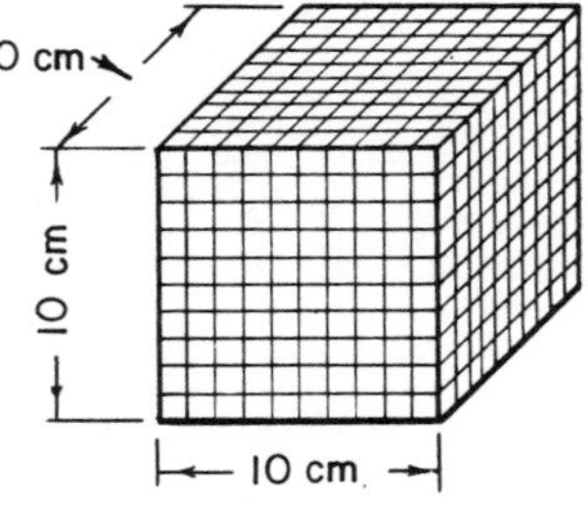

The same methods of computing the liquid capacity of a container are used regardless of whether the volume is expressed in British or metric units. Known values in one system may be changed readily to a desired unit in the other system.

Comparison of British and Metric Units of Liquid Measure	
British Units	**Equivalent in Metric Units (Approximate)**
1 qt.	0.946 liters
1 gal.	3.785 liters

RULE FOR CHANGING TO METRIC AND BRITISH UNITS OF LIQUID MEASURE

- Determine the equivalent value of one British or metric unit from a comparison table.
- Multiply the given value by the equivalent value in the desired unit.
- Express the product in the desired unit.

EXAMPLE: How many liters are there in 3 quarts?

Step 1 Determine the equivalent value in liters of one quart. 1 qt. = 0.946 liters

Step 2 Multiply the (3) quarts by (0.946). 3 x 0.946 = 2.838

Step 3 Express the product as liters. Ans. 3 qts. = 2.838 liters

ASSIGNMENT UNIT 36

A. CHANGING UNITS OF MEASURE

1. Change the linear dimensions given in either the conventional metric or British system to the units of measure specified in each case.

a. 200 cm to m
b. 70 dm to m
c. 3 000 mm to m
d. 575 cm to m
e. 312 cm to dm
f. 75 mm to cm
g. 675 mm to dm
h. 3 in. to cm
i. 5.4 in. to cm
j. 7 ft. to m
k. 3.2 ft. to m
l. 12 yds. to m
m. 6.5 yds. to m
n. 2 m to in.
o. 15.3 m to in.
p. 25.4 cm to in.
q. 12.7 cm to in.
r. 50.8 mm to in.

Ans.: b. 7 m e. 31.2 dm h. 7.62 cm k. .975 m n. 78.74 in. q. 5 in.

2. Change each conventional metric or British unit of surface measure to the unit of measure specified in each case.

a. 3100 sq. in. to m^2
b. 6925 sq. in. to m^2
c. 62 sq. in. to dm^2
d. 127.875 sq. in. to dm^2
e. 6 sq. in. to cm^2
f. 3 1/2 sq. in. to cm^2
g. 9 sq. ft. to m^2
h. 3 1/2 sq. yds. to m^2
i. 5.5 m^2 to sq. in.
j. 3.2 dm^2 to sq. in.
k. 7.25 cm^2 to sq. in.
l. 725.6 cm^2 to sq. in.

Ans.: b. 4.47 m^2 d. 8.25 dm^2 f. 22.582 cm^2 h. 2.926 m^2 j. 49.6 sq. in. l. 112.469 sq. in.

3. Change each conventional metric or British unit of volume measure to the unit of measure specified in each case.

   a. 2 000 dm^3 to m^3
   b. .75 dm^3 to cm^3
   c. 700.5 cm^3 to mm^3
   d. 10 m^3 to $ft.^3$
   e. 5 dm^3 to $in.^3$
   f. 4.5 m^3 to $yds.^3$
   g. 16 $in.^3$ to cm^3
   h. 3.6 $ft.^3$ to m^3

   Ans.: b. 750 cm^3 d. 352.14 cu. ft. f. 5.886 cu. yds. h. .101 88 m^3

4. Change each conventional metric or British unit of liquid or volume measure to the unit of measure specified in each case.

   a. 3 000 cm^3 to liters
   b. 17 dm^3 to liters
   c. 122.046 $in.^3$ to liters
   d. 5 liters to quarts
   e. 12 qts. to liters
   f. 3.171 qts. to liters
   g. 6.57 liters to gallons
   h. 31 1/2 gals. to liters

   Ans.: b. 17 liters d. 5.285 quarts f. 3 liters h. 119.228 liters

5. Establish the weight of each machine (A through E) in its metric equivalent. Round off each value to one decimal place. Then, give the metric weight of the five machines.

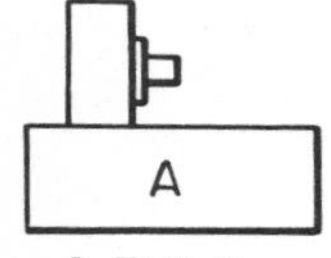

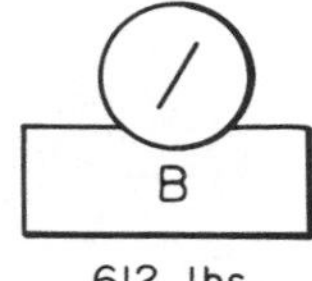

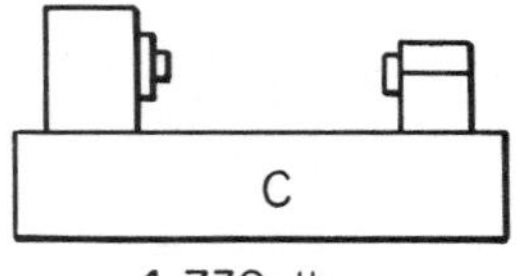

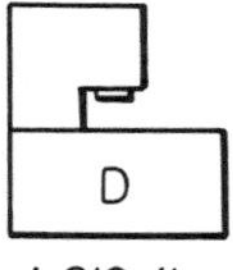

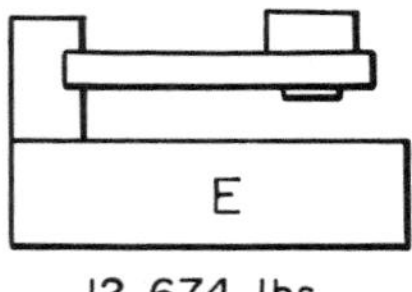

   Ans.: B. 278.2 kg D. 826.8 kg Total 10 249.1 kg

B. **DIRECT LINEAR MEASUREMENTS IN THE METRIC SYSTEM**

1. Read and record each metric measurement (A through J) as indicated. The first rule has graduations in millimeters. On the second rule the numbered graduations are in centimeters. Each division represents 1 millimeter. State dimensions F through J in terms of centimeter values.

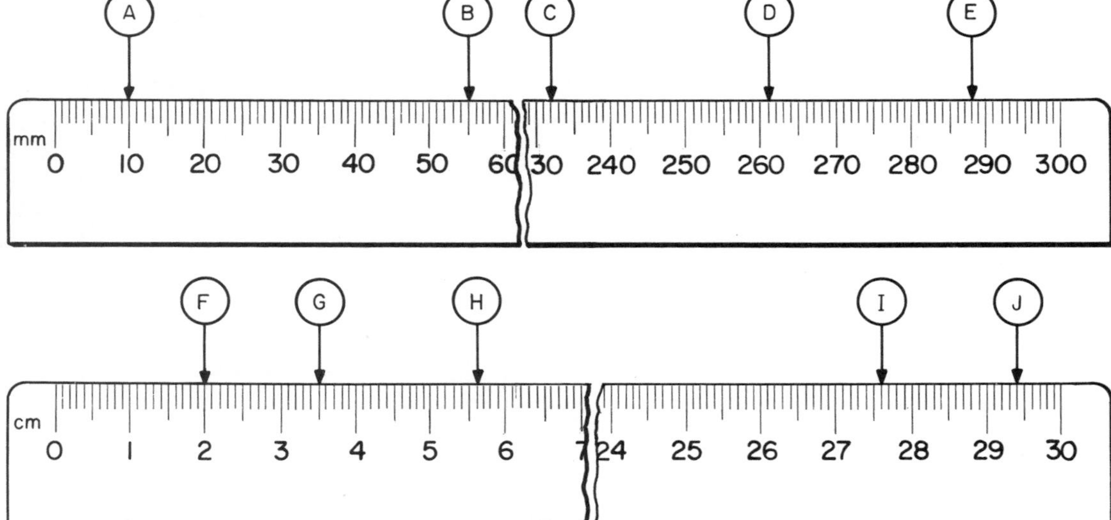

2. Measure the length of lines (a) through (i) to the degree of accuracy indicated. Measurements are to be metric.

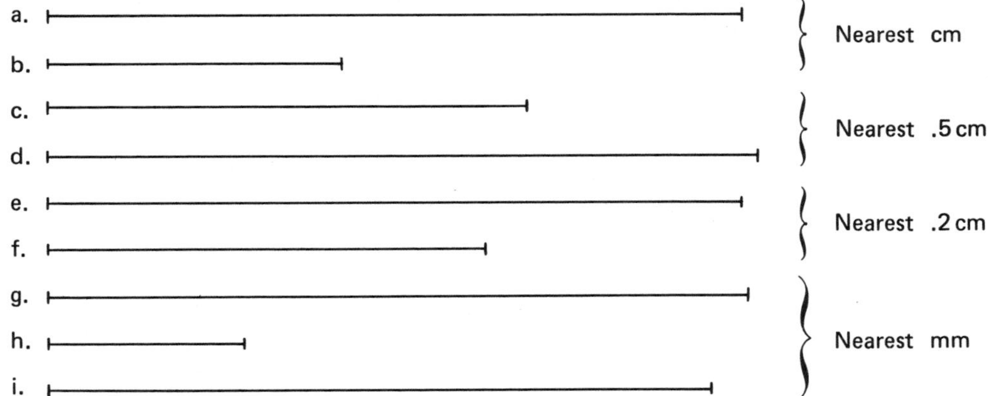

3. Measure and record lengths A, B, C and D. Dimensions are in cm. Add the centerline distance to the sum of A, B, C and D. Check this overall measurement with dimension E.

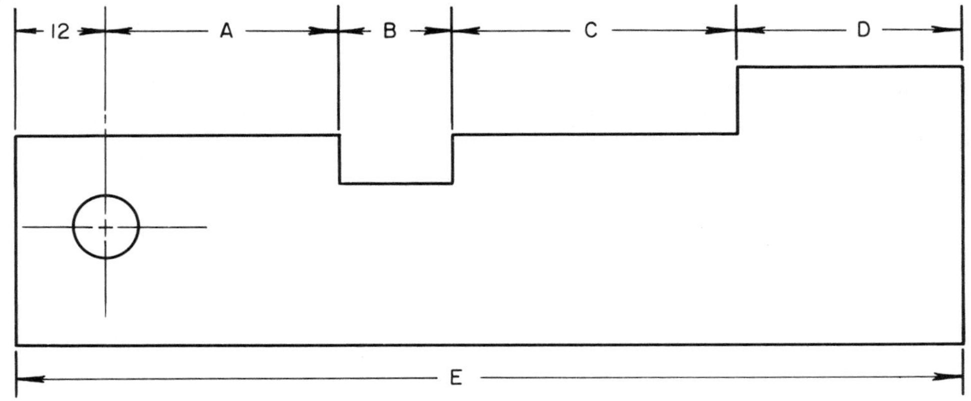

4. Measure the outside diameters of bars A, B, C, D and E with a caliper. Transfer this measurement to a rule. Record the diameter to the nearest 0.1 centimeter.

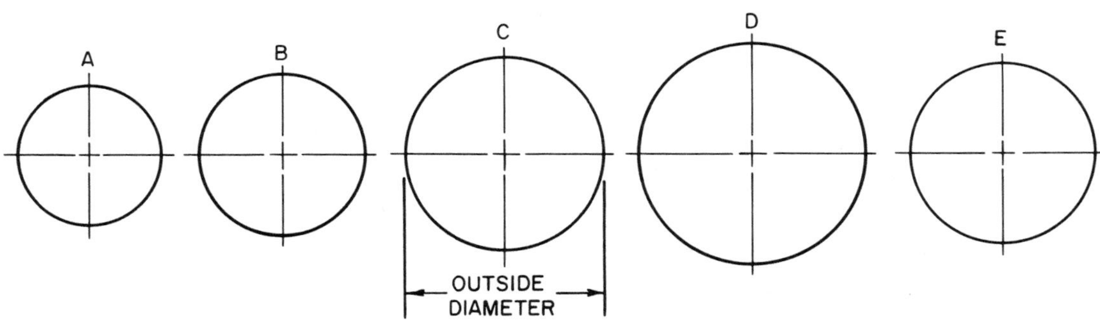

5. Use a metric scale of 1:100.
   a. Measure the lengths of sections A, B, C and D. Record each measurement to the nearest centimeter (cm).
   b. Give the overall length (E) of the structure. Then, add each dimension and check the sum against the overall length.

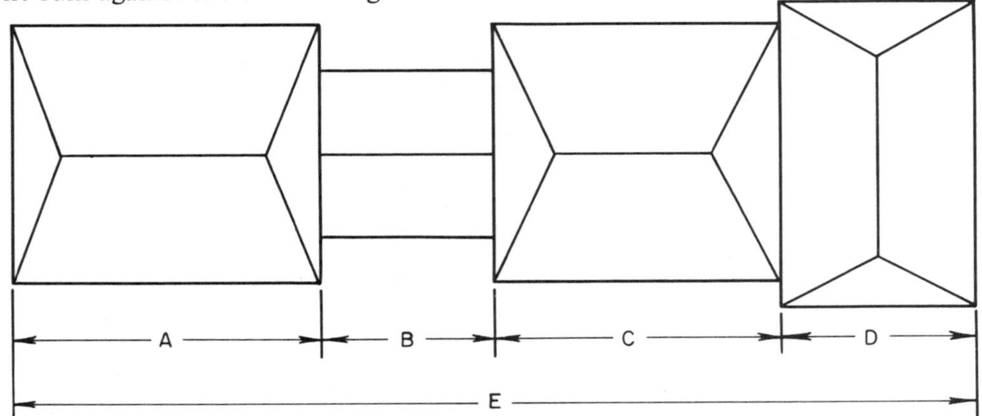

6. Read the linear dimensions on the metric micrometer readings at A, B and C. Estimate the third decimal place measurement for settings D and E. (Note: The sleeve graduations in the illustration are enlarged for easier reading.)

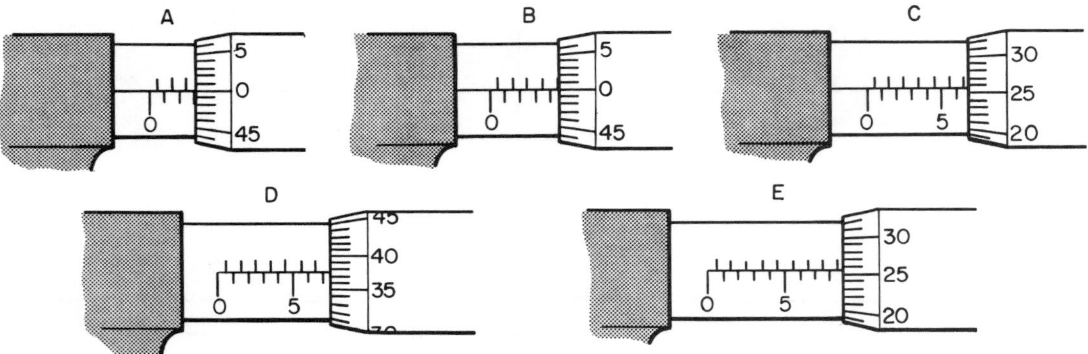

C. INDIRECT METRIC MEASUREMENTS

1. Compute dimensions A, B, C, D, E and F to the nearest 0.01 mm. State each dimension in terms of centimeters.

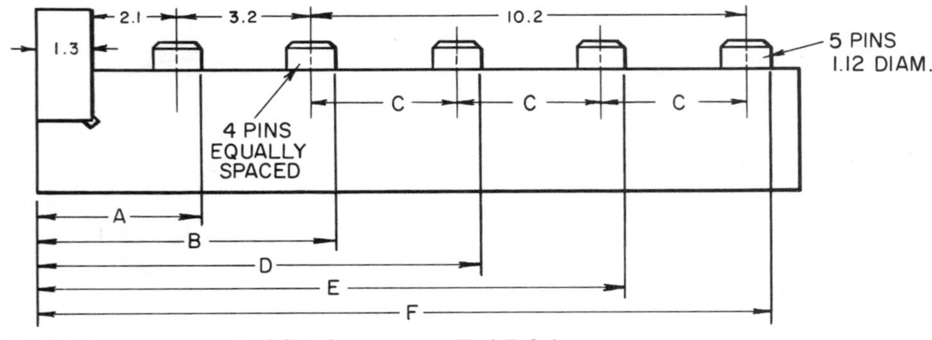

Ans.: B. 7.16 cm D. 10.56 cm F. 17.36 cm

2. Calculate dimensions A through J to which the shaft must be rough turned. Allow 1.6 mm on all diameters and 0.8 mm on all faces for finish machining.

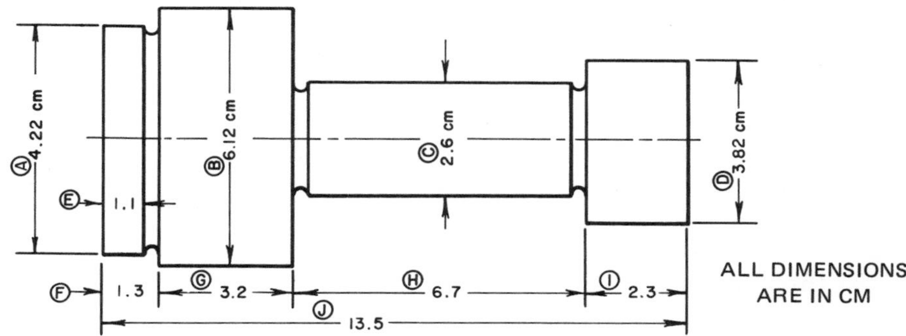

Ans.: C. 2.612 cm F. 1.38 cm I. 2.38 cm

3. Use the same drawing of the shaft. Determine dimensions A through J to which the part must be finish-turned before grinding. Allow 0.2 mm on all diameters and 0.16 mm on all faces for grinding.

Ans.: C. 2.62 cm F. 1.316 cm I. 2.316 cm

D. APPLICATION OF SQUARE MEASURE IN THE METRIC SYSTEM

1. Determine the area of square A in square centimeters and of rectangle B in square decimeters.

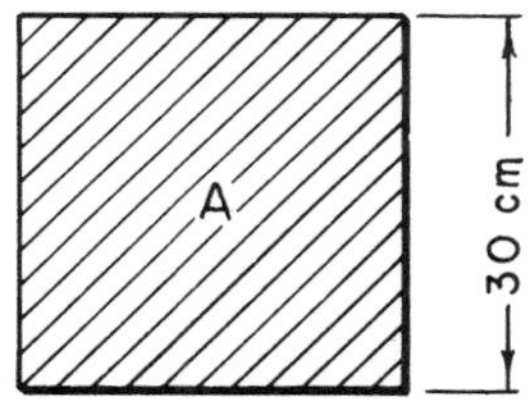

B

9 dm

2.5 m

Ans.: B. 225 dm^2

2. Determine the area of circles A and B from the given diameters, and the area of C and D from the given radii.

Ans.: B. 44.178 75 cm^2
D. 1 576.329 cm^2

	A	B	C	D
Diameter	4 dm	7.5 cm	—	—
Radius	—	—	2 m	22.4 cm

3. Determine the area of the sector of circle A and the shaded area of B.

Ans.: B. 34.410 992 cm^2

A

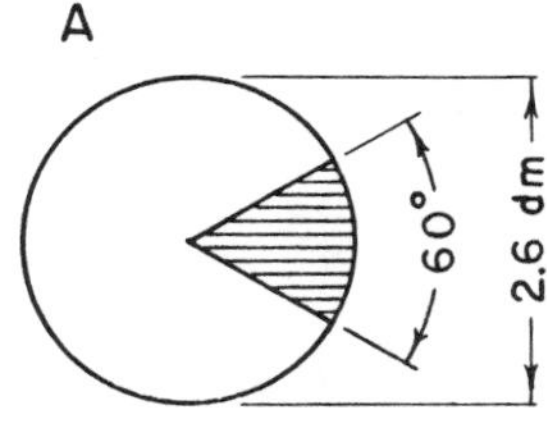

B

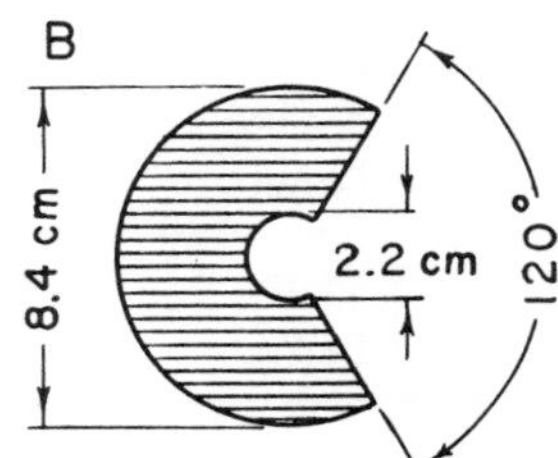

4. Compute the cross-sectional area of the link. Express the result in square inches correct to two decimal places.

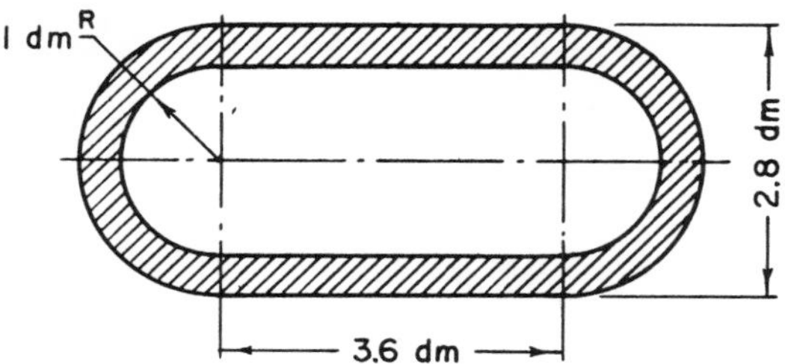

5. A form is to be built for a circular pool. The pool is 4.34 meters in diameter by 1.5 meters high. Find (a) the surface area and (b) the number of boards required to construct the form. The boards are 7.62 cm wide. Round off the surface area to two decimal places and the boards to the next board.

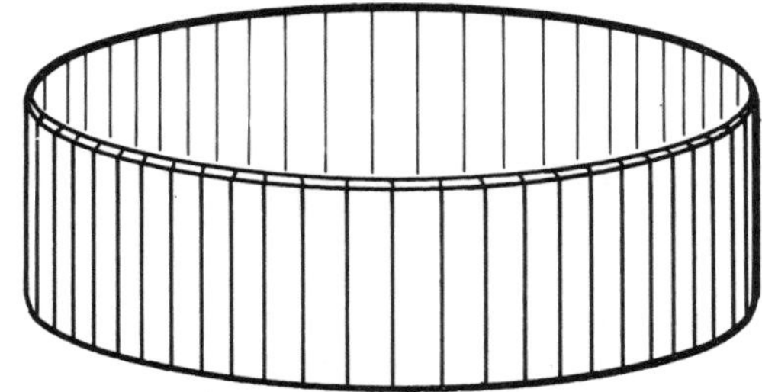

Ans.: (b) 179 boards

E. **APPLICATION OF VOLUME MEASURE IN THE METRIC SYSTEM**

1. Determine the volume of cube A in cubic decimeters and rectangular solid B in cubic meters.

	A	B
Length	6.2 dm	1.2 m
Depth	6.2 dm	18 dm
Height	6.2 dm	9.4 dm

Ans.: B. 2.030 4 m^3

2. Find the volume of the rectangular parts A and B.

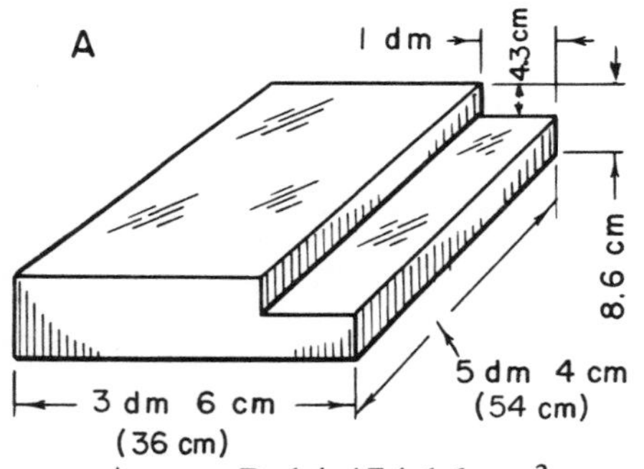

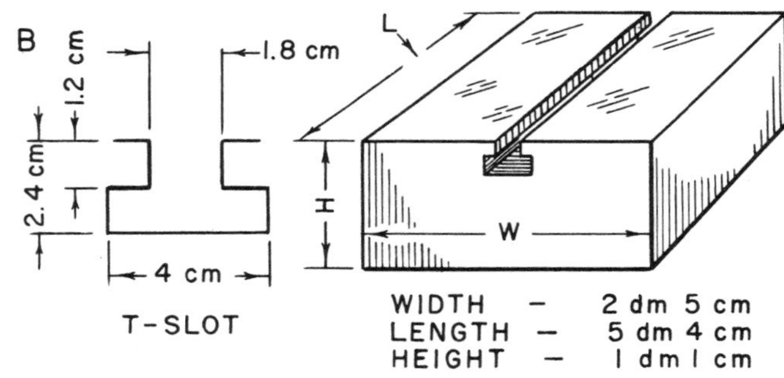

Ans.: B. 14 474.16 cm^3

3. Determine the volume of cylinders A, B, and C. Express the volume correct to two decimal places in the unit of measure indicated in each case.

			Volume in
A	Diam. Length	8.2 cm 24.6 cm	cm^3
B	Radius Length	2.4 dm 3.2 dm	dm^3
C	Diam. Length	6 cm 4 mm 4 dm 4 cm 8 mm	cm^3

Ans.: B. 57.91 dm^3

4. Find the volume of the bronze bushing in cubic decimeters.

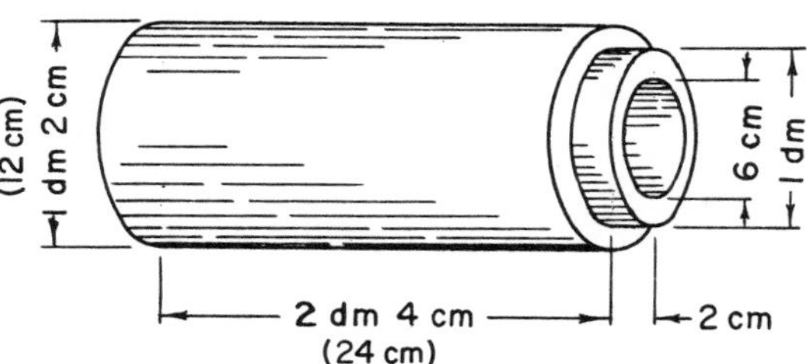

5. Determine the weight in pounds of the 15 bronze bushings described in the drawing.

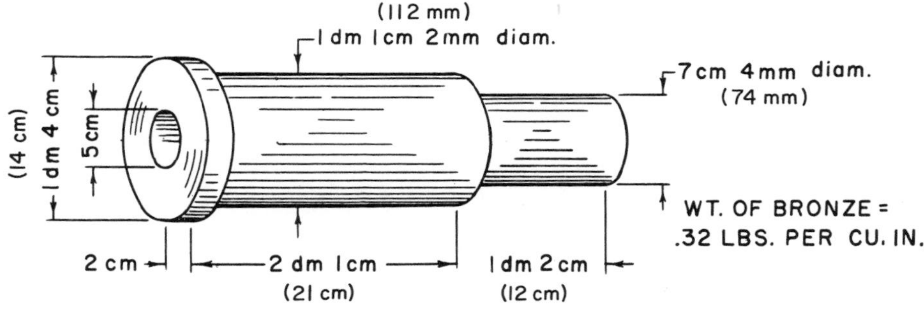

Ans.: 646.068 lbs.

6. Determine the weight of 50 cast iron castings conforming to the specifications given on the drawing.

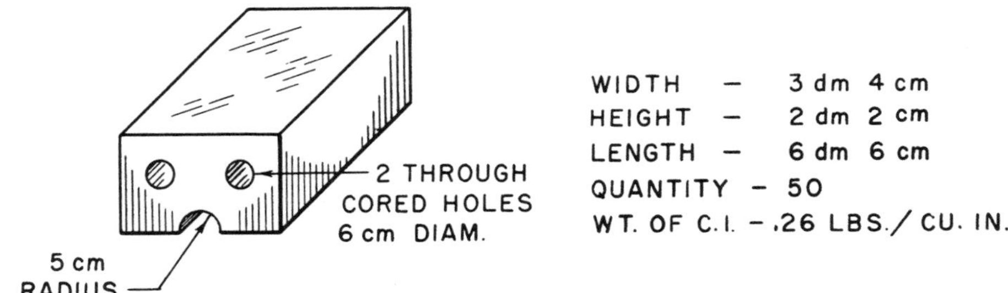

F. APPLICATION OF LIQUID MEASURE IN THE METRIC SYSTEM

1. Find the liquid capacity of the rectangular coolant tank to the nearest quart.

Ans.: 65 quarts

2. Determine the liquid capacity of the outer shell of the quenching tank to the nearest gallon.

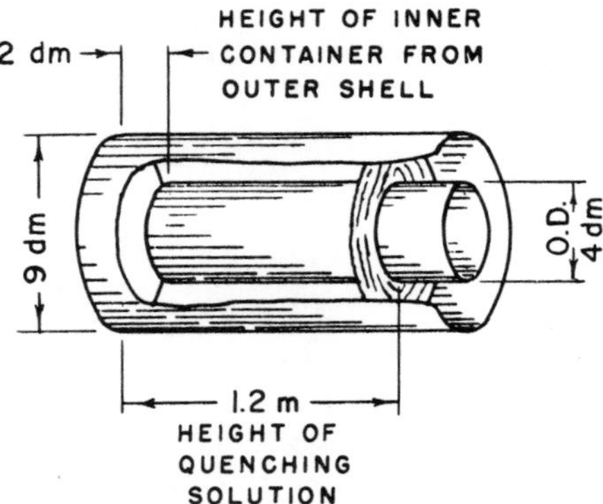

3. Compute the liquid capacity of containers A, B, C and D. State each capacity in the unit of measure indicated in the table, rounded to two decimal places.

Container	Diameter (d) or Radius (r)	Height (H)	Required Unit of Measure
A	(d) 25.4 cm	38.1 cm	cm^3
B	(d) 15.24 cm	11.43 cm	liters
C	(r) 64.77 cm	76.84 cm	qts.
D	(d) 1.3 m	2.36 m	gals.

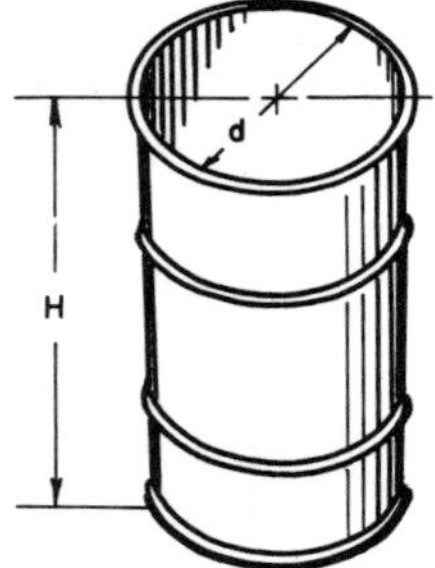

Ans.: B. 2.09 liters D.827.51 gals.

Unit 37 THE EVOLVING INTERNATIONAL SYSTEM – SI METRICS

Seven base units, two supplementary units and a series of derived units represent all units of measure in SI Metrics. This system has been stated to be adequate to measure all known physical quantities.

In review, everyday mathematical problems involving SI Metrics are solved using base decimal ten multiple and submultiple vaiues. Quantities, problems and solutions are stated according to guidelines for writing in SI Metrics.

Symbols are used in the system. These provide a convenient, consistent, simple method of designating a specific unit or combination of units. Prefixes further simplify the unit designations, mathematical processes and solutions.

Each SI Metric unit may be converted to customary units or conventional metric units of measure. Tables are readily available which give:

- The quantity to be measured (like density, D),
- The unit of measure (kilograms per cubic meter, kg/m^3),
- The formula ($D = kg/m^3$),
- The conversion units which may be in SI Metrics and conventional metric or customary units (for example: g/cm^3, or lb $(mass)/ft.^3$), and
- The conversion factor and mathematical processes like,

$$kg/m^3 = lb\ (mass)/in.^3 \cdot (2.768 \times 10^4).$$

A. SEVEN BASE UNITS OF MEASURE IN SI METRICS

The seven base units of measure cover: length, mass, time, electrical current, temperature, luminous intensity, and the substance of a system.

1. Unit of Length

The illustration shows how the meter as a measure of length is standardized. The $Krypton_{86}$ atom is designated by the symbol. The waveform in a vacuum of the radiation of an atom is shown graphically. The waveform indicates transition in energy levels of the $Krypton_{86}$ atom. This combination of scientific activity, transferred to the measuring bar represents the precise measurement of the meter.

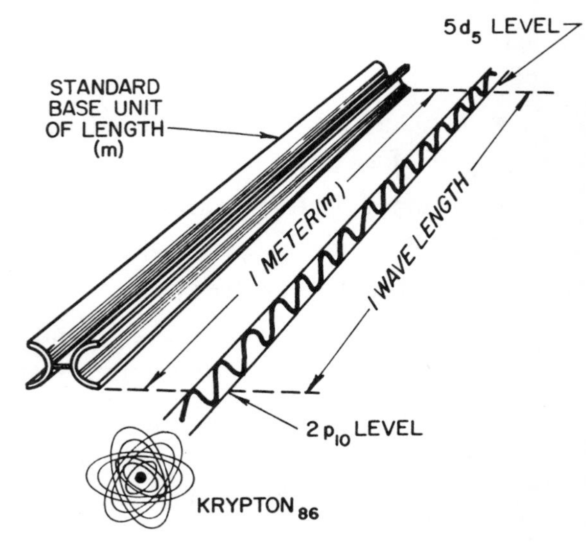

In SI Metrics (like all other metric systems) the meter (m) is the standard unit of length. One major difference between the earlier meter standard and the present one is in the definition and in the method of reproducing a standard meter measuring bar. Years ago the meter represented a fixed value in relation to the earth's circumference. Standard measuring bars were compared for precision and accuracy against a standard held by the International Bureau and the earlier scientific academy. The duplicate measuring bars were "prototypes." The prototypes were the standards for each participating nation.

The SI standard unit of length (the meter) may now be reproduced in a laboratory anywhere in the world. Restated, the meter refers to a "length." The "length" is equal to 1 650 763.73 wavelengths in a vacuum of the Krypton_{86} atom. The conditions of the atom are defined in terms of radiation of the atom and specific energy levels. The radiation corresponds to the transition of the atom between the $2p_{10}$ and $5d_5$ energy levels. These terms, values and conditions provide adequate description. The engineer, scientist, and measurement laboratory technologist may translate this meter definition into a precise measuring bar standard.

Measurements must be taken that range all the way from minute particles finer than a billionth part of a meter to earth-outer space dimensions, each representing great multi-digit quantities. Thus, a series of more practical units of measure are derived from the meter as the base unit.

2. Unit of Mass

The "kilogram" still represents a "unit of mass." The kilogram is equivalent to 2.2 pounds. Other recommended multiples of the SI unit are the megagram (Mg), gram (g), milligram (mg) and microgram (μg). The metric ton (t) is another unit that may be used. $1\,t = 10^3$ kg. Additional derived units that relate to mass are covered later.

3. Unit of Time

The "second" remains as the unit of time. Again, this unit is defined scientifically in terms of periods of radiation, an atom, and two levels of activity. The "second" is the duration of

- 9 192 631 770 periods of radiation of a
- cesium_{133} atom corresponding to the
- transition levels between
- two hyperfine levels of the ground state. All of these phenomena may be reproduced in the laboratory for the setting of standards.

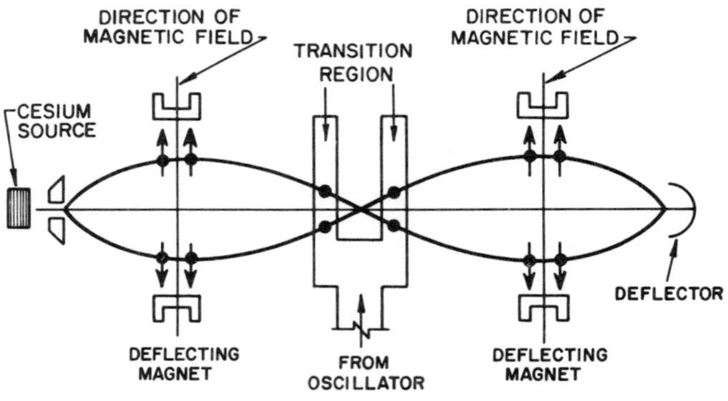

The duration, or time interval, of a second is still 1/86 400th of the mean solar day. The designation for second is (s). Recommended decimal multiple and submultiples of the SI unit include the kilosecond (ks), millisecond (ms), microsecond (μs) and the nanosecond (ns). Other units that may be used are the customary ones of minute, hour and day.

4. Unit of Electric Current

The "ampere" is the unit of intensity of electric current. As a common name, the ampere is designated by the capital (A). Other recommended values of this SI unit include the kiloampere (kA), milliampere (mA), microampere (μA), nanoampere (nA) and picoampere (pA). Note that most of these examples express submultiple decimal values of an ampere.

The illustration shows two straight parallel conductors of negligible cross section and infinite length. These are placed one meter apart in a vacuum. The "ampere" is that constant, which if maintained in the two conductors, produces a force equal to 2 x 10^{-7} newton/meter of length.

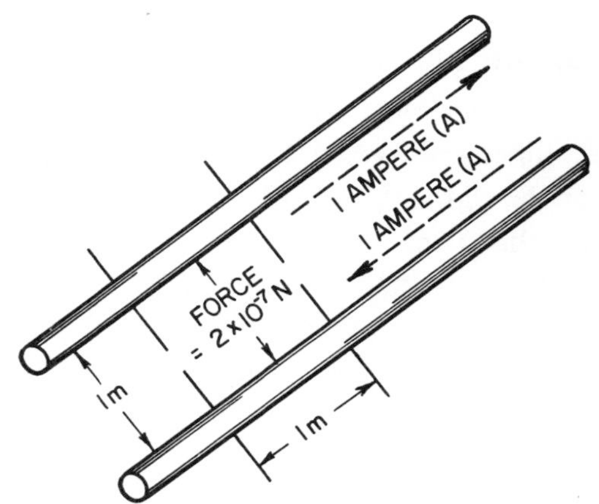

5. Unit of Temperature

The "kelvin" (K) is the SI unit of thermodynamic temperature. A kelvin temperature is expressed without the ° symbol. The boiling point of water on the kelvin scale is 373.15 K degrees (373.15 K). Water freezes at 273.15 K. The "kelvin" is defined as being equal to 1/273.16 of the thermodynamic temperature of the triple point of water.

The more commonly used temperature measurement unit is the derived "Celsius" degree. Temperatures are readily convertible between the kelvin and Celsius, and the kelvin and Fahrenheit readings by transposing values in these two formulas:

$$t_K = t_C + 273.15 \qquad t_K = \frac{(t_F + 459.67)}{1.8}$$

6. Unit of Luminous Intensity

The "candela" is the SI "unit of luminous intensity." The candela was adopted at the 13th CGPM in 1967. By scientific definition the candela represents

- the luminous intensity (in the perpendicular direction) of
- a surface 1/600 000 square meter of a blackbody
- at the temperature of freezing platinum under a pressure of
- 101 325 newtons per square meter.

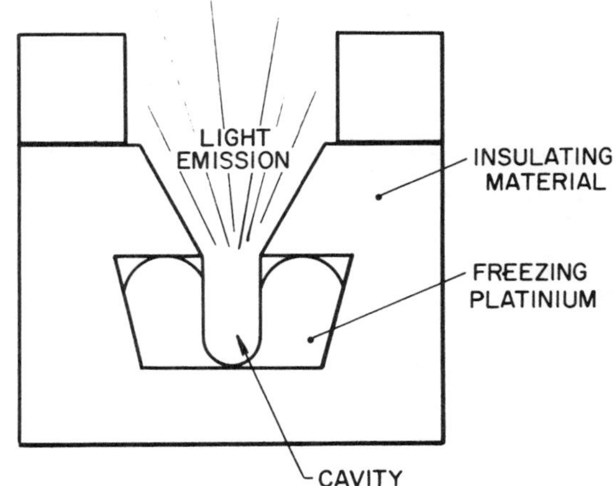

7. Amount of Substance of a System

The "mole" (mol) was introduced in physical chemistry and molecular physics. The mole represents a unit of measure of the quantity: "amount of substance." The SI definition states: "One mole is an amount of substance of a system which contains as many elementary units as there are carbon atoms in exactly 0.012 kg of C_{12}." The elementary unit must be specified. It may be an atom, molecule, ion, electron, or a selected group of particles.

The mole and kilomole (kmol) are used to denote amount of substance of a system. Molar mass is expressed in kilogram/mole (kg/mol) or gram/mole (g/mol). Molar volume quantities are stated as cubic meter/mole (m^3/mol) and cubic meter/kilomole (m^3/kmol).

B. SUPPLEMENTARY UNITS OF ANGULAR MEASURE

There are two types of angles in SI Metrics for which supplementary units have been developed. There is a "plane" angle and a "solid angle." The *"radian"* is the unit of measure of the plane angle. The "radian" (rad) represents an angle which has its vertex at the center of a circle. The sides of the angle are subtended by an arc. The arc is equal in length to the radius. The angle thus formed is a radian.

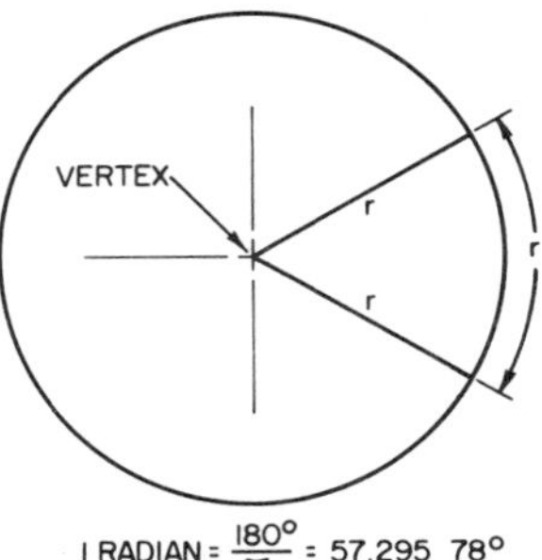

I RADIAN = $\frac{180°}{\pi}$ = 57.295 78°

Translating this definition into a simple mathematical statement, 1 rad = $180°/\pi$ = 57.295 78°. The recommended SI units for radian are milliradian (mrad) and microradian (μ rad). Other customary units that may be used include degree (°), minute (′), second (″) and grad (^{g}).

The "solid angle" is the other supplementary unit in SI. The "solid angle" (*"steradian,"* sr) has its vertex at the center of a sphere. The steradian encloses an area of the spherical surface. The enclosed area is equal to that of a square. The sides of the square are equal in length to the radius.

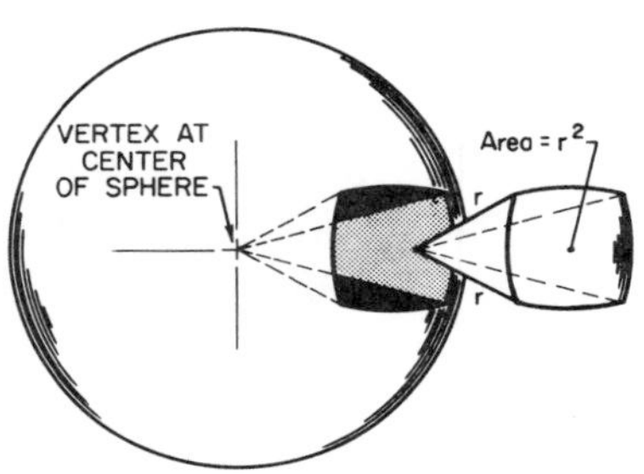

C. DERIVED UNITS OF MEASURE

There are many instances when base or supplementary units of measure are not suitable and "derived" units are required. These are derived from base or supplementary units. In general, the preferred units of measure in SI Metrics are multiples of three (3): like, kilo (k, 10^3), mega (M, 10^6), giga (G, 10^9) or milli (m, 10^{-3}), micro (μ, 10^{-6}) and pico (p, 10^{-12}).

1. Derived Length, Area and Volume Units

The decimal multiple and submultiples of SI units that are used for linear measurements include the kilometer (km), millimeter (mm), micrometer (μm) and nanometer (nm). The decimeter (dm) and centimeter (cm) are also accepted.

The derived units of area and volume are also related to the meter as the base unit. In area measure, the square kilometer (km^2) and square millimeter (mm^2) are recommended multiples. The dm^2 and cm^2 are accepted. For larger measurements the "are" and "hectare" are other units. 1 are (a) = $10^2 m^2$ (100 square meters); 1 hectare (ha) = $10^4 m^2$ (10 000 square meters).

In volume measure, the mm^3 is a recommended multiple of the base unit of m^3. The dm^3 and cm^3 are accepted units of volume measure. The "liter" has been declared as an acceptable SI unit. One liter equals one cubic decimeter ($1\ \ell = 1\ dm^3$). In terms of the meter, $1\ \ell = 10^{-3}\ m^3$ or $0.001\ m^3$ or $1\ cm^3$. The centiliter, milliliter and hectoliter are other accepted units of volume measure.

$1\ c\ell = 10^{-5}\ m^3$ (or $0.000\ 01\ m^3$); $1\ m\ell = 10^{-6}\ m^3$ (or $0.000\ 001\ m^3$) or $1\ cm^3$

2. Units Derived from the Unit of Mass

Units of force, work, power, pressure, and others are derived from the kilogram as the base unit of mass. Recommended multiples of the kg are Mg, g, mg, and μg. Repeating, the metric ton (t) = 10^3 kg. In measuring mass density (kg/m^3), the derived unit of $1\ t/m^3$ is the equivalent of $1\ kg/\ell = 1\ g/m\ell$. Other more common units follow.

Force. Force is measured in "newtons" (N). The SI unit of force is N · m. A force of one newton applied to a mass of one kilogram produces an acceleration of one meter per second per second. Expressed as a formula,

$$N = kg \cdot m/s^2$$

Work: Energy, Quantity of Heat. Work is measured in "joules." One joule of work is produced when a force of one newton is applied through a distance of one meter (J = N · m). Work is usually expressed in gigajoules, megajoules, kilojoules and millijoules (GJ, MJ, kJ and mJ). Another practical unit of measure is the kilowatt-hour (kWh) of work.

$$1\ kWh = 3.6 \times 10^6\ J \text{ or } 3.6\ MJ$$

Power. The "watt" (W) is the SI unit of power. It represents one joule of work completed in one second.

$$W = J/s \text{ or } N \cdot m/s$$

Pressure. The "pascal" (Pa) is the SI unit for measuring pressure. A pascal is equal to one newton per meter squared.

$$Pa = N/m^2$$

3. Units Derived from the Units of Time

Three commonly needed units of measure that are derived from the second include: frequency (f), velocity (v) and acceleration (a).

Frequency. Frequency denotes the number of cycles per second. The "hertz" is the SI unit of measure of frequency.

$$1\ Hz = 1\ s^{-1}$$

Velocity. Velocity (v) relates to distance and time. It is measured in terms of meters per second. v = m/s Velocity is also expressed in the derived unit of kilometer per hour

$$1\ km/h = \frac{1}{3.6}\ m/s$$

Acceleration. Acceleration (a) denotes a rate of change in velocity. Acceleration is equal to distance (meters) divided by time in seconds squared.

$$a = m/s^2$$

4. Units Derived from the Base Electrical Unit

Six common electrical measurements relate to: potential, resistance, capacitance, quantity, inductance and magnetic flux. These characteristics are measured by units which are derived from the "ampere" (A) as the base unit. The table indicates the derived unit in each case and the formula.

Base Electrical Unit: Ampere (A)		
Electrical Measurement	Derived Unit of Measurement	Formula
potential	volt (V)	V = W/A
resistance	ohm (Ω)	Ω = V/A
capacitance	farad (F)	F = A • (s/V)
quantity	coulomb (C)	C = A • s
inductance	henry (H)	H = Wb/A
flux	weber (Wb)	Wb = V • s

5. Units Derived from the Base Unit of Luminous Intensity

The "candela" (cd) is the base unit of luminous intensity. There are two major derived units from the candela. "Illumination lux" (lx) is defined in scientific terms as the luminous intensity given by a luminous flux of one "lumen" (lm) per square meter. $lx = lm/m^2$

Another derived unit is the "lumen" (lm, luminous flux). The lumen is equal to (candela) x (steradian). m = cd • sr In science, the lumen is equal to the luminous flux emitted in a solid angle of one steradian. The point source has a uniform intensity of one candela (cd). The "watt" (W), as a common unit of electrical power, equals 17 lumens. 1 W = 17 lm

6. Units Derived from the Base Unit of Temperature

The degree Celsius is the derived unit of temperature. It is used in general everyday applications. Unlike the kelvin (K) SI unit, a temperature on the Celsius scale is followed by the °C symbol. The degree Celsius replaced the Centigrade designation. The freezing and boiling point of water on the Celsius scale is 0°C and 100°C, respectively. The mathematical relationships between computing Celsius and the customary Fahrenheit degrees remain the same.

Many problems still require the conversion of temperature units between the customary and other metric systems. The same simple formulas that were used between the former Centigrade and Fahrenheit scales apply to Celsius/Fahrenheit conversions.

$$t_C = (t_F - 32) \cdot 5/9 \qquad t_F = (t_C \times 9/5) + 32$$

or

$$t_C = (t_F - 32) \div 1.8 \qquad t_F = 1.8t_C + 32$$

7. Units Derived from the Base Unit of Time

The day (d), hour (h), minute (min) and week, month and year are commonly used units of time. Each is derived from the "second" as the base unit. The value of each of these derived units and its use in mathematical computations follows the customary and conventional metric systems.

8. Units Derived from the Base Molar Unit

As stated earlier, the "mole" (mol) is the latest base unit in SI Metrics. Other units have been derived for the measurement of molar mass, volume, internal energy, heat energy and other molecular measurements. The derived unit for each quantity relates the mole to the nature of the quantity. For example, kg/mol to measure molar mass, J/mol for molar internal energy, and J/(mol • K) or J/(kmol • °C) for molar heat capacity.

D. CONVERSION FACTORS AND PROCESSES IN METRICATION

It is possible to remember some of the commonly used values and formulas for computing specific quantities. However, it is a more accurate practice to use tables containing both formulas and numerical values. These tables are identified as "tables of conversion factors."

Different tables are available depending on the degree of precision required. In engineering and scientific problems, tables are used that have a great number of least significant digits (decimal places). Tables ranging from six to eight place decimal values are adequate for general applications. The final result is then rounded off depending on the required accuracy.

A smaller unit of measure is changed to a larger unit in the metric system by moving the decimal point to the left. In the case of changing 1 700 millimeters to meters, the value is stated as 1.7 m. In reverse, zeros are added and the decimal point is moved to the right. 12 MHz = 12 000 000 Hz

When a conversion table is used, a conversion factor like 1 mm = 0.039 37″ may be changed to 1 cm = 0.393 7″, or 1 km = 39 370″. The prefix indicates the relationship of the numerical value to the unit of measure.

RECIPROCAL PROCESSES IN CONVERSION

While a table may give one set of conversion factors, other units of measure may be computed. The reverse process is performed by using reciprocals.

Mathematical processes involving reciprocals are covered in later units. For the present, "using the reciprocal" means dividing (1) by a numerical value. For example, to convert feet to meters the conversion factor is 0.304 8. Thus, 10 ft. = 10 • (0.304 8) or 3.048 m. The answer in meters may be converted to its feet equivalent by using the reciprocal of the multiplier (0.304 8). In this instance, the reciprocal is 1/0.304 8. Thus, 3.048/0.304 8 = 10 ft.

Tables are available for conversion of common quantities from SI or conventional metrics to customary units and the reverse. Other tables are detailed for specialized application. Part of Conversion Table·V that appears in the Appendix is reproduced. Selected units of measure are grouped according to use by categories (like: acceleration, area and density). Conversion factors are indicated for units of measure in the three common measurement systems.

CONVERSION FACTORS FOR SI, CONVENTIONAL METRIC AND CUSTOMARY UNITS (Abstract of Table V, Appendix)

Conversion of Customary Metric Units to SI Metrics				Conversion of SI Metrics to Customary and Conventional Metric Units		
Category	From ↓ Customary or Conventional Metric Unit →	To SI Metric →	Factor (A) (Multiply by) ↓	From ↓ SI Metric →	To Customary or Conventional Metric Unit →	Factor Multiply by the reciprocal of the multiplier (Factor A) which is used in conversion to the SI Metric unit
acceleration	ft./s^2	m/s^2	0.304 8	m/s^2	ft./s^2	↓
	in./s^2		$2.540\ 0 \times 10^{-2}$ *		in./s^2	↓
area	ft.^{2}	m^2	$9.290\ 3 \times 10^{-2}$	m^2	ft.^{2}	
	in.^{2}		$6.451\ 6 \times 10^{-4}$ *		in.^{2}	↓
density	g/cm^3	kg/m^3	$1.000\ 0 \times 10^{3}$ *	kg/m^3	g/cm^3	
	lb. (mass)/ft.^{3}		16.018 5		lb. (mass)/ft.^{3}	↓
	lb. (mass)/in.^{3}		$2.768\ 0 \times 10^{4}$		lb. (mass)/in.^{3}	

*Exact values

The abstracted table summarizes earlier descriptions of different parts of SI Metrics. Symbols, power of ten decimal multiple and submultiple quantities, positive and negative values and simple mathematical processes are illustrated.

Direct and computed measurement principles and applications related to customary units of measurement were treated in Section 2. This section dealt with direct and computed measurement in the conventional metric system and SI Metrics. The ability to make direct SI and conventional metric measurements and to compute others is essential in developing occupational competency and solving daily consumer problems.

ASSIGNMENT UNIT 37

1. Indicate three specific items of information that are contained in conversion tables of units of measure.

2. The following information on three derived units of measure in each of three categories (A, B and C) is required:

   a. Indicate the area or nature of the measurement.

   b. Give the symbol of the unit of measure used.

   c. State the formula for the derived unit of measure. Note the example A 1 under Mass.

	Base Units of Measure								
	A. Mass (kilogram, kg)			B. Electric Current (ampere, A)			C. Time (second, s)		
	Derived Units of Measure								
	Nature of Measurement (a)	Symbol (b)	Formula (c)	Nature of Measurement (a)	Symbol (b)	Formula (c)	Nature of Measurement (a)	Symbol (b)	Formula (c)
1	force	N	$N = kg \cdot m/s^2$						
2									
3									

3. Give the reciprocal factor to use to convert the three required unit values (A, B, C and D) to the given value. The table provides the initial conversion information to change from the given to the required unit value.

	Measurement Values		Conversion Factor and Process	Required Reciprocal
	Given Unit Value	Required Unit Value		
A	in.	mm	25.4 (x)	
B	kg/s	lb. • mass/min	0.007 560 (÷)	
C	psi	pascal (Pa)	6 894.757 (x)	
D	grains (g)	kilograms (kg)	15 432.9 (÷)	

Ans.: B. 0.007 560/1

4. Use the table of conversion factors for SI Metrics in the Appendix.

   a. Record the factors for converting the given A, B, C and D quantities to the required SI units.

   b. Compute the required unit values.

	Category	SI Metric Units		Conversion Factor	Converted Value
		Given	Required		
A	Density	10^{12} g/cm^3	kg/m^3		
B	Energy	75 kWh	J		
C	Pressure	10^2g (force)/cm^2	N/m^2		
D	Volume	7ℓ • 10^6	m^3		

Ans.: B. 3.6 x 10^6; 270 (10^6) J

5. Compute (a) the equivalent SI Metric pressures of systems A and B. (b) Determine the total force exerted by each piston to the nearest two decimal places.

Pa = psi (6 894.757) kg (force)/m^2 = Pa (9.806 650)

Piston System	System Pressure	Equivalent SI Metric Pressure (a)	Piston Area	Total Piston Force (b)
A	10 psi	Pa	10 in^2	
B	64 Pa	kg (force)/m^2	12.2 m^2	

Ans.: B. 627.63; 7 657 kg

Unit 38 ACHIEVEMENT REVIEW ON SI METRICS AND CONVENTIONAL METRICS

A. HISTORICAL PERSPECTIVE ON STANDARDS AND UNITS OF MEASURE

1. State three reasons why international units of measure and standards change slowly but continuously.

B. ADVANTAGES OF SI METRICS

1. a. List five of the seven base units in SI Metrics.

   b. Identify the physical property that each unit measures.

SI Base Unit					
Physical Property					

2. Give three advantages of SI Metrics over other systems of weights and measures.

C. METRICATION: GOVERNMENT AND PRIVATE SECTOR

1. Secure an organization chart of the American National Metric Council. Identify three different sector committees that will deal with units of measure and other SI standards for consumer products.

D. SCIENTIFIC NOTATION SYSTEM

1. Translate each of the four given values to its equivalent SI value in the required unit.

	Given Quantity and Unit	Required Unit	Quantity SI and Abbreviation
A	1 250 grams	kilograms (kg)	
B	2 500 000 volts	megavolts (MV)	
C	1.75 meters	millimeters (mm)	
D	9 835 800 000 hertz	gigahertz (GHz)	

2. Cite three rules for writing SI Metric units of measure.

E. DIRECT LINEAR MEASUREMENTS IN THE METRIC SYSTEM

1. Measure the diameter of each of the six bored holes with an inside caliper. Transfer each measurement to a rule. Record each diameter to the nearest millimeter.

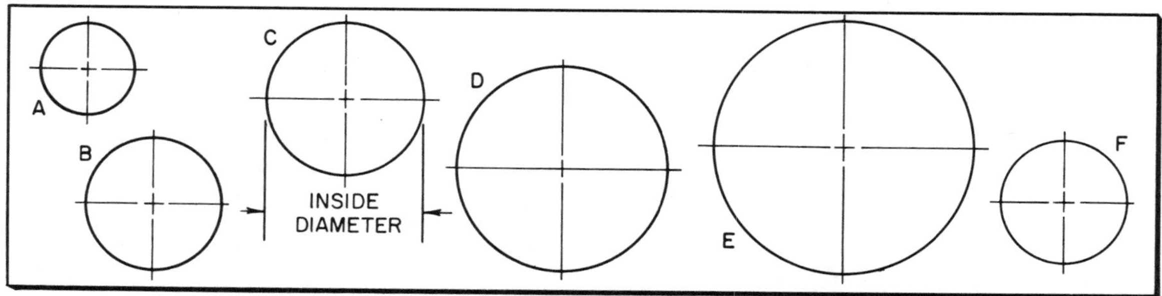

2. Read measurements A through F on the 1:50 metric drafting scale. State each measurement in terms of meter and fractional decimal values.

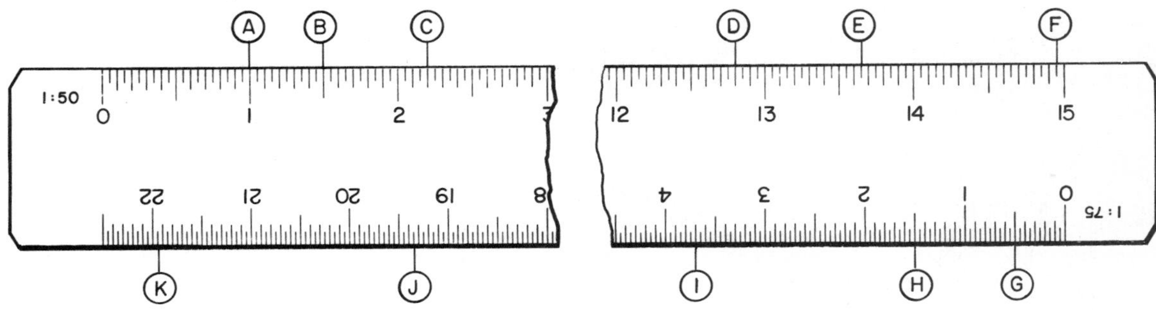

3. Read measurements G through K on the bottom 1:75 metric drafting scale. Give each reading in terms of its meter/centimeter value.
4. Determine the linear dimensions on the vernier micrometer settings A, B and C. (Note: The sleeve graduations in the illustration are enlarged for easier reading).

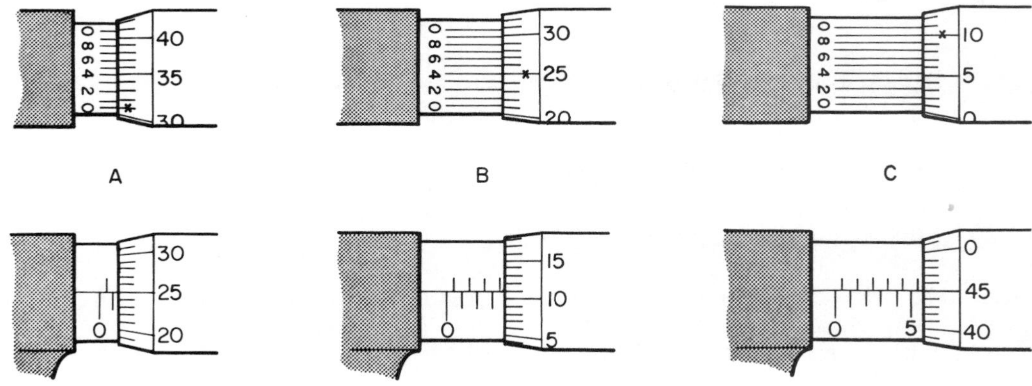

5. Read the three metric vernier caliper settings as indicated at A, B and C.

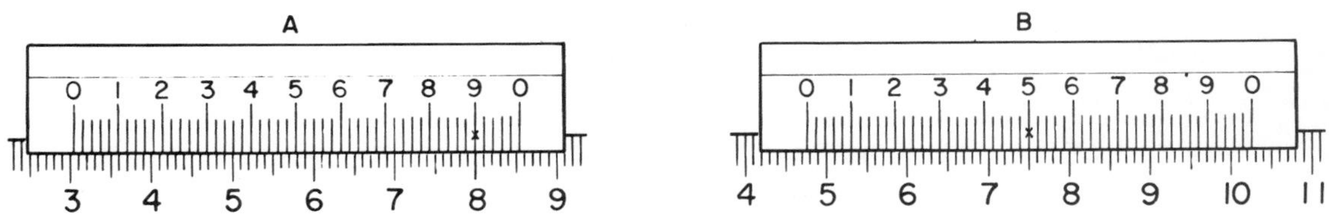

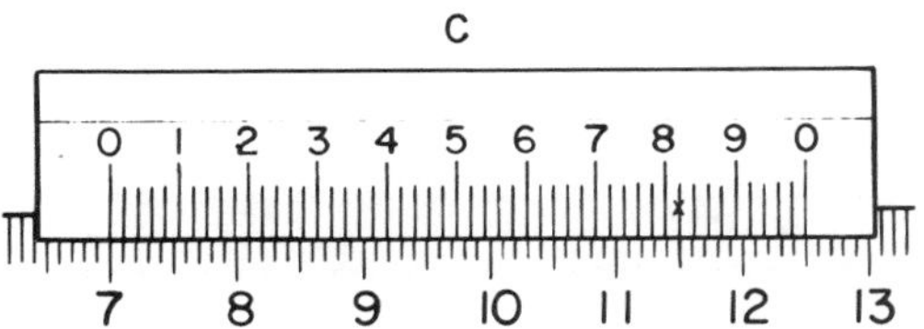

F. COMPUTED MEASUREMENTS IN THE METRIC SYSTEM

1. Determine the weight of 10 cast iron blocks to the nearest pound.

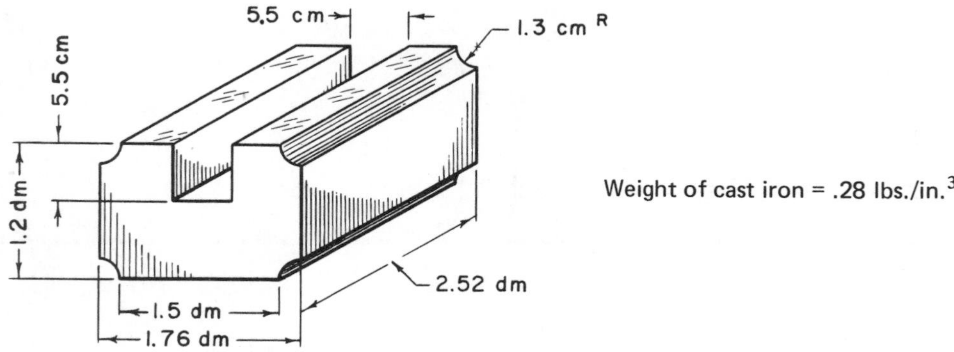

2. Compute the cost of the bronze castings illustrated correct to two decimal places.

OUTSIDE DIAMETER	1.2 dm
INSIDE DIAMETER	2.54 cm
HEIGHT	3.6 dm
NUMBER REQUIRED	12
WT. OF BRASS	.26 lbs./in.^{3}
COST	87¢ /lb.

120°

G. BASE AND DERIVED UNITS OF MEASURE IN SI METRICS

1. Make two brief statements about the need for derived units of measure in SI Metrics.
2. a. Name any one of the units of measure in SI Metrics.
   b. Give the base unit for the group or category.
   c. Name four recommended decimal multiple and submultiple units and give the symbol for each unit.

H. CONVERSION FACTORS AND PROCESSES IN METRICATION

1. Convert each of the temperature measurements (A, B, C and D) to its equivalent value in each of the two other temperature measurement units.

	SI Metric Temperature		Customary Temperature
	Celsius (°C)	Kelvin	Fahrenheit (°F)
A	-10		
B	40		
C		1 753.15	
D	3.43×10^3		

2. Secure a table of conversion factors.
   a. Record the conversion factor and mathematical process for values A, B, C and D.
   b. Convert the given measurement to the required measurement, correct to two decimal places.
   c. Give the reciprocal and mathematical process to use in converting the computed measurement back to the given measurement.
   d. Recompute the original given value to the nearest whole number.

	Measurements		Conversion Factor and Process	Computed Measurement	Reciprocal and Mathematical Processes	Recomputed Given Value
	Given	Required				
A	465 mm	in.				
B	150 kg	lb.(mass) avoirdupois				
C	125 Btu/sec	kW				
D	240 km/h	m/s				

3. Compute the required volume (mass) in systems A, B, C and D. Use the two formulas as indicated.
   a. State the conversion factor in each case.
   b. Compute and record each volume in the unit indicated in the table, correct to two decimal places.

	Volume (Mass)		Conversion Factor and Process
A	4 313.80 kg/m^3	lb. (mass)/gal(US)	
B	kg/m^3	22.6lb.(mass)/gal.(US)	
C	kg/m^3	32 lb. (mass)/ft.^{3}	
D	7 220 kg/m^3	lb. (mass)/ft^3	

$$\text{lb. (mass)/gal.(US)} = \frac{\text{kg/m}^3}{119.8264}$$

$$\text{kg/m}^3 = \text{lb. (mass)/ft.}^3 \times 16.0185$$

Section 9

SYMBOLS

Unit 39 THE CONCEPT OF SYMBOLS

Symbols are used as a shorthand and simplified way of saying what operations are to be performed. Symbols identify the quantities and units of measurement that are involved in the various steps. Typical examples of the everyday use of symbols are found in money problems ($), (¢), and (%) and the arithmetical signs of (+), (–), (x), and (÷).

Also, symbols are another form of worldwide communication. By their use it is possible to develop mathematical formulas. These have the same interpretation regardless of the part of the world in which they are applied.

Symbols may be used with ease and accuracy if, at first, certain basic concepts are developed. The concepts relate to: (1) the grouping symbols, (2) letters and subnumbers used as symbols, (3) signs and symbols which denote mathematical processes, (4) methods of handling symbols, (5) techniques of expressing quantities, and (6) symbols for constant values. These concepts and the application of symbols are covered in this section. Practical problems of addition, subtraction, multiplication, and division are included, involving symbols.

A. SYMBOLS USED FOR GROUPING QUANTITIES

Many problems daily are simplified by using what are called *grouping symbols.* The term refers to those symbols which are used to group quantities together for ease in reading and to simplify mathematical processes. There are four common grouping symbols. While they serve the same function, each one is also used to separate or differentiate one quantity from another.

The first of these grouping symbols, and the one most widely applied, is the *parenthesis* ( ). Some problems contain a number of parentheses and additional mathematical operations are to be performed with the quantities enclosed in the parentheses. A second grouping symbol called the *bracket* [ ] is used in such instances. Still more complex mathematical practices involve the quantities in parentheses ( ) and brackets [ ]. A third grouping symbol known as *braces* { } is used with parentheses and brackets. The *bar* —— (which is a straight line) is usually placed over or under a quantity to indicate that a required mathematical operation must be performed for the whole group or quantity.

APPLYING GROUPING SYMBOLS

EXAMPLES: Case 1 Parenthesis ( )

$$(4C) + (5D) + (6C - 4D) =$$

Case 2 Bar —— and Parenthesis ( )

$$\frac{(3A)}{2} + \frac{3.14\ (D) + 3.14\ (3D)}{4} - (6A) =$$

Case 3 Bar ——, Parenthesis ( ), and Brackets [ ]

$$5X + \frac{(7X + 4X)}{2} + [\frac{(8C)}{4} - (C) + \frac{12X + 10C}{2} + \frac{1.158C + 4X}{4}] =$$

Case 4 Bar ——, Parenthesis ( ), Brackets [ ], and Braces { }

$$\frac{16}{1.157\ (4D) + (2D)} + (4X) + \{\ [8X + (3X + 2D) - (4X + D)] + 2X\ \} =$$

RULES FOR SOLVING PROBLEMS WHICH CONTAIN GROUPING SYMBOLS

- Perform the mathematical operations indicated within the *parenthesis* and under or over the *bar,* first.
- Follow with the operations required for the quantities in the *brackets* [ ].
- Finally, do the operations indicated for the *braces* { } .

NOTE: The mathematical processes may be simplified by following this practice of solving the quantities in the parenthesis, brackets, and braces in that order.

LETTERS AND SUBNUMBERS USED AS SYMBOLS

Close examination of problems in mathematics and shop formulas reveals that the formula or problem in many instances is a combination of numbers and symbols. These, in a convenient form express the relationship of one quantity to another. The symbols which group the quantities may appear in any one of, or combination of, the four forms, parenthesis ( ), brackets [ ], braces { } , or bar ——.

A problem may be simplified further by using *letters.* In the case of the formula, the numerical values of letters or other symbols are substituted in the final solution of a problem. These letters are sometimes an abbreviation of a term or word. In other instances, just a single letter is used. The letter may become a *standard* when it always denotes a definite dimension. The dimension is established and accepted by national and international standards-setting organizations.

Notations or letters which appear in mathematical expressions or formulas have a fixed meaning. For example, in dealing with surface measurement, the area of a rectangle is determined by multiplying the linear dimension of the base by the height. This arithmetical process can be expressed in a simple and compact form in the formula (A = L x H).

In this case, the (A) is the letter symbol for area, (L) for length, and (H) for height. The letters are selected as representing a definite value and convey the same meaning as the written value.

CAPITALS AND LOWERCASE LETTERS AS SYMBOLS

Capital letters and *lowercase letters* are used as symbols to designate different quantities. For example, the capital letter (D) may denote the diameter of a bar of steel and (d), a lowercase letter, that of another. Care must be taken when using both capital and small or lower-case letters as symbols to make sure that the correct value of the letter is used in computations.

SUBNUMBERS USED AS SYMBOLS

In many formulas and problems the same letter may be used to denote a number of values. When such is the case, a *subnumber,* called a subscript, follows the letter or symbol for purposes of identification. These subnumbers are placed to the right of and slightly below the letter. The symbol (A_1) would be read "A sub-one." This quantity is differentiated from the next which may be (A_2) "A sub-two" or (A_3) "A sub-three" by using the subscript.

C. SYMBOLS DENOTING MATHEMATICAL PROCESSES

In common use are the four arithmetical signs. The signs are symbols which denote the mathematical operations required. Thus the plus sign (+) indicates addition; the minus sign (–), subtraction; the (x), multiplication; and (÷), division.

In addition to these signs, other symbols are used to denote multiplication. For instance, if the quantity (A) is to be multiplied by the quantity (B), the problem may be written five different ways to express the same process.

Case	Method of Expressing Multiplication Process
1	A x B
2	A · B
3	A B
4	(A) (B)
5	A(B) or (B)A

In the first case, the multiplication process is denoted by the sign (x). The symbol (•) in the second case indicates that A is to be multiplied by B. In case three, it is understood that A and B are to be multiplied together. Finally, the parentheses are used to indicate multiplication. The methods shown in case 4 and 5 are used when combinations of quantities must be multiplied.

While the multiplication process may be expressed in five different ways, the quantities indicated in each case have the same value. In other words,

$$A \times B = A \cdot B = A\,B = (A)\,(B) = A\,(B) \text{ or } (B)\,A$$

The operations involving the quantities within a parenthesis are carried out before the final value of a parenthesis is multiplied by another value in a second parenthesis.

D. METHODS OF HANDLING SYMBOLS

The letters or numbers which are used to express a fixed mathematical relationship are sometimes given or stated, as in the case of formulas. Otherwise, arbitrary symbols are selected to simplify the writing and solution of problems.

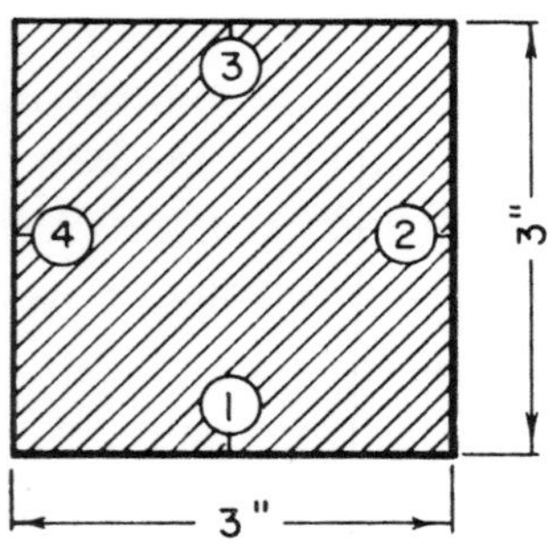

In the accompanying square, each side is three inches long. The distance around this square (which is called the *perimeter*) may be determined a number of different ways.

The perimeter may be found by adding the four sides (Method 1). In Method 2, the number of sides (4) is multiplied by the length of each side (3"). The multiplication process is preferred because it is easier and more accurate.

METHOD 1 ADDITION

① 3" + ② 3" + ③ 3" + ④ 3" = 12"

METHOD 2 MULTIPLICATION

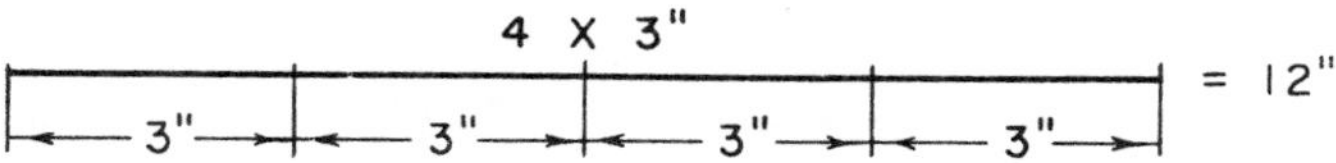

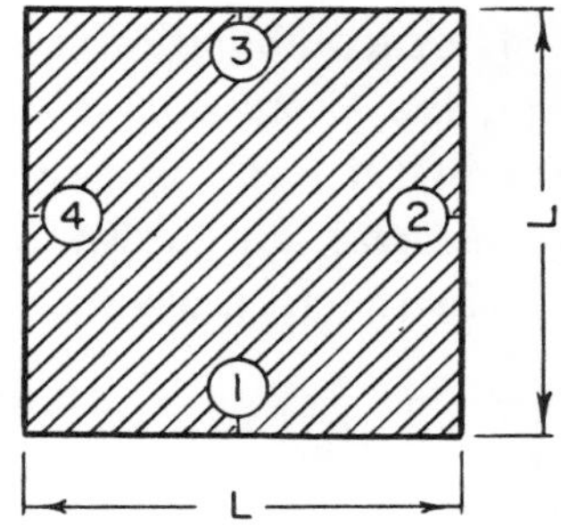

In the second square, the length of each side is given as dimension (L). The perimeter of this square is also equal to the sum of the four sides. However, instead of using a number to indicate the dimension of a side, the letter (L) is substituted. The perimeter which may be found either by multiplication or addition is equal to (4L).

METHOD 1 ADDITION

① L + ② L + ③ L + ④ L = 4 L

METHOD 2 MULTIPLICATION

4 X L

L L L L = 4 L

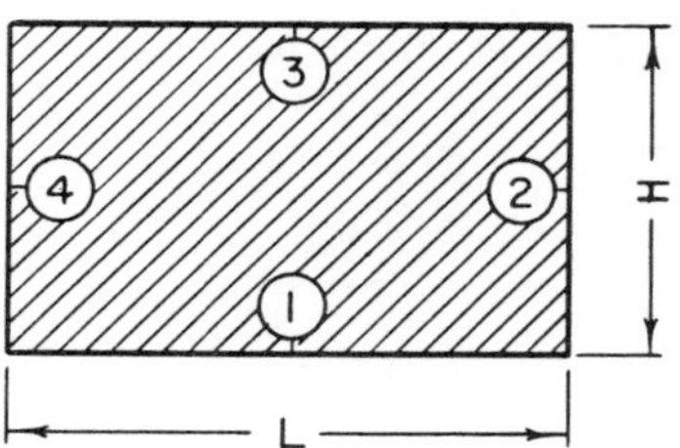

Symbols may be used as readily as numbers. In fact, where the numbers in a problem are large and unwieldy, it is far simpler to perform the mathematical operations by using symbols. The value of each symbol is substituted in one of the last steps.

The perimeter of a rectangle is equal to the sum of the four sides. Since both pairs of sides are equal, the perimeter, in terms of the base whose length is (L) and height is (H), is equal to 2 (L) + 2 (H).

METHOD 1 ADDITION

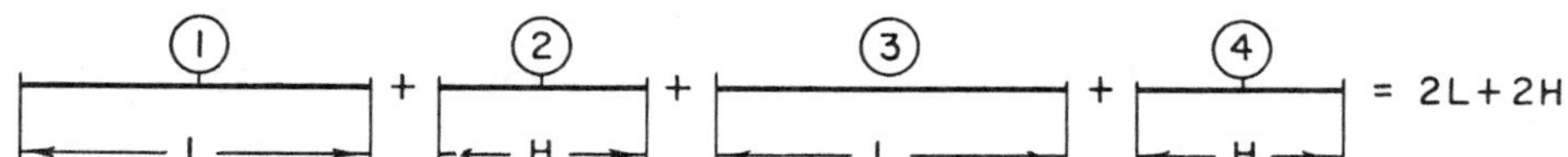

METHOD 2 MULTIPLICATION

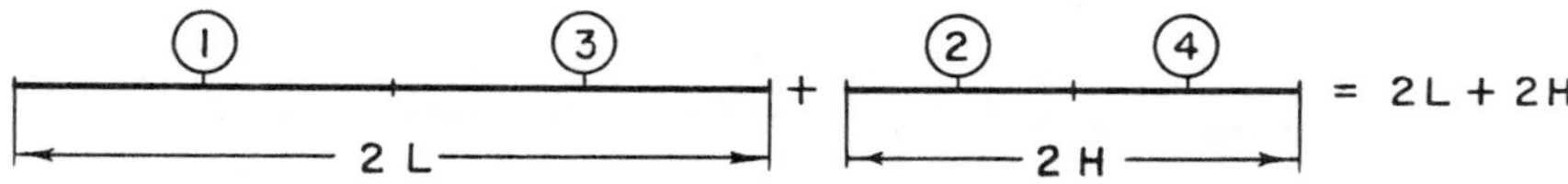

The relationship of the sides to the perimeter may be expressed as a formula where (P) denotes the perimeter of the rectangle: P = 2L + 2H. When simplified, P = 2 (L + H).

E. METHODS OF EXPRESSING QUANTITIES

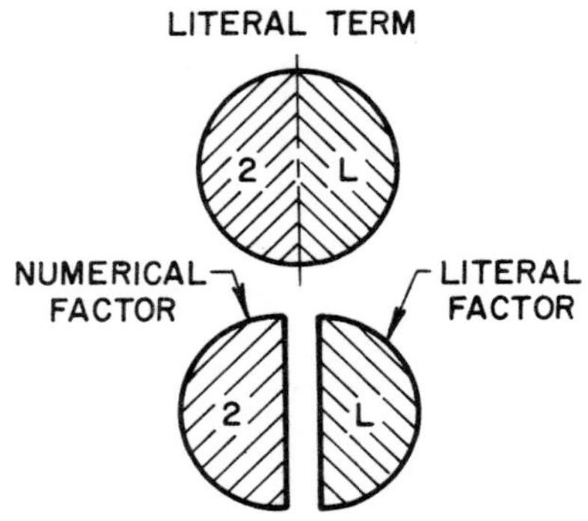

A quantity may be expressed either in terms of numbers, or a combination of numbers and symbols. Where only numbers are used, the quantity is said to be expressed in *numerical terms.* Where letters are used in combination with numbers, like (8A) and (4B), the expression is called a *literal term.* The parts of a literal term, namely the *numerical factor* and the *literal factor,* are shown in the illustration.

In the formula for the perimeter of a rectangle, the literal terms are (2L) and (2H).

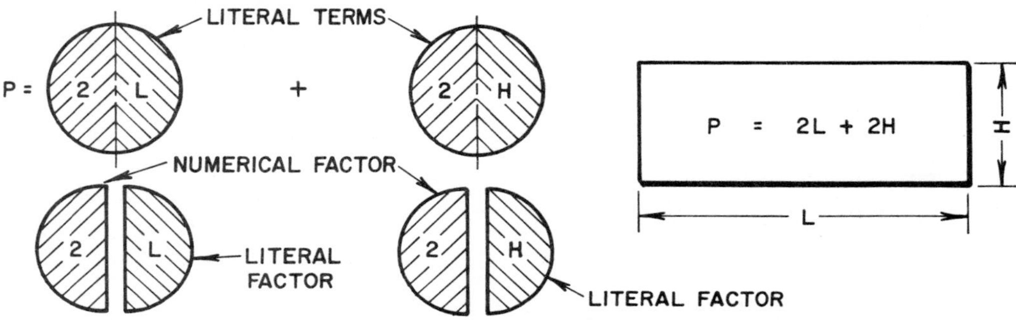

The numerical value of a literal factor is substituted in the final solution of a problem.

EXAMPLE: Determine the value of the literal term (4A) when dimension (A) is equal to (4).

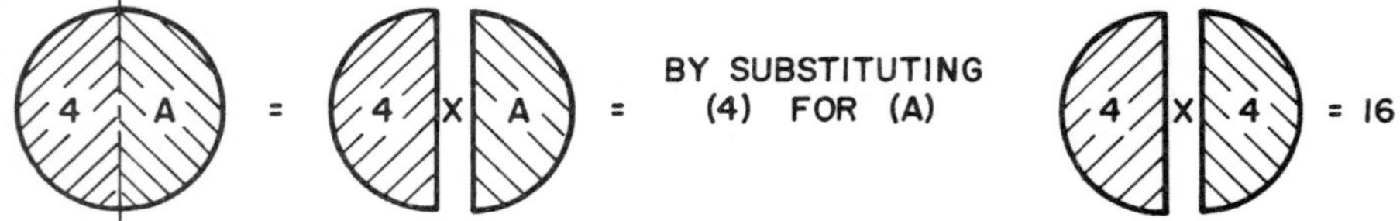

The terms used in expressing quantities may be identified easily. Remember that the numerical factor refers to a number value and the literal factor to a letter or other symbol. Symbols may be applied to the mathematical solution of triangles, circles, or any other shaped part. In fact, symbols may be used in most problems where simplicity of expression and ease of solution are required.

The word *expression* mathematically refers to the abbreviated form method of stating a problem in numerical and literal terms. For example, the total area of the two rectangular parts is found by adding the area of each rectangle.

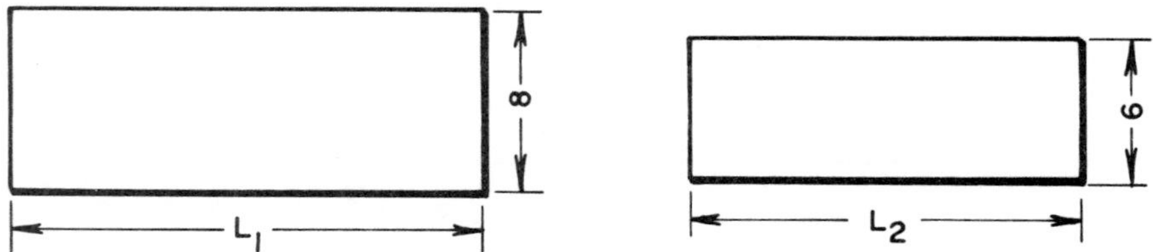

Since the area of a rectangle is equal to the length of the base multiplied by the altitude, this relationship may be expressed as

$$A = 8L_1 + 6L_2$$

where (A) refers to the total area and (L_1) and (L_2) the respective lengths of each rectangle. The value $A = 8L_1 + 6L_2$ is called an *expression.*

F. SYMBOLS USED FOR CONSTANT VALUES

Where a value has been established scientifically and a specific symbol is used universally to denote a fixed mathematical relationship, the value is then known as a *constant.* A constant never changes.

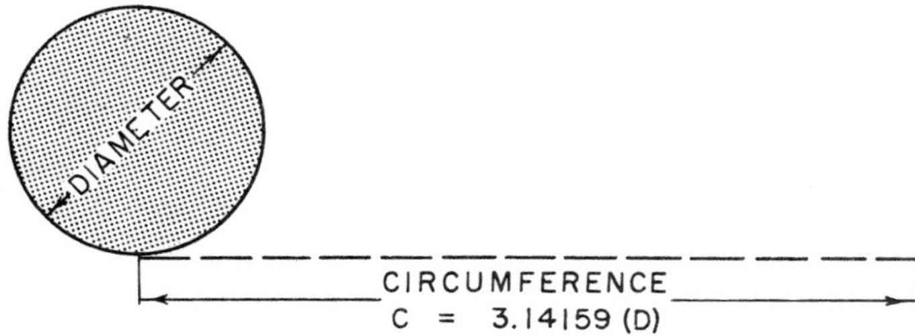

For example, to find the circumference of a circle, the diameter is multiplied by the constant 3.14159. This value is numerically correct to four decimal places. This relationship is sometimes expressed in the formula C = Pi (D).

The symbol (C) denotes the circumference; (D), the diameter; and the English letters (Pi) are the symbol for 3.14159. In most formulas, the Greek letter for (Pi), which is (π), is used. Since this 3.14159 is a fixed quantity which has been proved and is an established fact, it is called a constant value for (Pi).

When symbols indicate constant values in problems, the mathematical processes are simplified. The symbols may be added, subtracted, multiplied, or divided with greater ease than the numerical values. In most instances, it is comparatively simple in the final steps of solving a problem to substitute the numerical value of each literal factor.

ASSIGNMENT UNIT 39

1. Determine the dimensions of each shaded portion in the figures shown. Note that the objects are divided equally into the number of parts indicated in each instance.

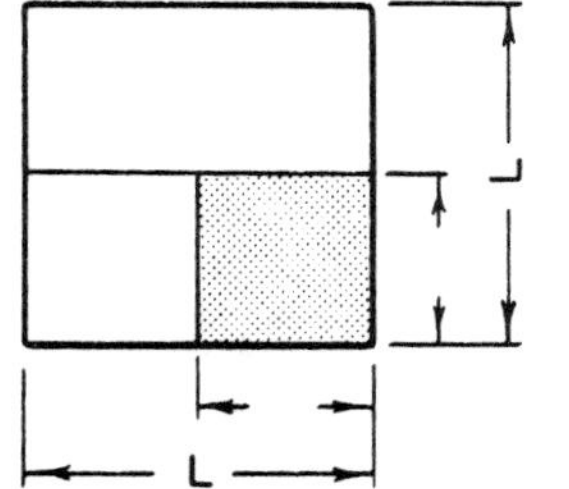

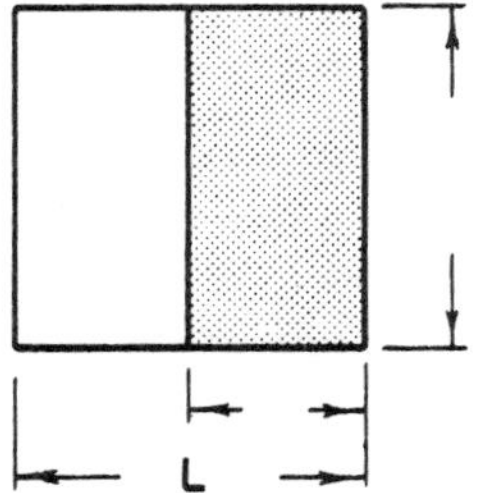

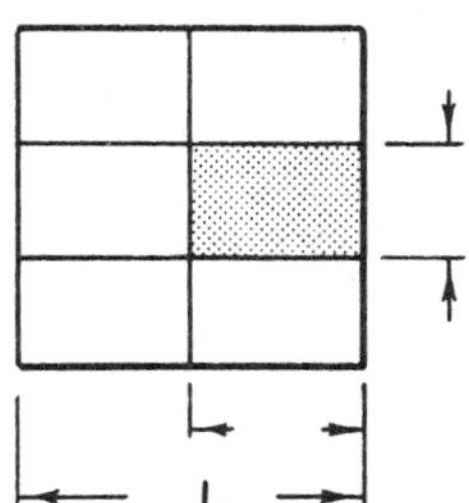

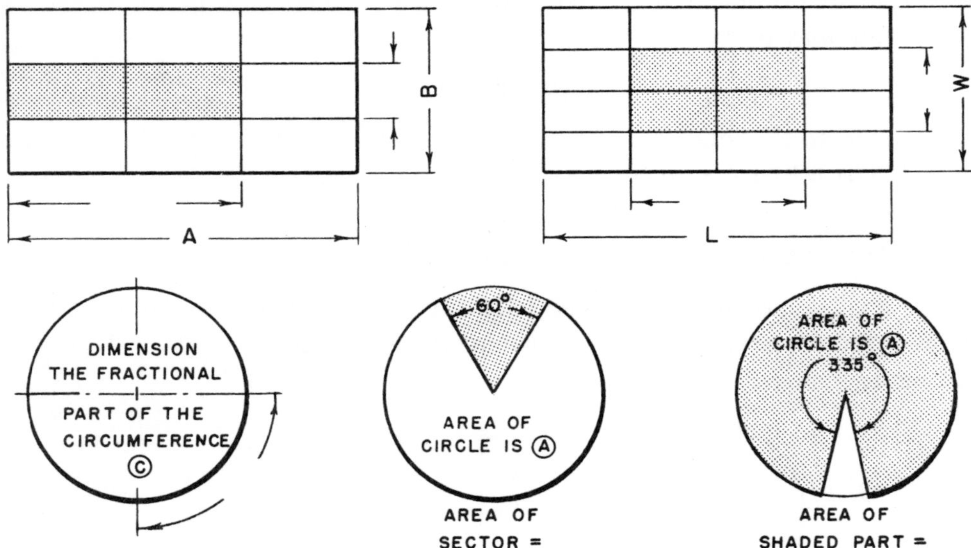

2. Dimension the copper stamping. Use the symbol (L) to denote length and (W) its width. The inner square is (3X) inches on a side. The rectangle is (5X) inches long and (2X) inches wide.

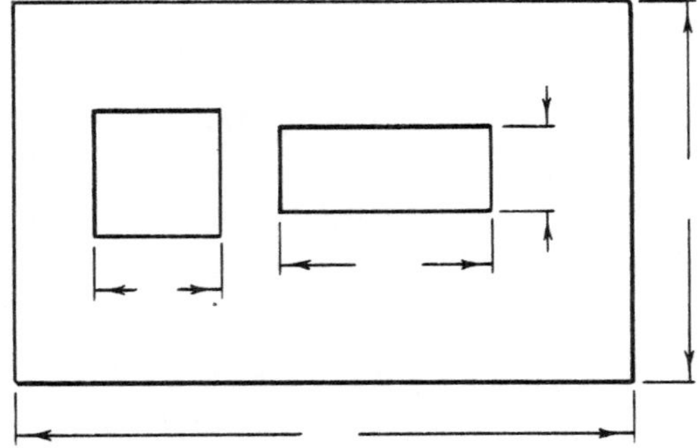

3. A Step Block which has four equal steps is (H cm) high, (W cm) wide, and (L cm) long. Dimension the sketch according to these known sizes.

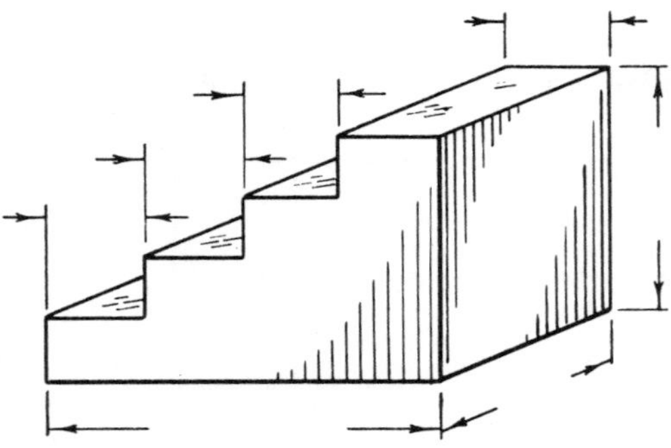

4. Dimension the square, rectangle, and triangles according to the specifications given in each instance.

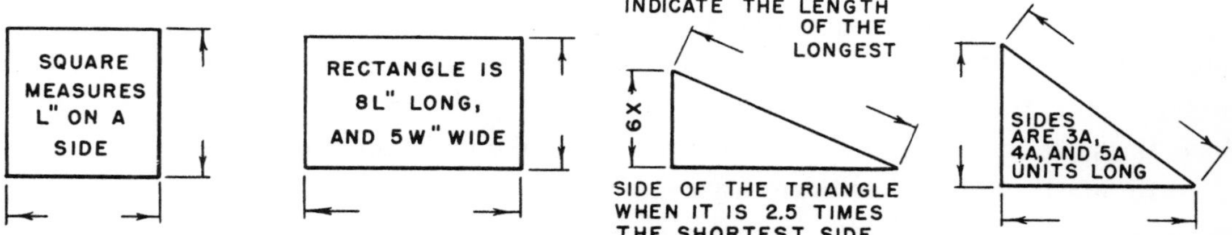

5. Dimensions on shop drawings are often given in terms of letters or symbols. The numerical value of each dimension is stated in table form. Where this practice is followed, one drawing is used for many different sizes of the same shaped part. Indicate on the drawing the letter symbol given in the table for each dimension.

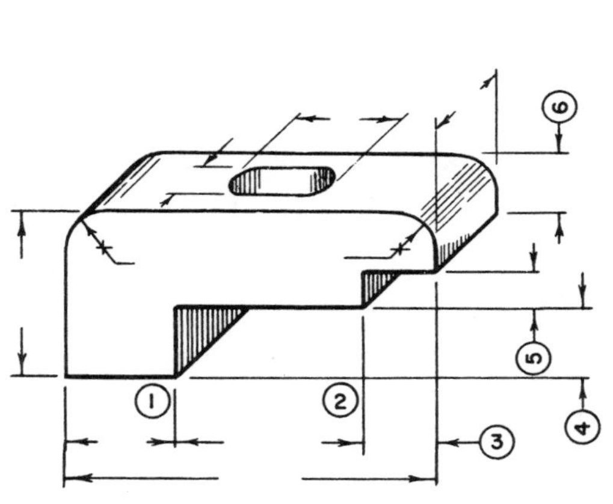

Linear Dimension on Drawing		Letter Symbol
Overall length		L
Overall height		H_1
Width		W
Radius at corners		R
Length of Step	1	A
	2	B
	3	C
	4	D
	5	E
	6	F
Elongated slot	width	G
	length	H

Unit 40 APPLICATION OF SYMBOLS IN ADDITION

In any mathematical expression, the parts which are separated by any of the signs like plus (+) and (–) are called *terms.* When the various terms in an expression have the same literal factor, they are called *like terms.* In the expression 8A + 9A + 4A all of the terms have the same literal factor (A). These terms are like terms and may be added.

In any problem of addition involving the use of symbols, the like terms are added the same as any other numerical values. However, attention must be given to expressing the sum in terms of the literal factor. In the above case, when the three terms are added, the sum of (21A) has the same literal factor (A) as each of the terms.

RULE FOR ADDING LIKE TERMS

- Locate all like terms in the expression.
- Add the numerical factors.
- Express the sum in terms of the literal factor.

EXAMPLE: Add 5S + 3S + 4S + 6S

Step 1 Locate the like terms in the expression.

Step 2 Add the numerical factors (5 + 3 + 4 + 6).

Step 3 Express the sum (18) in terms of the literal factor (S). 5S + 3S + 4S + 6S = 18S

The words *unlike terms* are used when the literal factors are different or unlike. Unlike terms cannot be added or subtracted. For example, in the rectangle illustrated, the base is 8L units long and 5W units wide. The perimeter, which is equal to the sum of all the sides, may be expressed as:

8L + 5W + 8L + 5W

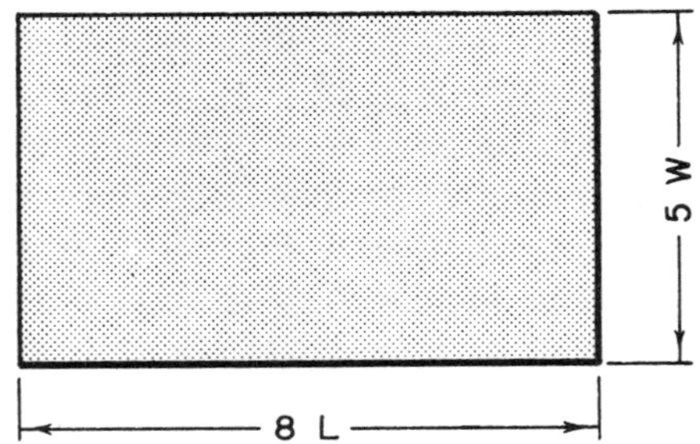

In this expression, the first and third terms (8L and 8L) and the second and fourth (5W and 5W) are like terms and can be added: (8L + 8L = 16L); (5W + 5W = 10W).

The 16L and 10W are unlike terms and cannot be added because the value of the literal factor is different in each instance. The perimeter which is equal to 10L + 16W is expressed in as simple terms as possible.

ASSIGNMENT UNIT 40

1. Add the columns A through F.

A	B	C	D	E	F
9X	3 1/2L	7.2W	13.63H	19.25A	16.5AB
16X	14 3/4L	19.4W	17. H	13.88A	17.7AB

Ans.: B. 18 1/4 L D. 30.63 H F. 34.2 AB

2. Add the following like terms.

a. X + X + 4X =
b. 9H + 7H + H =
c. 1 1/2 B + 9 1/4 B + 6B =
d. 3C + 4.7C + 5.2C =
e. (5.5X) + (92.6X) + (4.7X) + .5X =
f. (7 1/2 X) + (8 1/4 X + 5 1/8 X) =
g. (3.2A) + [8.5A + (19.2A + 6.4A)] + 2.8A =
h. [2 1/2 B + (7 1/4 B + 3 3/4 B)] + 16 1/2 B =

Ans.: b. 17H d. 12.9C f. 20 7/8 X h. 30B

3. Simplify the following expressions by grouping all like terms.

a. 6L + 7L + 5W =
b. 7AB + (8B + 15AB + 3B) =
c. 14 3/4 CD + 12 1/2 D + 9 1/6 CD =
d. 19.25XY + 17.45Y + 12.75XY + 32.50XY =
e. (12.38AB) + (16.72C) + (12.90AB + 70.22AB) =
f. [10 1/4 LW + (15 1/2 X + 9 3/8 LW + 12 3/4 X)] + 6 1/4 LW =

Ans.: b. 22AB + 11B d. 64.50XY + 17.45Y f. 25 7/8 LW + 28 1/4 X

4. Determine dimensions B through F.

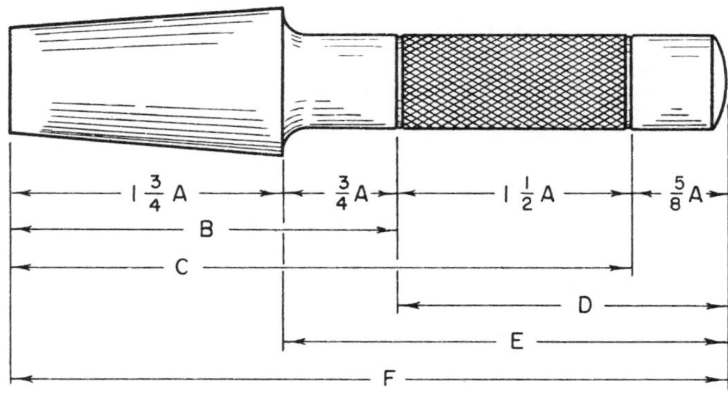

Ans.: B = 2 1/2 A D = 2 1/8 A F = 4 5/8 A

5. Find the length of the hardened plugs (A and B), the length of the body (C) and the overall length of the Plug Gage (D).

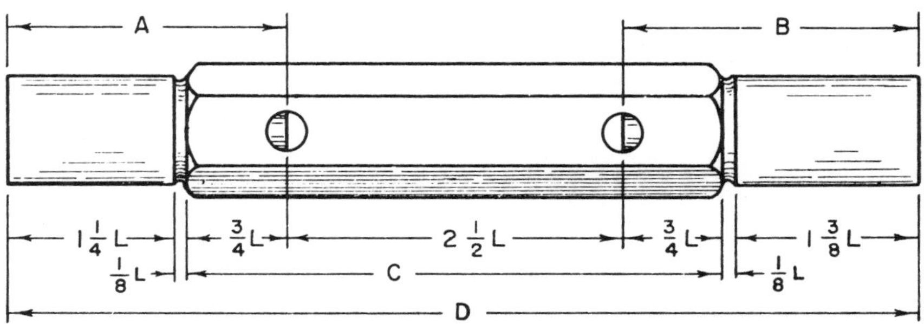

Ans.: B = 2 1/4 L D = 6 7/8 L

6. Find the literal values of dimensions A through G.

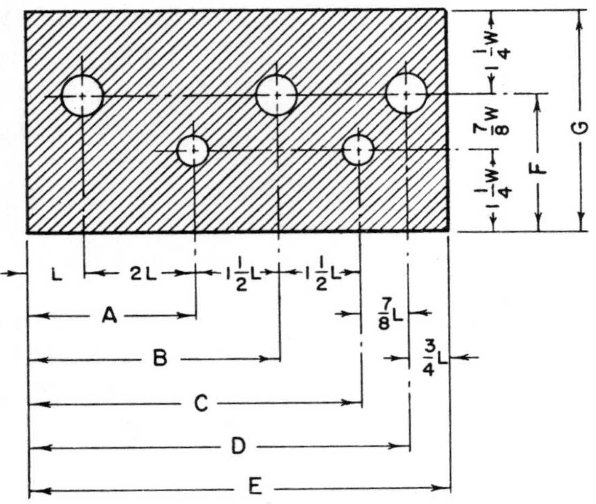

Ans.: B = 4 1/2 L D = 6 7/8 L F = 2 1/8 W

7. Determine the literal dimensions A through F for the Plate.

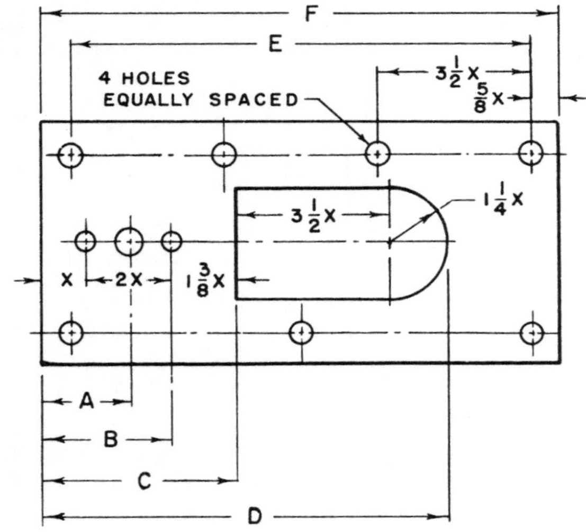

Ans.: B = 3X D = 9 1/8 X F = 11 3/4 X

Unit 41 APPLICATION OF SYMBOLS IN SUBTRACTION

The two mathematical operations which workers use daily are addition and subtraction. Most answers can be easily obtained by simple arithmetic. However, there are numerous occasions when it is necessary to subtract quantities which contain symbols. Here, as in addition, only like terms may be subtracted.

RULE FOR SUBTRACTING LIKE TERMS

- Locate or determine the like terms in the expression.
- Subtract the numerical factors.
- Express the difference in terms of the literal factor.

EXAMPLE: Subtract (17A – 3 1/2 A – 5A – 4 1/2 A).

Step 1 Locate all like terms in the expression. $(17A,\ 3\frac{1}{2}A,\ 5A,\ 4\frac{1}{2}A)$

Step 2 Subtract the numerical factors. $(17 - 3\frac{1}{2} - 5 - 4\frac{1}{2}) = 4$

Step 3 Express the difference (4) in terms of the literal factor (A). $(17A - 3\frac{1}{2}A - 5A - 4\frac{1}{2}A) =$ 4A Ans.

When the terms in the same expression are connected by both plus and minus signs, the plus terms are collected separately. The minus terms are next collected. Then the difference between the plus and minus quantities is determined. The practice of collecting terms which involve the same mathematical operation simplifies the actual work involved in arriving at the answer.

Here again, the mathematical processes indicated in the parenthesis are performed first, the brackets next and finally, the braces. Once these operations are completed, all like terms may be combined by adding or subtracting.

EXAMPLE: Determine the value of the following expression which involves addition and subtraction: (6D – 4D + 1.5D + 8B) + (5B – 1.25B – 2.75B + 6D) =

Step 1 Locate all like terms in each parenthesis. (6D, 4D, 1.5D)
(5B, 1.25B, 2.75B)

Step 2 Add or subtract the numerical factors as indicated by the signs in each parenthesis. (6D – 4D + 1.5D) = 3.5D
(5B – 1.25B – 2.75B) = 1B

Step 3 Combine any remaining like terms in the original parentheses (8B) and (6D). (8B + 1B) = 9B
(6D + 3.5D) = 9.5D

The value of the expression
(6D – 4D + 1.5D + 8B) + (5B – 1.25B –2.75B + 6D) = 9B + 9.5D Ans.

Occasionally the literal factors contain more than one letter like 6AB and 9XY. In such cases, where the terms in the expression are identical, they are still referred to as like terms and may be added or subtracted.

EXAMPLE: Subtract (14AB – 7AB + 8BC – 4.2BC – 2.4AB) =

Step 1 Locate all like terms. (14AB – 7AB – 2.4AB) and (8BC – 4.2BC)

Step 2 Subtract the numerical factors in each case. (14 – 7 – 2.4) = 4.6 and (8 – 4.2) = 3.8

Step 3 Express the differences in terms of the literal factor. (14AB – 7AB – 2.4AB) = 4.6AB (8BC – 4.2BC) = 3.8BC

The value of the expression

(14AB – 7AB + 8BC – 4.2BC – 2.4AB) = 4.6AB + 3.8BC Ans.

ASSIGNMENT UNIT 41

1. Simplify the quantities A through F.

A	B	C	D	E	F
25X – 12X	$19\frac{3}{4}$ W $-10\frac{1}{2}$ W	$16\frac{3}{8}$ L $-7\frac{9}{16}$ L	20.6N – 14.0N	23.38YZ – 17.86YZ	144.2XYZ – 92.8XYZ

Ans.: B. 9 1/4 W D. 6.6 N F. 51.4 XYZ

2. Simplify the following expressions.

a. 35X – 16X – 7X =
b. 75 A – 19 1/2 A – 12 1/2 A =
c. 144 1/2 B – 64 1/4 B – 17 7/8 B =
d. 8Y – 4.6Y – 1.62Y =
e. (92.4A) – (16.8A) – (12.6A) =
f. (15 1/2 C) – (9 3/4 C + 2 1/4 C + 1 1/4 C) =
g. [(8.8D + 6.6D) – (1.4D + 6D)] – 3.9D =
h. 76.75BC – [2.50BC + (7.25BC + 3.38BC)] =

Ans.: b. 43A d. 1.78Y f. 2 1/4 C h. 63.62 BC

3. Simplify the following expressions.

a. 17P + 9L – 6P =
b. 16AB – (9AB + 12 BC – 2AB) =
c. 14 1/2 X – 10 1/4 X + (3X + 7Y + X) =
d. 75.38LW – 20.25WD – 20.63LW + 43.12WD =
e. (16.25HD) – (17.50CD) + (12.62HD + 7.88HD) =
f. [9 1/8 L + (22 3/4 WD – 6 3/8 L – 8 1/2 WD – 2 1/8 WD)] – 1 1/16 L =

Ans.: b. 9AB – 12BC d. 54.75LW + 22.87WD f. 1 11/16 L + 12 1/8 WD

4. Find the numerical value of A through F for each given value by subtracting (8.6) in each case.

Given Value					
A	B	C	D	E	F
12	9.8	12.2	$10\frac{5}{8}$	$16\frac{1}{4}$	17.312

Ans.: B. 1.2 D. 2.025 F. 8.712

5. Determine the value of A through F by subtracting (2 1/2) from each numerical value.

A	B	C	D	E	F
12	$20\frac{3}{4}$	$11\frac{3}{8}$	4.5	9.38	12.125

Ans.: B. 18 1/4 D. 2 F. 9.625

6. Determine the numerical value of A through H by multiplying the given value by (3) and subtracting (2 1/4).

A	B	C	D	E	F	G	H
8	14	$3\frac{1}{2}$	$5\frac{1}{16}$	$7\frac{1}{32}$	4.25	6.04	7.063

Ans.: B. 39 3/4 E. 18 27/32 H. 18.939

7. Determine the value of dimensions A through G in terms of the literal dimension L.

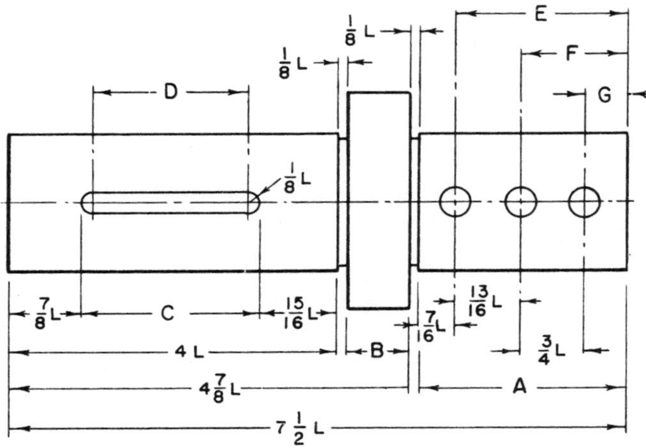

Ans.: B = 3/4 L D = 1 15/16 L F = 1 1/4 L

8. Determine the literal dimensions A through G for the Drill Plate.

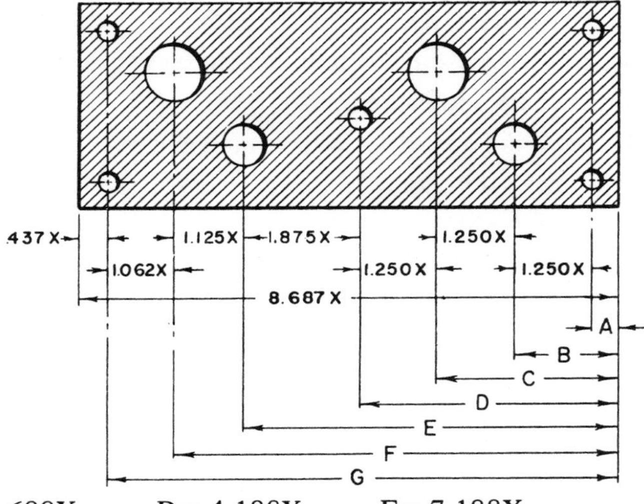

Ans.: B = 1.688X D = 4.188X F = 7.188X

Unit 42 APPLICATION OF SYMBOLS IN MULTIPLICATION

The multiplication of quantities involving the use of symbols differs somewhat from either addition or subtraction. It is possible in multiplication to multiply all terms in an expression regardless of whether they are like or unlike.

To perform this mathematical operation, the numerical factors and expressions are multiplied together the same as any whole or mixed numbers. The literal factors are next multiplied. The answer is expressed in terms of the numerical product followed by the product of the literal factors.

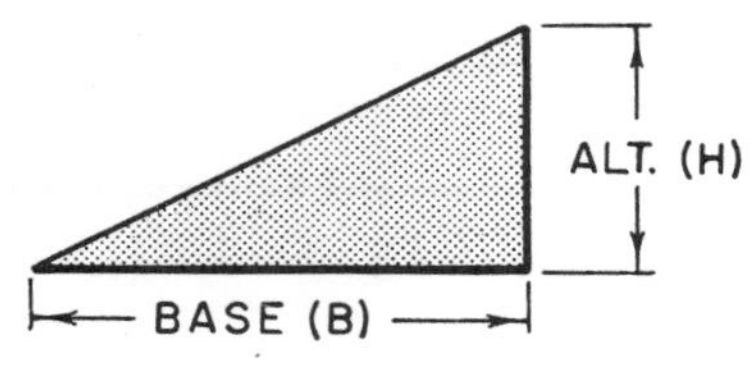

For example, if the quantities A, B, and C are multiplied, the product is ABC. In the case of a triangle, its area is equal to the product of one-half the base multiplied by the altitude.

If the letter (B) is used to denote the length of the base and (H) its altitude, then the area A = B/2 x H or BH/2.

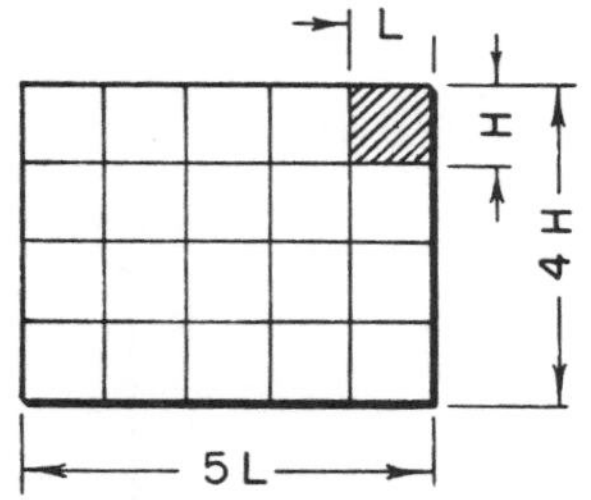

In the rectangle illustrated, if the length of the base is (5L) and the height (4H), the rectangle contains five units of (L) length and 4 units (H) high. The area of the rectangle is equal to 5(L) x 4(H) = 20 LH. This area is identical with that composed of 20 of the smaller shaded rectangles. Since the area of one of the shaded rectangles is equal to its length (L) x height (H), the total area is equal to 20 LH.

There are times when the signs in an expression indicate that certain of the quantities must be added, subtracted, and multiplied. When such is the case, like quantities which must be added are added. Next, those quantities to be subtracted are subtracted. Finally, the multiplying of like and unlike quantities is performed. This method of doing each of the three operations separately in the sequence indicated simplifies the solution of a problem.

RULE FOR MULTIPLYING LIKE OR UNLIKE TERMS

- Add all like terms in the expression where indicated by (+) signs.
- Subtract all like terms where indicated by (–) signs.
- Multiply either like or unlike quantities where indicated by (x) signs.

  Multiply numerical factors.
  Multiply literal factors.
  Combine numerical and literal factors.
  Express product in literal terms.

EXAMPLE: Case 1 Multiply (6A) by (7B).

Step 1	Multiply *numerical factors* (6) and (7).	6 x 7 = 42
Step 2	Multiply the literal factors (A) and (B).	A x B = AB
Step 3	Combine numerical and literal factors (42) and (AB).	Ans. (6A) (7B) = 42AB

EXAMPLE: Case 2 Solve (2A + 4A − 3A −A) (2.2B) (4C).

Step 1 Add all like terms as indicated. 2A + 4A = 6A

Step 2 Subtract all like terms as indicated, from this sum. 6A − 3A − A = 2A

Step 3 Multiply the result (2A) by the literal term (2.2B).

Multiply numerical factors. (2) (2.2) = 4.4

Multiply the literal factors. (A) (B) = AB

Combine the numerical and literal factors. (2A) (2.2B) = 4.4AB

Step 4 Repeat these processes with the remaining literal term (4C). (4.4AB) (4C) =

Multiply numerical factors. (4.4) (4) = 17.6

Multiply the literal factors. (AB) (C) = ABC

Combine and express in literal terms. (4.4AB) (4C) = 17.6ABC

Ans. (2A + 4A − 3A −A) (2.2B) (4C) = 17.6ABC

ASSIGNMENT UNIT 42

1. Multiply each term given in problems A through F.

A	B	C	D	E	F
10X x 5Y	9.2A x 5B	6.8L x 8.4M	5.25AB x 7.5C	8 1/2X x 12Y	6 1/4AD x 3 1/2C

Ans.: B. 46AB D. 39.375ABC F. 21 7/8 ADC

2. Perform the operations indicated in problems (a) through (e), and simplify.

a. (6P) (7) + 5 (P)

b. (12X) (5Y) + (17XY)

c. [(9L) (8W) (6H)] + (12LWH)

d. 16 1/2 LH + [(5 1/4 W − 3 1/2 H) (4 1/2 L)]

e. 32.5XY + [(8.25X − 3.13X − 6.38Z) (2.5Y)]

Ans.: b. 77XY d. 3/4 LH + 23 5/8 LW

3. Compute the value of A through F by substituting the values for N given in the table in the formula, 12 (N + 6.5).

	A	B	C	D	E	F
Value of N	7 1/2	5	4 1/4	6.5	7.75	5.063

Ans.: B. 138 D. 156 F. 138.756

4. Determine the area of the shaded portion of each object. Note the number of equal parts in each object. Round off answers, where possible, to two decimal places.

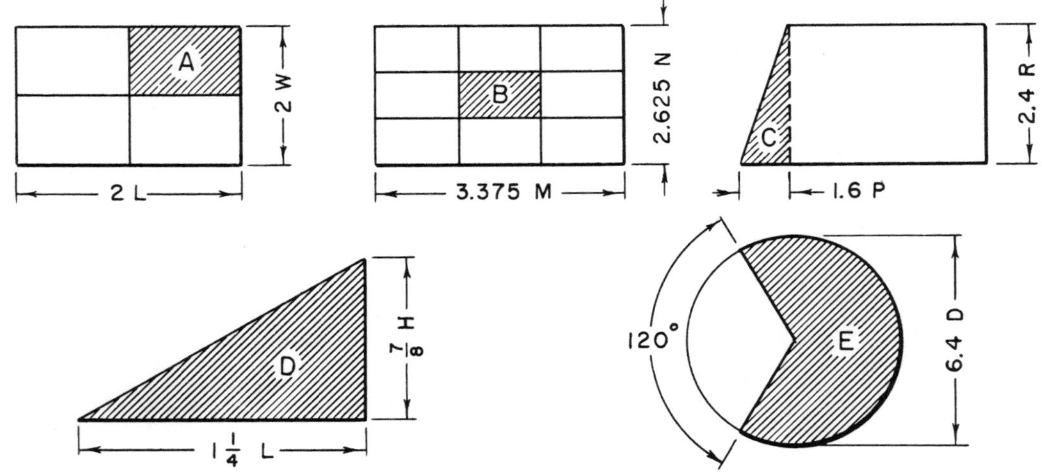

Ans.: B. .98MN D. .55LH

5. Compute the volume of parts A through F accurate to two decimal places.

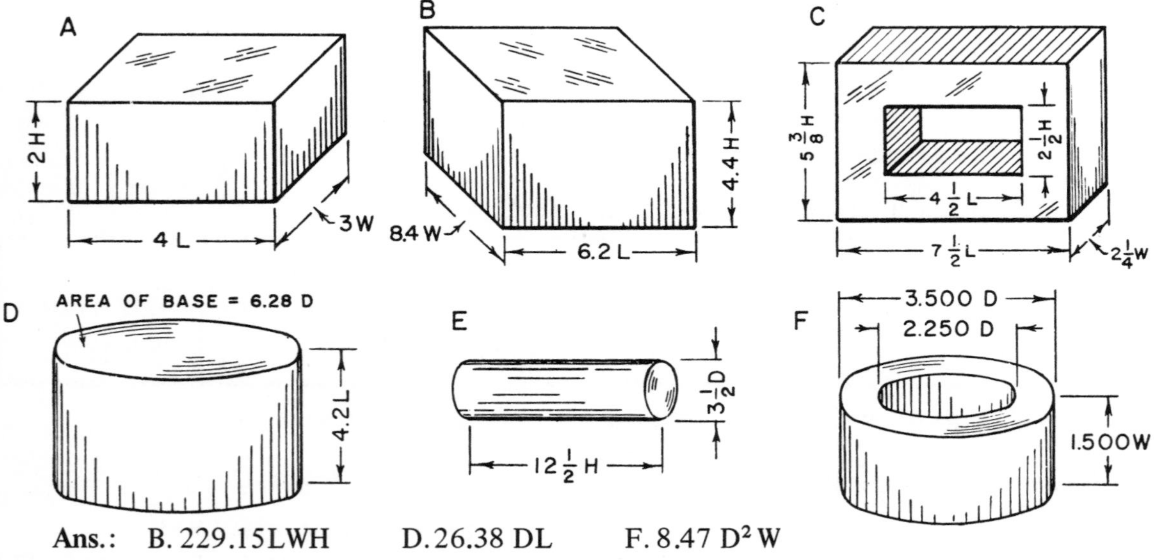

Ans.: B. 229.15LWH D. 26.38 DL F. 8.47 D^2 W

6. Find the center distances A through F and overall dimension G for any one of the three sheet metal templates.

Template Number	Dimension (L)
1	10 cm
2	15 cm
3	20 cm

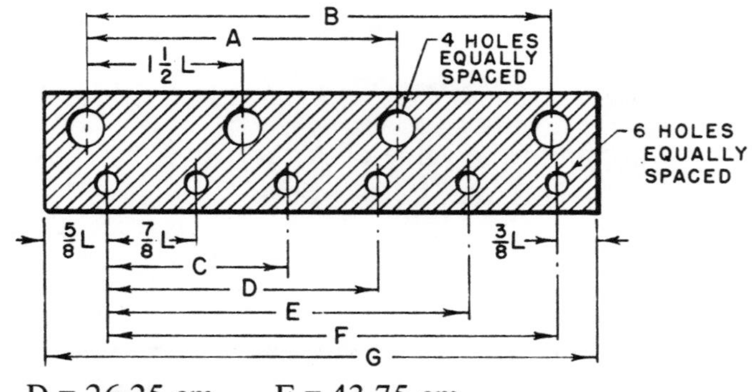

Ans.: Number 1 B = 45 cm D = 26.25 cm F = 43.75 cm

Unit 43 APPLICATION OF SYMBOLS IN DIVISION

While the three other fundamental processes of addition, subtraction, and multiplication are used more extensively than division, there are many times when both the like and unlike terms of an expression must be divided. The division process is comparatively simple if the basic steps described in this unit are followed. The numerical factors of like or unlike terms are divided first. These are followed by the division of any literal factor that appears in both the numerator and denominator.

RULE FOR DIVIDING LIKE TERMS

- Place the numerator above the denominator.
- Divide the *numerical factors* in numerator and denominator.
- Cancel the *literal factors* which are identical for both numerator and denominator.
- Express the result as a numerical factor where the literal factors cancel each other.

EXAMPLE: Divide (24XY) by (8XY).

Step 1 Place the numerator (24XY) above the denominator (8XY).

Step 2 Divide the numerical factors (24) and (8).

$$\frac{\overset{3}{\cancel{24}}\ XY}{\underset{1}{\cancel{8}}\ XY}$$

Step 3 Divide through by (X) in both numerator and denominator to get (1). Then divide through with Y.

$$\frac{\overset{3\cdot 1\cdot 1}{\cancel{24}\ \cancel{X}\cancel{Y}}}{\underset{1\cdot 1\cdot 1}{\cancel{8}\ \cancel{X}\cancel{Y}}}$$

Step 4 Express the result as a numerical factor (3) because the literal factors cancel each other.

$$3$$

RULE FOR DIVIDING UNLIKE TERMS

- Form a fraction.
- Divide the numerical factors in both numerator and denominator.
- Cancel any literal factor which appears in both the numerator and denominator.
- Express the result in terms of the numerical quotient followed by all literal factors that do not cancel out.

EXAMPLE: Divide 12ST by 4S.

Step 1 Form a fraction.

Step 2 Divide the numerical factors.

$$\frac{\overset{3}{\cancel{12}}ST}{\underset{1}{\cancel{4}}S}$$

Step 3 Cancel any literal factor which appears in both numerator and denominator.

NOTE: In this case the symbol (S) is common to numerator and denominator.

$$\frac{\overset{3}{\cancel{12}}\cancel{S}T}{\underset{1}{\cancel{4}}\cancel{S}} =$$

Step 4 Express the combined results in terms of the numerical quotient (3) followed by the literal factor (T).

$$\frac{\overset{3}{\cancel{12}}\cancel{S}T}{\underset{1}{\cancel{4}}\cancel{S}} = 3T$$

Occasionally, both the multiplication and division signs appear in the same expression. When this happens, the multiplication process must be completed before division.

EXAMPLE: Divide (6L x 4H x 6D) by (12D).

Step 1	Form a fraction and indicate the required mathematical processes.	$\frac{6L \times 4H \times 6D}{12D}$
Step 2	Multiply all literal terms in the numerator.	$\frac{144LHD}{12D}$
Step 3	Divide the numerical factors in both numerator and denominator.	$\frac{\overset{12}{\cancel{144}}LHD}{\cancel{12}D}$
Step 4	Divide the literal factors common to both the numerator and denominator (D in this case).	$\frac{\overset{12}{\cancel{144}}LH\cancel{D}}{\cancel{12}\cancel{D}}$
Step 5	Express the combined result in terms of the numerical quotient (12) followed by all literal factors that did not cancel out (LH).	12LH

$$\frac{6L \times 4H \times 6D}{12D} = \frac{\overset{12}{\cancel{144}}LH\cancel{D}}{\underset{1}{\cancel{12}\cancel{D}}} = 12LH$$

ASSIGNMENT UNIT 43

1. Find the result in problems A through I.

a. LH ÷ H =
b. 12A ÷ 6 =
c. 16 1/2 B ÷ 4 =
d. 9.62X ÷ 6 =
e. 16C/4C =
f. 12.75AB/4.25B =
g. 6 3/8 BC ÷ 1 1/16 BC =
h. .76LWH/.019WH =
i. (.3X + .6XY)/.02X =

Ans.: b. 2A d. 1.603X f. 3A h. 40L

2. Compute the value of A through E according to the formula D = C ÷ 3.14.

	A	B	C	D	E
Value of C	31.40	25.12	20.41	$10\frac{1}{2}$	$30\frac{3}{8}$

Ans.: B. 8 D. 3.344

3. Determine dimension M.

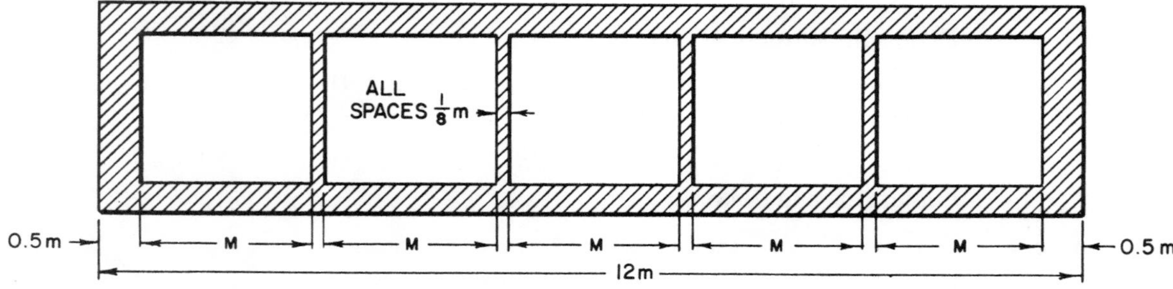

4. A gallon of paint covers 35.2 square meters of surface area.

   a. (1) Compute the surface area of each room and (2) the total area for both rooms A and B.

   b. Determine the total amount of paint required for the job.

   c. Convert the gallons required to equivalent full liters.

   Ans.: a. (2) 1 920.73 m²
   b. 54.57 gallons

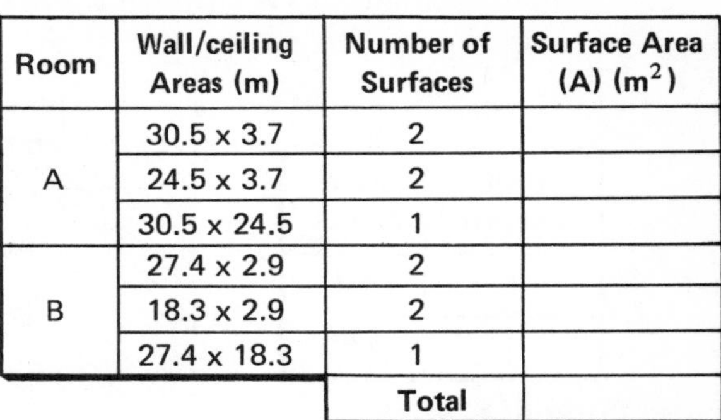

Room	Wall/ceiling Areas (m)	Number of Surfaces	Surface Area (A) (m^2)
A	30.5 x 3.7	2	
	24.5 x 3.7	2	
	30.5 x 24.5	1	
B	27.4 x 2.9	2	
	18.3 x 2.9	2	
	27.4 x 18.3	1	
		Total	

5. Determine dimensions A, B, C, D, and E for each of five sections when L = 254.0, 381.0, 317.5, 479.4, and 622.3 millimeters respectively.

   Ans.: When L = 254.0 mm, B = .826
   D = 1.778

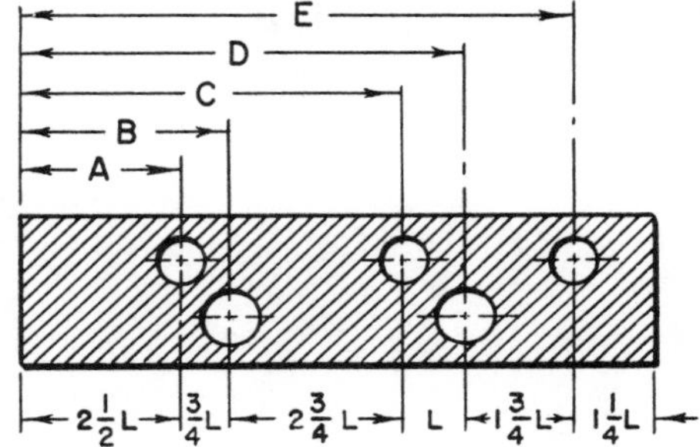

6. Compute the center distances (C) between the holes on Links A through E.

Link	Overall Distance (O)	No. Equally Spaced Holes
A	14	6
B	32	20
C	24 11/16	11
D	16.4	8
E	20.576	12

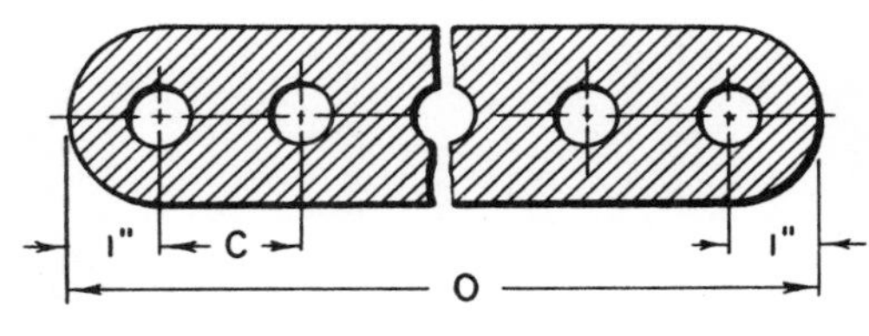

Ans.: B. 1.579″ D. 2.057″

7. Determine dimensions A, B, C, D, and E for the four different Test Bars indicated in the table.

Test Bar	Value of L	Value of M
1	4.500	.750
2	6.500	1.000
3	8.750	1.250
4	10.875	1.750

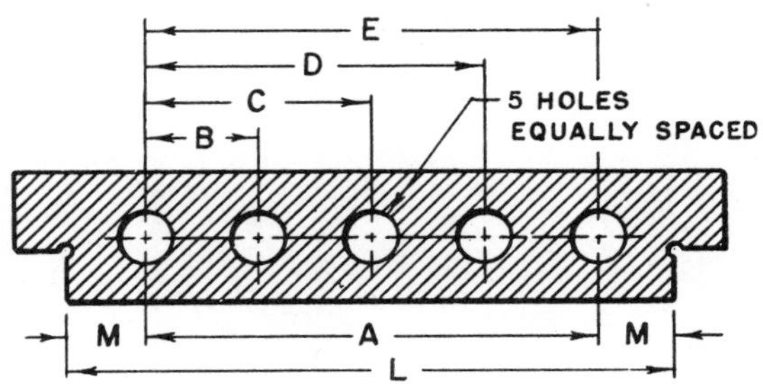

Ans.: For Test Bar 1, B = .75″ D = 2.25″

8. Compute dimensions A through E for Drill Templets (1) and (2).

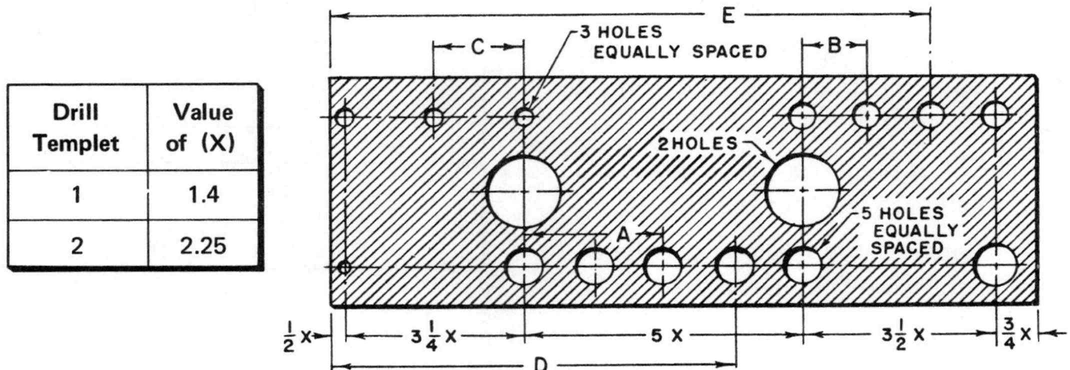

Drill Templet	Value of (X)
1	1.4
2	2.25

Ans.: For templet 1, B = 1.633″ D = 10.5″

Unit 44 ACHIEVEMENT REVIEW ON THE USE OF SYMBOLS

A. THE CONCEPT OF SYMBOLS

1. Determine dimensions A through E in the sketch of the train of discs.

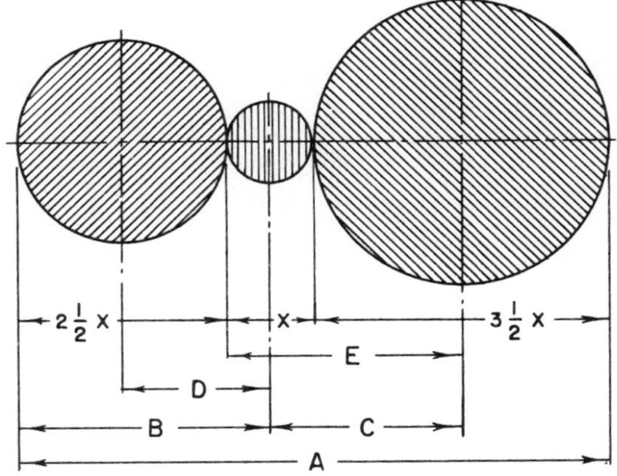

2. Place the letter symbols in the table in one set of circles on the sketch of the Trip Plate. Place the numerical value of each symbol in the second set of circles.

Linear Dimensions on Drawing	Letter Symbol	Numerical Value
Overall Length	L	4.6
Overall Height	H	2.8
Width of Plate	W	.5
Radius at Corners	r	.6
Included Angle	Δ	45°
Length to Angle	A	2.5
Elongated Slot-Width	B	.6
Elongated Slot-Length	C	1.0

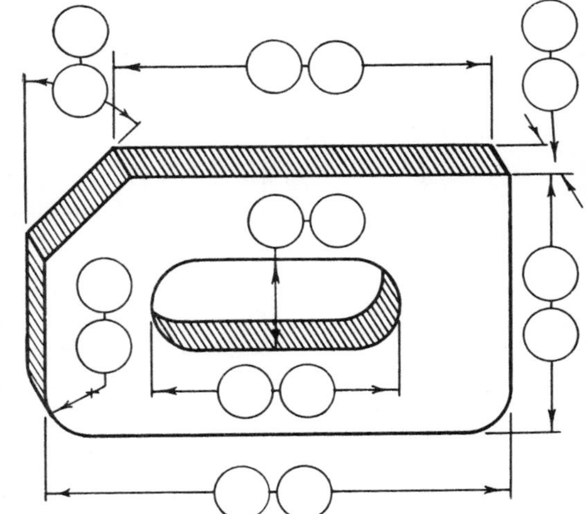

B. APPLICATION OF SYMBOLS IN ADDITION

1. Determine the literal dimensions A through F for the Parallel Bar.

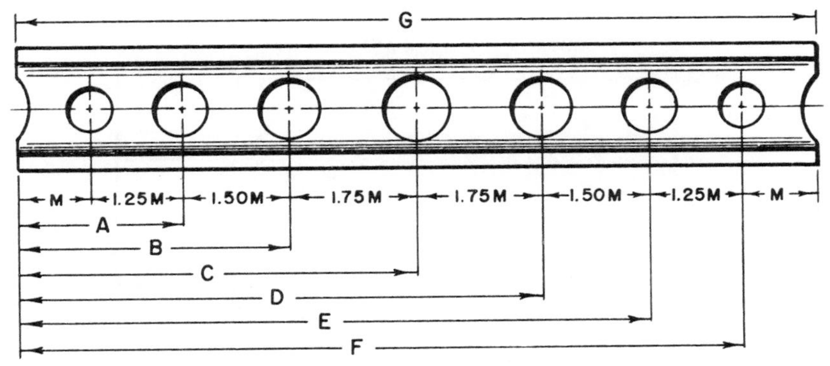

2. Find the literal dimensions A through H for the End Plate.

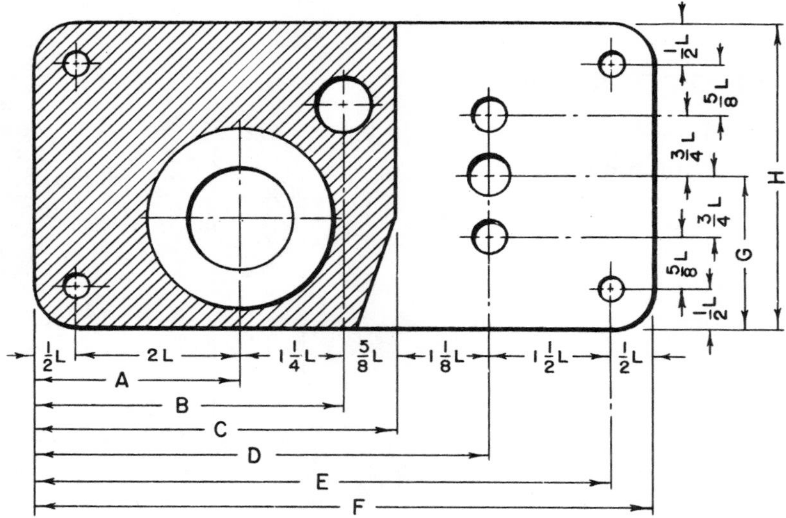

C. APPLICATION OF SYMBOLS IN SUBTRACTION

1. Determine the literal values of dimensions A through E.

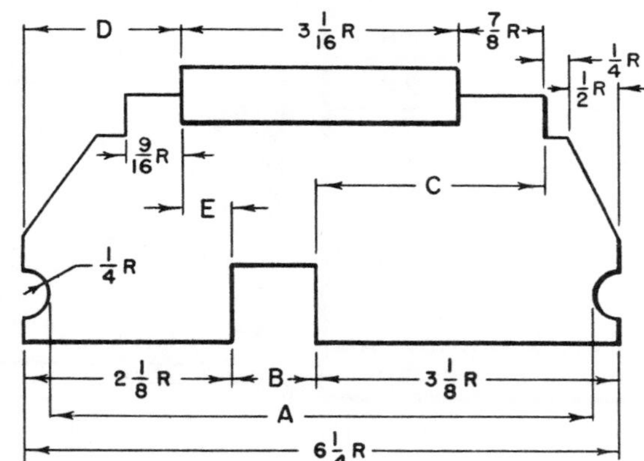

2. Compute literal dimensions A through E for the Gage Plate.

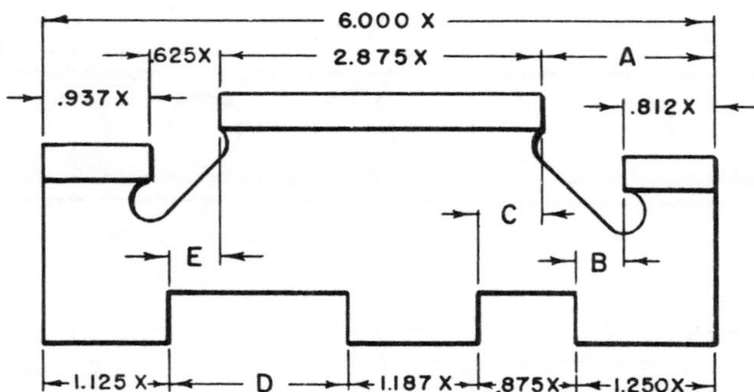

D. APPLICATION OF SYMBOLS IN MULTIPLICATION

1. Use the values of A_1 and A_2 in the formula $2\ 1/2\ (A_1 - A_2) + 2$ to determine values for dimensions A through D.

Dim.	A_1	A_2
A	20	10
B	8 1/2	4 1/2
C	6 3/8	3 7/8
D	10.50	6.25

2. By using letters as symbols, only one drawing is required for different sizes of the same template. Determine dimensions A through O which are needed for machining each of the five templates.

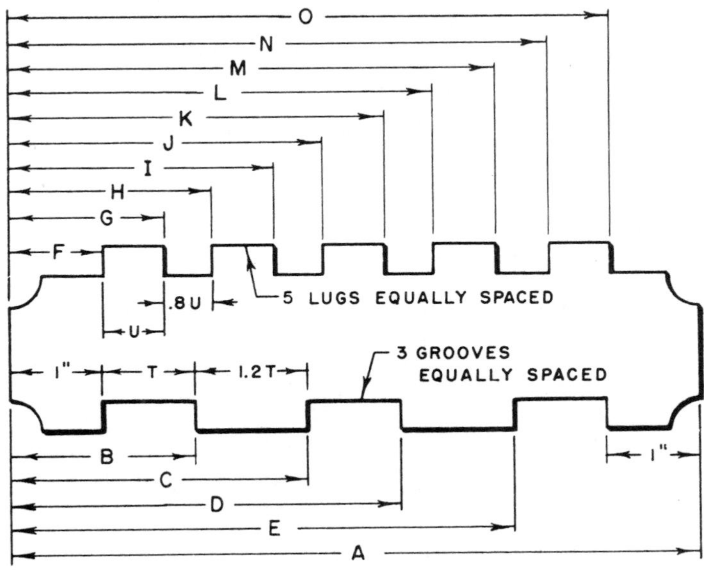

Table of Values		
Template No.	T	U
1	1	.66
2	1.5	1.0
3	2	1.32
4	2.5	1.66
5	3	1.98

E. APPLICATION OF SYMBOLS IN DIVISION

1. Determine the dimensions A through K to which the three different sized gages must be machined.

NOTE: Express all dimensions as decimals, correct to three places.

	Gage No.		
	1	2	3
X =	107.5 mm	40.96 cm	19.146 cm

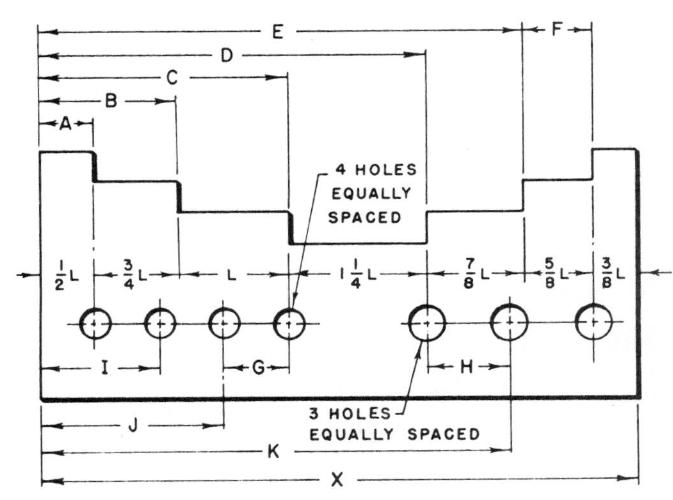

Section 10

EQUATIONS

Unit 45 A CONCEPT OF EQUATIONS

Equations, like symbols, are used in higher mathematics to solve problems which would otherwise be difficult and complicated. Symbols are widely applied in equations to represent unknown quantities which must be computed. Symbols also represent given known quantities which would be difficult to use in a problem except in the final steps in the solution.

In this section, the term *equations* is defined. The common principles which apply in the daily use of equations are also stated. The concept regarding the term *equations* and the principles underlying their use are applied in problems involving addition, subtraction, multiplication, and division. The use of equations is essential to a study of basic algebra. In this unit equations are treated as a method of applying higher mathematics to the solution of everyday problems.

A. DEFINING EQUATIONS

An equation is a statement expressed in mathematical terms. An equation indicates that the quantities or expressions on both sides of an (=) sign are equal. An *equation* is said to be an equality of two quantities. An expression like ($C = \pi D$) is a simple equation. The (C) is the symbol for circumference; (D), for the diameter of the circle; and (π) the Greek letter symbol, for the constant (3.1416). The equation $C = \pi D$ indicates that the circumference (C) is equal to the product of (π) times the diameter (D). The symbols (C) and (D) are used in this case to represent unknown quantities.

An equation is, therefore, a combination of numerical quantities and symbols which when added, subtracted, multiplied, or divided (as indicated by the signs in an expression) are equal to another stated quantity. An equation usually asks a question:

> What number added to (7) will equal (21)? The letter (X) is commonly used to represent the unknown quantity. This problem can be stated as a simple equation which may be solved by inspection.
>
> $$X + 7 = 21$$
>
> $$\boxed{14} + 7 = 21$$
>
> Therefore, $$X = 14$$

Where subtraction, multiplication, and division processes are indicated, a question is also asked. For example:

What number subtracted from 10 equals 4?

What number multiplied by 6 equals 30?

What number divided by 5, a given number (or any symbol), equals 10, a stated quantity?

B. PARTS OF AN EQUATION

In all equations, the expressions which appear on either side of the equality sign (=) are called *members.* Usually, the term *first member* is used to indicate the quantity to the left of the sign, and *second member,* the expression on the right of the equality sign.

The first member in the illustration is (5A + 4); the second member, (24).

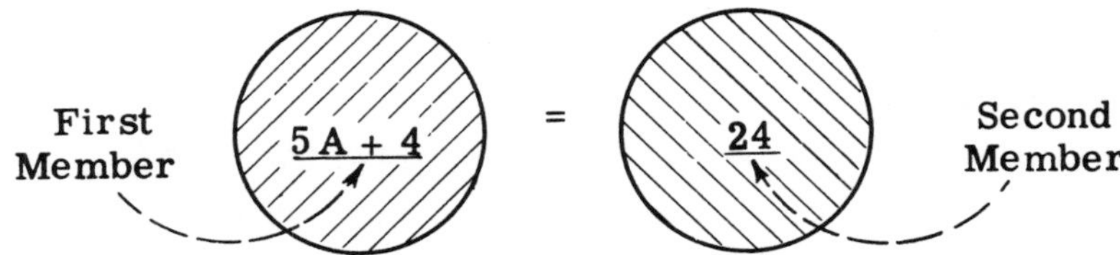

C. BALANCING AN EQUATION

In every equation both members must be equal and the equation is said to *balance.* To keep an equation in balance, the equal members must be increased or decreased, multiplied or divided by equal amounts.

After an equation has been solved, the value obtained for an unknown quantity is substituted in the equation. If the equation is *balanced,* as indicated by the equality of both members, the solution is correct.

This process of checking is essential at all times to prove the accuracy of dimensions and quantities. It is comparatively simple to substitute computed values in the original equation to determine the accuracy of computation.

RULE FOR CHECKING AN EQUATION

- Substitute the computed value of any letter or symbol in the original equation.
- Perform each operation as indicated.

NOTE: The equation is balanced when the values on both sides of the equation are equal.

EXAMPLE: Case 1 Check the answer B = 4 in the equation 6B = 24.

Step 1	Substitute the value of B in the original equation. (B = 4)	$6(4) = 24$
Step 2	Multiply.	$6 \times 4 = 24$
Step 3	Check the answer. Since both sides of the equation are equal, the answer B = 4 is correct.	$24 = 24$

EXAMPLE: Case 2 Solve the equation 8Y + 7Y = 45 and check.

Step 1	Perform operations indicated for first member (left side) of equation.	$8Y + 7Y = 15Y$ $15Y = 45$
Step 2	Divide the value of both members by 15.	$\frac{15Y}{15} = \frac{45}{15}$ Ans. Y = 3
Step 3	Check by substituting the value of Y in the original equation. Y = 3	$8(3) + 7(3) = 45$

Step 4	Perform the mathematical operations as indicated. Multiply. Then add.	$24 + 21 = 45$
Step 5	Check the final value on both sides of the equation. NOTE: If these values are not equal, start at the beginning in the original problem and check each successive step.	$45 = 45$

D. COLLECTING TERMS

The expression *collecting terms* refers to the process of combining letters or numbers within brackets, parentheses, or other grouping symbols. The terms are collected or combined as indicated by the signs of operation either to determine a final result or to simplify additional mathematical operations.

RULE FOR COLLECTING TERMS TO DETERMINE FINAL RESULT

- Combine letters, numbers, or other symbols in the first member; then, the second member.
- Add, subtract, multiply, or divide as indicated in each case.

  NOTE: Follow the practice of starting with the quantities in parentheses first, brackets next and, finally, those in braces.
- Write the resulting simplified equation.
- Perform the operations as indicated.
- Simplify the result by reducing to lowest terms when needed.

EXAMPLE: Solve the equation $2R = 7 + (4 + 3) + 6$.

Step 1	Collect terms in the right member of the equation by adding the numerical terms.	$7 + (4 + 3) + 6 = 20$
Step 2	Restate the simplified equation to simplify the next step.	$2R = 7 + (4 + 3) + 6$ (Original Equation) $2R = 20$ (Simplified Equation)
Step 3	Solve this simple equation for (R) by inspection.	Ans. $2R = 20$, $R = 10$

COLLECTING TERMS TO SIMPLIFY OPERATIONS

EXAMPLE: Solve the equation $(4X + 7X) - 3X = 5 + (18 - 3) + (14 - 2)$.

Step 1	Perform the mathematical operations indicated within the grouping symbols of the right (second) member of the equation.	$(18 - 3) = 15$ $(14 - 2) = 12$
Step 2	Collect terms in the right member of the equation.	$5 + 15 + 12 = 32$
Step 3	Perform the mathematical operations indicated in the parenthesis of the left member.	$(4X + 7X) = 11X$
Step 4	Collect terms in left member.	$11X - 3X = 8X$
Step 5	Restate equation in simplified terms.	$8X = 32$
Step 6	Solve for the unknown.	Ans. $X = 4$

CHECK: The accuracy of the computed value of X may be checked by substituting 4 for X in the original equation.

Step 1	Start with original equation.	$(4X + 7X) - 3X = 5 + (18 - 3) + (14 - 2)$
Step 2	Substitute 4 for X.	$(4 \times 4 + 7 \times 4) - 3 \times 4 = 5 + (18 - 3) + (14 - 2)$
Step 3	Perform the mathematical operations as indicated.	$(16 + 28) - 12 = 5 + (15) + (12)$ $44 - 12 = 5 + 15 + 12$
	Check both sides of equation to be sure that they balance.	$32 = 32$

E. REMOVING COMMON FACTORS

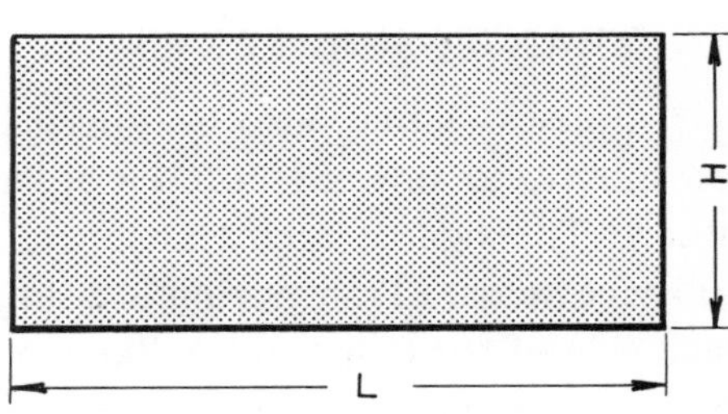

Formulas or other expressions of equality may often be reduced to simplest terms without changing their value. Where a factor is common to an expression, it may be removed. For example, the perimeter of a rectangle is equal to the sum of all four sides. Expressed as a formula, $P = 2L + 2H$. This formula may also be written $P = 2(L + H)$. The (2) is common to both literal terms and the way in which it is written does not change its value: $2L + 2H = 2(L + H)$.

This practice may be applied also when only letter symbols or combinations of letters and numbers are used in an expression. The common factor may be a single numeral, letter, or symbol, or any combination of one or more of these.

RULE FOR REMOVING FACTORS

- Examine the letters, numbers, and symbols on the left side of the equation.
- Determine which number or letter (if any) may be removed as a common factor.
- Place the common factor outside a parenthesis.
- Remove the common factor from each term.
- Perform the same operations for the right side of the equation.

EXAMPLE: Case 1 Simplify the expression AB – AC + AD.

Step 1	Determine which factor is common to AB, AC, and AD.	
Step 2	Place the common factor (A) outside a parenthesis.	A ( )
Step 3	Factor each term by removing the common factor and writing the remainder in the parenthesis.	A (B – C + D)
	The new expression	

A (B – C + D) is equal to AB – AC + AD.

EXAMPLE: Case 2 Simplify the expression (3XY - 6Y).

Step 1	Determine the factor which is common to both terms (3Y).	
Step 2	Place common factor (3Y) outside parenthesis.	3Y ( )
Step 3	Factor each term.	3XY = 3Y (X) 6Y = 3Y (2)
Step 4	Combine terms and keep the original signs.	3Y (X) - 3Y (2) = 3Y (X - 2)

The new expression 3Y (X – 2) is equal to 3XY – 6Y.

F. TRANSPOSING TERMS

Equations may also be solved by transposing terms. By this method, all known terms are moved to one side of the equation (usually the right) and all unknown terms to the other. The sign of each transposed quantity is changed. Hence, + becomes –; x becomes ÷; and vice versa. Transposing is a simple form of adding, subtracting, multiplying, or dividing each side of the equation by like amounts.

RULE FOR SOLVING EQUATIONS BY TRANSPOSING

- Determine which terms should be moved from one side of an equation to the other.
- Take one term at a time, of those to be transposed, and move it to the opposite side.
- Change the sign of each term as it is moved from one side of the equal sign to the other.
- Continue to transpose by collecting the known and unknown terms.
- Divide the equation by the numerical value or letter (known as the coefficient) preceding the unknown quantity.
- Check the equality of the equation by substituting the computed value of the unknown in the original equation.

EXAMPLE: Solve the equation 5X + 4 = -2X + 25.

Step 1 Transpose known quantity (4) from left to right in the original equation.

5X + (4) = -2X + 25 (-4)

Change sign + → -

- Change sign

Step 2 Transpose unknown quantity from right to left.

5X (+2X) = (-2X) + 25 -4

5X (+2X) = 25 (-4)

Equation with known and unknown terms transposed.

Step 3 Collect all terms.

7X = 21

Step 4 Divide the known term (21) by the coefficient of the unknown (7).

$X = \frac{21}{7}$

Ans. X = 3

CHECK:

Step 1	Substitute the computed value 3 for the unknown X in the original equation.	$5X + 4 = -2X + 25$ (Original Equation)
Step 2	Collect terms on both sides of the equation by performing the operations as indicated.	$5(3) + 4 = -2(3) + 25$
Step 3	Check final values on both sides of the equation to see that they are equal.	$19 = 19$

ASSIGNMENT UNIT 45

A. DEVELOPING A CONCEPT OF EQUATIONS

1. Develop an equation to show the amount of metal machined from the gear casting as illustrated. Use the letter (X) to denote the amount of metal removed during machining.

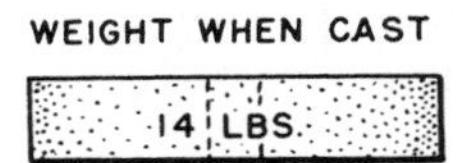

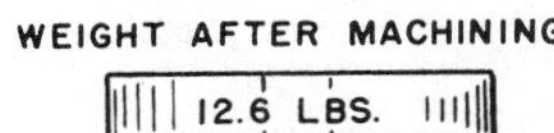

2. Express the circumferences (C_1) and (C_2) as equations in terms of diameters (D_1) and (D_2) respectively.

   Ans.: $C_2 = \pi D_2$

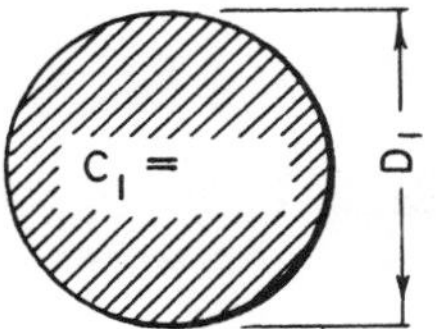

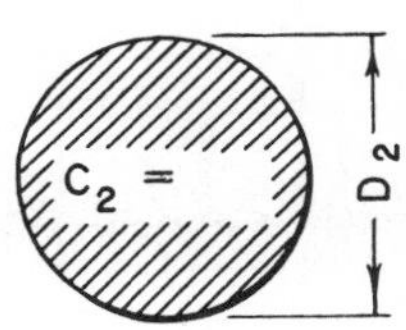

3. Develop an equation for finding the center distance (C) for the discs in the illustration.

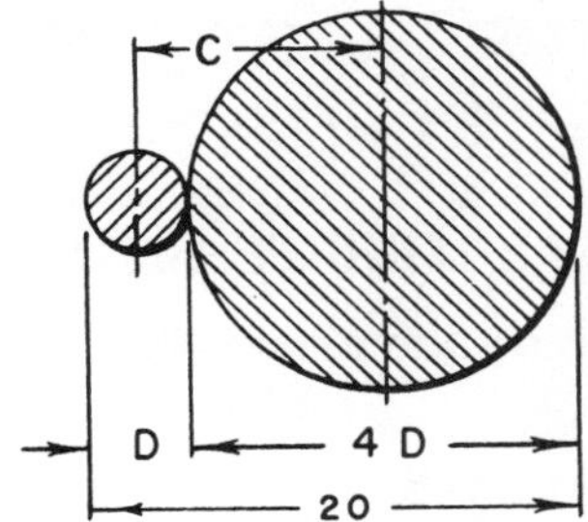

4. Indicate by an equation how the root diameter of the thread illustrated may be computed.

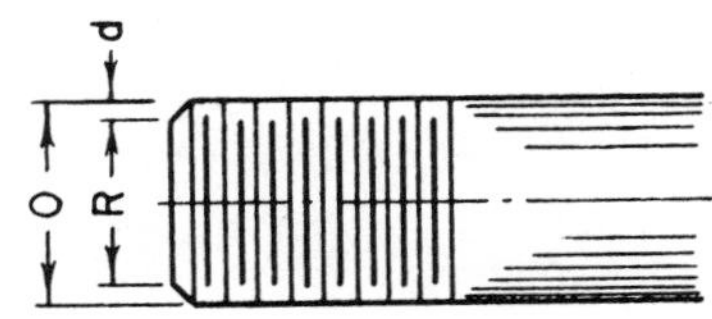

O = OUTSIDE DIAMETER
R = ROOT DIAMETER
d = SINGLE DEPTH OF THREAD

   Ans.: $R = O - 2d$

5. Show by an equation how the pitch of a thread may be computed. The pitch is equal to the unit (1) divided by the number of threads per inch.

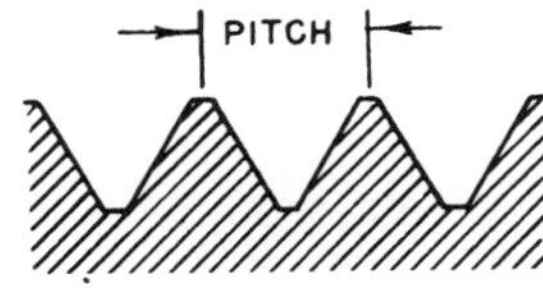

P = PITCH
N = NUMBER OF THREADS PER INCH

6. Write an equation in terms of the inside diameter (I) and wall thickness (W) for computing the outside diameter (O) of the tube illustrated.

   Ans.: $O = I + 2W$

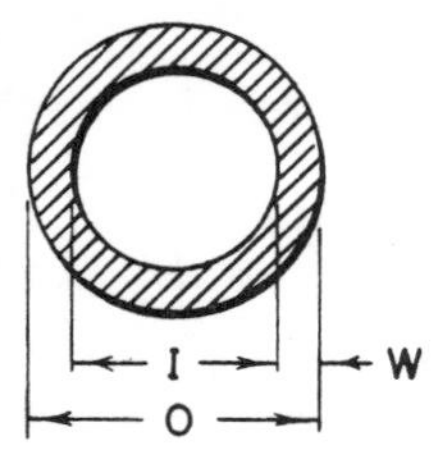

7. Determine the equations for computing dimensions A, B, C, D, and E given on the drawing. Express each equation in terms of the letter symbol indicated in the table.

   NOTE: Simplify each equation by collecting terms and removing any common factor.

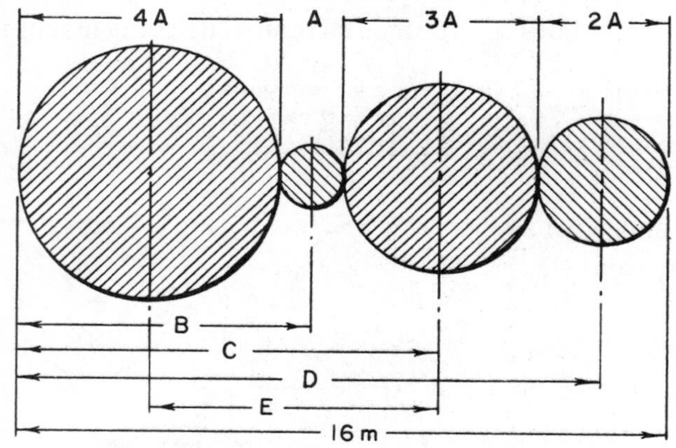

Req'd. Dimen.	Terms
A	16 m
B	A
C	B and A
D	C and A
E	16 and A

Ans.: $B = 4\ 1/2\ A = 7.2$ m; $D = C + 2\ 1/2\ A = 14.4$ m

B. COLLECTING TERMS AND REMOVING COMMON FACTORS

1. Simplify the expressions A through J.

   a. $2X + Y$
   b. $4N - 2LN$
   c. $3XY + 6LM$
   d. $\pi D_1 + \pi D_2$
   e. $2\pi R_1 - 2\pi R_2$
   f. $3\ 1/7\ D_1 - 3\ 1/7\ D_2$
   g. $1.28P_4 - .64P_5$
   h. $1\ 1/2\ L + 3N$
   i. $6A + 18B - 30C$
   j. $1.57(AB) + 1.57(BC) - 3.14(BD)$

   Ans.: b. $2N(2 - L)$ e. $2\pi(R_1 - R_2)$ h. $1\ 1/2\ (L + 2N)$

2. Solve equations A through F by inspection. Check results.

   a. $4A = 24$
   b. $21 = 3X$
   c. $22 + 6 = 7B$
   d. $5\ 1/2\ Y = 34 + 32$
   e. $18C - 13\ 1/2\ C = 126 - 58\ 1/2$
   f. $7M - 3M = 44 + 16$

   Ans.: b. $X = 7$ d. $Y = 12$ f. $M = 15$

Unit 46 POSITIVE AND NEGATIVE QUANTITIES

A. SIGNS OF MATHEMATICAL OPERATIONS

The four mathematical signs of (+), (–), (x), and (÷) denote the same processes regardless of whether used in simple arithmetical problems or in computations requiring the use of higher mathematics. The (+) and (–) signs are referred to here as *signs of operation.* Signs of operation are used to indicate what operation is to be performed with specific quantities.

In performing mathematical operations with equations and formulas, the result is often a minus quantity. The minus quantity is referred to as a *negative quantity.* A negative quantity is indicated by a minus (–) sign; a *positive quantity,* by a plus (+) sign. These signs are now used to indicate the quality of a number, that is, whether a number is a *positive* or a *negative quantity.* Such signs are called *signs of quality.*

EXAMPLE: Add the following:

$$(+10) + (+15) + (+6) = +31$$

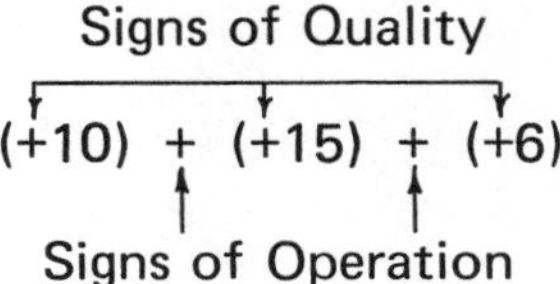

In the (+31) the (+) is the sign of a positive quantity or a sign of *quality.* The plus (+) signs between the parentheses are signs of *operation.*

B. ADDITION OF POSITIVE AND NEGATIVE QUANTITIES

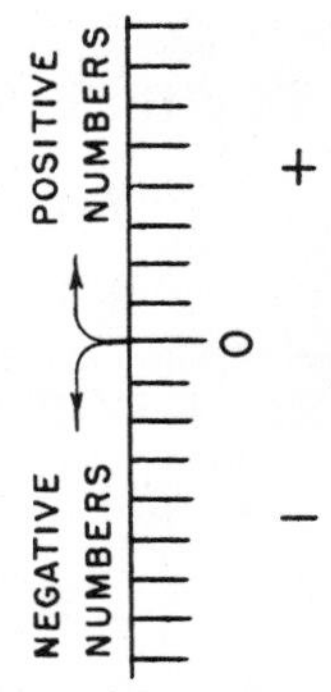

In addition, either numerical or literal quantities are combined in a unit. If all the numbers added are positive and the sign of operation is (+), the answer is a positive number.

The words *positive number* refer to all numbers greater than zero. All numbers less than zero are *negative numbers.* Positive numbers are preceded by a (+) sign; negative numbers, a (–) sign. A quantity like (–10) is a negative number as indicated by the minus (–) sign. When no sign appears before a number it is assumed to be positive.

When it is necessary to find the sum of two or more quantities with different signs, subtract the smaller value from the larger. Give the result the same sign as the larger unit.

There are four possible combinations in addition:

- Two positive quantities.
- Two quantities with unlike signs where the positive term is larger than the negative one.
- Two quantities with unlike signs where the negative quantity is larger than the positive.
- Two negative quantities.

The possible combinations are illustrated as four cases.

Case 1	Case 2	Case 3	Case 4
+4 +1 +5	+4 –1 +3	–4 +1 –3	–4 –1 –5

RULE FOR ADDING NUMBERS WITH LIKE SIGNS

- Find the arithmetical sum.
- Place the common sign before this sum.

EXAMPLE: Case 1 Add (+4) + (+5).

Step 1	Find the arithmetical sum.	(4 + 5) = 9
Step 2	Place the common sign (+) before this sum.	(+4) + (+5) = +9

EXAMPLE: Case 2 Add (–4) + (–5).

Step 1	Find the arithmetical sum.	(4 and 5) = 9
Step 2	Place the common sign (–) before this sum.	(–4) + (–5) = –9

RULE FOR ADDING TWO NUMBERS WITH UNLIKE SIGNS

- Subtract the smaller number from the larger.
- Place the sign of the larger before the sum.

EXAMPLE: Case 3 Add (–9) + (+5).

Step 1	Subtract the smaller number (5) from the larger (9).	(9 – 5) = 4
Step 2	Place the sign of the larger (–) before the sum.	(–9) + (+5) = –4

EXAMPLE: Case 4 Add (+8) + (–4).

Step 1	Subtract the smaller (–4) from the larger (+8).	(8 – 4) = 4
Step 2	Place the sign of the larger (+) before the sum.	(+8) + (–4) = +4

RULE FOR ADDING MORE THAN TWO NUMBERS WITH UNLIKE SIGNS

- Add all the positive numbers.
- Add all the negative numbers.
- Subtract the smaller quantity from the larger.
- Place the sign of the larger before the final sum.

EXAMPLE: Add (+6) + (+5) + (–4) + (–3).

Step 1	Add all the positive numbers.	(+6) + (+5) = +11
Step 2	Add all the negative numbers.	(–4) + (–3) = –7
Step 3	Subtract the smaller from the larger.	(+11) + (–7) = 4
Step 4	Place the sign of the larger (+) before the final sum (+4).	Ans. +4

C. SUBTRACTION OF POSITIVE AND NEGATIVE QUANTITIES

The subtraction of any quantity or expression is indicated by the minus (–) sign. However, the subtraction of positive and negative numbers is the inverse of addition.

The possible combinations for subtracting two numbers are illustrated as four cases.

Case 1	Case 2	Case 3	Case 4
(+4) - (+1) (+3)	(+4) -(-1) (+5)	(-4) - (-1) (-3)	(-4) - (+1) (-5)

RULE FOR SUBTRACTING POSITIVE AND NEGATIVE NUMBERS

- Change the sign of the quantity to be subtracted (subtrahend).
- Proceed as in addition.

EXAMPLE: Subtract (–8a) – (+4a) – (–3a).

Step 1 Change the signs of the quantities to be subtracted. (Subtrahends) — (-8a) - (-4a) - (+3a)

Step 2 Change signs of operation to plus (+). — (-8a) + (-4a) + (+3a)

Step 3 Proceed as with addition. Add all negative quantities. — (-8a) + (-4a) = -12a

Step 4 Subtract the smaller quantity (3a) from the larger (12a). — (-12a) + (+3a) = -9a

Step 5 Place the sign of the larger quantity (–) before the final sum. — Ans. -9a

D. ADDITION AND SUBTRACTION INVOLVING GROUPING SYMBOLS

When the plus sign precedes a parenthesis or other grouping symbol, all the terms inside the parenthesis are to be added to the preceding terms. The parenthesis may be removed without changing the signs of any of the terms if it is preceded by a (+) sign.

EXAMPLE: Add 8 + (5 – 3) + (6 – 2).

Step 1 Remove all parentheses preceded by a plus sign. The quantity + (5 – 3) is the same as 5 – 3; + (6 – 2) = 6 – 2. — (8 + 5 + 6) = 19

Step 2 Add all the positive numbers. — (8 + 5 + 6) = 19

Step 3 Add all the negative numbers. — (-3) + (-2) = -5

Step 4 Subtract and place the sign of the larger before the final sum. — Ans. 19 - 5 = 14

When a minus (–) sign precedes a parenthesis or other grouping symbol, it indicates that all the terms within the parenthesis are to be subtracted from preceding terms. The signs of all the terms in the parenthesis are changed and the same procedure is followed as in addition.

EXAMPLE: Perform the operations indicated: 6 – (5 – 2) – (3 – 6).

Step 1 Change the signs of quality in each parenthesis preceded by a (–) sign. — –(5 - 2) becomes (-5 + 2); -(3 - 6) becomes (-3 + 6)

Step 2 Remove parentheses and proceed as in addition. — 6 - 5 + 2 - 3 + 6 = +6

E. MULTIPLICATION OF POSITIVE AND NEGATIVE QUANTITIES

When two numbers with *like signs* are multiplied, the product is plus (+) as illustrated in the table in Cases 1 and 2. The product of two numbers with *unlike signs* is minus (–), Cases 3 and 4.

Case 1	Case 2	Case 3	Case 4
$\begin{array}{r} +4 \\ \underline{\times (+3)} \\ +12 \end{array}$	$\begin{array}{r} -4 \\ \underline{\times (-3)} \\ +12 \end{array}$	$\begin{array}{r} -4 \\ \underline{\times (+3)} \\ -12 \end{array}$	$\begin{array}{r} +4 \\ \underline{\times (-3)} \\ -12 \end{array}$

PRINCIPLES APPLIED TO MULTIPLYING POSITIVE AND NEGATIVE TERMS

1. When an even number of negative terms is multiplied, the product is (+).
2. When an odd number of negative terms is multiplied, the product is (–).
3. When any number of positive terms are multiplied, the product is always plus (+).

F. DIVISION OF POSITIVE AND NEGATIVE QUANTITIES

The rules governing the use of signs for multiplication apply also in division because of the relationship between these two processes. When dividing quantities with *like signs,* the quotient is plus (+); for quantities with *unlike signs,* minus (–).

RULE FOR DIVIDING TWO QUANTITIES WITH LIKE SIGNS

- Divide as in arithmetic.
- Place the plus (+) sign before the quotient.

RULE FOR DIVIDING TWO QUANTITIES WITH UNLIKE SIGNS

- Divide as in arithmetic.
- Place the minus (–) sign before the quotient.

These rules are applied in the four instances cited in the table.

Case 1	Case 2	Case 3	Case 4
$\frac{+12}{+4} = +3$	$\frac{-12}{-4} = +3$	$\frac{-12}{+4} = -3$	$\frac{+12}{-4} = -3$

ASSIGNMENT UNIT 46

A. ADDITION OF POSITIVE AND NEGATIVE QUANTITIES

1. Add the following combinations of positive and negative values for the numerical and literal terms indicated.

a.	b.	c.	d.	e.	f.	g.	h.
$\begin{array}{r} +5 \\ \underline{+4} \end{array}$	$\begin{array}{r} +8 \\ \underline{-3} \end{array}$	$\begin{array}{r} -6 \\ \underline{+4} \end{array}$	$\begin{array}{r} -10 \\ \underline{-4} \end{array}$	$\begin{array}{r} +6X \\ \underline{+7X} \end{array}$	$\begin{array}{r} +9Y \\ \underline{-2Y} \end{array}$	$\begin{array}{r} -6AB \\ \underline{+3AB} \end{array}$	$\begin{array}{r} -4XYZ \\ \underline{-12XYZ} \end{array}$

i. +6 1/2L
+9 1/4L

j. +6.25A
−3.75A

k. -5 1/8L
-8 1/4L

l. -3.063B
-8.875B

m. +5 1/2
+6 1/2
+9
-3

n. 17
+6 1/4
−3 1/4
−4 1/2

o. −12 7/8
-5 3/8
−4 1/4
+6 1/2

p. +9.625A
−7.125A
−2.250A
+3.375A

Ans.: d. −14 h. −16XYZ l. − 11.938B p. +3.625A

2. The gains and losses in temperature are recorded in degrees Celsius. Give the temperature readings at each of the following four points. Each temperature reading starts at −17°C.

   a. Temperature drop −10°C
   b. Rise +33°C
   c. Drop −17°C
   d. Rise +21°C

   Ans.: b. 16°C d. 4°C

3. A merchant showed the following six monthly profits (+) and losses (-). Determine the total profit or loss for this six-month period.

Month	Profit (+) or Loss (-)
1	+ $4,275
2	+ 2,017
3	− 200
4	− 639
5	+ 2,794
6	+ 5,226

B. SUBTRACTION OF POSITIVE AND NEGATIVE QUANTITIES

1. Subtract each of the combinations a through h.

   a. +6
   +4

   c. −7
   +4

   e. +5a
   +7a

   g. −35A
   +16A

   b. +8
   −5

   d. −5
   −7

   f. +9b
   −12b

   h. −17XY
   −33XY

   Ans.: b. +13 e. −2a h. +16XY

2. Subtract each of the following.

   a. 12 − (+7)
   b. (−16) − (+6)
   c. (−32) − (−10)
   d. (5A) + (6A) + (3A) from (22A) − (−9A)
   e. (−6abc) + 9XY from (24abc − 7XY)
   f. (5X − 3YZ) from (8X + 2YZ)

   Ans.: b. −22 d. 17A f. 3X + 5YZ

3. Solve problems a through d.

   a. 8A − (+5A + 2A)
   b. 3Y + 7X − (−6X + 2Y)
   c. 4AB − (−2AB − 3LM)
   d. −3M − (−12M −6B)

   Ans.: b. 13X + Y d. 9M + 6B

C. MULTIPLICATION OF POSITIVE AND NEGATIVE QUANTITIES

1. Multiply the numerical values a through d.

a. $\begin{array}{r} 4 \\ \underline{\times\ 3} \end{array}$ b. $\begin{array}{r} (+2.2) \\ \underline{\times\ (\ -5)} \end{array}$ c. $\begin{array}{r} (-6.4) \\ \underline{\times\ (+3.4)} \end{array}$ d. $\begin{array}{r} (\quad -8) \\ \underline{\times\ (-6\ 1/4)} \end{array}$

Ans.: b. –11 d. 50

2. Multiply each of the combinations a through i.

a. (+8)(+9) d. (–5)(–8) g. (–3)(+6)(–4)
b. (+7)(–8) e. (+6)(+4)(+3) h. (–17)(–2)(–3)
c. (–6)(+3) f. (+15)(–10)(+2) i. (+12)(–11)(–5)(+8)

Ans.: b. –56 e. 72 h. –102

3. Perform the operations indicated at a, b, c, and d.

a. (5) + (6) (–4) (–3) c. –(+75) + (80) + (–3) (12) (–4)
b. (–35) – (–4) + 3 (4) (–5) d. (–3) (+2) – [3 (–5) (–2) + 6]

Ans.: b. –91 d. –42

D. DIVISION OF POSITIVE AND NEGATIVE QUANTITIES

1. Divide each of the following.

a. $\frac{14}{7}$ b. $\frac{28}{-2}$ c. $\frac{-16}{4}$ d. $\frac{-75}{-15}$

Ans.: b. –14 d. 5

2. Divide.

a. (–72) ÷ 9 c. (–36) ÷ (–2.4)
b. 64 ÷ (–8) d. (–11.9) ÷ (–1.7)

Ans.: b. –8 d. 7

3. Perform the operations indicated.

a. [(5) + (6)] ÷ (.3) c. [(+16) – (5)] ÷ (–.08)
b. [(–8) + (7)] ÷ (–5.6) d. [(7) (–4) + (17)] – (–69) ÷ (–1.6)

Ans.: b. .179 d. –36.25

E. ADDITION, SUBTRACTION, MULTIPLICATION, AND DIVISION OF POSITIVE AND NEGATIVE QUANTITIES

1. Perform the operations indicated for the three positive and negative quantities given in the table. Round off each answer to one decimal place.

a.	[(17) (11) – (14.2) (15) ÷ (.6) (.04)] x (–4.3)
b.	[(–25.6) (.4) + (–17.338) (20) x (14.5) (–4)] ÷ (–.6) (4.2)
c.	[(12) (–4.6) (3.5) – (15) (13.7) (–.09) x (19) (–4.3) (5.2)] ÷ (.02) (–35) (10.1)

Ans.: b. –7976.92

Unit 47 SOLVING EQUATIONS BY ADDITION

The solution of equations by addition may be simplified by adding the same quantity to both members. This process does not change the value of the equation.

RULE FOR SOLVING AN EQUATION BY ADDITION

- Add the same quantity to both sides.
- Check the answer by substituting the computed value for the unknown quantity in the original equation.

EXAMPLE: Case 1 Solve the equation (A) – (4) = 15.

Step 1 Add (4) to both members of the original equation.

Step 2 Add both sides of the equation.

$$\begin{array}{r} A - 4 = 15 \\ +4 = +4 \\ \hline A \quad = 19 \end{array}$$

Step 3 Check by substituting the numerical value (19) for (A) in the original equation.

$$\begin{array}{r} A - 4 = 15 \\ 19 - 4 = 15 \\ 15 = 15 \end{array}$$

EXAMPLE: Case 2 Solve the equation (2 1/2) = (B) – (7).

Step 1 Add (7) to both members of the original equation.

$$\begin{array}{rcl} 2\frac{1}{2} & = & B - 7 \\ +7 & & +7 \\ \hline \end{array}$$

Step 2 Determine the sum (9 1/2 = B).

$$9\frac{1}{2} = B$$

Step 3 Check. Substitute the numerical value (9 1/2) for (B) in the original equation.

$$\begin{array}{rcl} 2\frac{1}{2} & = & B - 7 \\ 2\frac{1}{2} & = & 9\frac{1}{2} - 7 \\ 2\frac{1}{2} & = & 2\frac{1}{2} \end{array}$$

ASSIGNMENT UNIT 47

NOTE: Each dimension computed for each problem must be checked for accuracy.

1. Determine dimensions A and B for the block illustrated.

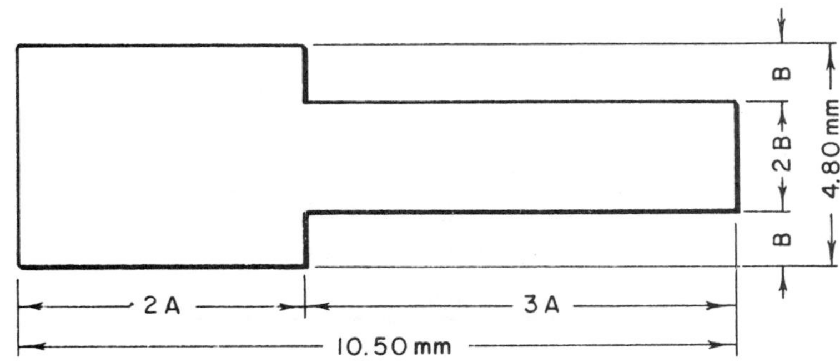

Ans.: B = 1.2 mm

2. Find dimensions A, B, and C for the following shaft.

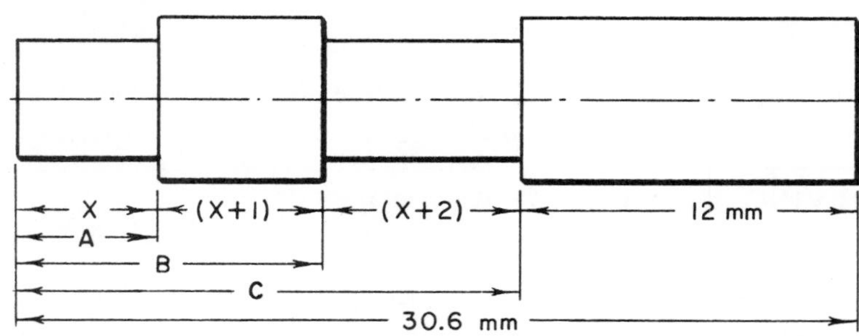

Ans.: B = 11.4 mm

3. Determine the outside diameter (mm) of each size bushing given in the table. Round off each value to two decimals.

	Inside Diameter (I)	Single Wall Thickness (T)
A	31.75 mm	6.35 mm
B	15.875 mm	4.7625 mm
C	14.2875 mm	3.175 mm
D	26.9875 mm	4.7625 mm
E	27.7876 mm	3.9624 mm

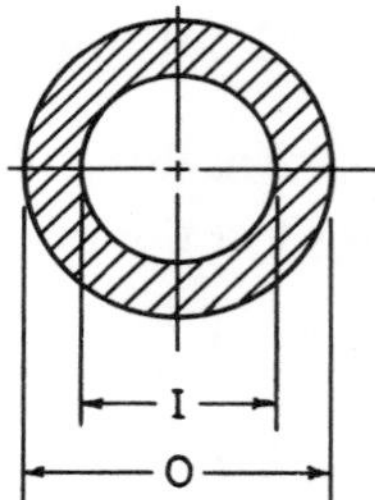

Ans.: B = 25.40 mm D = 36.51 mm

4. Determine dimensions A, B, C, and D for the special roll.

Ans.: B = 6.8″
D = 5.7″

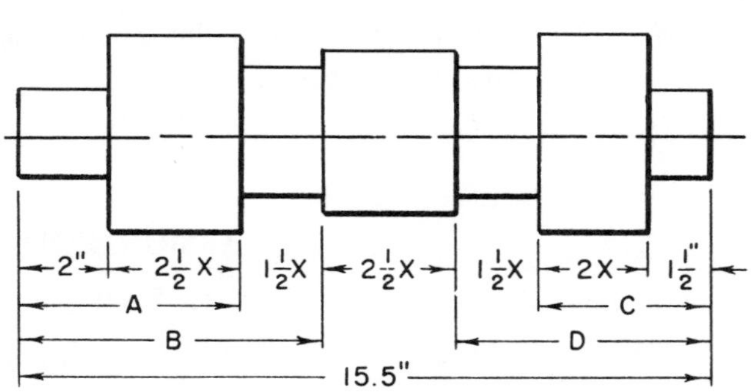

5. Solve for dimension L for each value of M and H given in the table of dimensions for the plug.

Dimension	A	B	C	D	E	F
M	8	10	6 1/4	2.500	1 3/4	1.250
H	2	3	2 1/4	.500	1/4	.375

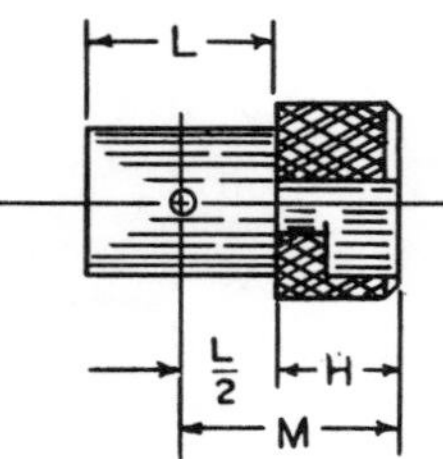

Ans.: B. 14″ D. 4″ F. 1.75″

6. Find the overall dimension (O) for each size given in the table of dimensions for the special gage.

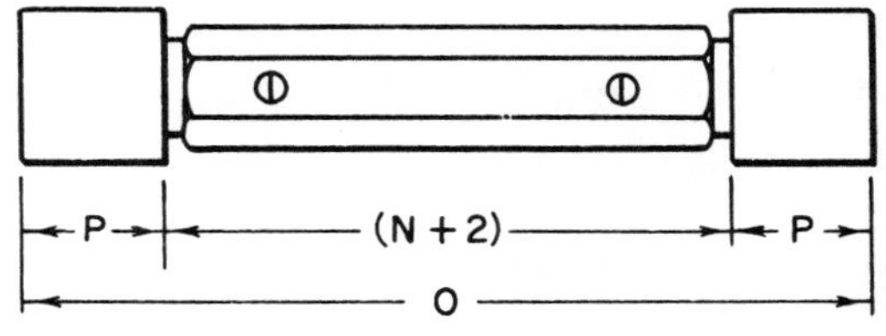

	Dimension			Dimension	
	(P)	(N)		(P)	(N)
A	1	3	D	1 3/4	4 1/4
B	2	4 1/2	E	.800	2.600
C	1 1/2	3 1/2	F	.625	2.375

Ans.: B. 10.5″ D. 9 3/4″ F. 5.625″

7. Compute the total resistance (R_t) and total voltage (V_t) of the four dry cells connected in series.

$V_t = e_1 + e_2 + e_3 + e_4$

$R_t = r_1 + r_2 + r_3 + r_4$

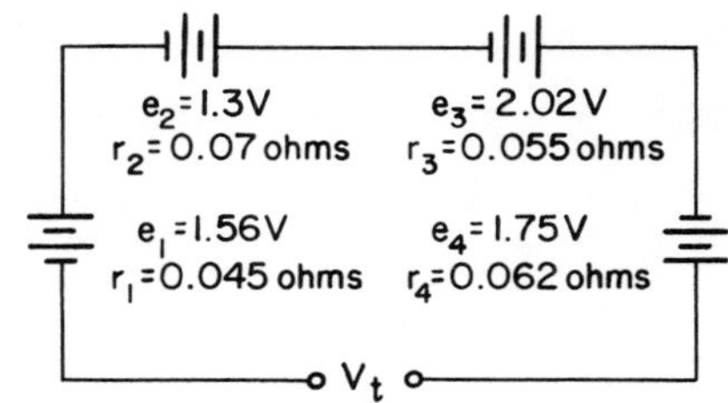

Ans.: $R_t = 0.232$ ohms

Unit 48 SOLVING EQUATIONS BY SUBTRACTION

When the same number quantity is subtracted from both sides of an equation, it does not change the value of the equation.

RULE FOR SOLVING AN EQUATION BY SUBTRACTION

- Subtract the same number or quantity from both sides.
- Check the computed value by substituting it in the original equation.

EXAMPLE: Case 1 Solve the equation X + 9 = 13.

Step 1 Subtract (9) from both sides of the equation.

NOTE: The difference (4) indicates the value of (X).

$$\begin{array}{rcr} X + 9 & = & 13 \\ -9 & & -9 \\ \hline X & = & 4 \end{array}$$

Step 2 Check by substituting the numerical value (4) for (X) in the original equation.

$$\begin{array}{rcr} X + 9 & = & 13 \\ (4) + 9 & = & 13 \\ 13 & = & 13 \end{array}$$

EXAMPLE: Case 2 Solve the equation 22.50 = M + 6.25.

Step 1 Subtract (6.25) from both sides of the equation.

NOTE: The difference (16.25) indicates the value of (M).

$$\begin{array}{rcll} 22.50 & = & M & +6.25 \\ -6.25 & & & -6.25 \\ \hline 16.25 & = & M & \end{array}$$

Step 2 Check. Substitute the numerical value (16.25) for (M) in the original equation.

$$\begin{array}{rcll} 22.50 & = & M & +6.25 \\ 22.50 & = & 16.25 & +6.25 \\ 22.50 & = & 22.50 & \end{array}$$

ASSIGNMENT UNIT 48

1. Find the center distance (L) for each set of dimensions given in the lever table. Check all computed center distances.

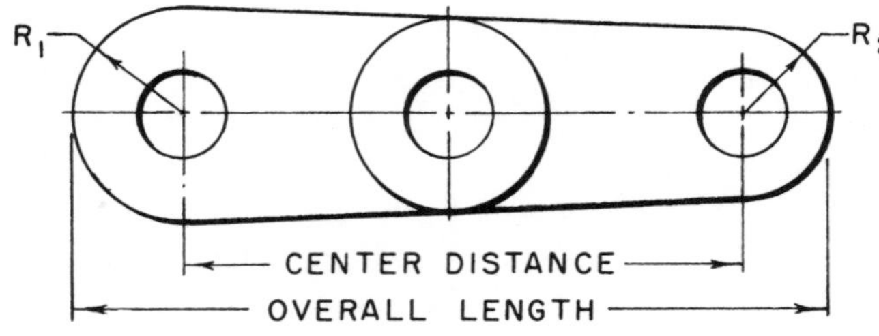

	Overall Length (O)	Radius (R_1)	Radius (R_2)
A	12″	2	1 1/2
B	11″	1 1/2	1 3/8
C	10″	1 1/4	1 1/16
D	9 1/2″	1 1/8	15/16
E	8.25″	1.125	.875
F	7.625″	.875	.687

L = Center Distance

O = Overall Length

R_1 and R_2 = Radii of Ends

Ans.: B. 8 1/8″ D. 7 7/16″ F. 6.063″

2. Convert each computed center distance (Problem 1) to its equivalent metric dimensions. Round off each dimension to an accuracy of two decimal places.

   Ans.: B. 206.38 mm D. 188.91 mm F. 154.00 mm

3. Determine the value of N for the drill plate. Check answer.

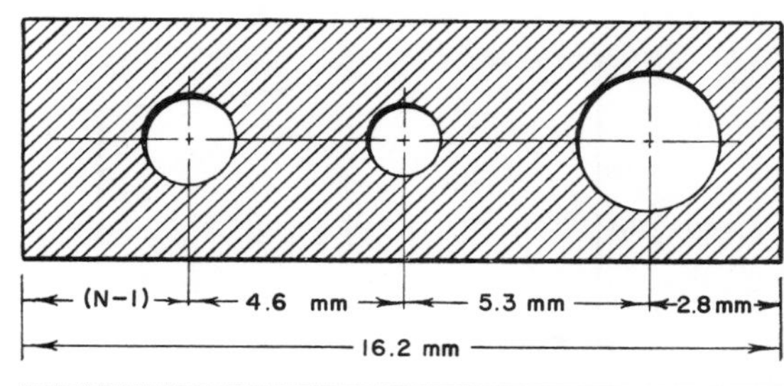

4. Solve for dimension E by using equations. Check the computed value of E. All dimensions are in millimeters (mm).

   Ans.: E = 1.8 mm

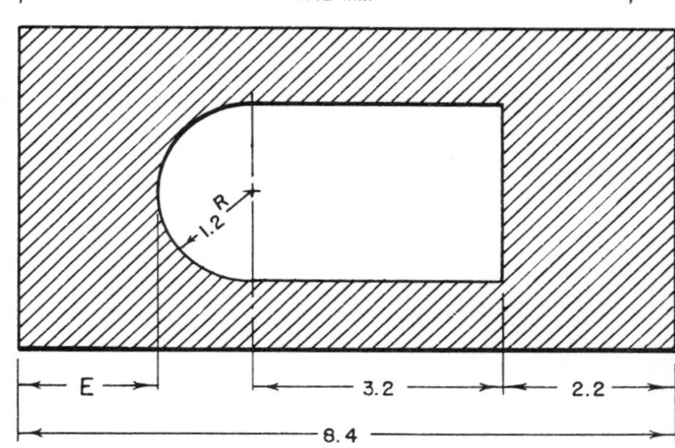

5. Solve for the internal resistance (r) or external resistance (R_1) of circuits A, B, C and D.

$$r = R_t - R_\ell$$

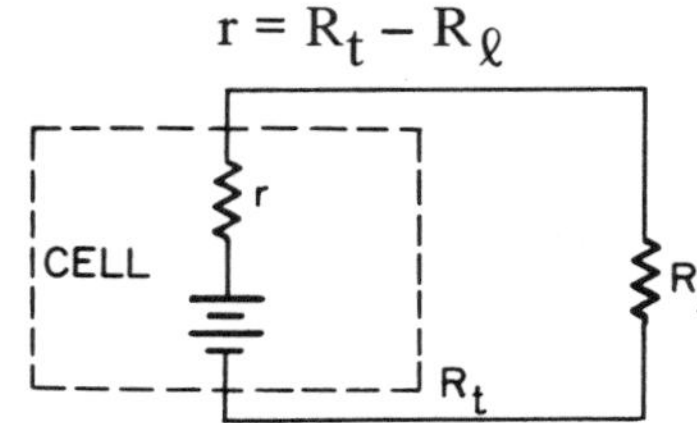

Circuit	Total Circuit Resistance (R_t)(ohms)	External Resistance (R_ℓ) (ohms)	Internal Resistance (r) (ohms)
A	2.25	1.7	
B	3.262		0.787
C	6.073		1.294

Ans.: B. 2.475

6. Find wall thickness T and 2T for each size of tubing specified in the table.

T — I D — T
O D

T = Single Wall Thickness
2T = Double Wall Thickness

	Diameters	
	Outside (OD)	Inside (ID)
A	2	1 3/4
B	4	3 1/2
C	1 1/2	1 1/8
D	5.000	4.500
E	3.750	3.375
F	1.063	1.000

Ans.: B. T = 1/4″ D. T = .25″ F. T = .0315″

7. Determine the minimum taper of machined parts A through E. The minimum taper (T) is equal to the difference between the large diameter D_1 and the small diameter D_2 at the ends of the taper, minus the tolerance (t).

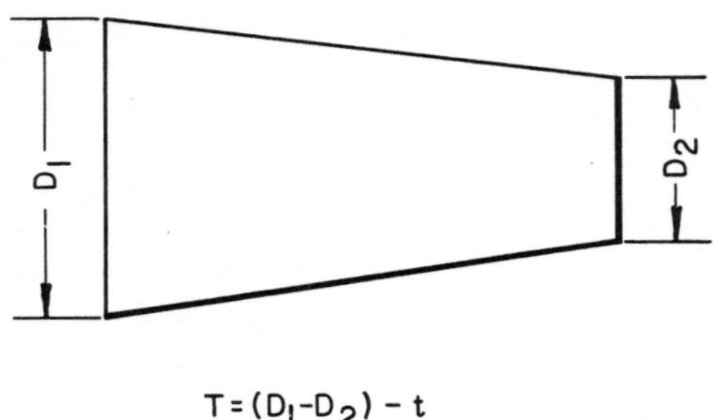

	Large Diameter (D_1)	Small Diameter (D_2)	Tolerance (t)
A	1.000"	.875"	.005"
B	8 1/2"	7 5/16"	1/64"
C	4.4x	3.2x	.03x
D	4.25A	3.125A	.19A
E	2.4 cm	.9 cm	.07 cm

Ans.: B. 1 11/64" D. .935A

Unit 49 SOLVING EQUATIONS BY MULTIPLICATION

A. MULTIPLYING BOTH MEMBERS BY THE SAME QUANTITY

The value of an equation does not change when both sides are multiplied by the same quantity.

RULE FOR SOLVING AN EQUATION CONTAINING A FRACTION

- Multiply each side by the same quantity.
- Substitute the computed value in the original equation and check the answer.

EXAMPLE: Solve the equation A/5 = 10.

Step 1 Multiply both sides of the equation by (5). $\frac{A}{5} \times (5) = 10 \times (5)$

Step 2 Cancel like factors in the numerator and denominator. The computed value of A is 50. $\frac{A}{\not{5}} \times (\not{5}) = 10 \times (5)$; $A = 50$

Step 3 Check by substituting 50 in the original equation. $\frac{50}{5} = 10$; $10 = 10$

B. CROSS-MULTIPLYING

Where the right and left members of an equation are fractions, the denominators may be removed by *cross-multiplying.* The term implies that the numerator of each member of the equation is multiplied by the denominator of the other.

RULE FOR REMOVING FRACTIONS BY CROSS-MULTIPLYING

- Multiply the numerator of the right member by the denominator of the left.
- Multiply the numerator of the left member by the denominator of the right.
- Collect terms as may be required.
- Check accuracy of result by substituting the computed value in the original equation.

EXAMPLE: Solve and check the equation $\frac{4}{6 + B} = \frac{2}{7}$.

Step 1 Multiply the numerator (2) by the denominator of the left member (6 + B). $4 = \frac{2\,(6 + B)}{7} = \frac{12 + 2B}{7}$

Step 2 Multiply the left numerator (4) by the right denominator (7). $4\,(7) = 12 + 2B$

Step 3 Move known term (12) to left side of the equation and change sign to (–). $28 - 12 = 2B$; $16 = 2B$

Step 4 Divide known term (16) by the coefficient (2) of the unknown term. $\frac{16}{2} = B;\ 8 = B$

Step 5 Check by substituting the computed value of B in the original equation.

$\frac{4}{6 + B} = \frac{2}{7}$ (Original equation)

$\frac{4}{6 + 8} = \frac{2}{7}$ (Substituting (8) for B)

$\frac{4}{14} = \frac{2}{7};\ \frac{2}{7} = \frac{2}{7}$ Check

ASSIGNMENT UNIT 49

A. MULTIPLYING BOTH SIDES OF AN EQUATION

1. Solve equations a through h by multiplication. Check each answer.

a. $\frac{X}{4} = 12$ c. $\frac{U}{5} = 2.2$ e. $\frac{c}{3.14} = 2$ g. $3.1416 = \frac{c}{2.25}$

b. $\frac{M}{2\ 1/2} = 10$ d. $\frac{1}{6}n = 5$ f. $.62 = \frac{a}{8.2}$ h. $\frac{B}{.5} = .063$

Ans.: b. M = 25 e. c = 6.28 h. B = .0315

B. CROSS-MULTIPLYING

1. Find the value of the unknown in equations a through e by cross-multiplying. Check the value of each computed value.

a. $\frac{X}{2} = \frac{6}{4}$ c. $\frac{10}{8.4} = \frac{4A}{60.48}$ e. $\frac{1 - 4\ (L - 3L)}{200} = \frac{.6}{1}$

b. $\frac{2}{4Y} = \frac{12}{72}$ d. $\frac{4B + 6}{3} = \frac{4}{5}$

Ans.: b. Y = 3 d. B = –.9

C. EQUATIONS USED IN PRACTICAL PROBLEMS

1. A circuit with a total line resistance of 0.54 ohms (R) draws 72 amperes (I) of current. Compute the power (P) of the circuit in watts.

$$P = (I) \cdot (I) \cdot (R)$$
$$P = I^2 (R)$$

2. Find the wattage for appliances A, B and C. The amperes and volts in each circuit are given in the table.

P = E x I P = watts (W) E = volts (V) I = amperes (A)

Appliance	Amperes (I,A)	Volts (E,V)	Watts (P,W)
A	1.136	110	
B	0.68	220	
C	2.174	230	

Ans.: B. 150 watts

3. Determine the number of threads per inch for screws A through F from the single depths indicated in the table.

NOTE: Compute to the nearest whole number of threads.

	Single Depth (D)		
A	.0649	D	.0361
B	.1299	E	.0101
C	.0203	F	.0232

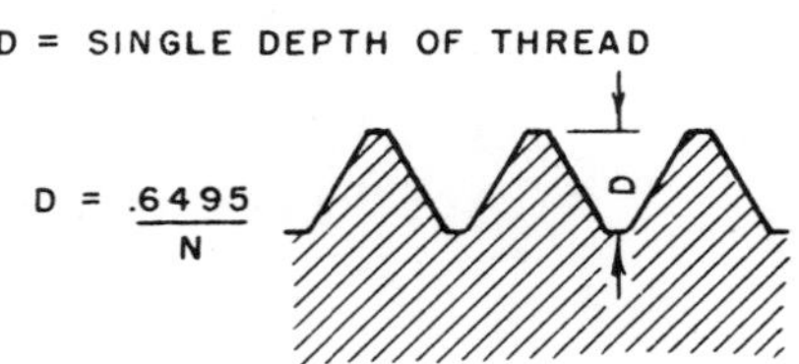

Ans.: B. N = 5 D. N = 18 F. N = 28

4. Determine the cutting speed (CS) in feet per minute for machining parts A, B, C, D, E, and F. Use the given equation and the 3.14 value of (π) in solving for (CS).

$$CS = \frac{\pi \text{ x D x rpm}}{100} = \text{m/min.}$$

CS = Cutting Speed in ft./min.
D = Diameter of Work
rpm = Revolutions per minute for work

	Diameter of Work (D)	Revolutions per Minute (rpm)
A	20 cm	24
B	8.2 cm	96
C	2.86 cm	514

	Diameter of Work (D)	Revolutions per Minute (rpm)
D	38 mm	260
E	19.1 mm	1200
F	158.75 mm	44

Ans.: B. 24.72 m/min. D. 31.02 m/min. F. 21.93 m/min.

Unit 50 SOLVING EQUATIONS BY DIVISION

When both sides of an equation are divided by the same number, symbol, or other quantity, the value remains unchanged.

RULE FOR SOLVING AN EQUATION BY DIVISION

- Divide both members of the equation by the same quantity.
- Cancel like factors in each numerator and denominator.
- Check the answer in the original equation.

EXAMPLE: Solve the equation 5A = 20.

Step 1 Divide both members of the equation by (5).

$$5A = 20 \quad \frac{5A}{5} = \frac{20}{5}$$

Step 2 Cancel like factors in each numerator and denominator.

$$\frac{\cancel{5}A}{\cancel{5}} = \frac{\cancel{20}^{\,4}}{\cancel{5}_{\,1}} \quad A = 4$$

Step 3 Check by substituting the computed value of A in the original equation.

5A = 20 (original equation)

5(4) = 20 (Substituting (4) for A)

20 = 20

ASSIGNMENT UNIT 50

1. Solve for the unknown value in each problem (a through f). Check each answer.

a. 4X = 8 c. 21 = 4Z e. 4 1/8 L = 33.66

b. 5Y = 32 d. 1 1/2 N = 30 f. 7.6875 = .375A

Ans.: b. y = 6.4 d. N = 20 f. A = 20.5

2. The perimeter of a square die block is 40.88". Find the length of each side. Check result.

PERIMETER 40.88"

L

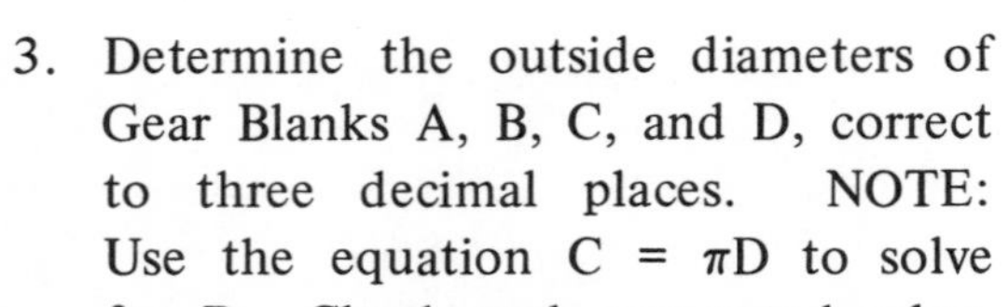

3. Determine the outside diameters of Gear Blanks A, B, C, and D, correct to three decimal places. NOTE: Use the equation C = πD to solve for D. Check each computed value.

Ans.: B. 18.183" D. 1.799"

Circumference (C)	
A	31.416
B	57.124
C	4.7124
D	5.652

OUTSIDE DIAMETER

4. The area of a rectangular blank 10.6 cm high is 261.82 sq. cm. Determine the length of the blank and check the result.

AREA = 261.82 sq. cm

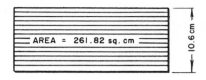

10.6 cm

5. Convert the five Celsius degree temperatures to equivalent Fahrenheit degrees.

$$C = \frac{(F - 32)\,5}{9}$$

Ans.: B. 399.2°
D. 161.6°

	Oven Temperatures (°C)	Equivalent Temperature (°F)
A	176.67°	
B	204°	
C	429.33°	
	Motor Temperature Rise (°C)	
D	72°	
E	97.30°	

6. One method used to calculate a child's dosage of certain medication is based on weight.

Child	Weight (lbs.)	Adult Dose	Child Dose
A	50	12.6 mg	
B	85	27.0 mg	
C	97	1.3 cm^3 (cc)	

$$\frac{\text{Weight of child in lbs.}}{150} \text{ x adult dose} = \text{child's dose}$$

Give the dosages of three different medications for A, B and C.

Ans.: B. 15.3 mg.

7. Determine the unknown quantity in each of the following equations (A through E). Check computed value.

	Given Equation	Given Values	Determine
A	$G = AB$	$G = 3,\ A = 6$	B
B	$L = \frac{2n}{N}$	$L = 40,\ N = 25$	n
C	$4X = \frac{A - b}{3P}$	$X = 1.25,\ A = 4.75,\ b = 2.13$	P
D	$1\frac{1}{2}M = \frac{Fd}{r}$	$M = 4.6,\ d = 1\frac{1}{4},\ r = \frac{3}{4}$	F
E	$2.2C = \frac{HM}{25}$	$H = 2200,\ M = 1.8$	C

Ans.: B. n = 500 D. F = 4.14

8. What is the efficiency of engines A, B, and C (correct to two decimal places)?

$$\text{Efficiency} = 100 \cdot \frac{\text{Useful output (O)}}{\text{Input (I)}}$$

$$E = 100 \cdot \frac{O}{I}$$

Ans.: B. E = 60%

Engine	Useful Output (O)	Input (I)
	Horsepower	
A	20	60
B	1 1/2	2 1/2
C	.162	2.12

9. Find the brake horsepower (B) of engines A, B, and C (correct to the nearest 1/4 horsepower). Check each answer.

$$B = \frac{2\left(\frac{22}{7}\right)(L)(W)(R)}{33{,}000}$$

L = Length of arm (")
W = Weight (lbs.)
R = Revolutions per minute

Ans.: B = 76 1/4

Engine	(L) inches	(W) pounds	(R) rpm
A	14	15	550
B	17 1/2	30 1/2	750
C	36 3/4	75 1/4	66

Unit 51 SOLVING PRACTICAL PROBLEMS WITH EQUATIONS

A definite sequence for analyzing practical problems should be followed because the solution may require more than one method of computation. This practice simplifies the solution of a problem and reduces the possibility of error.

RULE FOR ANALYZING, EXPRESSING, AND SOLVING PRACTICAL PROBLEMS INVOLVING EQUATIONS

- Read the entire problem through.
- Represent unknown quantities either by standard symbols assigned, or select symbols which may be easily associated with unknown dimensions.
- Determine whether a formula may be used to express the required relationship or if an equation is needed to show an equality between two expressions.
- Solve the equation by any one or combination of the four fundamental processes.
- Check all results by substituting the computed values for the unknowns in the original problem.

EXAMPLE: Determine the number of revolutions per minute that a 12-inch grinding wheel will revolve for an allowable surface speed of 6280 feet per minute.

Step 1 Select symbols to use.

(S) surface speed of wheel.
(D) diameter of wheel.
(N) rpm of grinder spindle.

Step 2 Select or derive a formula to determine the surface speed.

$$S = \frac{\pi \times D \times N}{12}$$

Step 3 Substitute known values in the formula. $S = 6280$; $\pi = 3.14$; $D = 12$.

$$6280 = \frac{3.14\ (12)\ (N)}{12}$$

Step 4 Cancel like factors in numerator and denominator of the right member.

$$6280 = \frac{3.14\ (\overset{1}{\cancel{12}})\ (N)}{\underset{1}{\cancel{12}}}$$

Step 5 Divide both members by (3.14).

$$\frac{\overset{2000}{\cancel{6280}}}{\underset{1}{\cancel{3.14}}} = \frac{\overset{1}{\cancel{3.14}}\ (N)}{\underset{1}{\cancel{3.14}}}$$

$$2000 = (N)$$

Step 6 Check. Substitute the computed value of N and other known values, in the original formula.

$$S = \frac{\pi \times D \times N}{12} \quad \text{(Original Formula)}$$

$$6280 = \frac{3.14\ (12)\ (2000)}{12} \quad \text{(Substituting values)}$$

Step 7 Cancel like factors in numerator and denominator.

$$6280 = \frac{3.14\ (\overset{1}{\cancel{12}})\ (2000)}{\underset{1}{\cancel{12}}}$$

Step 8 Multiply the remainder and compare the results. The equation is balanced when both sides are equal.

$$6280 = 6280$$

Unit 52 ACHIEVEMENT REVIEW ON EQUATIONS

A. APPLICATION OF POSITIVE AND NEGATIVE QUANTITIES

1. Add the following combinations.

a. $3A + 2B$ $\underline{4A + 6B}$	c. $4L + 6R$ $\underline{-2L - 8R}$	e. $-5X - 3Y$ $+4X + 2Y$ $\underline{+3X + 8Y}$	g. $-1.2XY - 3.22$ $-2.2XY - 8.02$ $\underline{-2.6XY - 9.62}$
b. $6a - 4b$ $\underline{-2a + 7b}$	d. $-5AB + 4CD$ $\underline{+3AB - 6CD}$	f. $5AB - 3C$ $4AB - C$ $\underline{-2AB + 8C}$	h. $-4.25YZ + 3.50PQ$ $-2.75YZ - 1.75PQ$ $\underline{+3.25YZ - .50PQ}$

2. Perform the operations indicated at A and B.

A	$17.2A - [3A + (5A - 2B) - (-3A - 4B)]$
B	$-16\frac{1}{2}L - [-5\frac{1}{2} - (8 + 3L) - (-15 + 14\frac{1}{2}L)]$

3. Two liter vessels contain 75% and 35% solutions, respectively, of the same nutrient. Determine the volume in milliliters, (mℓ) of each solution that is required to produce one liter of a 55% solution. Use the equation

   $(X) + (\ell - X) =$ required solution

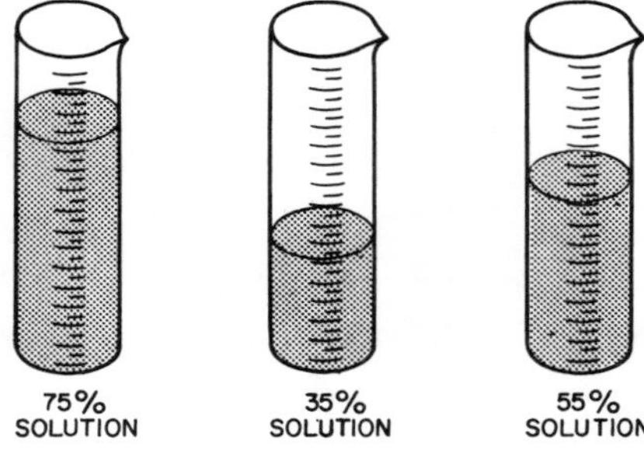

$X =$ volume of 75% solution
$(\ell - X) =$ volume of 35% solution

B. SOLVING EQUATIONS BY ADDITION

1. Determine the numerical value of X and each dimension of the step gage. Check the accuracy of the computed value.

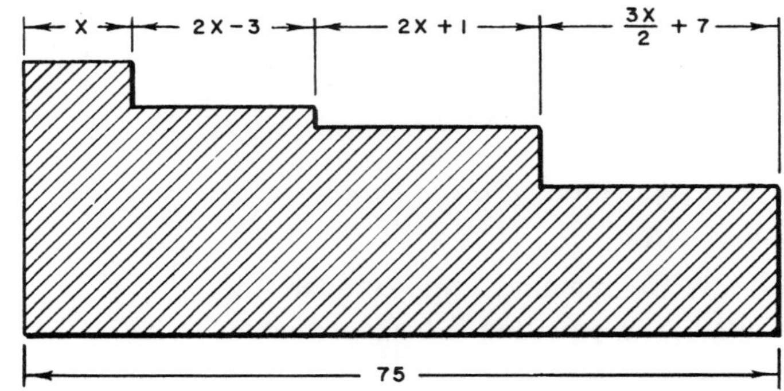

2. Solve for dimension L and check.

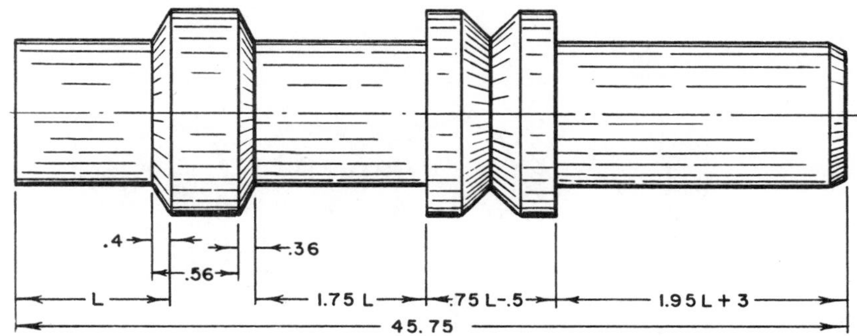

3. Determine the decimal value of dimensions O, T_1, and T_2 correct to three places. Then determine the value of each unknown dimension on the large drawing of the perforating and blanking die and the small drawing of the perforated ring.

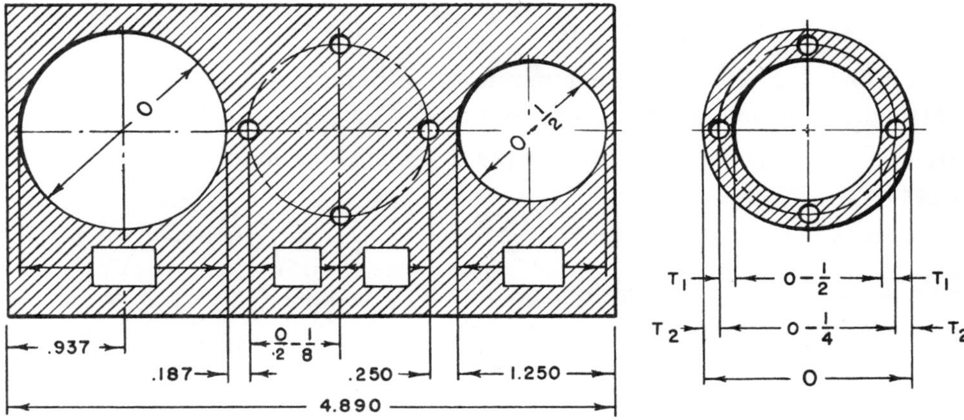

C. SOLVING EQUATIONS BY SUBTRACTION

1. Find dimensions X and Y for the bearing illustrated in both customary and metric units. Check each dimension. NOTE: Dual dimensions: $\frac{\text{customary (inches)}}{\text{metric (millimeters)}}$.

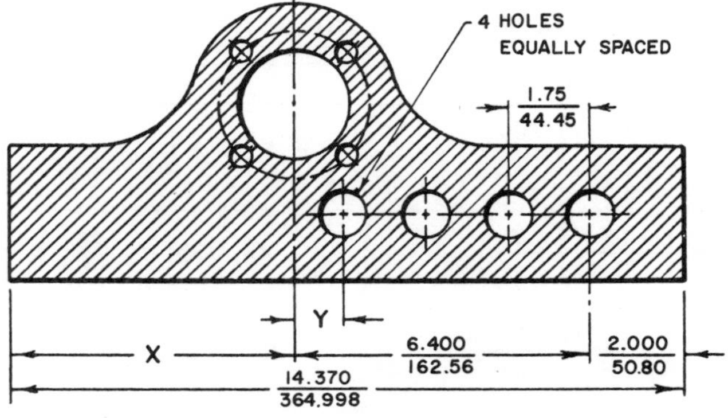

2. Solve for dimension Y in both customary and metric units. Use the numerical value $\frac{1.26''}{32.0 \text{ mm}}$ for dimension A. Give each answer correct to two decimal places. Check.

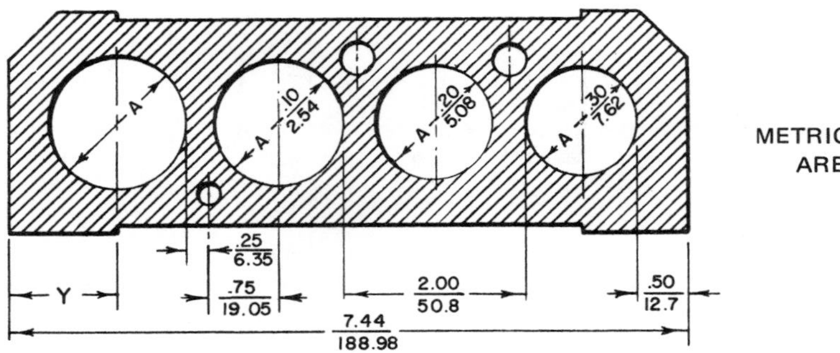

D. SOLVING EQUATIONS BY MULTIPLICATION

1. Solve for the unknown term by cross multiplying.

   a. $\frac{1.6}{2.1} = \frac{14.4}{6.2B}$ b. $\frac{8.2}{5X + 4} = \frac{2.2}{16.1}$ c. $\frac{6}{22} = \frac{15}{8(r+1)}$ d. $\frac{6 - 3(5 - 2P)}{6} = \frac{7(4P - 20)}{32}$

2. Determine the revolutions per minute of a milling machine spindle to produce the cutting speeds indicated for operations A, B, C, and D.

   NOTE: State answers in terms of the nearest whole number. Use 3.14 for the value of (π).

   Expressed as an equation, rpm $= \frac{12 \text{ CS}}{\pi D}$

   rpm is the number of revolutions per minute
   CS is the cutting speed in feet per minute
   D is the diameter of the milling cutter

Milling Operations	A	B	C	D
Diameter of Milling Cutter (D)	4	6	3 1/2	4.75
Cutting Speed in Ft/Min (CS)	100	35	800	1500

E. SOLVING EQUATIONS BY DIVISION

1. Substitute the given value in each equation and solve for the unknown. Check results.

	Given Equation	Given Value
A	$\frac{L_1}{T_1} = \frac{L_2}{T_2}$	$L_1 = 1\frac{5}{8}$, $L_2 = 3\frac{1}{4}$, $T_2 = 280$
B	$Xa = \frac{1 - (3\,Xa - 7)}{3\pi t_1 z}$	$Xa = 72$, $\pi = \frac{22}{7}$, $z = .5$
C	$5C = \frac{12\,(C - A)}{B_1 - B_2\,(2A - 3B_1 + 4)}$	$C = 4.2$, $B_1 = 3.6$, $B_2 = 2.8$

2. Determine dimensions A, X, R_1, and r_2 for the spacing gage illustrated. Check the accuracy of each computed dimension.

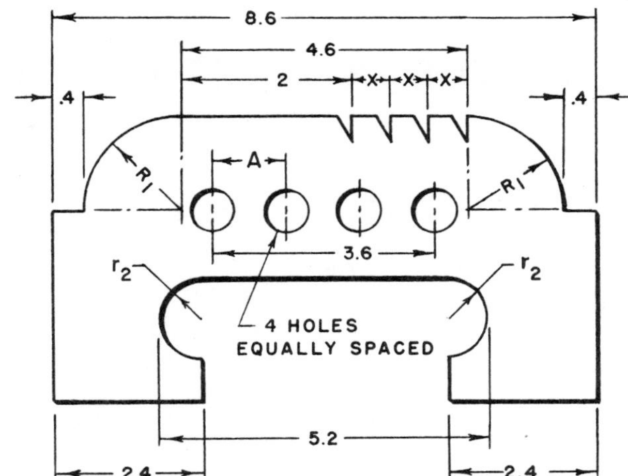

3. The total resistance (R_t) of the two line wires in the diagram is 0.415 ohms (R). The area of the copper wire is 16,724 circular mills (d^2).

   Compute the length of each wire in meters.

$$R_t = \frac{(K) \cdot (L)}{d^2}$$

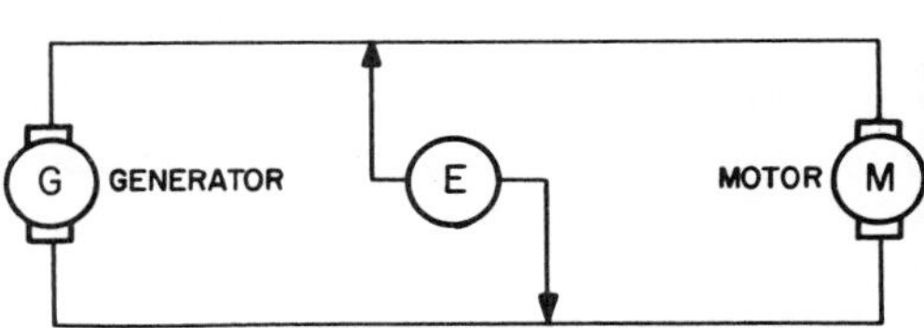

K = 10.8 (constant for copper)
L = Length of wire in feet
d^2 = circular mills

1m = 3.281 ft.

Section 11

RATIO AND PROPORTION

Unit 53 THE CONCEPT OF RATIO

A ratio is a comparison of one quantity with another like quantity or value. In other words, ratio is simply a statement of the relationship between two things. The ratio of corresponding sides of two squares, like A and B, may be stated as 4 to 6. Both objects are alike in that each is a square, but they differ in their lengths as 4 to 6.

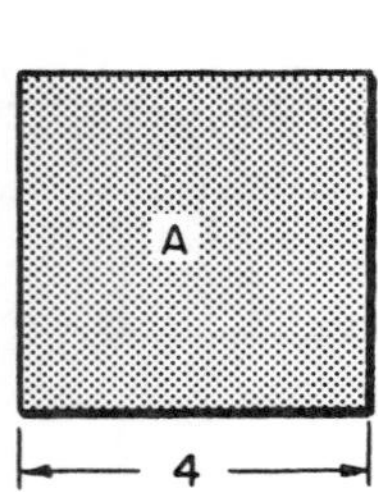

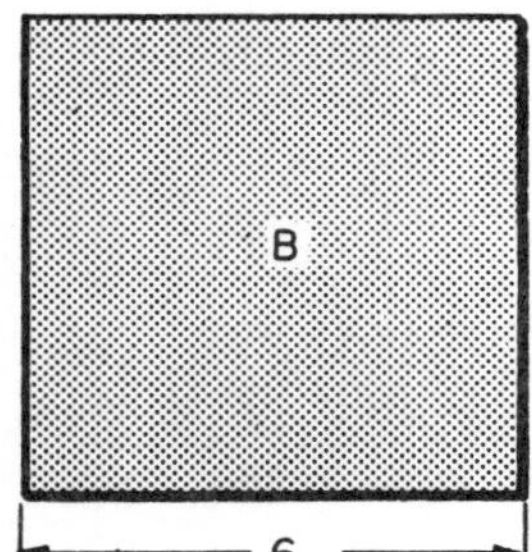

A. FORMS FOR EXPRESSING RATIO

In squares A and B the ratio is 4 to 6. This same ratio or comparison may be given in two other ways: (1) by the use of a colon, as 4:6; (2) by the use of a division sign, as 4 ÷ 6 or 4/6.

The two numbers 4 and 6 are the terms of the ratio: (4) is the *first term* and (6), the *second term.* Since a ratio indicates division, the number may be reduced to lowest terms without changing the value.

RULE FOR APPLYING PRINCIPLES OF RATIO

- Read the problem to determine like quantities.
- Compare two quantities by writing the first and second terms of a ratio.
- Reduce ratio to lowest terms.
- Apply the ratio to other parts of the problem, if required, to determine other dimensions.

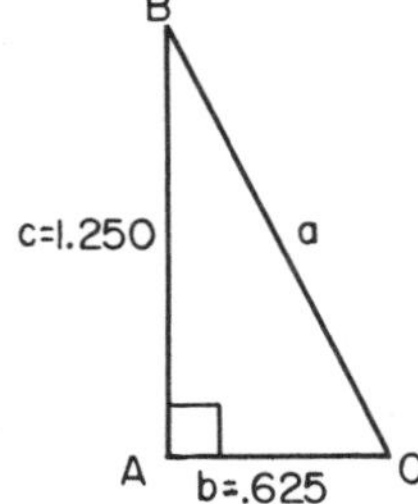

EXAMPLE: Express the relationship of sides b and c of triangle ABC as a ratio.

Step 1 Measure the lengths of sides b and c.

Step 2 Write as a ratio. b:c or .625:1.250

Step 3 Reduce to lowest terms. 1:2

ASSIGNMENT UNIT 53

A. APPLICATION OF RATIO IN MEASUREMENT

1. Measure the length of each line, (a through e), to the nearest 1/32″. Using these lengths, indicate the ratios given in the table.

a.

b.

c.

d.

e.

Required Ratio
b:a
a:c
d:b
c:e

Ans.: a:c = 23:24 c:e = 48:41

2. Measure the lengths indicated for each object. Then, with these values, give the ratio of dimensions for the combinations given.

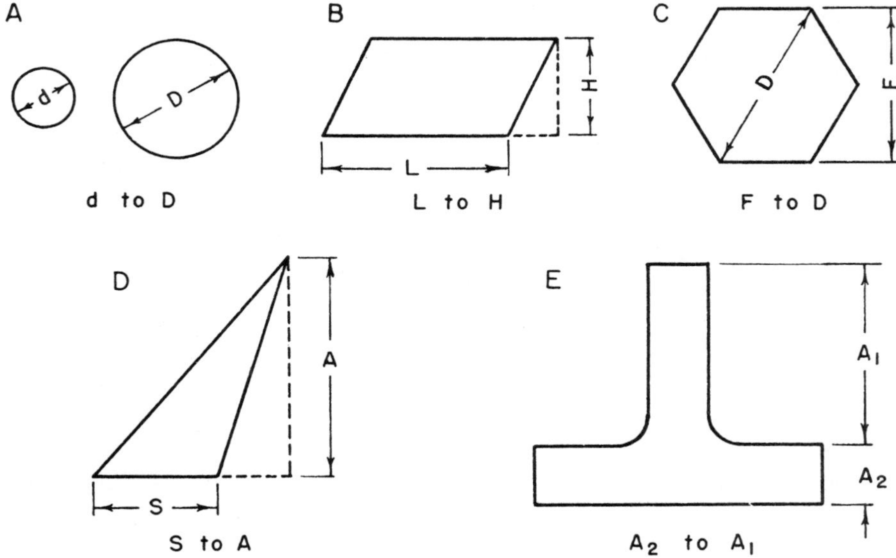

Ans.: B. 31:17 D. 21:37

3. A pinion driver gear has 24 teeth; the driven gear, 84 teeth. What is the ratio of the driver gear to the driven gear?

4. Give the ratio of a primary winding of 350 turns to a secondary winding of 17 1/2 turns.

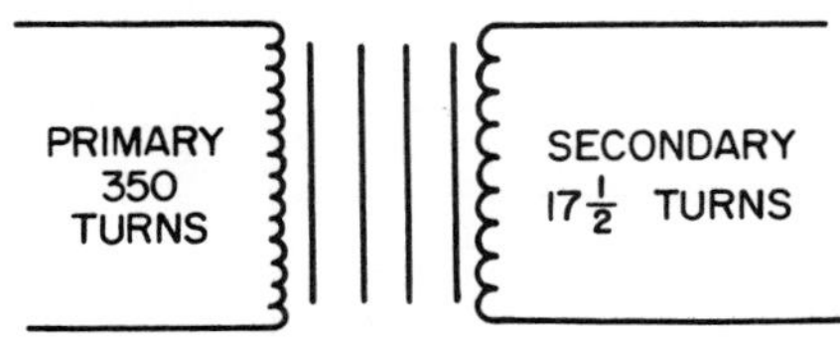

Ans.: 20:1

5. The rise and span of three roof layouts are given in the table. Determine the pitch in each case, rounded to whole numbers. P = R/S

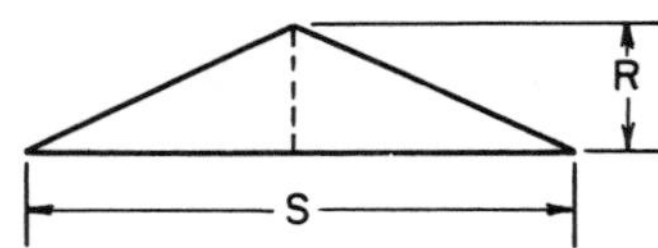

Roof Layout	Rise (R)	Span (S)	Pitch (P)
A	.91 m	3.66 m	
B	1.82 m	3.66 m	
C	.91 m	5.49 m	

Ans.: B. 1:2

6. Determine the ratio of the shaft diameter (D) to bearing length (L) in problems A through E.

Shaft	A	B	C	D	E
Shaft Diameter	1.000″	.750″	1.250″	.312″	.625″
Bearing Length	2 1/2″	1.500″	3.750″	1″	1 7/8″

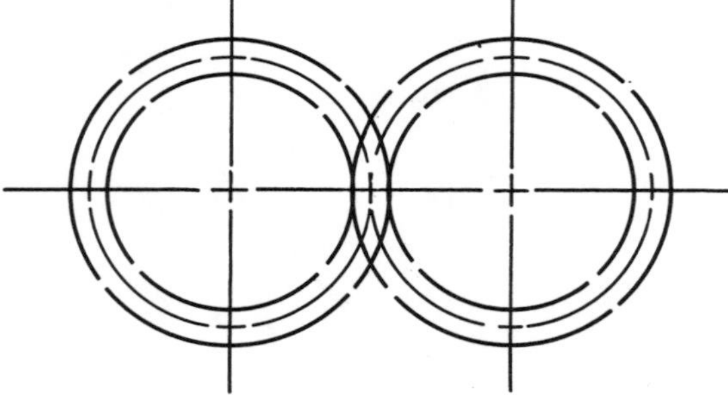

Ans.: B. 1:2 D. 39:125

7. a. Determine the gear ratio of each driver gear to each driven gear for the five sets of gears in the table.

Gear Set	Gear Teeth	
	Driver	Driven
A	32	32
B	32	64
C	32	80
D	96	108
E	54	132

Ans.: B. 1:2 D. 8:9

b. Express the gear ratios a second way, this time in terms of the driven gear to the driver gear.

Ans.: B. 2:1 D. 9:8

8. Give the compression ratio of each piston and cylinder combination for each compressed volume listed in the table. Express each ratio in terms of how many times the gas in cylinder B is compressed in relation to cylinder A.

Combination	Cubic Inches	
	Full Cylinder (A)	Compressed Cylinder (B)
1	24	12
2	24	4.8
3	12 1/2	9 3/8
4	13.6	2.2

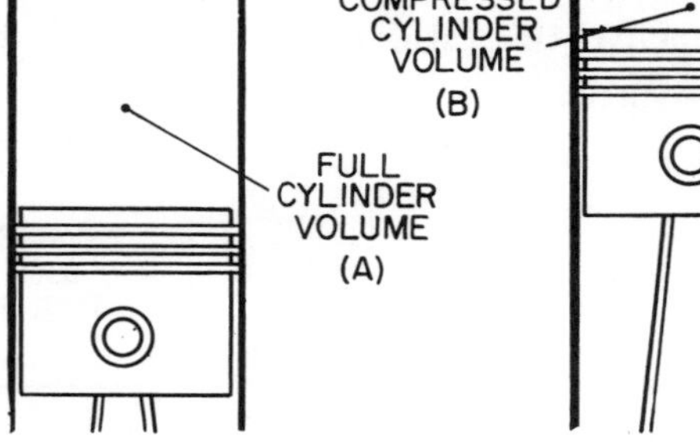

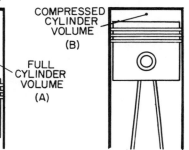

Ans.: 2) 5:1 4) 6.2:1

Unit 54 THE CONCEPT OF PROPORTION

Two ratios, equal in value and placed on opposite sides of an equal sign, make up a *proportion.* A proportion, therefore, is an equality of two ratios.

EXPRESSING A PROPORTION

Two ratios like 1:2 and 4:8, representing equal quantities, may be expressed as a proportion.

TERMS OF A PROPORTION

The two outside terms (1 and 8) are known as *extremes,* while the two inner terms (2 and 4) are called the *means.* In any proportion, the product of the means is equal to the product of the extremes.

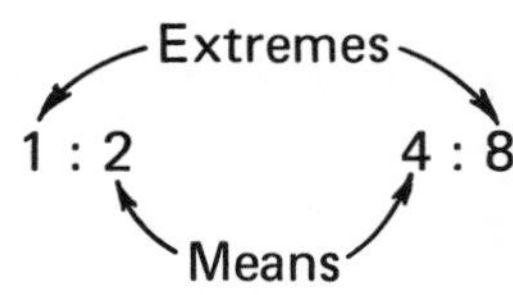

A. APPLICATION OF DIRECT PROPORTION

This principle is important because if three of the four terms of a proportion are known, the fourth term may be computed easily.

RULE FOR FINDING MISSING TERM IN A PROPORTION

- Read the problem and set up two sets of ratios.
- Examine each ratio to make certain that there is an equality of the two ratios. Then write as a proportion.
- Determine whether the missing term is a mean or an extreme term.
- Multiply the means and divide the product by the known extreme to find the missing extreme, or,
- Multiply the extremes and divide the product by the known mean to get the missing mean.

EXAMPLE: A wire 1320 feet long has a resistance of .42 ohms. What resistance is there in one mile of the same wire?

Step 1	Set up two like ratios. X = the missing value.	1320:5280 .42 ohms:X 1320:5280 = .42:X
Step 2	Multiply the two means and place on one side of = sign.	5280 x .42 = 2217.6
Step 3	Multiply the two extremes and place on the opposite side of the = sign.	1320 x (X) = 1320X 1320X = 2217.6
Step 4	Divide 2217.6 by 1320.	$X = \frac{2217.6}{1320} = 1.68$ ohms
Step 5	Check by substituting 1.68 ohms for X in the original proportion.	1320:5280 = .42:1.68
Step 6	Multiply extremes.	1320 x 1.68 = 2217.60

Step 7	Multiply means.	5280 x .42 = 2217.60
Step 8	Compare both products to make certain the values on both sides of the equation are equal. If they vary, start at the first step and recheck.	2217.60 = 2217.60

B. APPLICATION OF INDIRECT PROPORTION

Proportion, thus far, has been covered as *direct* because the relationship of one ratio to another is direct. A proportion may also be *indirect,* in which case the ratios vary inversely. In writing an *indirect* or *inverse proportion,* the two terms in the first or second ratio are reversed.

Use is made of indirect proportion in velocity and speed problems. If the ratios of the speeds of two different sized pulleys were written as a direct proportion, the larger pulley would have to rotate faster. Since just the opposite is true, the proportion is an inverse one.

To illustrate, determine what rpm an 8-inch diameter pulley, turning at 100 rpm, will drive a 4-inch diameter pulley.

Direct Proportion (Incorrect)	Indirect Proportion (Correct)
8:4 = 100:X	8:4 = X:100 (Terms 3 and 4 reversed)
8X = 400	800 = 4X
X = 50	200 = X

It is readily apparent that by using indirect proportion the correct rpm of 200 is obtained.

RULE FOR APPLYING INDIRECT PROPORTION

- Determine the three values that are given and the fourth value which is to be computed.
- Set up the first ratio the same as for direct proportion.
- Set up the second ratio by arranging the terms in inverse order.
- Check by inserting the computed value in the original problem and reworking.

EXAMPLE: A larger gear of 96 teeth revolves at 250 rpm and drives a smaller gear of 48 teeth. Determine the rpm of the smaller gear.

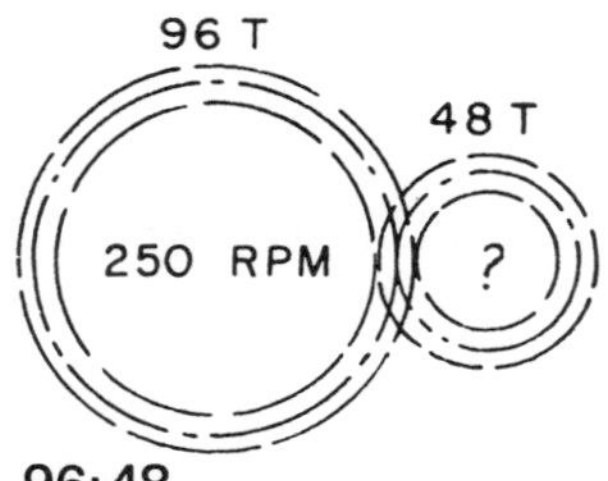

Step 1	Set up ratio of the number of teeth in the *driver* to the number of teeth in the *driven* gear.	96:48
Step 2	Set up ratio of rpm in *driven* gear to *driver* gear.	X:250
	NOTE: This places the third and fourth terms in inverse order.	96 (250) = 24,000
Step 3	Multiply the extremes.	96 (250) = 24,000
Step 4	Divide the product of the extremes by the known mean.	$\frac{24000}{48}$ = 500 rpm
Step 5	Label answer and check by substituting computed value in the original equation.	Ans. 500 rpm

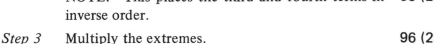

ASSIGNMENT UNIT 54

A. APPLICATION OF DIRECT PROPORTION TO PRACTICAL PROBLEMS

1. Determine how many milliliters of an 8.5 percent saline solution are needed to prepare 450 milliliters of a 3.5 percent solution.

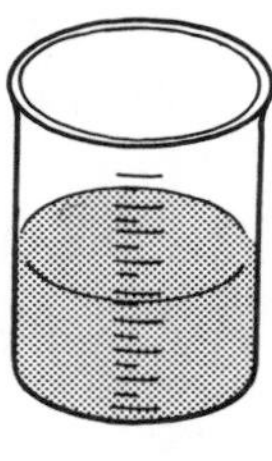

2. A cylindrical container holds 1000 gallons of oil when filled to a depth of 8 feet. How many gallons are there when the level is 3 1/2 feet? **Ans.:** 437.5 gallons
3. One cubic inch of water weighs .58 ounces. The specific gravity of cast iron is 7.82.
   a. What is the weight of 1 cubic foot, 864 cubic inches of cast iron?
   b. Convert the weight to its equivalent metric value.
   Ans.: b. 339.29 kg
4. What is the weight of tin, antimony, and copper in 40 pounds of Babbit metal? Babbit is made up of 96 parts tin, 8 parts antimony, and 4 parts copper. **Ans.:** tin = 35.56 lbs.
5. A motor driven pump discharges 560 liters of water in 2.5 minutes. How long does it take to discharge 10,900 liters?
6. A wire that is 925 feet long has a resistance of 2.92 ohms. Determine the length of copper wire of the same area that has a resistance of 4.24 ohms. **Ans.:** 1343.147 ft.

B. APPLICATION OF INDIRECT PROPORTION TO PRACTICAL PROBLEMS

1. In the direct drive illustrated, the 4″ drive pulley revolves at 1700 rpm. What size pulley is needed to increase the rpm of the driven pulley to 3200? Round off pulley diameter to nearest 1/2″.

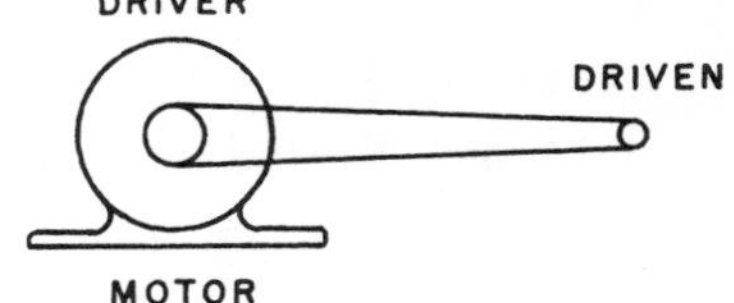

2. Compute the missing value for gears A through E.

	No. Teeth in Driver	No. Teeth in Driven	Rpm of Driver	Rpm of Driven
A	24		200	150
B	56	72		300
C	8	36	70	
D		144	50	32
E	72	96	60	

Ans.: B. 386 rpm D. 92 teeth

3. Determine the spindle speed for each step of the step cone pulley and drive illustrated.

   Ans.: Step 2 231 rpm
   Step 4 686 rpm

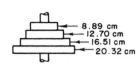

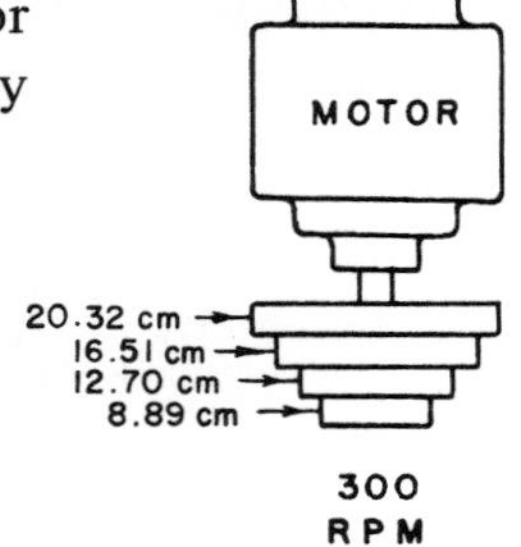

4. The pressure of a contained gas is indirectly proportional to its volume. Determine the compression at the four different stages of compression (A through D) given in the table. State the compression as pounds per square inch, rounded to the nearest pound.

   NOTE: The pressure on the original volume is 20 lbs/□″.

Stage of Compression	Volume of Gas (Cubic Inches)
Original	20
A	16
B	12
C	9
D	7.5

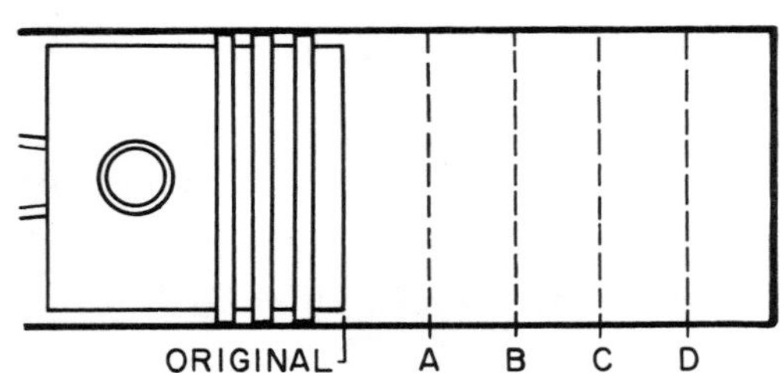

   Ans.: B. 33 D. 53

5. The applied force on a simple machine is indirectly proportional to the generated force. Calculate the weight that can be lifted (generated force) for the four lever combinations. Round off answers to the nearest pound.

   Ans.: B. 222
   D. 2,173

Lever	Distances in Centimeters		Applied Force (kg)
	D_1	D_2	
A	8	4	120
B	6 1/4	4 1/2	160
C	15.2	16.8	88
D	19.6	24.9	2760

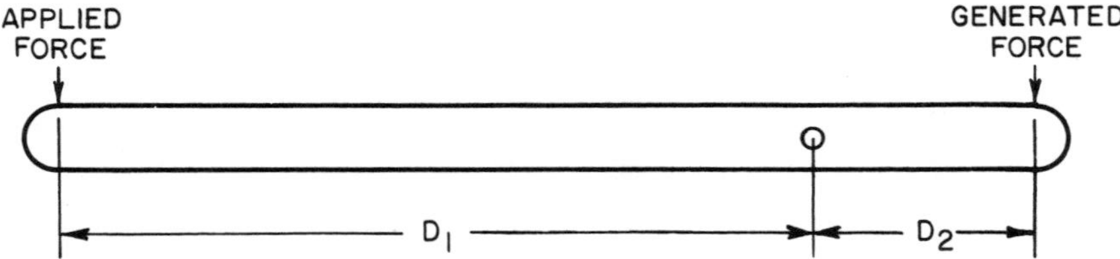

6. An electrical conductor wire of 34.221 mills diameter has a resistance of 6.032 ohms. Determine the resistance of a wire 42.610 mills in diameter of the same material and diameter. The resistance varies inversely as the square of the diameter.

Unit 55 APPLICATION OF RELATIONSHIPS TO PROPORTION

Two quantities that depend on one another for their values are related and any change in one quantity produces a change in the other.

One of the most widespread applications of relationships is in the use of scale drawings. A drawing that says Scale 1″ = 1′ - 0″ means that for every measurement on the drawing, the actual size is 12 times larger. The scale, therefore, indicates a relationship between the size of the drawing and the actual size of the part.

Wherever a scale is indicated, it should be used in the order in which the terms or numbers are arranged. A scale 1:2 means that the drawing is one-half the size of the part.

RULE FOR APPLYING RELATIONSHIPS TO PROPORTION PROBLEMS

- Determine the relationship of the part to an established scale.
- Form a proportion with the scale ratio on one side of the equals sign and a ratio of known to unknown size on the other side.
- Multiply the extremes.
- Multiply the means.
- The product of the extremes equals the product of the means; solve for the unknown.

EXAMPLE: Determine dimensions A, B, C, and D.

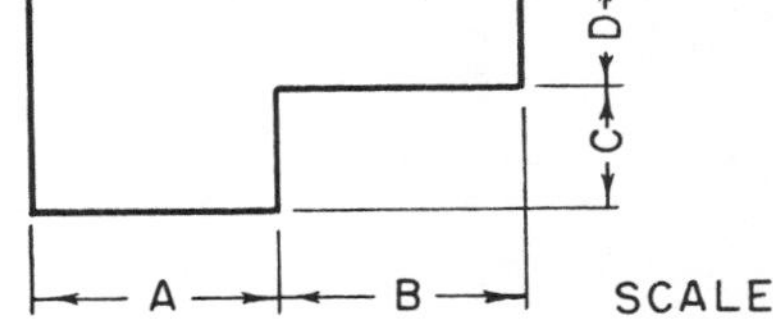

Step 1 Measure the length of A.

Step 2 Form a proportion.

1:2 = measured length:actual length of A.

Step 3 Multiply extremes.

Step 4 Multiply means, using the measured length of A.

Step 5 Product of means equals product of extremes; solve for actual length A.

Step 6 Repeat same steps for B, C, and D.

ASSIGNMENT UNIT 55

1. The specific weight of bronze is 8.3 as compared with a specific weight of 7.8 for cast iron. Determine how much castings A through E will weigh in cast iron.

Castings	A	B	C	D	E
Weight of Parts in Bronze	3 oz.	1 lb.	2 lbs., 8 oz.	8 lbs., 4 oz.	12 lbs., 2 oz.

Ans.: B. .94 lbs. D. 7.753 lbs.

2. Determine the cutting speed for the five diameters of work given in the table. Then give the rate of change in cutting speeds as a ratio.

$$CS = \frac{\text{rpm} \times \pi D}{12}$$

Work Pieces	A	B	C	D	E
Work Diameter	2″	1 1/2″	1″	3/4″	1/2″
Spindle rpm	250	250	250	250	250
Required Rate of Change		A to B	A to C	B to D	A to E

Ans.: B. 98 Rate 4:3 D. 49 Rate 2:1

3. Measure the various lengths and diameters as shown on each drawing. Then, using the scale given for each drawing, compute the actual size.

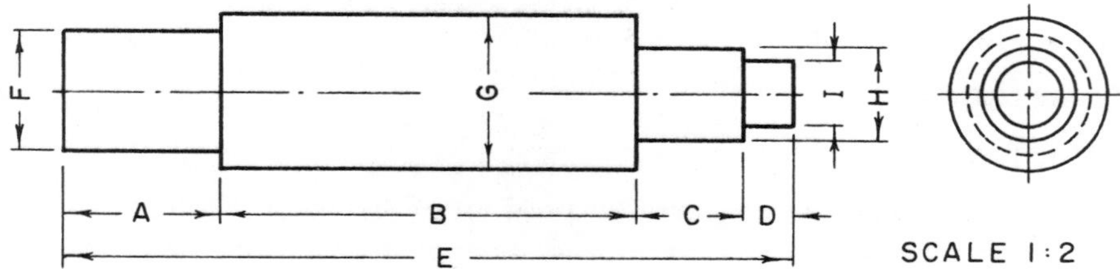

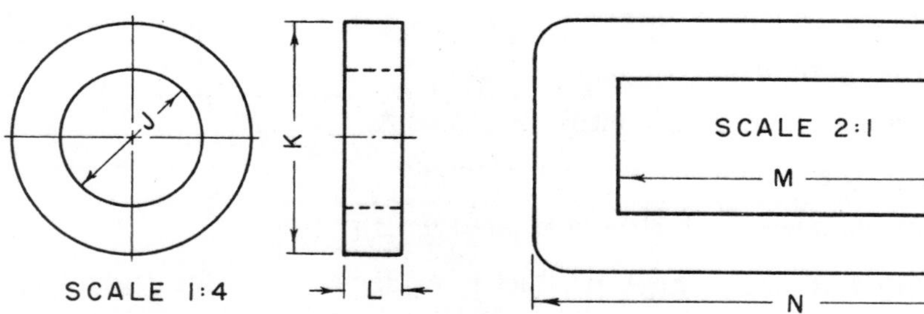

Ans.: B = 3 7/16″ E = 6″ H = 13/16″ K = 4 3/8″ N = 1 1/8″

Unit 56 ACHIEVEMENT REVIEW ON RATIO, PROPORTION AND RELATIONSHIPS

A. THE CONCEPT OF RATIO

1. Express in lowest terms the rise of each roof to the span (also known as *pitch*).

	Rise	Span
A	9′ - 0″	26′ - 0″
B	10′ - 0″	30′ - 0″
C	8′ - 0″	26′ - 6″
D	14′ - 6″	32′ - 6″
E	9′ - 6″	28′ - 8″

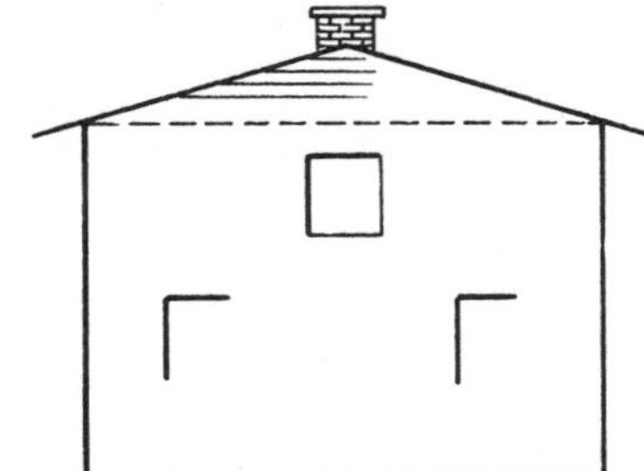

2. Determine what scale is used on drawings A, B, and C.

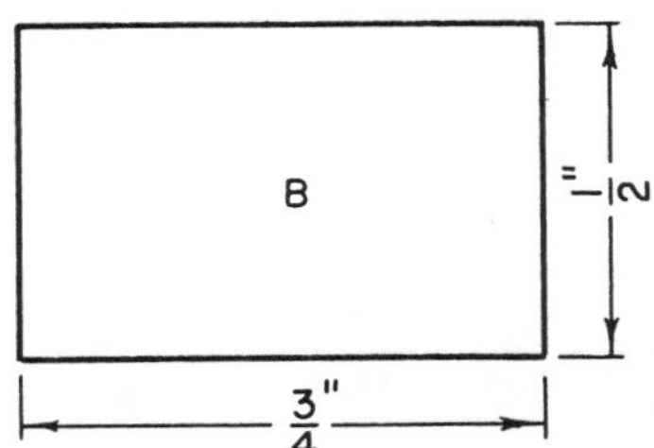

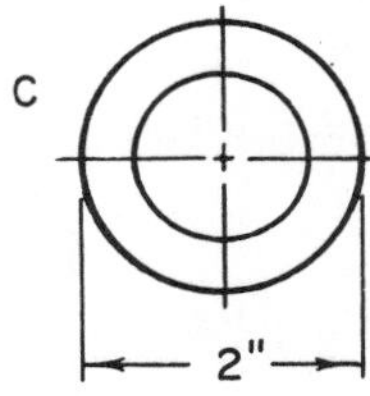

B. APPLICATION OF DIRECT PROPORTION TO PRACTICAL PROBLEMS

1. Find the value of each unknown quantity.

a. A:2 = 5:10
b. 4:B = 9:4 1/2
c. 17 1/2:8 3/4 = 32.5:C
d. 8.25:10.50 = D:36.75
e. E/16 = 7/15
f. 22/F = 3.6/4.7
g. 9.2/13.8 = G/6.50
h. 22.250/36.750 = 12.5/H

2. Four actual measurements on a job were 30, 45, 68, and 104 inches. To what length will each line be drawn if a scale of 1:2 is used for a drawing of the job?

3. A crew of 12 men assemble 45 units a day. If the production is to be increased to 80 units a day, how many additional men will be needed?

4. The label of a large quantity of a medical solution reads: 1 mℓ = 1/3 gr. A prescribed dose of 1/2 gr is needed.

   Find the volume of the required medical solution.

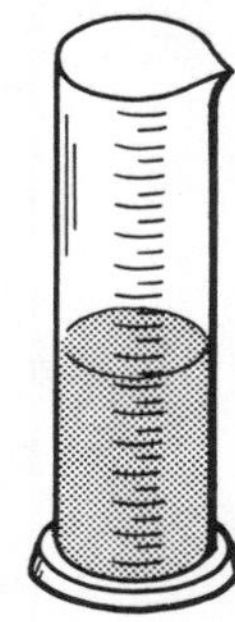

Prescribed Dose: Required Volume of Medicine
=
Amount of Medicine in Preparation: Amount in Stock Solution

5. Compute the liquid capacity of reservoirs A, B and C for the depth stated in each case. Give answers in kiloliters, correct to three decimal places.

Reservoir	Total Capacity		Required Capacity Depth
	Volume	Depth	
A	11 358 ℓ	2.74 m	1.83 m
B	27 465 ℓ	4.69 m	2.47 m
C	92.397 kℓ	6.75 m	4.29 m

C. APPLICATION OF INVERSE PROPORTION TO PRACTICAL PROBLEMS

1. A crankshaft turns at 1,250 rpm. Referring to the pulley diameters in the sketch, compute the rpm of
   a. the generator pulley and
   b. the fan pulley.

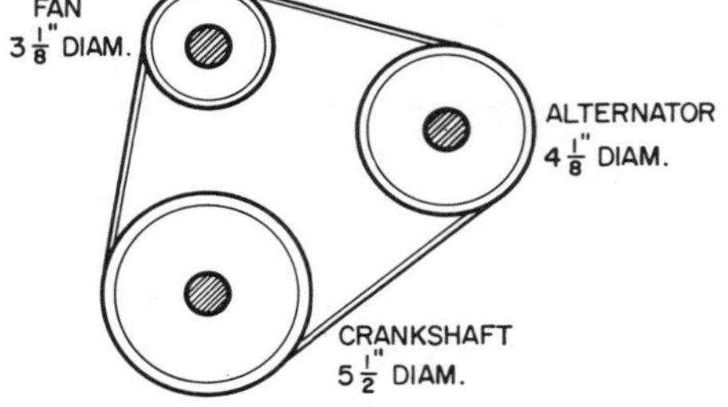

2. Find the values that are missing in the table.

	Driver Gear		Driven Gear	
	No. Teeth	Rpm	No. Teeth	Rpm
A	36	120	48	
B	44	200		160
C		320	96	240
D	82		104	140
E	18	400	80	

D. RELATIONSHIPS IN RATIO AND PROPORTION

1. Determine the circumferences and areas of circles A through F. Then express the relationship between the circumferences and areas as ratios.

	Diameters (Inches)	Required Ratio
A	5	Circumference A to C
B	8	Circumference D to B
C	3	Circumference E to C
D	4	Area F to D
E	9	Area E to A
F	6	Area F to B

Section 12

EXPONENTS

Unit 57 THE CONCEPT OF EXPONENTS

A simplified method of stating mathematically that one quantity is to be multiplied by itself a number of times is to write a small number to the right of and slightly above the original quantity. This number, called an *exponent*, shows that the quantity is to be *raised* (multiplied) to the power as indicated.

A. EXPONENTS USED WITH NUMERICAL VALUES

If the number 3 is to be multiplied by itself four times, the mathematical operation may be stated a number of ways. In each case, the *factored* form indicates that (3) is to be taken as a factor four times. A more convenient way of expressing this problem is to use the exponent and the *exponential* form, 3^4. The quantity 3 is to be raised to the fourth power. The results of either the factored or exponential forms are equal, as the meanings are the same.

Method 1	(3) (3) (3) (3)	=
Method 2	$3 \cdot 3 \cdot 3 \cdot 3$	=
Method 3	$3 \times 3 \times 3 \times 3$	=

The area of a square .6 inch on a side is .36 sq. in. This area may be determined by multiplying .6″ x .6″. The problem may be stated as, A = .6″ x .6″. The same problem may be written more conveniently as, A = $.6^2$. The exponent ^{2} shows that .6″ is to be raised to the second power, or is to be taken as a factor two times.

.6"

1"

1"

.6"

Exponents, therefore, serve a two-fold purpose:

1. They provide a simplified technique of expressing a problem mathematically.
2. They simplify the mathematical processes required to solve a problem.

When exponents are used, attention must be paid to the unit of measurement in which the result is expressed. A dimension given in a linear unit, when multiplied by itself, becomes a unit in square measure. A dimension multiplied three times by itself is expressed in terms of cubic measure.

RULE FOR USING EXPONENTS (with Single Literal or Numerical Values)

- Substitute the value given for a literal term.
- Multiply the numerical value by itself the number of times indicated by the exponent.
- Express the result in the appropriate unit of measure.

EXAMPLE: Case 1 Find the area of a square 8 inches on a side. The area = 8^2.

Step 1 Multiply 8 by itself the number of times indicated by the exponent (^{2}). $8^2 = 8 \times 8 = 64$

Step 2 Express the area in square inches. Ans. 64 sq. in.

EXAMPLE: Case 2 Determine the volume of a sphere 6 inches diameter, correct to two places. The volume is equal to $\frac{\pi D^3}{6}$

Step 1	Substitute the known diameter (6) for D and 3.1416 for π.	$V = \frac{3.1416\ (6)^3}{6}$ $= \frac{3.1416\ (6)\ (6)\ (6)}{6}$
Step 2	Cancel like factors in numerator and denominator.	$= \frac{3.1416\ (6)\ (6)\ (\not{6})^{1}}{\not{6}_{1}}$
Step 3	Multiply and round off the result to two places.	$= 113.0976$
Step 4	Express in appropriate unit of measure (″) x (″) x (″) = cu. in.	$= 113.10$ $= 113.10$ cu. in.

B. FACTORING

The term *factoring* refers to the steps used in determining the series of smaller numbers which, when multiplied by each other, produce the original number. If the factors are all the same, they may be written in exponential form. In a problem like 3 x 3 x 3 x 3 x 3, the 3 is a common factor. The exponential form 3^5 is the preferred method of stating that "three is to be raised to the fifth power."

In some instances, a product is given and it becomes necessary to find the factors. If the product is 27, this number may be divided by 3 to get 9. The nine may also be divided by 3. Therefore, when 3 is multiplied three times by itself (3^3), it is equal to 27.

RULE FOR FACTORING

- Divide the original number by any number that will divide into it exactly.
- Divide the quotient by the same number, if possible.
- Continue to divide until the last number may no longer be divided.
- Determine what factor, if any, is common.
- Simplify the result.

EXAMPLE: Factor 125.

Step 1	Divide original number by any number that will divide exactly.	$\frac{125}{5} = 25$
Step 2	Divide the quotient by the same number.	$\frac{25}{5} = 5$
Step 3	Determine the common factor (5).	$5 \cdot 5 \cdot 5 = 125$

ASSIGNMENT UNIT 57

A. APPLICATION OF EXPONENTS

1. Express the quantities A through H in exponential form.

a. Two to the second power
b. Four to the fourth power
c. Ten to the seventh power
d. Five to the fourth power
e. Four-tenths to the second power
f. One and two-tenths to the second power
g. One-half to the third power
h. Six and one-fourth to the second power

Ans.: b. 4^4 e. $.4^2$ h. 6.25^2

2. Find the numerical value of numbers (a) through (l) when raised to the power indicated in each case.

a. 15^2	d. 10^5	g. 1.5^3	j. $(.25'')^2$
b. 12^3	e. 2^8	h. $(1/4)^2$	k. $(.50'')^3$
c. 8^4	f. $.5^2$	i. $(2\ 1/2)^3$	l. $(1.25')^3$

Ans.: b. 1728 e. 256 h. 1/16 k. .125 cu. in.

B. FACTORING

Prepare a table similar to the one illustrated. Factor each value A through N and include the factors in the appropriate column. Then write in exponential form in the next column.

		Factors	Exponential Form
A	4		
B	16		
C	25		
D	64		
E	.09		
F	.36		
G	.81 sq. in.		

		Factors	Exponential Form
H	1/16		
I	1/64		
J	125		
K	1000		
L	512 cu. in.		
M	.729 cu. in.		
N	1.728 cu. ft.		

Ans.: B. 2^4 E. $.3^2$ H. $(1/2)^4$ K. 10^3

C. APPLICATION OF EXPONENTS IN PRACTICAL PROBLEMS

1. Compute the areas of circles A through D correct to three decimal places.

	Given
A	Diameter = 22.5 cm
B	Diameter = 18.75 cm
C	Radius = 2.4 cm
D	Radius = 10.32 mm

Ans.: B. 276.117 cm^2 D. 334.588 mm^2

2. Find the area of squares A through H. Round off answers to three decimal places.

	Given
A	3″
B	15″
C	14′
D	.8″

	Given
E	1.5 m
F	5.625 cm
G	6.35 mm
H	109.54 mm

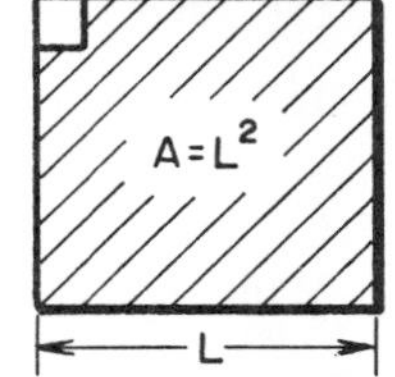

Ans.: B. 225 sq. in. E. 2.25 m^2 H. 11 999.011 mm^2

3. Determine the power (P, in watts) required for each of three electrical circuits that draw 12 amperes (I) of current and have a resistance (R) of (a) 10 ohms, (b) 8 1/2 ohms, and (c) 17.62 ohms, respectively. $P = I^2 \ (R)$

   Ans.: (b) 1224 watts

4. Use the horsepower formula given and find the horsepower ratings of motors A through D, to the nearest whole number value.

$$\text{Horsepower ratings} = \frac{(\text{Diameter of cylinder})^2 \times (\text{Number of Cylinders})}{2.6}$$

$$H = \frac{(D)^2 \ (N)}{2.6}$$

Motor	Number Cylinders (N)	Diameter (Bore) of Cylinders (D)
A	2	4"
B	4	4.2"
C	6	3 1/4"
D	12	3.75"

Ans.: B. 27 D. 65

Unit 58 ALGEBRAIC MULTIPLICATION OF NUMBERS AND LETTERS

The same principles of using exponents which apply to numerical values may be used with literal values or any combination of numbers and letters. If the quantity A is to be taken as a factor 5 times, it may be written in exponential form as A^5. The form A^5 has the same value as A x A x A x A x A.

A. MULTIPLICATION OF LIKE FACTORS WITH EXPONENTS

When the factors of a number are the same, the original number may be stated in exponential form. The number 9, when factored, is equal to 3 x 3. Written in exponential form, the value of 3^2 is the same as 9.

Occasionally, like factors are to be multiplied. A shortcut method of doing this is to add the exponents. Thus, $3^2 \times 3^4 = 3^{(2+4)}$, or 3^6. This process may be checked easily by multiplying each factor "long hand" and then comparing the end results.

Step 1 $3^2 = 3 \times 3 = 9$

Step 2 $3^4 = 3 \times 3 \times 3 \times 3 = 81$

Step 3 $3^2 \times 3^4 = 9 \times 81 = 729$

Check by adding exponents — Check

Step 4 $3^2 \times 3^4 = 3^{(2+4)} = 3^6$

Step 5 $3^6 = 3 \times 3 \times 3 \times 3 \times 3 \times 3 = 729$

These same steps are followed when letters are used in place of numerical values.

RULE FOR MULTIPLYING LIKE FACTORS

- Determine like numerical or literal factors.
- Add the exponents of all like factors.

NOTE: If no exponent is given, the exponent is understood to be ^{1}

EXAMPLE: Multiply $S^3 \times S \times S^2$ and express the result in exponential form.

Step 1 Add exponents of all like factors. $S^{(3+1+2)} = {}^6$

Step 2 Express in exponential form. $S^3 \times S \times S^2 = S^6$

B. MULTIPLICATION OF UNLIKE FACTORS, SCIENTIFIC NOTATION SYSTEM (SI METRICS)

Prefixes, multiple and submultiple values and symbols of the "scientific notation system" were covered in an earlier unit on SI Metrics. Unlike factors expressed in this system may be multiplied. The steps are similar to those followed for like factors. The answer may be a positive or negative quantity, depending on the quantities involved.

EXAMPLE: Multiply 6.6 (10^{-2}) hertz by 3.2 (10^{-4}) hertz.

Step 1 Multiply the unlike factors. $(6.6) \cdot (3.2) = 21.12$

Step 2 Add the exponents. $10^{(-2\ +\ -4)} = 10^{-6}$

Step 3 Combine the results and label the answer. $21.12\ (10^{-6})$ hertz (Hz)

NOTE: The 10^{-6} value may be expressed by using the prefix ("micro-") or symbol (μ) with the unit of measure (hertz, Hz).

21.12 (10^{-6}) hertz may be written 21.12 microhertz or 21.12 μHz.

The same steps are used for positive power of ten values. For instance, $6.6(10^3) \times 3.2 (10^4) = 21.12(10^7)$. Positive and negative exponents may be combined in a similar manner.

EXAMPLE: Multiply 6.6 (10^{-3}) Hz by 3.2 (10^5) Hz.

Step 1 Multiply the unlike factors. $(6.6) \cdot (3.2) = 21.12$

Step 2 Add the exponents. $(10^{-3}) + (10^5) = (10^2)$

Step 3 Combine the values. $21.12\ (10^2)$

Step 4 Add the appropriate unit of measure in the answer. $21.12\ (10^2)$ Hz

Using these simple steps and the scientific notation system simplifies the multiplication process. This is particularly important where quantities involve a great number of digits.

C. EXPONENTS USED WITH NUMERICAL AND LITERAL VALUES COMBINED

Sometimes a quantity containing several terms may be included within a parenthesis. The exponent indicates the number of times the quantity is to be multiplied by itself. The expression $(A + 1)^2$ means that each number and letter in the parenthesis is to be multiplied by every other number and letter. Further, $(A + 1)^2$ means that $(A + 1)$ must be multiplied by $(A + 1)$.

RULE FOR MULTIPLYING EXPONENTS (with Quantities Combining Literal and Numerical Values)

- Determine the terms that are affected by the exponent.
- Multiply each literal and/or numerical term in the parenthesis first by one term, then by the next.
- Add like terms.
- Express the product in the appropriate units of measure.

EXAMPLE: Solve the problem $(A + 1)^2$.

Step 1 Multiply each term by 1.

Step 2 Multiply each term by A.

Step 3 Add and combine like terms.

Step 4 Arrange the terms with the term having the highest power first.

$$\begin{array}{r} A + 1 \\ \times\quad 1 \\ \hline A + 1 \end{array}$$

$$\begin{array}{r} A + 1 \\ \times A \quad\ \ \\ \hline A^2 + A \end{array}$$

NOTE: This step is known as *arranging the terms in the descending order of power.*

The quantity $A^2 + 2A + 1$ is the same as $(A + 1)^2$.

ASSIGNMENT UNIT 58

A. MULTIPLICATION OF LIKE NUMERICAL FACTORS

1. Write the results of each multiplication in exponential form.

a. $2^2 \times 2^2$
b. $3^2 \times 3 \times 3^3$
c. $10^5 \times 10^7$
d. $9^4 \times 9^7 \times 9^5$
e. $(1/2)^2 \times (1/2)^3$
f. $(1/4)^3 \times (1/4)^5$
g. $(1.2)^4 \times (1.2)^9$
h. $(3.02)^3 \times (3.02)^5 \times (3.02)^6$

Ans.: b. 3^6 e. $(1/2)^5$ h. $(3.02)^{14}$

2. Multiply the following literal values and express in exponential form.

a. $A^3 \times A$
b. $C^5 \times C^2$
c. $X^6 \times X^3$
d. $f^2 \times f^{12} \times f^3$
e. $E^4 \times E^6 \times E^0 \times E$
f. $y^2 \times y^9 \times y^3 \times y^5$
g. $d^{10} \times d^{12}$
h. $A^3 \times A^2 \times A^5$
i. $L^2 \times L^4 \times L^6 \times L^{10}$
j. $D^4 \times D^6 \times D \times D^8$
k. $Z \times Z^3 \times Z^6 \times Z^2$
l. $P^4 \times P^2 \times P^{12} \times P$

Ans.: b. C^7 e. E^{11} h. A^{10} k. Z^{12}

B. MULTIPLICATION OF UNLIKE FACTORS IN THE SCIENTIFIC NOTATION SYSTEM

1. Multiply each of the following quantities.

a. $3.6\ (10^2)$ volts x $4.7\ (10^4)$ volts
b. $17.92\ (10^6)$ grams x $12.8\ (10^3)$ grams
c. $27.15\ (10^{-8})$ hertz x $14.6\ (10^{-4})$ hertz
d. $422.7\ (10^{-18})$ meters x $6.5\ (10^{12})$ meters

Ans.: b. $229.376\ (10^9)$ grams d. $2\ 747.55\ (10^{-6})$ meters

2. Rewrite each answer in the preceding problem. Give the (a) computed quantity, (b) appropriate prefix, (c) unit of measure, and (d) symbol. Then, simplify the writing of the answer.

Computed Quantity	Numerical Value	Prefix	Symbol	Unit of Measure	Simplified Answer

C. MULTIPLYING EXPONENTS WITH QUANTITIES COMBINING LITERAL AND NUMERICAL VALUES

1. Multiply the number and letter values and simplify the results in each case.

a. $(A + 2)^2$
b. $(C + 5)^2$
c. $(B + 8)^2$
d. $(y + 3)^2$
e. $(X + 4)^2$
f. $(d + 3)^3$
g. $(n + 1)^3$
h. $(Z + 6)^2$
i. $(g + 2)^3$
j. $(m + 7)^3$
k. $(R - 1)^2$
l. $(S - 1)^3$

Ans.: b. $C^2 + 10C + 25$
h. $Z^2 + 12Z + 36$
e. $X^2 + 8X + 16$
k. $R^2 - 2R + 1$

Unit 59 ALGEBRAIC DIVISION OF NUMBERS AND LETTERS

Division has been described as a shortcut method of repeated subtraction of one quantity from another quantity in the same unit of measure. Where a number, followed by an exponent, is to be divided by another number with an exponent, the division process is the reverse of algebraic multiplication.

A problem like $3^4 \div 3^2$ may be solved by either one of two methods.

Method 1 $\quad \frac{3 \times 3 \times 3 \times 3}{3 \times 3} = \frac{81}{9} = 9$

Method 2 $\quad \frac{3^4}{3^2} = 3^{(4-2)} = 3^2 = 9$

The second method is simplified because only a few simple subtraction and multiplication steps need to be followed. The exponent of the divisor (^{2}) is subtracted from the exponent of the dividend (^{4}). The difference between these exponents ($^4 - ^2 = ^2$) becomes the exponent of the quotient factor (3), as 3^2.

A. DIVISION OF LIKE FACTORS

The division of letters, or numbers and letters in combination, in exponential form is possible only when the letter in both dividend and divisor is the same.

RULE FOR DIVIDING NUMBERS AND LETTERS WITH EXPONENTS

- Determine the factor common to both dividend and divisor. This becomes the quotient factor.
- Subtract the exponent of the divisor from the exponent of the dividend.
- Write the difference between the exponents as the exponent of the quotient factor.

  NOTE: If the exponent of the divisor is greater than that of the dividend, the difference will be a negative value.

EXAMPLE: Case 1 Divide B^6 by B^2.

Step 1 Determine the quotient factor. $\quad \frac{B^6}{B^2} = B$

Step 2 Subtract the exponents. $\quad (^{6-2}) = {}^4$

Step 3 Combine the quotient factor and exponent. $\quad \frac{B^6}{B^2} = B^4$

EXAMPLE: Case 2 Divide $\frac{C^6 \times C^b}{C^2 \times C^{2b}}$.

Step 1 Multiply the quantities in the numerator. $\quad C^6 \times C^b = C^{(6+b)}$

Step 2 Multiply the quantities in the denominator. $\quad C^2 \times C^{2b} = C^{(2+2b)}$

Step 3 Determine the common factor. $\quad = C$

Step 4 Subtract the exponents of the divisor from the exponents of the dividend.

NOTE: Change the signs and add.

$$\begin{array}{rl} & (6 + b) \\ - & (2 + 2b) \\ + & \underline{(-2 - 2b)} \\ = & (4 - b) \end{array}$$

Step 5 Write the result $(4 - b)$ as the exponent of the quotient factor (C). $\quad \frac{C^6 \times C^b}{C^2 \times C^{2b}} = C^{(4-b)}$

The same rule of division applies when the quotient factor is common to both dividend and divisor but the exponents are different.

EXAMPLE: Case 3 Divide 8^X by 8^Y.

Step 1	Write quotient factor.	$\frac{8^X}{8^Y}$, 8
Step 2	Subtract exponents. Since (X − Y) cannot be reduced, the answer is $8^{(X - Y)}$.	$= 8^{(X - Y)}$

B. DIVISION OF UNLIKE FACTORS, SCIENTIFIC NOTATION SYSTEM (SI METRICS)

Scientific and other occupational problems often require the division of unlike factors. In the scientific notation system these are expressed as powers of ten. Like multiplication, the division process is carried out first. The sign of the exponent in the denominator is changed. The value of the exponent is then added to the exponent in the numerator.

The resulting answer may be expressed in a power of ten form. Otherwise, an appropriate prefix may be used. The prefix is followed by the unit of measure.

EXAMPLE: Divide 7.5 x (10^3) pascal by 1.5 x (10^{-6}) pascal

Step 1	Divide the numerator by the denominator.	7.5/1.5 = 5.0
Step 2	Change the sign of the exponent in the denominator.	(10^{-6}) to (10^{+6})
Step 3	Add the values of the exponents.	$(10^{3+6}) = 10^9$
Step 4	Combine the values.	5.0 and (10^9) = 5.0 x $(10)^9$
Step 5	Express the answer in the appropriate unit of measure (pascal, Pa). Simplify the writing of the answer by using the symbol of the prefix and the abbreviation of the unit of measure.	5.0 (10^9) pascal G Pa 5.0 gigapascal = 5.0 GPa

Exponential values may result in a submultiple value. In the case of 7.5 (10^2)/1.5 (10^5) = 1.5 (10^{-3}) pascal. The negative exponential value 10^{-3} is associated with the prefix "milli-." The value may be stated as 1.5 millipascal or 1.5 mPa.

ASSIGNMENT UNIT 59

A. ALGEBRAIC DIVISION OF LIKE NUMBERS

1. Divide each combination of numbers.

a. $\frac{4^4}{4^2}$ c. $\frac{12^8}{12^6}$ e. $\frac{2.5^4}{2.5^2}$ g. $\frac{(\frac{1}{2})^4}{(\frac{1}{2})^2}$

b. $\frac{3^6}{3^3}$ d. $\frac{132^7}{132^5}$ f. $\frac{.63^3}{.63^2}$ h. $\frac{(\frac{5}{8})^6}{(\frac{5}{8})^4}$

Ans.: b. $3^3 = 27$ e. $2.5^2 = 6.25$ h. $(5/8)^2 = 25/64$

B. ALGEBRAIC DIVISION OF UNLIKE FACTORS, SCIENTIFIC NOTATION SYSTEM (SI METRICS)

1. Divide each of the following quantities.

a. $\frac{6.9\,(10^{-6})\text{ meters}}{2.3\,(10^{-4})\text{ meters}}$

b. $\frac{72.45\,(10^{2})}{16.1\,(10^{5})}$ liters

c. $\frac{112.95\,(10^{9})}{150.6\,(10^{6})}$ meters

d $\frac{2.746\,(10^{3})}{2.288\,(10^{-6})}$ volts

Ans.: b. $4.5\,(10^{-3})$ liters d. $1.2\,(10^{9})$ volts

2. Express each answer (a through d) in the preceding problem in terms of the appropriate

a. Numerical value
b. Prefix
c. Symbol
d. Unit of measure

Then, restate as a simplified answer.

Computed Quantity	Numerical Value	Prefix	Symbol	Unit of Measure	Simplified Answer

C. ALGEBRAIC DIVISION OF LETTERS

1. Divide each combination of letters.

a. $\frac{A^3}{A^2}$

b. $\frac{B^4}{B}$

c. $\frac{X^{15}}{X^{12}}$

d. $\frac{A^c}{A^d}$

e. $\frac{Y^{4m}}{Y^{2m}}$

f. $\frac{C^{10a}}{C^{14a}}$

Ans.: b. B^3 d. $A^{(c-d)}$ f. C^{-4a}

2. Perform the operations indicated in each case.

a. $\frac{c^2 \text{ x } c^4}{c^3}$

b. $\frac{B^3 \text{ x } B^{3d}}{B^2 \text{ x } B^{2d}}$

c. $\frac{X^4 \text{ x } X^Y}{X^2 \text{ x } X^{2Y}}$

d. $\frac{A^7 \text{ x } A^3 \text{ x } A^{2m}}{A^2 \text{ x } A^4 \text{ x } A^{3m}}$

Ans. : b. $B^{(1+d)}$ d. $A^{(4-m)}$

Unit 60 ACHIEVEMENT REVIEW ON EXPONENTS

A. THE CONCEPT OF EXPONENTS

1. Raise each number to the power indicated by the exponent.

   a. 10^2 c. 3^5 e. $(1/2)^3$
   b. 8^3 d. $(.10)^4$ f. $(.15')^3$

2. Compute the volume of cubes A, B, C, and D in cubic inches correct to three decimal places.

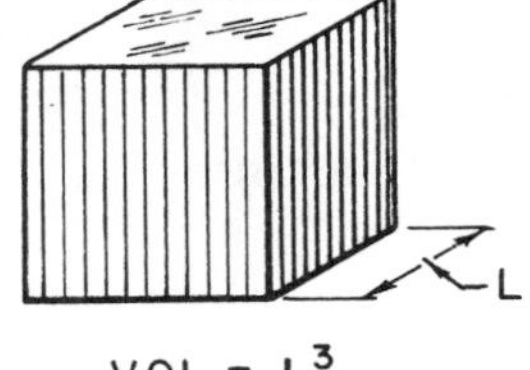

	Given Length of Side
A	4"
B	5"
C	4.25"
D	3 1/8"

3. Determine the area of circles A through D correct to two decimal places. Use the value of 3.14 for π.

	Given Radius
A	4"
B	.8"
C	2.75"
D	3 5/8"

4. Compute the volume of spheres A through D correct to three decimal places. Use the value of 3.14 for π.

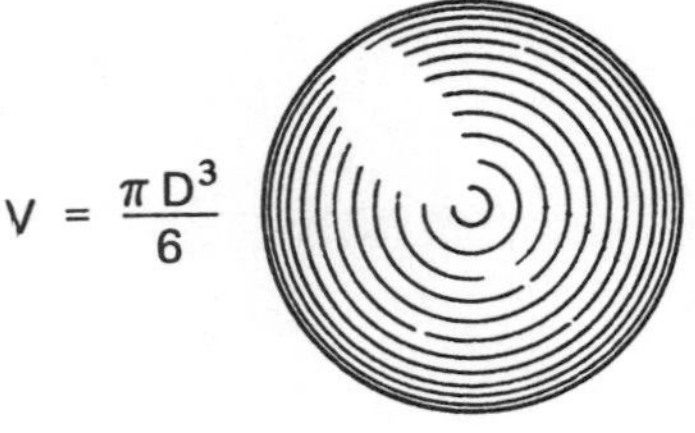

	Given Diameter
A	5.08 cm
B	8.255 cm
C	31.75 mm
D	0.92 m

5. Determine the area of the square part with the cutouts as illustrated. Give the areas in both customary and metric units. Round off answer correct to three places.

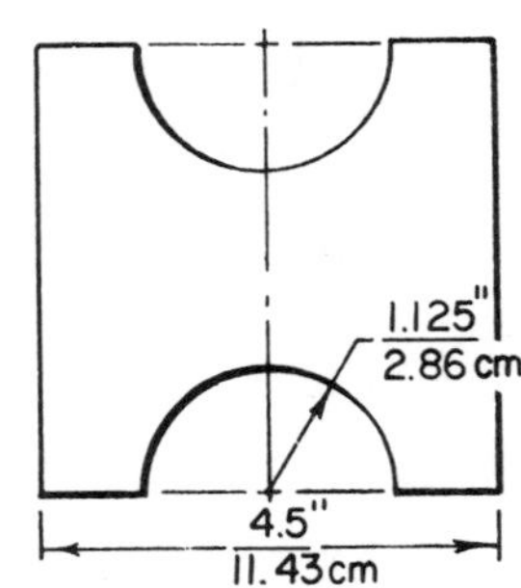

B. ALGEBRAIC MULTIPLICATION OF NUMBERS AND LETTERS

1. Multiply each set of factors and raise to the power indicated at (a) through (d). Round off decimal values correct to two places.

   a. $2^2 \times 2^3$
   b. $(1/6)^2 \times (1/6)^4$
   c. $.8^3 \times .8$
   d. $(.15)^3 \times (.15) \times (.15)^2$

2. Multiply the number and letter values (a) through (d) and simplify.

   a. $(B + 3)^2$
   b. $(5 + C)^3$
   c. $(X + 4)^2$
   d. $(3 + AB)^3$

C. ALGEBRAIC MULTIPLICATION OF QUANTITIES IN SCIENTIFIC NOTATION

1. Multiply each of the four quantities. Express each answer in terms of the appropriate symbols of the prefix and unit of measure.

   a. $2.9\ (10^3)$ joules (J) x $6.2\ (10^6)$ joules
   b. $272.4\ (10^{-8})$ lumen (lm) x $4.8\ (10^{-10})$ lumen
   c. $16.72\ (10^{-12})$ amperes (A) x $7.56\ (10^{15})$ amperes
   d. $8.56\ (10^{-18})$ coulomb (C) x $12.97\ (10^{12})$ coulomb

D. ALGEBRAIC DIVISION OF NUMBERS AND LETTERS

1. Divide each number in problems (a) through (d) and raise the quotient factor to the resulting exponential value. Round off decimal values to two places.

   a. $\frac{242^5}{242^3}$
   b. $\frac{.625^4}{.625^2}$
   c. $\frac{1.125^5}{1.125^2}$
   d. $\frac{2.25^7}{2.25^3}$

2. Perform the operations indicated at (a) through (d).

   a. $\frac{X^{7m}}{X^m}$
   b. $\frac{L^3 \times L^3}{L^5}$
   c. $\frac{P^7 \times P^4 \times P}{P^6 \times P^3}$
   d. $\frac{A^9 \times A^{12} \times A^{10} \times A}{A^8 \times A^2 \times A^3}$

E. ALGEBRAIC DIVISION OF QUANTITIES IN SCIENTIFIC NOTATION

1. Divide each of the four quantities. Express each answer in terms of the symbols for the appropriate prefix and unit of measure.

   a. $\frac{7.5\ (10^{-5})}{1.25\ (10^{-2})}$ amperes (A)
   b. $\frac{54.6\ (10^{-6})}{4.55\ (10^{-12})}$ watts (W)
   c. $\frac{242.8\ (10^6)}{192.7\ (10^{12})}$ newtons (N)
   d. $\frac{5.426\ (10^6)}{0.096\ (10^9)}$ meters (m)

Section 13

RADICALS

Unit 61 SQUARE ROOT OF WHOLE NUMBERS

A working knowledge of how to find the square root of whole numbers, fractions, and algebraic numbers is important because of constant applications of these principles in business, industry, health occupations, distribution and merchandising, and the home.

A. PERFECT SQUARES OF WHOLE NUMBERS IN SQUARE ROOT

The phrase, *extracting the square root*, refers to the process of finding the equal factors which, when multiplied together, give the original number. The process is identified by the use of the *radical symbol* ($\sqrt{\ }$). This *radical sign* is a shorthand way of saying, mathematically, that the equal factors of the number under the radical sign are to be determined.

The $\sqrt{16}$ is read "the square root of 16." This number consists of the two equal factors 4 and 4. Thus, when 4 is raised to the second power or *squared*, it is equal to 16. The term *squaring a number* merely means to multiply the number by itself.

The 16 is also referred to as a "perfect" square. Numbers that are perfect squares have whole numbers as square roots. For example, the square roots of perfect squares 4, 25, 36, 121, and 324 are all whole numbers.

RULE FOR EXTRACTING THE SQUARE ROOTS OF WHOLE NUMBERS WHICH ARE PERFECT SQUARES

- Determine what number when multiplied by itself is equal to the whole number under the radical sign.

  NOTE: This number is known as the square root of the original number.
- If the factors cannot be determined readily,

  Break the original number into more than one factor.

  Extract the square root of each of the smaller numbers to get the factors.
- Multiply the factors. The product of these factors equals the square root of the original number. This square root multiplied by itself equals the original number which was a perfect square.

EXAMPLE: Find the square root of 1024.

Step 1	Break original number into a series of smaller numbers.	$\sqrt{1024} = \sqrt{4 \times 256} = \sqrt{4 \times 4 \times 64}$
Step 2	Extract the square root of each smaller number.	$\sqrt{4} \times \sqrt{4} \times \sqrt{64} = 2 \times 2 \times 8$
Step 3	Multiply the factors. The product (32) is the square root of 1024.	$2 \times 2 \times 8 = 32$ Ans.

B. COMPUTING THE SQUARE ROOT BY APPROXIMATION

RULE FOR EXTRACTING THE SQUARE ROOT BY APPROXIMATION

All numbers under a radical sign are not necessarily "perfect" squares. In such instances, an approximate square root may be computed to a specified degree of accuracy. Problems of this type are simplified by first extracting the square root of the perfect square. Then the square root of the number remaining under the radical sign is determined. The product of the square root of the perfect square and the approximate square root of the other number is the approximate square root of the original number.

EXAMPLE: Find $\sqrt{32}$ correct to two decimal places.

Step 1 Break the original number into smaller numbers which may be perfect squares.

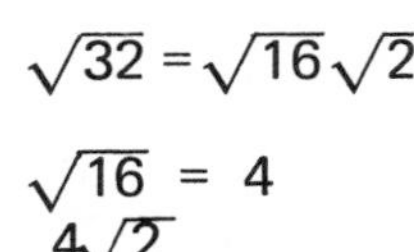

Step 2 Extract the square root of any perfect square. Place this number in front of the radical sign of remaining number.

NOTE: If there is more than one perfect square, multiply the roots of these to get the number to place in front of the radical sign.

Step 3 Examine the remaining number under the radical sign and determine the approximate number of the square root. In this case, the square root is closer to 1 than 2 because $1^2 = 1$ and $2^2 = 4$.

Step 4 Place the 1 outside the radical sign above the 2. Multiply the 1 by itself and place the product (1) under the 2.

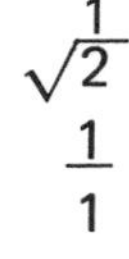

Step 5 Subtract as in division to get the remainder.

Step 6 Add a decimal point following the 2, and one more set of zeros (00) than the required number of decimal places.

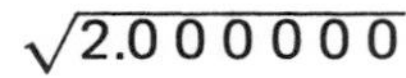

NOTE: The zeros are added because the square root is a whole number and a decimal fraction.

Step 7 Carry down one set of zeros (00) and add to the remainder.

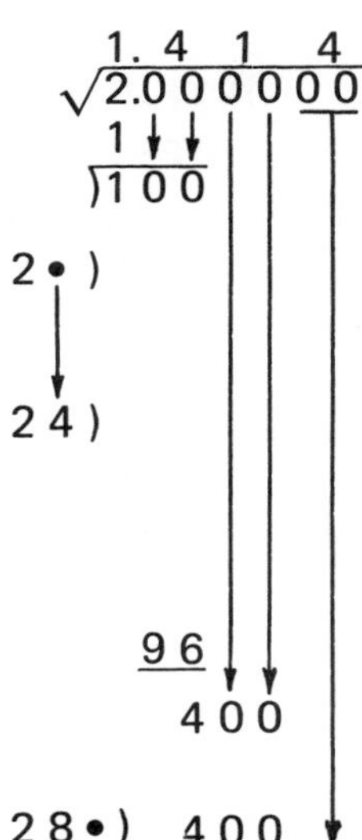

Step 8 Double the first number (1) and write outside the division frame in the tens column.

Step 9 Determine how many times the "two tens" plus a number in the units place may be divided into the 100. In this instance, 24 will go into 100, 4 times.

Step 10 Place the 4 above the radical sign following the decimal point. Multiply the 24 x 4 and place the product (96) under the 100.

Step 11 Subtract and bring down next set of zeros.

Step 12 Double the 1.4 above the radical sign and place the result in the hundreds and tens digits as a divisor into the 400.

Step 13 Determine how many times the 280 will divide into 400. Add the 1 to the 280 and place 1 above the radical sign.

Step 14 Multiply the 281 x 1 and place the product under the 400.

```
28•  )    400
↓
281  )
          281
2824)   11900
        11296
```

Step 15 Subtract and continue the same processes until the factor is determined correct to a specified number of places.

Step 16 Multiply the factor 4 as the square root of $\sqrt{16}$ and 1.414 as the approximate square root of $\sqrt{2}$.

$4 \times 1.414 = 5.656$

Step 17 The $\sqrt{32} = 5.66$ correct to two decimal places.

The four separate mathematical processes used in determining the approximate square root of $\sqrt{32}$ are illustrated as they are carried out in actual practice.

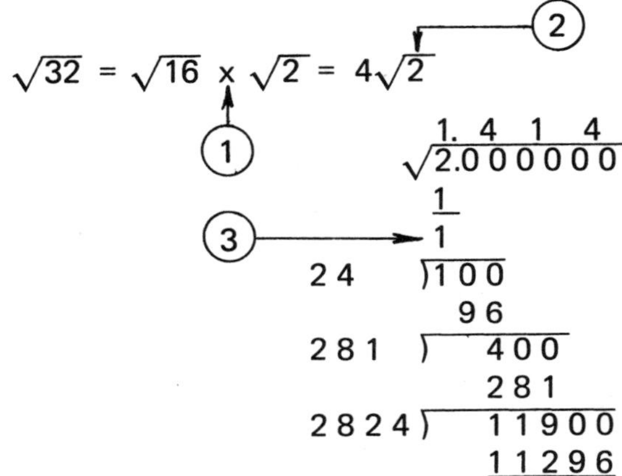

(4) → 4 (1.414) = 5.656 = 5.66 NOTE: The 5.66 is the approximate square root of 32.

ASSIGNMENT UNIT 61

A. DETERMINING SQUARE ROOTS OF WHOLE NUMBERS WHICH ARE PERFECT SQUARES

1. Determine, by observation, the square root of each perfect square under a radical sign.

a. $\sqrt{36}$	d. $\sqrt{625}$	g. $\sqrt{.25}$	j. $\sqrt{2.25}$
b. $\sqrt{64}$	e. $\sqrt{144}$	h. $\sqrt{1.21}$	k. $\sqrt{3600}$
c. $\sqrt{100}$	f. $\sqrt{256}$	i. $\sqrt{1.44}$	l. $\sqrt{2.89}$

Ans.: b. 8 e. 12 h. 1.1 k. 60

2. Compute the square root of each perfect square in (a) through (i). If necessary, factor the original number to simplify a problem.

a. $\sqrt{1024}$	d. $\sqrt{5184}$	g. $\sqrt{12.25}$
b. $\sqrt{4096}$	e. $\sqrt{6.25}$	h. $\sqrt{.2025}$
c. $\sqrt{1296}$	f. $\sqrt{9.61}$	i. $\sqrt{.5625}$

Ans.: b. 64 e. 2.5 h. .45

B. EXTRACTING SQUARE ROOT BY APPROXIMATION

1. Extract the square root of (a) through (i) by the approximation method. Give each answer correct to two decimal places and check the accuracy of each result.

   a. $\sqrt{2}$ d. $\sqrt{5}$ g. $\sqrt{24}$
   b. $\sqrt{3}$ e. $\sqrt{15}$ h. $\sqrt{320}$
   c. $\sqrt{7}$ f. $\sqrt{17}$ i. $\sqrt{431}$

   Ans.: b. 1.73 e. 3.87 h. 17.89

2. Find the value of the following:

   a. $\sqrt{(3)^2 + (6)^2 + (8)^2 + (4)^2}$
   b. $\sqrt{(10)^2 + (5.2)^2 + (6.4)^2 + (3.1)}$
   c. $\sqrt{(9.3)^2 + (4.8)^2 + (5.2) + (7.4)^2}$
   d. $\sqrt{(2)^2 + (7)^2 + (9)^2 + (4)^2}$
   e. $\sqrt{(1.2)^2 + (2.5)^2 + (5.5)^2 + (3.9)^2}$

   Ans.: b. 13.33 d. 12.25

C. PRACTICAL PROBLEMS IN SQUARE ROOT

1. Determine the length of side (L) for triangles A through E. Substitute the values given in the table in the equation. $L = \sqrt{X^2 + Y^2}$

	A	B	C	D	E
X =	3″	6.6″	1′	10″	5.6″
Y =	4″	8.8″	2′	16″	7.8″

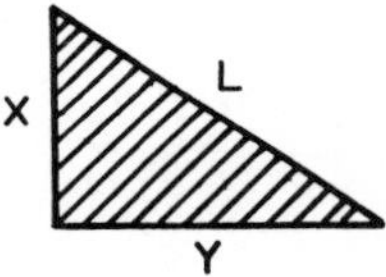

   Ans.: B. 11″ D. 18.868″

2. Compute the value of D correct to two decimal places for each value of S. Use 3.142 for π. $D = \sqrt{S/\pi}$

	A	B	C	D
Value of S	9.426	31.42	38.704	62.84

   Ans.: B. 3.16 D = 4.47

3. Find dimension (S) for each of the four square sheet metal ducts, according to the cross-sectional areas given in the table. Reduce answers to feet and inches and round off to the nearest whole inch.

Duct	Cross-Sectional Area (X)
A	3715.2 cm²
B	7901.25 cm²
C	0.93 m²
D	2.51 m²

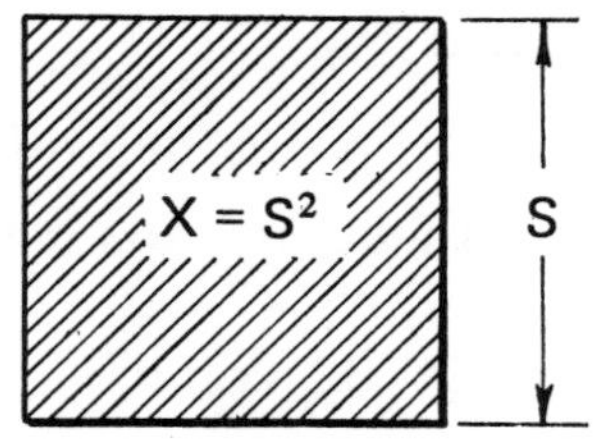

   Ans.: B. 88.89 cm D. 1.58 m

4. The voltage diagram shows voltage E_R is 82.2 volts. E_X is 66.4 volts. Compute the line voltage voltage E_L correct to two decimal places.

$$E_L = \sqrt{(E_R)^2 + (E_X)^2}$$

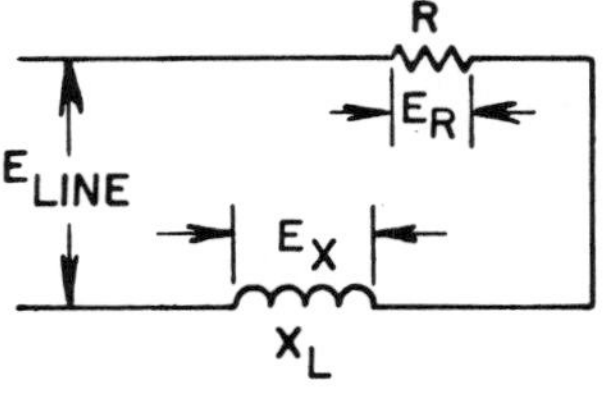

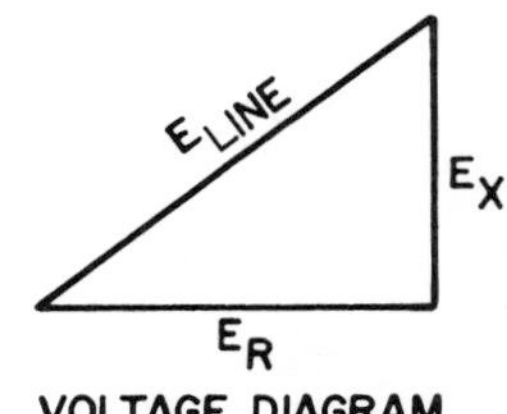

VOLTAGE DIAGRAM

Unit 62 SQUARE ROOT OF FRACTIONS AND ALGEBRAIC NUMBERS

A. EXTRACTING THE SQUARE ROOT OF A FRACTION (Perfect Square)

Extracting the square root of a fraction is a double process of first finding the square root of the numerator and then of the denominator.

RULE FOR EXTRACTING THE SQUARE ROOT OF A FRACTION (Perfect Square)

- Determine the factors of the numerator. If any factor is a perfect square, remove from under the radical sign and place its square root as a numerator.
- Determine the factors of the denominator and proceed as with the numerator.
- Combine the terms of the fraction and simplify.

EXAMPLE: Find the square root of 4/9.

$$\sqrt{\frac{4}{9}} = \frac{\sqrt{4}}{\sqrt{9}}$$

Step 1 Determine the square root of the numerator. $\sqrt{4} = 2$

Step 2 Determine the square root of the denominator. $\sqrt{9} = 3$

Step 3 Place the numerator (2) over the denominator (3). The result is 2/3.

$$\sqrt{\frac{4}{9}} = \frac{2}{3} \text{ Ans.}$$

B. APPROXIMATING THE SQUARE ROOT OF FRACTIONS

When neither the numerator nor the denominator of a fraction (or both) can be factored as perfect squares, then the approximate method is used to compute the square root of the fraction under the radical sign.

RULE FOR DETERMINING SQUARE ROOT OF A FRACTION (Approximate Method)

- Place the numerator under a radical sign.
- Place the denominator under a radical sign.
- Extract the square root of the numerator by the approximate method the same as for a whole number.
- Perform the same operation for the denominator.
- Express the resulting fraction in lowest terms.

EXAMPLE: Solve $\sqrt{\frac{2}{3}}$ correct to two decimal places.

Step 1 Place the numerator and denominator under separate radical signs.

$$\sqrt{\frac{2}{3}} = \frac{\sqrt{2}}{\sqrt{3}}$$

Step 2 Extract the square root of the numerator; then of the denominator.

$$\frac{\sqrt{2}}{\sqrt{3}} = \frac{1.414}{1.732}$$

NOTE: Carry out to three decimal places.

$$= \frac{.707}{.866}$$

Step 3 Express in lowest terms and round off to two decimal places.

$$= \frac{.71}{.87}$$

C. SQUARE ROOT OF ALGEBRAIC NUMBERS

An algebraic number contains letters and numbers used in combination. The square root of an algebraic number is the product of the square root of the number and the square root of the letter or letters.

RULE FOR DETERMINING THE SQUARE ROOT OF ALGEBRAIC NUMBERS

- Determine the square root of the numerical value. See if the number may be factored as a perfect square. Otherwise, use the approximate method.
- Place the result outside the radical sign.
- Factor the literal value.
- Multiply the numerical and literal values outside the radical sign.

EXAMPLE: Find $\sqrt{9Y^2}$.

Step 1 Break up $\sqrt{9Y^2}$ into numerical and literal terms. $\sqrt{9Y^2} = \sqrt{9} \times \sqrt{Y^2}$

Step 2 Determine the square root of the numerical term. $\sqrt{9} = 3$

Step 3 Determine the square root of the literal term. $\sqrt{Y^2} = Y$

Step 4 Multiply the square roots of the terms. $3 \times Y = 3Y$ Ans.

This same procedure is followed for both the numerator and denominator of algebraic fractions.

ASSIGNMENT UNIT 62

A. DETERMINING SQUARE ROOTS OF FRACTIONS (Perfect Squares)

1. Determine, by observation, the square root of each fraction (perfect square) under a radical sign.

a. $\sqrt{\frac{4}{25}}$ d. $\sqrt{\frac{25}{36}}$ g. $\sqrt{\frac{64}{81}}$ j. $\sqrt{\frac{.25}{.36}}$

b. $\sqrt{\frac{16}{25}}$ e. $\sqrt{\frac{36}{49}}$ h. $\sqrt{\frac{100}{121}}$ k. $\sqrt{\frac{1.00}{1.21}}$

c. $\sqrt{\frac{9}{16}}$ f. $\sqrt{\frac{9}{25}}$ i. $\sqrt{\frac{.16}{.25}}$ l. $\sqrt{\frac{.64}{1.44}}$

Ans.: b. 4/5 e. 6/7 h. 10/11 k. 1/1.1

2. A heating coil in a dryer uses 16 watts (W). The heat resistance is 25 ohms (O). How many amperes (A) are there in the circuit when $A = \sqrt{W/O}$?

3. Compute the square root of each fraction. Wherever practical, factor to simplify.

a. $\sqrt{\frac{1600}{2025}}$ b. $\sqrt{\frac{1764}{2704}}$ c. $\sqrt{\frac{10.89}{42.25}}$ d. $\sqrt{\frac{110.00}{129.6}}$

Ans.: b. 21/26 d. 10.488/11.384

B. EXTRACTING THE SQUARE ROOT OF FRACTIONS BY APPROXIMATION

1. Extract the square root of fractions (a) through (f). Reduce and/or factor, where practical. Also, reduce to lowest terms and round off answers correct to two decimal places.

a. $\sqrt{\frac{5}{7}}$ c. $\sqrt{\frac{44}{35}}$ e. $\sqrt{\frac{5.0}{12.5}}$

b. $\sqrt{\frac{10}{24}}$ d. $\sqrt{\frac{3}{32}}$ f. $\sqrt{\frac{7.84}{15.36}}$

Ans.: b. $\frac{2.24}{3.46}$ d. $\frac{1.73}{5.66}$ f. $\frac{.35}{.49}$

C. EXTRACTING THE SQUARE ROOT OF ALGEBRAIC NUMBERS

1. Find the square root of each algebraic number and fraction.

a. $\sqrt{4a^2}$ d. $\sqrt{.25X^2}$ g. $\sqrt{\frac{16A^2}{25B^2}}$

b. $\sqrt{9b^2}$ e. $\sqrt{1.44Y^2}$ h. $\sqrt{\frac{27b^2}{32c^2}}$

c. $\sqrt{36c^2}$ f. $\sqrt{2.56Z^2}$ i. $\sqrt{\frac{2.42X^2}{7.2Y^2}}$

Ans.: b. 3 b e. 1.2 Y h. 5.196 b/5.657 c

2. Determine length (b) of $\triangle ABC$ when $b = \sqrt{c^2 - a^2}$.

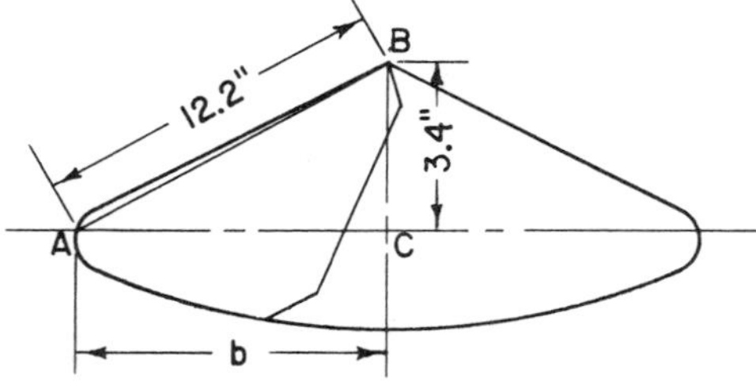

Unit 63 APPLICATION OF SQUARE ROOT TABLES

The simplest method of finding the square root of a number is to use a *table of square roots.* This practice is widespread in the business and industrial world. It conserves time and, what is more important, it insures accuracy.

While the form in which tables are prepared varies, the factual information they contain is the same. All square root tables list in sequence and in one column all whole numbers. The square root of each of these numbers is given in another column. The square root values, except in the case of perfect squares, are approximate. The values are accurate to the degree indicated for the entire table. The tables are called *two-point, three-point,* or the like. The "point" indicates that the approximate values are correct to two or three decimal places, respectively.

Larger square root tables are accurate to four and five places. Also, these tables contain the approximate square roots of whole numbers and tenths.

TABLES OF SQUARE ROOT VALUES

Table I	
1 through 10	
No.	Square Root
1	1.00
2	1.41
3	1.73
4	2.00
5	2.24
6	2.45
7	2.65
8	2.83
9	3.00
10	3.16

Table II										
1.0 through 9.9										
No.	.0	.1	.2	.3	.4	.5	.6	.7	.8	.9
1	1.00	$1.0\overline{5}$	1.10	1.14	1.18	1.22	1.26	1.30	1.34	1 38
2	1.41	$1.4\overline{5}$	1.48	1.52	$1.5\overline{5}$	1.58	1.61	1.64	1.67	1.70
3	1.73	1.76	1.79	1.82	1.84	1.87	1.90	1.92	$1.9\overline{5}$	1.97
4	2.00	2.02	$2.0\overline{5}$	2.07	2.10	2.12	2.14	2.17	2.19	2.21
5	2.24	2.26	2.28	2.30	2.32	$2.3\overline{5}$	2.37	2.39	2.41	2.43
6	$2.4\overline{5}$	2.47	2.49	2.51	2.53	2.55	2.57	2.59	2.61	2.63
7	$2.6\overline{5}$	2.67	2.68	2.70	2.72	2.74	2.76	2.77	2.79	2.81
8	2.83	$2.8\overline{5}$	2.86	2.88	2.90	2.92	2.93	2.95	2.97	2.98
9	3.00	3.02	3.03	3.05	3.07	3.08	3.10	3.11	3.13	3.15

Note: Wherever a line appears over the second place digit of 5, like $1.5\overline{5}$, drop the last digit in rounding-off. The $1.5\overline{5}$ correct to one decimal place is 1.5.

A. READING TABLES OF SQUARE ROOTS

Portions of these types of tables are illustrated. Table I lists whole numbers from 1 to 10 in one column. The square root of each number is given in a second column. Note that the square root is correct to two decimal places. Table II contains the square root values of numbers from 1.0 through 9.9, correct to two decimal places. Table III shows only a small part of a larger table of square root values for numbers ranging from 1.00 to 9.99 in steps of .01. This three-point table is accurate to the nearest thousandth.

Table III										
Square Root Values of Numbers from 1.00 through 9.99										
No.	**0**	**1**	**2**	**3**	**4**	**5**	**6**	**7**	**8**	**9**
1.0	1.000	$1.00\overline{5}$	1.010	$1.01\overline{5}$	1.020	$1.02\overline{5}$	1.030	1.034	1.039	1.044
1.1	1.049	1.054	1.058	1.063	1.068	1.072	1.077	1.082	1.086	1.091
1.2	1.095	1.100	$1.10\overline{5}$	1.109	1.114	1.118	1.122	1.127	1.131	1.136
1.3	1.140	$1.14\overline{5}$	1.149	1.153	1.158	1.162	1.166	1.170	1.175	1.179

RULE FOR READING A TABLE OF SQUARE ROOTS

- Determine the degree of accuracy required. Then select a table of square roots that will provide the desired accuracy.

  NOTE: If tables are not available, it may be necessary to compute by the approximate method.
- Find the given number in the column which is so marked.
- Locate the square root value of the given number in the column in which the square roots are given.

  NOTE: If the number contains a decimal, look for the square root value in the column to the right of the whole number and below the decimal value.
- Round off answer to as many places as may be required.

EXAMPLE: Case 1 Use a table to find $\sqrt{2}$ correct to one decimal place.

Step 1 Locate the whole number 2 in the first vertical column of a table of square roots.

Step 2 Read the square root to the right of the given number in the column of square roots.

Step 3 Round off to one decimal place. Ans. $1.41 = 1.4$

No.	Sq. Root
1	1.00
2	1.41
3	1.73
4	2.00

EXAMPLE: Case 2 Find in a table of square roots the $\sqrt{3.1}$ correct to one decimal place.

Step 1 Select a table of square roots which gives values of numbers in steps of .1.

Step 2 Locate the 3 in the vertical column of whole numbers.

Step 3 Read the square root value in the column to the right of 3 and below .1. $\sqrt{3.1} = 1.76$

Step 4 Round off the square root value of 1.76 to one decimal place. Ans. $1.76 = 1.8$

	.0	.1	.2
1	1.00	1.05	1.10
2	1.41	1.45	1.48
3	1.73	1.76	1.79
4	2.00		

B. COMPUTING THE SQUARE ROOT OF NUMBERS OUTSIDE THE RANGE OF TABLES

Sometimes, the range of a table of square roots is not large enough to take care of all numbers. When such is the case, the number may be factored so the perfect square is removed. The number remaining under the radial sign may then fall within the range of the table.

RULE FOR COMPUTING THE SQUARE ROOT OF ANY NUMBER
(Factoring, Approximate Method and Use of Tables)

- Factor the given number as far as possible.
- Locate the square root value of the remainder under the radical sign in a table of square roots.
  NOTE: If no table is available, compute this value by the approximate method.
- Multiply the first factor (or combination of factors) by the square root obtained from a table or by the approximate method.
- Round off the result, if required.

EXAMPLE: Case 1 Find $\sqrt{192}$ to two decimal places.

Step 1 Factor. $\sqrt{192} = \sqrt{64} \times \sqrt{3}$

Step 2 Determine $\sqrt{64}$. $\sqrt{64} = 8$

Step 3 Find $\sqrt{3}$ from a table. $\sqrt{3} = 1.73$
NOTE: Compute this value if no table is available.

Step 4 Multiply both factors 8 and 1.73. $\sqrt{192} = (8) \times (1.73)$ $= 13.84$ Ans.

EXAMPLE: Case 2 Find $\sqrt{.24}$ to two decimal places.

Step 1 Express $\sqrt{.24}$ in terms of a fraction. $\sqrt{.24} = \sqrt{\dfrac{24}{100}} = \dfrac{\sqrt{24}}{\sqrt{100}}$

Step 2 Factor the numerator. $\sqrt{24} = \sqrt{4} \times \sqrt{6} = 2\sqrt{6}$

Step 3 Find the value of $\sqrt{6}$. $\sqrt{6} = 2.45$

Step 4 Multiply both factors in the numerator. $\sqrt{24} = (2) \times (2.45) = 4.90$

Step 5 Factor the denominator. $\sqrt{100} = 10$

Step 6 Place the square root of the numerator (4.90) over the square root of the denominator (10) and divide. $\dfrac{4.90}{10} = .49$

$\sqrt{.24} = .49$ Ans.

The square root values of numbers may be checked readily by simply multiplying the square root of the original number by itself. When the square root value has been determined by the approximate method, the result should fall within the range of the required degree of accuracy. The square roots, particularly of decimal numbers, should be checked for accurate placement of the decimal point.

ASSIGNMENT UNIT 63

NOTE: Refer to the Table of Square Roots in the Appendix to solve those problems in this unit which require the use of a table.

A. READING TABLES OF SQUARE ROOTS

1. Find the square root of each number correct to two decimal places.

a. $\sqrt{2}$ b. $\sqrt{3}$ c. $\sqrt{5}$ d. $\sqrt{6}$ e. $\sqrt{7}$ f. $\sqrt{10}$

Ans.: b. 1.73 d. 2.45 f. 3.16

2. Find the square root of each number correct to one decimal place.

a. $\sqrt{1.1}$ d. $\sqrt{2.3}$ g. $\sqrt{9.3}$

b. $\sqrt{1.7}$ e. $\sqrt{5.2}$ h. $\sqrt{8.7}$

c. $\sqrt{3.3}$ f. $\sqrt{6.3}$

Ans.: b. 1.3 e. 2.3 h. 3.0

B. COMPUTING SQUARE ROOT VALUES

1. Compute the square root of each number by factoring, approximation or table. Give answers to two places.

a. $\sqrt{32}$ d. $\sqrt{324}$ g. $\sqrt{3.2}$

b. $\sqrt{80}$ e. $\sqrt{1694}$ h. $\sqrt{2501.7}$

c. $\sqrt{63}$ f. $\sqrt{27.5}$

Ans.: b. 8.94 e. 41.12 h. 50.02

C. APPLICATION OF SQUARE ROOT TO PRACTICAL PROBLEMS

1. Compute dimension Z of the part illustrated, for each dimension given for X and Y, correct to three decimal places. Wherever practical, use the table of square root values.

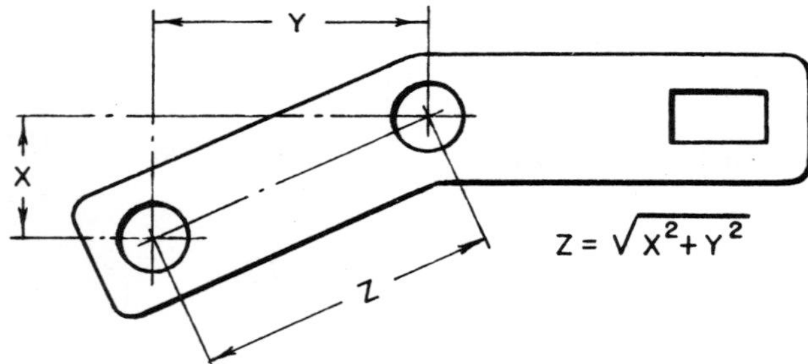

	Given Values	
	X	Y
A	3	4
B	6	7
C	12.5	15
D	8.6	10.5

Ans.: B. 9.220″ D. 13.572″

2. A series of rectangular pipes is to be constructed. The width of each pipe is to be five times the height. Find the dimensions of sheet metal pipes A through E for the area given in each instance.

Pipe	Area
A	80 cm^2
B	100 cm^2
C	245 mm^2
D	366.25 mm^2
E	5.5 m^2

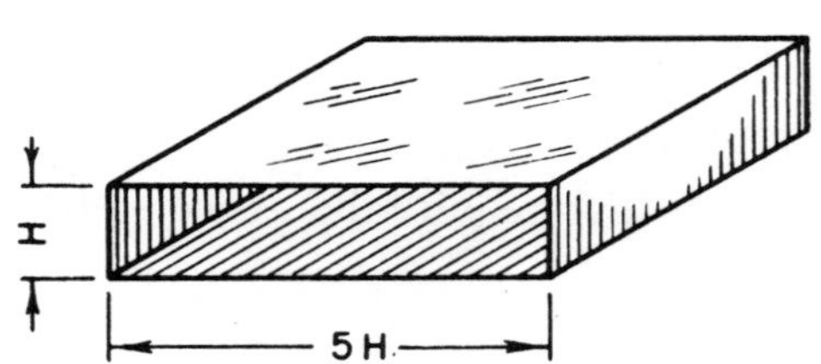

Ans.: B. H = 4.472 cm; 5H = 22.36 cm
D. H = 8.56 mm; 5H = 42.8 mm

3. What amperage is flowing through an electrical circuit when the wattage is 440 and the resistance is 200?

$$\text{Amperage} = \sqrt{\frac{\text{Watts}}{\text{Resistance}}}$$

4. An electrical heating unit has a 20-ohm resistance and uses power at the rate of 2420 watts. Determine the voltage that the heater works on when,

$$\text{Voltage} = \sqrt{(\text{Watts}) \times (\text{Ohms Resistance})}$$

Ans.: 220 volts

5. Calculate the cylinder diameter (c) of an eight-cylinder engine (N) rated at 96.4 horsepower (h.p.) when,

$$c = \sqrt{\frac{\text{h.p.} \times 2.5}{N}}$$

6. The resistance of an electric heating device is 672 ohms. It uses 34 watts of power. Determine the amperes required by the resistance. Round off the answer to three decimal places.

$$A = \sqrt{\frac{\text{watts}}{\text{ohms}}}$$

Ans.: 0.225 amperes

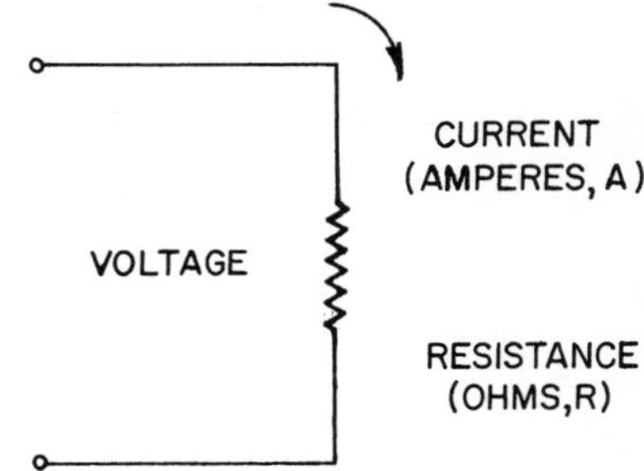

Unit 64 ACHIEVEMENT REVIEW ON RADICALS

A. DETERMINING SQUARE ROOTS OF WHOLE NUMBERS (Perfect Squares)

1. Determine the square root for (a) through (d).

   a. $\sqrt{729}$ b. $\sqrt{361}$ c. $\sqrt{18.49}$ d. $\sqrt{30.25}$

B. EXTRACTING SQUARE ROOT BY APPROXIMATION

1. Find the square root of (a) through (d) by the approximation method. Round off each answer to two decimal places.

   a. $\sqrt{7}$ b. $\sqrt{30}$ c. $\sqrt{28}$ d. $\sqrt{5.6}$

2. Determine the diameter (d) in mils of a #8 wire having a cross-sectional area of 16,510 circular mils (C.M.), when $d = \sqrt{C.M.}$

C. DETERMINING SQUARE ROOTS OF FRACTIONS (Perfect Squares)

1. Determine the square roots of each fraction.

   a. $\sqrt{\frac{2209}{3364}}$ b. $\sqrt{\frac{50.41}{8.41}}$ c. $\sqrt{\frac{.1521}{.3969}}$ d. $\sqrt{\frac{.0625}{.1024}}$

D. EXTRACTING SQUARE ROOT OF FRACTIONS BY APPROXIMATION

1. The amperes (A) in a circuit $= \sqrt{\frac{\text{watts (W)}}{\text{ohms (O)}}}$. Determine the amperes for the four circuits whose values appear in the table.

W =	1	2	8	1
O =	3	5	11	7

2. Find the square root of each fraction by approximation.

   a. $\sqrt{\frac{1.7}{3.2}}$ b. $\sqrt{\frac{.75}{.25}}$ c. $\sqrt{\frac{30.2}{37.3}}$ d. $\sqrt{\frac{2.15}{1.25}}$

E. DETERMINING THE SQUARE ROOT OF ALGEBRAIC NUMBERS

1. The largest side (hypotenuse) of a 90° triangle equals $\sqrt{a^2 + b^2}$. Find the hypotenuse for triangles A, B, and C.

Triangle	A	B	C
Side a =	6 1/2″	7 1/2″	11.5″
Side b =	2″	3 1/2″	4.5″

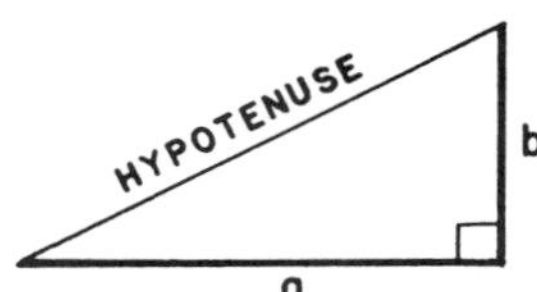

2. Find the value of each algebraic fraction.

   a. $\sqrt{\frac{A^2}{3}}$ b. $\sqrt{\frac{2b^2}{5}}$ c. $\sqrt{\frac{a^2\ b^2}{11}}$ d. $\sqrt{\frac{X^2\ Y^2}{7}}$

3. The vector diagram shows a voltage of 27 between L_3 and L_2 and 35 volts between L_1 and L_2. What is the voltage across L_1 and L_3? This voltage is equal to the square root of the sum of the squares of the other two sides of the triangle.

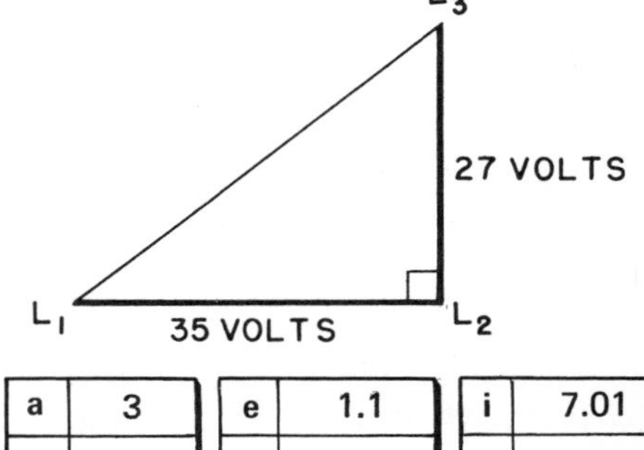

F. READING TABLES OF SQUARE ROOTS

1. Refer to a table of square root values. Find the square root of numbers (a) through (h) correct to two decimal places and (i) through (l) to three decimal places.

a	3	e	1.1	i	7.01
b	5	f	2.1	j	1.02
c	7	g	3.9	k	3.03
d	8	h	5.5	l	1.38

G. APPLICATION OF SQUARE ROOT TABLES, FACTORING, AND APPROXIMATION

1. Determine the square root of the following numbers which are outside the range of a table. Solve each number by factoring, approximating or using tables, whichever method or combination is appropriate.

   a. $\sqrt{200}$ b. $\sqrt{156}$ c. $\sqrt{.32}$ d. $\sqrt{224.8}$

2. The diameter of a wire in mils is equal to the square root of the circular mils area. Find the diameter of each of three wires where the cross-sectional areas equal 5.232, 3.109, and 4.378 circular mils, respectively.

3. Find distance D, when $D = \sqrt{X^2} - \sqrt{Y^2}$.

Section 14

FORMULAS

Unit 65 THE CONCEPT AND USE OF FORMULAS

A formula is an abbreviated way of expressing a combination of mathematical processes which, when solved, always give the same result. Formulas are used widely in the shop, and laboratory and clinic to obtain dimensions and other data. Formulas are applied in banking, business, marketing, agriculture and in the home for determining dimensions, costs, and the like.

A formula also provides a technique of simplifying the solution of a problem. It gives very specific directions for computing unknown quantities. A formula is an equality. In many cases, the formula requires the application of the principles covered thus far. These relate to the use of symbols, exponents, radicals, and the four basic processes of addition, subtraction, multiplication, and division of numerical and literal values. Formulas, therefore, express basic mathematical truths in a simplified form. Values may be substituted in formulas and comparatively simple processes followed to solve for a required dimension or quantity.

Formulas are found in farm journals, industrial publications, technical handbooks, and household publications. In fact, formulas are used wherever it is practical to take a shortcut in solving a problem. The use of a formula may be simplified if the basic steps for developing and applying formulas are followed.

RULE FOR DEVELOPING AND APPLYING FORMULAS

- Analyze the problem by reading it carefully.
- Determine what quantities are given and what values are required.
- Review the formula for the meaning of each literal and numerical value.
- Write the formula to one side with sufficient room around it to work the problem.

  NOTE: Where no formula is available, it is practical to develop one for solving the whole problem or parts of one.
- Perform the mathematical operations as indicated.
- Simplify the answer.
- Label the answer with the correct unit.
- Recheck the final result.

If an orderly procedure is followed for writing the formula, substituting values in the formula, and computing for missing values, the solution of the problem is simplified and the chance for error is lessened.

Note, too, that as the formula is written, the unknown quantity does not have to be written for each step. The unknown quantity is understood to be there before the equals sign.

ASSIGNMENT UNIT 65

A. INTRODUCTION TO AND USE OF FORMULAS

1. Develop a formula from the information furnished in each rule.

   a. The diameter (D) of a circle is equal to twice the radius (R).
   b. The area of a square (A) is found by squaring a side (S).
   c. The list price (L) is equal to the cost of an article (C) plus 25% markup.
   d. The length of one side of a right triangle (A) is equal to the square root of the sum of the squares of the other two sides, (B and C).
   e. The cutting speed (CS) of a drill is the product of the circumference of the drill times the revolutions per minute.

   Ans.: b. $A = S^2$ d. $A = \sqrt{B^2 + C^2}$

2. Interpret formulas A through E by writing the rule which each one expresses.

	Formula	
A	$A = \frac{\pi D^2}{4}$	A = Area of Circle D = Diameter
B	$V = .785\ D^2H$	V = Volume of cylinder D = Diameter H = Height
C	$\frac{OD}{N + 2} = P$	P = Diametral pitch OD = Outside diameter N = Number of teeth
D	$CS = \frac{\pi D\ (rpm)}{12}$	CS = Cutting speed in feet per minute D = Diameter of cutter rpm = Revolutions per minute
E	$L = \sqrt{r^2 + (\frac{S}{2})^2}$	L = Length of roof slope r = Rise S = Span

3. Rule three vertical columns (I, II, III) on a sheet of paper.

   a. Write five formulas from trade handbooks, technical journals, catalogs or any other printed material in column I.
   b. Identify each letter or symbol by writing in column II what each stands for.
   c. Translate each formula into a rule in column III.

B. FORMULAS WITH APPLICATIONS TO PRACTICAL PROBLEMS

1. Translate each of the following three mathematical statements into formulas.

   a. The root diameter (R) of a thread is equal to the outside diameter (o) minus twice the depth of the thread (d) and twice the clearance (c).
   b. The length of metal (L) required to make a right-angle bend is equal to the length of the two legs (L_1 and L_2) plus one half the thickness of the metal (t).

c. The approximate length (L) of a flat belt is equal to twice the distance between the centerlines (c) of the two pulleys (D_1 and D_2) plus 3.25 times the sum of the pulley diameters divided by two.

NOTE: All dimensions used in the formula must be in the same unit of measurement.

Ans.: b. $L = L_1 + L_2 + (t/2)$

2. Use the appropriate formula and solve each of the three following problems.

a. Determine the length of metal required to produce right-angle parts A, B, and C.

Right-Angle Parts	Dimensions of Legs		Metal Thickness (t)
	L_1	L_2	
A	10.2 cm	15.2 cm	0.32 cm
B	13.98 cm	22.72 cm	0.24 cm
C	0.165 m	0.244 m	0.005 m

Ans.: B. 36.82 cm

b. Find the root diameter of threaded parts A, B, and C.

Threaded Part	Outside Diameter (O)	Depth of Thread (D)	Clearance (C)
A	1.125″	.125″	.015″
B	3.3125″	.1875″	.022″
C	4 1/16″	5/32″	1/64″

Ans.: B. 2.8935 inches

c. Calculate the approximate lengths of flat belt that are required to fill the three conditions given in the table. Round off answers to the nearest 1/8″ and reduce to feet and inches.

Condition	Centerline Distance (c)	Pulley Diameters	
		(D_1)	(D_2)
A	36″	10″	14″
B	4′-6″	9″	13″
C	8′-7″	15″	18 1/2″

Ans.: B. 11 feet 11 3/4 inches.

Unit 66 APPLICATION OF FORMULAS TO SQUARES, RECTANGLES, AND REGULAR SOLIDS

Typical applications of the square and rectangle are found in the ductwork of buildings and homes for heating and ventilating, the shape of building lots, and the layout of rooms. As dimensions are added to these shapes, problems in areas, perimeters, cubical contents, and the like need to be solved. Formulas, which are comparatively simple to develop, are used for such problems.

A. DEVELOPING FORMULAS FOR SQUARE OBJECTS

Formula for Perimeter of a Square

Considering the square first, the distance around it (called *perimeter*) is equal to the sum of the four sides. Since each one of the four sides is equal, the perimeter (P) is equal to four times the length of a side (S). $P = 4S$

Formula for Area of a Square

The area of a square is equal to the width times the height. Here again, since each side is equal, the area (A) is found by multiplying a side (S) by itself. Expressed as a formula, $A = S^2$.

Formula for Volume of a Cube

Where the length of each side of a regular solid is equal, the object is called a cube. The volume of a cube is equal to its length multiplied by its width multiplied by its height. Since each of these sides is the same length, $V = S^3$.

Formula for Area of a Stretchout

The area of a stretchout (A) of a square surface is equal to the length of the four sides (S) multiplied by the height of the object. The formula $A = 4S\ (H)$ is the abbreviated way of saying the same thing. Note the selection of letters in the formula: A for Area, S for the length of one side, and H for height.

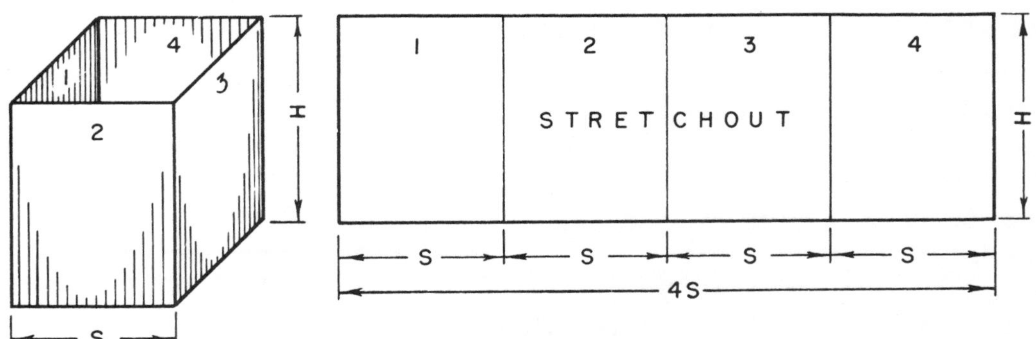

If the object has a seam or overlap, the overall length is equal to 4S plus the seam allowance.

B. DEVELOPING FORMULAS FOR RECTANGULAR OBJECTS

Rectangles differ from squares in that in place of four sides of equal length, the two sets of opposite sides are the same length.

Formula for Perimeter of a Rectangle

The perimeter of a rectangle is equal to 2W + 2H. W is the width of one side and H the height or length of the other. P = 2 (W + H) is a simpler way of stating the formula.

An allowance is usually added to this perimeter for overlapping the ends or for seams.

Formula for Area of a Rectangle

The area of a rectangle is the product of its two adjacent sides. The formula is $A = (S_1) \times (S_2)$. A denotes Area, (S_1) the length of one side, and (S_2) the length of the other side.

Formula for Volume of a Rectangular Solid

As the rectangle takes on height, it becomes a rectangular solid. The volume, then, is equal to the area of the base x the height. $V = (S_1) \times (S_2) \times (H)$

C. FORMULA FOR SIDES OF A RIGHT TRIANGLE

The dimension of a third side of a right triangle may be computed by a simple formula, when the two remaining sides are given. The formula is often referred to as the "Pythagorean Theorem." The theorem is a proven mathematical law. The formula expresses the relationship among the three sides of a right triangle. The square of the hypotenuse of a right triangle is equal to the sum of the squares of the remaining two sides. Expressed as a formula,

$$H^2 = (S_1)^2 + (S_2)^2$$

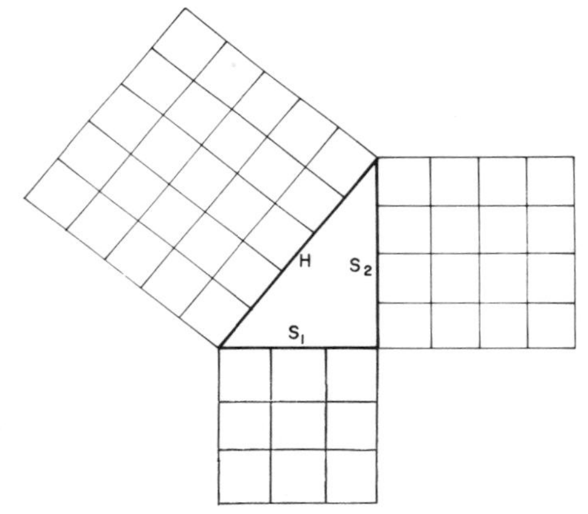

D. CONSERVING MATERIALS IN STRETCHOUTS

Once the sizes of a stretchout are determined, the next step is to determine the most economical use of the material from which one or more of the same object may be made. This process calls for simple calculations.

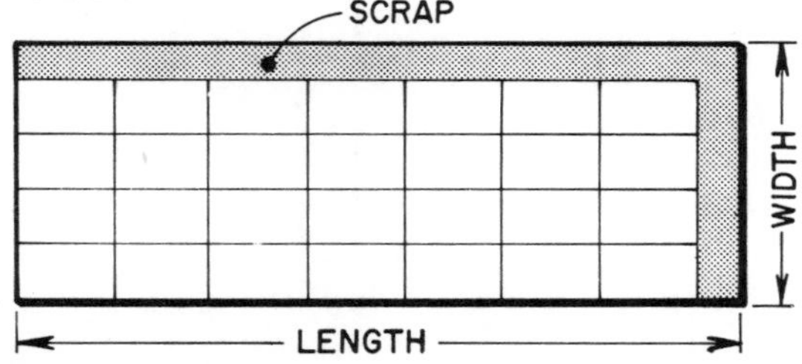

RULE FOR CONSERVING MATERIAL FOR STRETCHOUTS

- Make a simple sketch of the shape of the material and dimension.
- Lay out the pattern in one of the extreme corners.

- Divide the length of the material by the length of the stretchout.
- Divide the width in the same manner.
- Multiply quotients in both cases.
- Turn the pattern around 90°.
- Repeat the same steps.

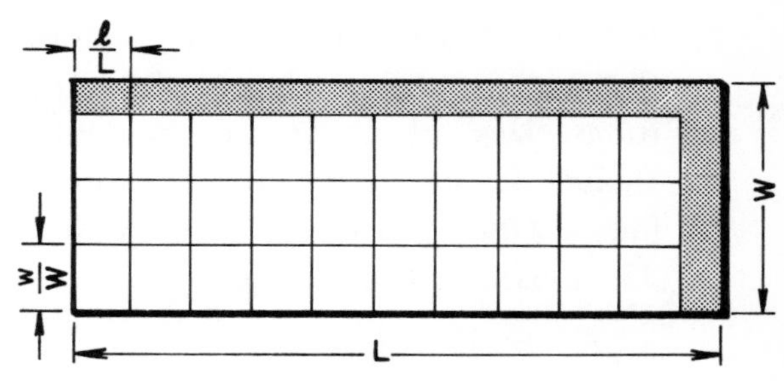

Compare the number of pieces that may be cut from the material with the pattern in both positions.

EXAMPLE: How many parts 7 inches in diameter by 12 inches high may be cut from a sheet 36″ x 120″. Add 1/2 inch to the length of each part for a lap seam and use 22/7 for π.

Step 1 Find the length of the stretchout, using the circumference formula and adding 1/2″.

$$C = \pi D + \frac{1}{2} = \frac{22}{7}(7) + \frac{1}{2} = 22\frac{1}{2}$$

Step 2 Make a simple sketch of the materials with dimensions.

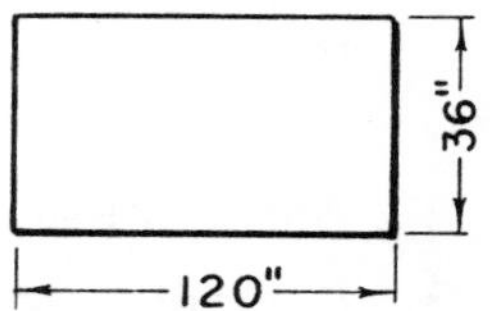

Step 3 Divide the length of the sheet by the length of the stretchout.

$$\frac{120}{22\frac{1}{2}} = 5\frac{1}{3}$$

Step 4 Divide the width of the sheet by the height of the part.

$$\frac{36}{12} = 3 \text{ pieces}$$

Step 5 Multiply the whole numbers only, to determine the number of pieces that may be cut.

$5 \times 3 = 15$ pieces Ans.

Step 6 Turn the pattern around 90° and repeat the same steps.

Step 7 Compare both products to determine the position in which to place the pattern to make the most economical use of the material.

ASSIGNMENT UNIT 66

A. APPLICATION OF FORMULAS TO SQUARE OBJECTS

1. Determine the number of cubic yards of topsoil required for an area 48 feet square. The topsoil is to be 4 inches deep.

2. How much paint is needed to cover five rooms with two coats? The room sizes are shown in the table. Deduct 25 square feet for each opening. One gallon of paint covers 350 square feet of surface.

   Ans.: B. 2.5 gallons D. 1.3 gallons

	Room Size			No. of
	Width	Length	Height	Openings
A	12′	12′	8′	2
B	16′	16′	8′	3
C	8′	8′	8′	4
D	10′	10′	7′-6″	3
E	12′	12′	7′-6″	4

3. Find the area of each of the stretchouts for square parts A through E. Add 1/2 inch to the length of the seam allowance.

	A	B	C	D	E
Length of Side	8″	9 1/2″	3′-3″	5′-4″	4′-9 1/2″

   Ans.: B. 365.75 sq. in. D. 114 sq. ft.

B. APPLICATION OF FORMULAS TO RECTANGULAR OBJECTS

1. What is the total area in square yards of two sections of a roof, 32′ x 28′ and 24′-8″ x 30′?

2. A bathroom 7′-6″ wide x 8′-3″ long has four sidewalls to be covered with metal lath to a height of 4′-6″. Allow 20 square feet for a door and window opening and determine to the nearest whole number the square yards of wall surface to be covered.

   Ans.: 14 sq. yds.

3. Determine the capacities of the containers as indicated at A through E.

   Use:

   1 cubic foot = 7.48 gallons

   1 gallon = 231 cubic inches

   1 barrel = 31 1/2 gallons

	Given Dimension			Required
	L	W	H	Capacity
A	24″	36″	30″	Gals.
B	12 1/2″	25″	28″	Gals.
C	2′-4″	3′-3″	2′	Gals.
D	5′-6″	6′-4″	10′-6″	Bbls.
E	20′-8″	15′-6″	12′-6″	Bbls.

   Ans.: B. 37.875 gallons D. 86.851 barrels

C. APPLICATION OF FORMULAS TO RIGHT TRIANGLE SIDES

1. Find the length of the cross braces for structural trusses A, B, and C. State each length correct to two decimal places.

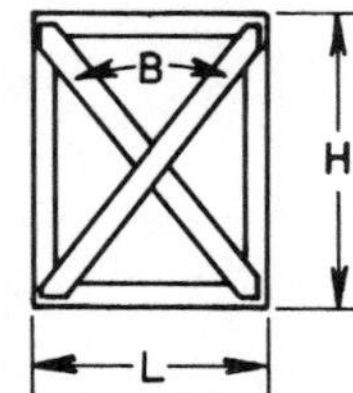

Truss	Length (L_1)	Height (H)	Cross Brace (B)
A	2.3 m	1.98 m	
B	2.84 m		3.69 m
C		2.92 m	4.86 m

   Ans.: B. 2.36 m

2. The 20.93 kilometer power line shown in the sketch is to be shortened by a new right of way. Determine the length of the new line, correct to two decimal places.

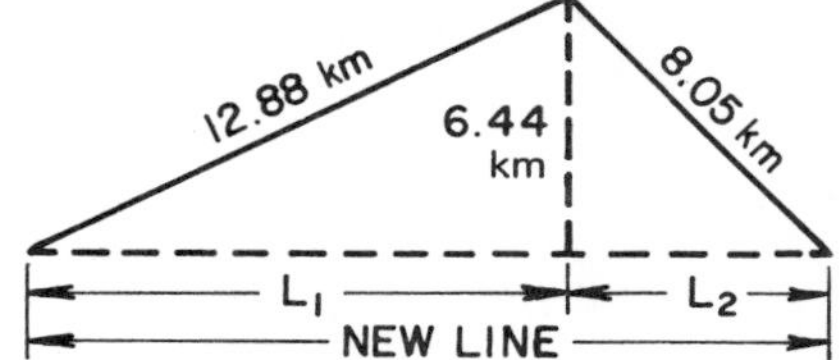

D. APPLICATION OF FORMULAS TO STRETCHOUTS

1. Find the number of rectangular pieces that may be cut from each of the material sizes given in the table for parts A through E.

	Sizes of Rectangular Parts			Allowance on Length and Height for Seams	Dimension of Materials
	L	W	H		
A	6″	12″	12″	1/4″	24″ x 60″
B	8″	10″	12″	1/4″	30″ x 96″
C	8½″	12″	12″	1/4″	36″ x 96″
D	1′-4″	1′	1′	1/2″	36″ x 96″
E	1′-6″	10″	2′	1/2″	48″ x 120″

Ans.: B. 4 D. 2

2. Determine the number of pieces that can be cut from a sheet 36″ x 96″ to make the rectangular part as illustrated.

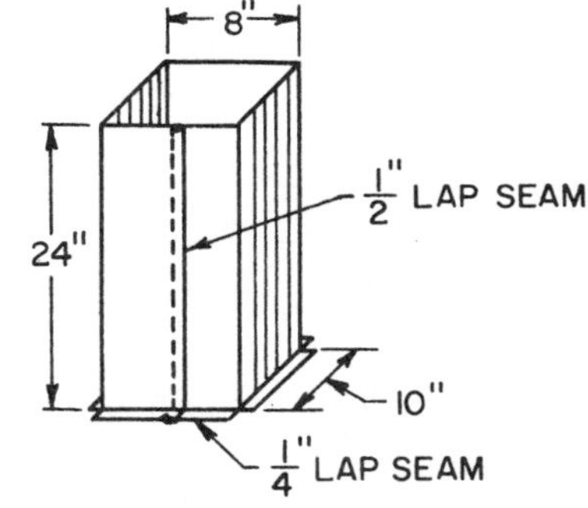

3. Three square ducts having cross-sectional areas of (a) 930 square centimeters, (b) 1648 square centimeters, and (c) 3721 square centimeters, respectively, are needed. A lap seam of 1.3 cm is added. What length of metal is required to make each square duct?

Ans.: (b) 163.7 cm

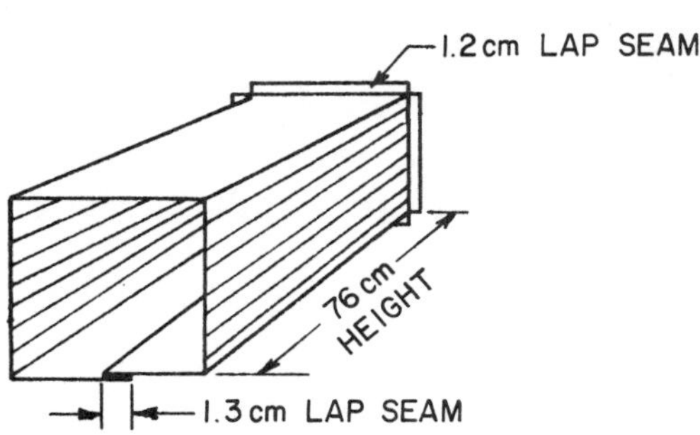

Unit 67 APPLICATION OF FORMULAS TO CIRCLES AND PARTS OF CIRCLES

One of the most widely known and used formulas deals with the circumference and diameter of a circle. The formula, $C = \pi D$, like all other formulas, serves more than one purpose, as it may be used to find the value of any letter or missing quantity. In this case, when the circumference is given and substituted in the formula, the diameter may be computed.

A. APPLICATION OF FORMULAS TO CIRCLES

EXAMPLE: Determine the diameter of a circle with a 22-inch circumference.

Step 1 Analyze the problem. The diameter (D) is required. The circumference (C) is given.

Step 2 Select the formula.

Step 3 Substitute given values for letters in the formula. Use the value of 22/7 for π.

Step 4 Perform mathematical operations as indicated.

Step 5 Label answer with correct unit of measure.

Step 6 Recheck answer by substituting the computed values in the formula.

$$C = \pi D$$
$$22 = \pi D$$
$$22 = \frac{22}{7} D$$
$$\overset{1}{\cancel{22}} \left(\frac{7}{\underset{1}{\cancel{22}}} \right) = D$$
$$7'' = D \text{ Ans.}$$
$$C = \pi D$$
$$22 = \frac{22}{7} \times 7$$
$$22 = 22$$

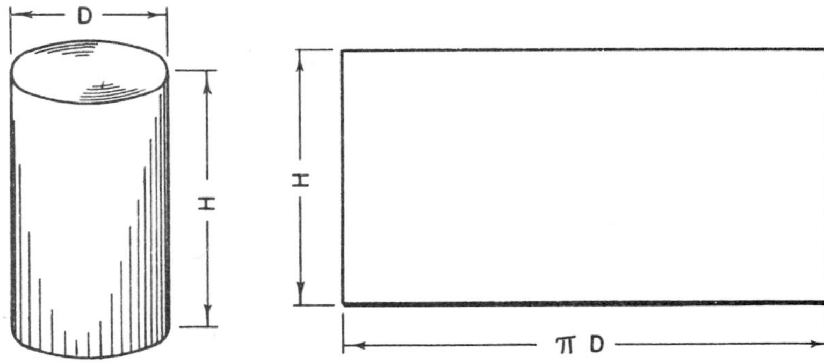

Formula for Stretchout of Circular Parts

The application of the circumference formula is especially helpful in finding the length of the *stretchout* of a circular job. In the illustration, it is apparent that the length of the stretchout is the same as the circumference; the height, the same as H.

B. APPLICATION OF FORMULAS TO PARTS OF CIRCLES

Formula for Lengths of Arcs

An arc is part of a circle, and a circle contains 360°. The ratio of the length of the arc to the circumference is the same as the ratio of the angle of the arc to 360°. With this information, a formula may be derived for computing arc length.

RULE FOR DEVELOPING FORMULA FOR ARC LENGTH

- Analyze problem.
- Select appropriate letters for given values and values to be computed.

  Let N = Number of degrees in angle of arc
  D = Diameter of circle
  C = Circumference
  L = Length of arc

- Write in abbreviated form, the statement which explains what the length of arc is equal to, using letters and numbers.

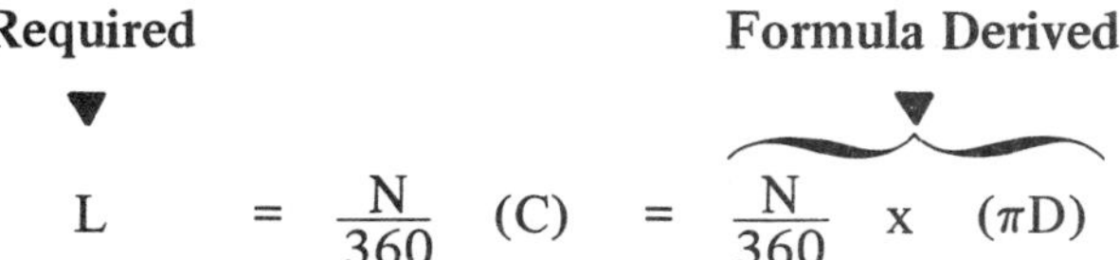

EXAMPLE: Find the length of arc in an angle of 45° in a 7-inch diameter circle. Use 22/7 for π.

Step 1 Read problem for what is given and what is required. $N = 45°,\ D = 7''$

Step 2 Select formula and substitute given values for letters. $L = \frac{N}{360} \times (\pi D)$

Step 3 Perform the operations as indicated.

Step 4 Label answer with correct unit of measure.

$$= \frac{\cancel{45}^{1}}{\cancel{360}_{8}} \times \left(\frac{22}{\cancel{7}_{1}} \cdot \cancel{7}^{1} \right)$$

$$= \frac{22}{8} = 2\frac{3}{4}'' \text{ Ans.}$$

C. APPLICATION OF FORMULAS TO CIRCULAR SOLIDS

As a third dimension of height is added to a circle, the object becomes a *circular solid*. The volume of this cylinder is equal to the area of the base x the height. In abbreviated form, $V = \pi r^2 H$. Note that three dimensions are multiplied so the product is in cubic measure.

EXAMPLE: Find the volume in cubic inches of a cylindrical container having a radius of 7 inches and a height of 10 inches.

Step 1 Read problem for given and required values.

Step 2 Select formula and substitute values.

Step 3 Perform mathematical operations.

Step 4 Label answer.

$$V = \pi r^2 H$$

$$= \frac{22}{\cancel{7}_{1}} \left(\cancel{7}^{1} \cdot 7 \cdot 10\right)$$

$$= 1540 \text{ cu. in. Ans.}$$

ASSIGNMENT UNIT 67

A. APPLICATION OF FORMULAS TO CIRCLES

1. Determine the circumference of blanks A through E for each diameter given in the table. Use 22/7 for the value of π.

Blanks	A	B	C	D	E
Given Diameter	14″	70″	3 1/2′	10.5′	9″

Ans.: B. 220″ D. 33′

2. Compute the circumference of pipes A through E for the diameters and radii given. Use $\pi = 3.1416$ and give each answer correct to three decimal places.

NOTE: D = Diameter, R = Radius.

Pipes	A	B	C	D	E
Given Diameter	D = 8 1/7″	D = 5 1/2′	R = 3″	R = 4.2′	R = 4.10″

Ans.: B. 17.279′ D. 26.389′

3. Find the diameter of pulleys A through E for each given circumference. Use the formula $C = \pi D$ and the value of 3.1416 for π. Give each diameter to three decimal places.

Pulleys	A	B	C	D	E
Given Circumference	63.84 cm	35.92 cm	88.9 mm	142.88 mm	1.524 m

Ans.: B. 11.434 cm D. 45.480 mm

B. APPLICATION OF FORMULAS TO PARTS OF CIRCLES

1. Compute the circular length at A, B, C, using the dimensions given on the sketch of the cam plate.

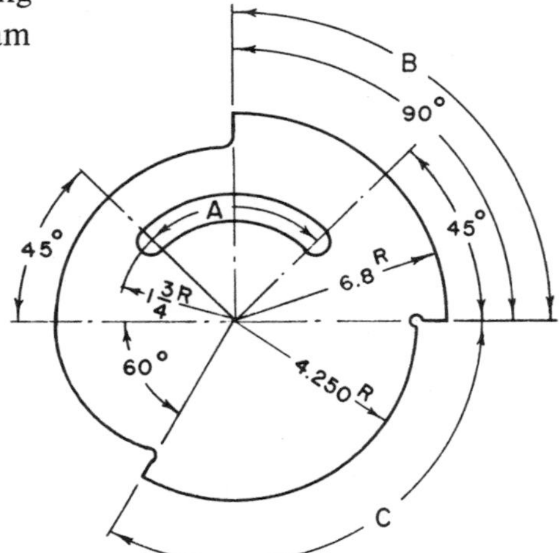

Ans.: B. 10.6814″

2. Determine the length of stretchout for (a) the throat and (b) the heel of sheet metal elbows A, B, C, and D. Use the dimensions given in the table.

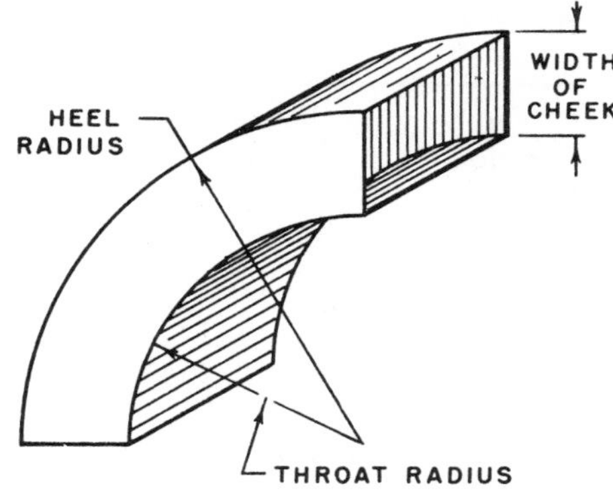

	A	B	C	D
Throat Radius	9″	8″	30″	6″
Central Angle	90°	60°	45°	135°
Width of Cheek	4″	5″	15″	3 1/2″

Ans.: B. (a) 8.378″ (b) 13.614″ D. (a) 14.137″ (b) 22.384″

3. Compute the circular length for each central angle and dimension as given in the accompanying table. Use π = 3.142.

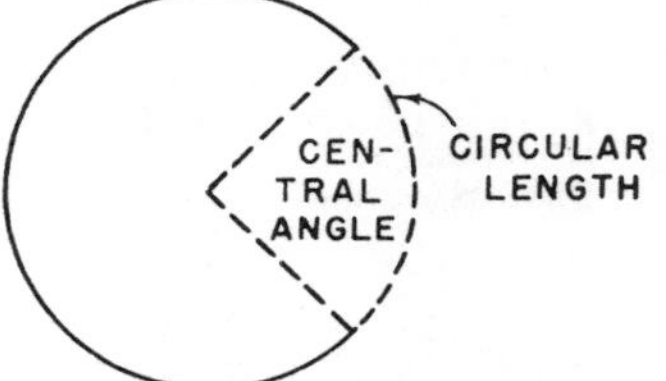

	A	B	C	D	E
Central Angle	180°	90°	60°	135°	72°
	Diameter	Diameter	Diameter	Radius	Radius
Dimension	10″	12 1/4″	12.6″	8″	6.250″
	25.4 cm	31.12 cm	.320 m	20.32 cm	158.75 mm

Ans.: B. 9.622″; 24.445 cm D. 18.852″; 47.884 cm

C. APPLICATION OF FORMULAS TO CYLINDRICAL SOLIDS

1. Find the volumes of containers A, B, and C and the capacities of D and E in the units of measure indicated in the table. Use 22/7 for π and the formula $V = \pi r^2 H$.

	Diameter	Height	Unit of Measure
A	14″	10″	Cubic Inch
B	20″	32″	Cubic Inch
C	14 1/2″	18″	Cubic Inch
D	28′	15′	Barrel
E	20 1/2′	12 1/2′	Barrel

Ans.: B. 10057 cu. in. D. 2194.133 barrels

2. Determine the liquid capacities of containers A, B, and C. Give the volumes in the measure indicated in each case. Use $\pi = 22/7$ and the formula $V = \pi r^2 H$ for both sections which make up each container. Round off decimal answers to two places.

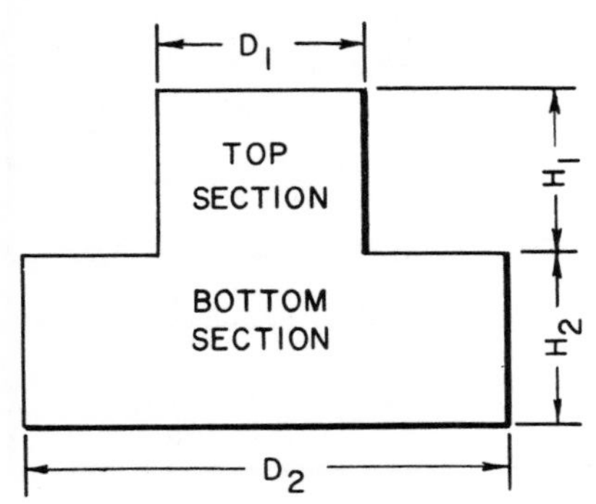

Container	Top Section		Bottom Section		Unit of Measure
	$Dia._1$	$Hgt._1$	$Dia._2$	$Hgt._2$	
A	14″	10″	28″	20″	Cubic Inch
B	21″	1′-8″	35″	2′-4″	Cubic Inch
C	3′-8″	8″	4′-10″	1′-9″	Cubic Inch

Ans.: B. 33,880 cu. in.

3. Determine the quantity of concrete required for the concrete pipes A and B. Use $\pi = 3.1416$. Give the answers in cubic meters, correct to the nearest two decimal places.

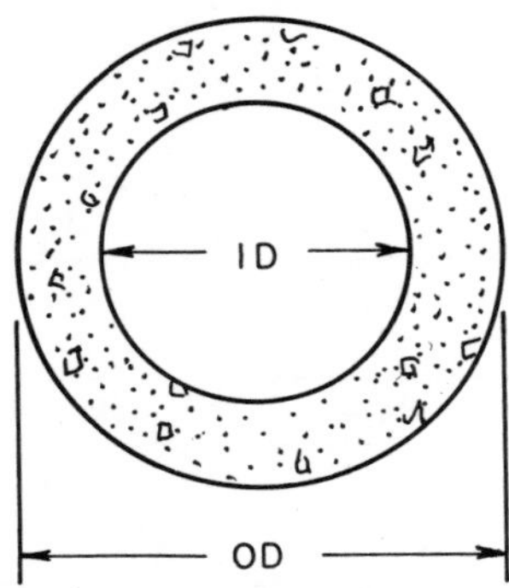

Concrete Pipe	Inside Diameter (ID)	Outside Diameter (OD)	Length
A	71.12 cm	99.06 cm	1.8 m
B	88.9 cm	124.46 cm	2.4 m

Ans.: B. 1.43 m^3

Unit 68 APPLICATION OF SPECIAL FORMULAS AND HANDBOOK DATA

Thus far, the units on the concept and application of formulas cover the abbreviated form of stating problems. The formulas used relate to square, rectangular, round, and parts of cylindrical shapes and solids. With this background information it is possible to compute the dimensions and sizes for many variations of regular shapes.

A. APPLICATION OF FORMULAS TO SEMICIRCULAR-SIDED OBJECTS

Formula for Area

A semicircular-sided object is an example of how the information about rounds and rectangles may be combined to solve a modified shape. The area of a semicircular-sided object is a composite of the area of a circle plus the area of a rectangle.

Expressed as a formula,

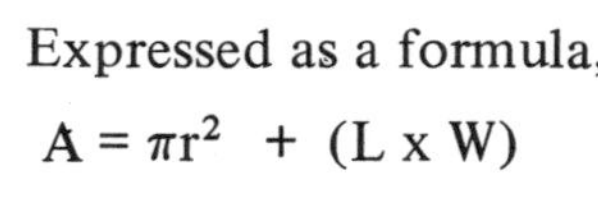

$$A = \pi r^2 + (L \times W)$$

Where A = Area
π = 22/7 or the decimal equivalent
r = Radius of semicircular end
L = Length of rectangle
W = Width of rectangle

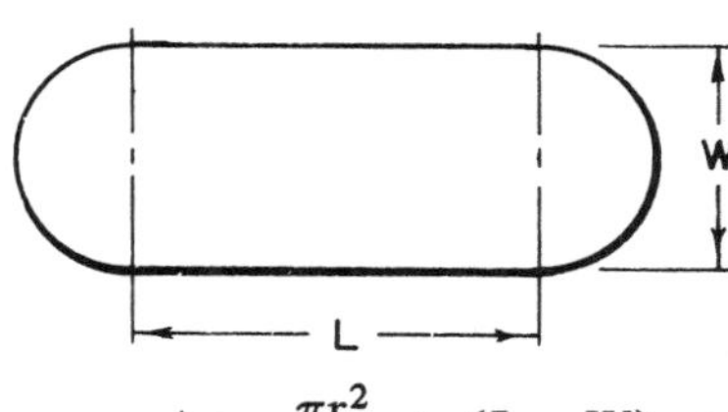

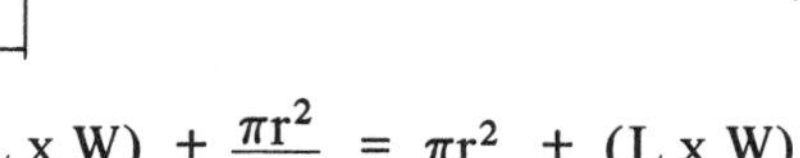

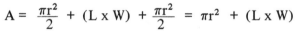

$$A = \frac{\pi r^2}{2} + (L \times W) + \frac{\pi r^2}{2} = \pi r^2 + (L \times W)$$

Formula for Volume

As the sides of the semicircular-sided object are extended, a solid is formed. The volume of this solid is equal to the area of the base times the height (H) of the object.

$$V = [\pi r^2 + (L \times W)]\ H$$

EXAMPLE: Find the capacity of a semicircular-sided tank in cubic feet. The end radius is 7 inches, the length of the rectangular center section is 12 inches, and the height is 10 inches.

$$V = [\pi r^2 + (L \times W)]\ H$$

Step 1 Select or develop formula.

$$V = \left[\frac{22}{7}(7)(7) + (12 \times 14)\right]10$$

Step 2 Substitute given values for letters.

$$V = \left[\frac{22}{\cancel{7}_1}(\cancel{7}^1)(7) + (12 \times 14)\right]10$$

Step 3 Perform mathematical operations.

$$= [154 + 168]\ 10$$

$$= 322 \times 10 = 3220$$

Step 4 Divide 3220 cu. in. by 1728 to get answer in cu. ft.

$$\frac{3220}{1728} = 1 \text{ cu. ft. } 1492 \text{ cu. in.}$$

B. APPLICATION OF HANDBOOK DATA

The number and variety of formulas are limitless, as their use cuts across many activities in life like science, industry, and the home. Most simple formulas that are used daily may be developed and applied with the knowledge obtained through the mastery of all the units in this section on Applied Algebra. Essentially, the parts of a formula are similar, as each formula represents an equality between values that are given and those that are required.

The spur gear is a common example of how handbook data is supplied as a series of formulas. These may be used in combination to compute all the required dimensions for machining the object. Some of the essential parts are illustrated and identified. A partial table of the kind of information furnished in trade handbooks is given with the drawing. Note the designation of letter symbols in the formulas.

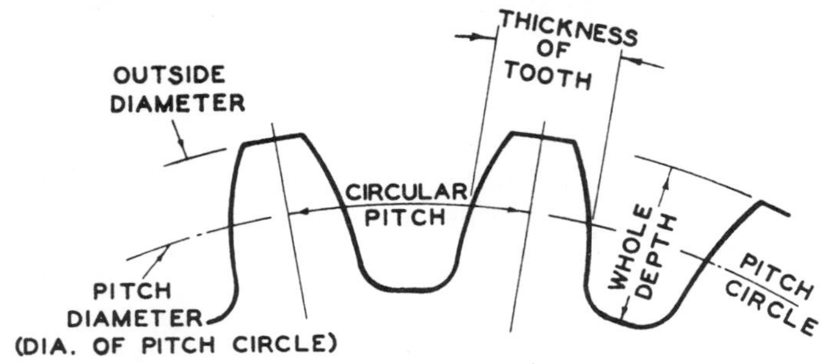

Formulas for Spur Gear Teeth				
Required Dimension	Outside Diameter (O)	Pitch Diameter (D)	Whole Depth of Tooth (W)	Thickness of Tooth (T)
Formula	$O = \frac{N + 2}{P}$	$D = \frac{N}{P}$	$W = \frac{2.157}{P}$	$T = \frac{1.5708}{P}$
N = Number of Teeth in Gear P = Diametral Pitch				

In this particular table, four major dimensions may be computed. Simply substitute given values for letters in the formulas and perform the mathematical operations indicated in each case. In like manner, other formulas may be used to solve for missing dimensions.

ASSIGNMENT UNIT 68

A. APPLICATION OF FORMULAS TO MODIFIED REGULAR SHAPES

1. Develop three formulas for volumes of square, rectangular, and cylindrical solids.

2. Develop a formula and determine the weight of the bronze castings from the tabular data given.

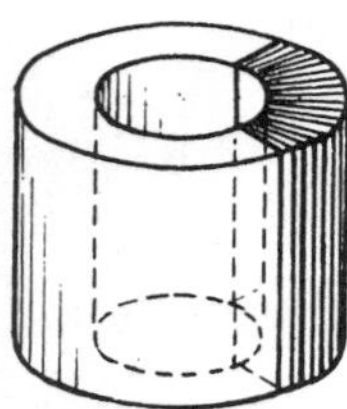

	Part Specification	
1	Outside Diameter	3 1/4″
2	Inside Diameter	1 3/8″
3	Sector Angle	135°
4	Height	4″
5	Number Required	24
6	Weight	.28 lbs./cu. in.

3. Compute the required measurement as identified in the table for ducts A, B, C and D. Use $\pi = 22/7$; $1\ m^3 = 264.17$ gal.

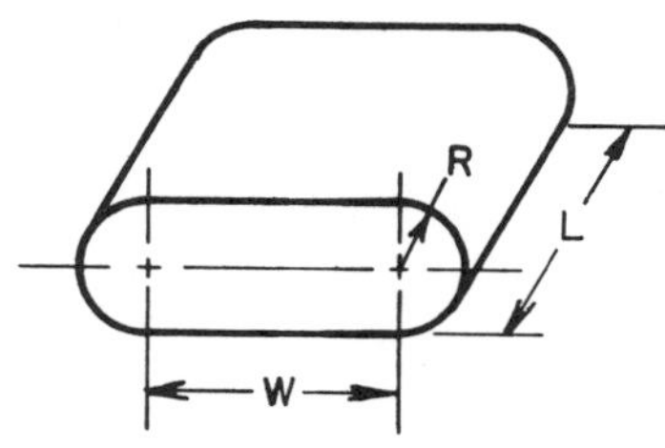

Duct	Given Dimensions			Required Dimension
	Diameter	Width	Length	
A	7 ft.	8 ft.		Perimeter
B	6.50 ft.	3.75 ft.		Area of end
C	1.54 m	2.50 m	4.62 m	Area of stretchout
D	.88 m (radius)	176.2 cm	1.46 m	Liquid capacity (gallons)

Ans.: B. 57.57 sq. ft. D. 2134.78 gal.

B. APPLICATION OF HANDBOOK DATA

A 96-tooth webbed spur gear of 10 diametral pitch (P) to fit a 1 1/4″ diameter shaft (B) is needed. The handbook data relating to the six dimensions required for machining the gear is given in table form. Use the formulas in the table to compute the dimensions. Label each dimension with the appropriate unit of measure.

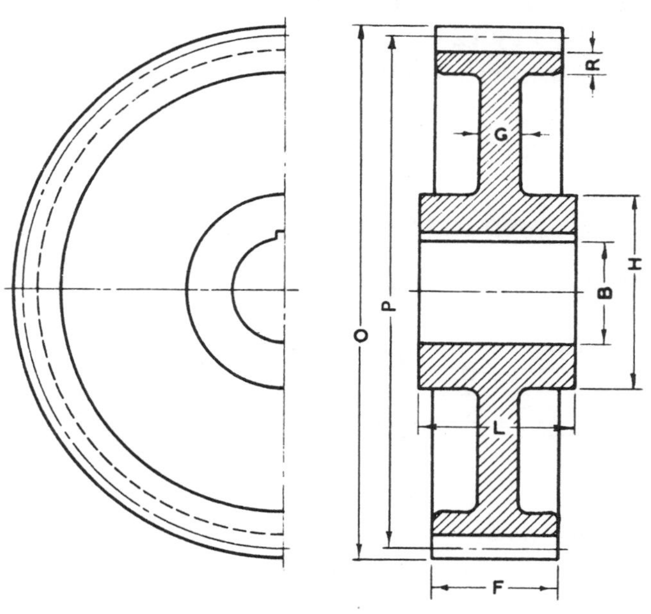

Required Dimensions	Solution
Outside Diameter	$O = \frac{N+2}{P}$
Width of Face	$F = \frac{3\pi}{P}$
Length of Hub	$L = 1\frac{1}{4}F$
Diameter of Hub	$H = 1\frac{3}{4}B$
Thickness of Web	$G = \frac{F}{3}$
Thickness of Rim	$R = \frac{\pi}{2P}$
N = Number of Teeth in Gear P = Diametral Pitch B = Bore	

Ans.: F = .942″ H = 2 3/16″ R = 5/32″

Unit 69 ACHIEVEMENT REVIEW ON FORMULAS AND HANDBOOK DATA

A. CONCEPT OF FORMULAS

1. State briefly two characteristics of formulas.
2. Give three main reasons why formulas are used.
3. Interpret what is meant by each formula.

   a. $C = \pi D$ (Circle)
   b. $A = S^2$ (Square)
   c. $P = 2(L + H)$ (Rectangle)
   d. $A = \pi r^2$ (Circle)

4. State each rule as a formula.

   a. To convert a Celsius reading to a Fahrenheit (F) reading, multiply the Celsius (C) reading by 1.8 and add 32.
   b. The area of a sector (A) is equal to the sector angle (n) over 360° times the area of the circle.
   c. The cutting speed of a drill is the product of the circumference of the drill (πD) times the revolutions per minute (rpm) divided by 12.
   d. The mechanical efficiency (E) is equal to the output (O) divided by the input (I).
   e. The S.A.E. horsepower rating formula states that the horsepower (h.p.) is equal to the cylinder bore (D) squared times the number of cylinders, divided by 2.5.

B. APPLICATION OF FORMULAS TO CIRCLES AND PARTS OF CIRCLES

1. The diameters of a series of parts are given in table form. Compute each circumference accurate to two decimal places.

	A	B	C	D	E
Diameter	7 mm	5.5 mm	9.25 cm	3.25 m	5.438 m

2. The accompanying table gives the circumference of pulleys A through E. Determine the diameter in each case to three places, using $\pi = 3.1416$.

	A	B	C	D	E
Circumference	28.274 mm	20.422 mm	25.918 cm	10.603 cm	9.623 m

3. Determine the weight of A and B for the part as illustrated. Use the tabular data and $\pi = 3.1416$. Round off the answer to one place.

	Outside Diameter	Inside Diameter	Height	Sector Angle	Weight per cu. in.
A	6.750″	3.125″	8 1/4″	135°	.33 lbs.
B	6.750″	3.125″	8 1/4″	225°	.15 lbs.

C. APPLICATION OF FORMULAS TO SQUARES AND RECTANGLES

1. Determine the greatest number of pieces (A through E) that may be cut from the sheets given in the table.

	Shape	Dimension			Allowance in Length for Seams	Sheet Size
		Length	Width	Height		
A	Square	4″	4″	6″	1/8″	24″ x 72″
B	Square	1′-3″	1′-3″	8″	1/2″	36″ x 96″
C	Rectangle	5″	8″	12″	1/4″	30″ x 72″
D	Rectangle	7.6″	9.8″	11.2″	.4″	36″ x 96″
E	Rectangle	2′-9″	1′-3″	10″	3/8″	48″ x 120″

D. APPLICATION OF FORMULAS TO SPECIAL PROBLEMS

1. What length of copper wire 2.743 mm in diameter gives a resistance (R) of 4.2 ohms?

$$R = \frac{KL}{D^2}$$

R = Resistance
K = 10.8 (for copper)
D = Diameter in mils = Diameter (mm) x 0.03937

2. Determine the S.A.E. horsepower rating of an 8-cylinder (N) automobile engine with a bore (D) of 3.375 inches.

$$\text{H.p.} = \frac{D^2 N}{2.5}$$

3. Find the value of the missing letter in each formula. Use $\pi = 3.1416$ and label each answer, where possible.

A	$C = \frac{5}{9}(F - 32)$	$F = 77°$
B	$E = \frac{O}{I}$	O = 22,000 Btu, I = 32,000 Btu
C	$A = .7854\ D^2$	D = 75 cm
D	$I = \frac{E}{R}$	E = 12 volts, R = 4.5 ohms
E	$S = \frac{n}{2}(a + L)$	n = 72, a = 9, L = 165
F	$A = ab + \frac{d}{2}(a + c)$	a = 6.4, b = 5.2, c = 12, d = 8.6
G	$V = \frac{\pi H}{3}(3A^2 + 3B^2 + H^2)$	A = 9.4, B = 7.6, H = 8.4
H	$A = \sqrt{B^2 + C^2}$	B = 27.2 m C = 24.6 m
I	$S = \sqrt{\frac{B}{6}}$	B = 612
J	$Z = 5 + \sqrt{\frac{25 - (4 \times Y)}{2X}}$	X = 1.5, Y = 3.4

4. Determine the pitch (P) of threads A through E, the single depth (d) for screw threads F through J, and the major diameter (D) of numbered screws K through O. Round off answers to three decimal places.

$P = \frac{1}{N}$	
	Threads per Inch (N)
A	10
B	20
C	8
D	16
E	24

$d = \frac{.6495}{N}$	
	Threads per Inch (N)
F	10
G	20
H	8
I	16
J	24

D = W (.013) + .060	
	Wire Size (W)
K	2
L	3
M	4
N	6
O	8

5. The revolutions per minute that the work, or a drill, or a cutter turns, is equal to the cutting speed in feet per minute divided by πD. Find the rpm for each operation indicated in table form. Use π = 22/7.

$$\text{rpm} = \frac{\text{CS in ft. x 12}}{\pi D}$$

	Cutting Speed Ft./Min.		Given Diameter	Required
A	100	Work Diameter	7/8″	Rpm of Lathe Spindle
B	80		2 1/8″	
C	60		3 1/2″	
D	55	Drill Diameter	1/2″	Rpm of Drill Press Spindle
E	42		1″	
F	80		7/8″	
G	90	Cutter Diameter	2 3/4″	Rpm of Milling Machine Spindle
H	60		5 1/2″	
I	40		6″	

6. Use the necessary formula to find the dimensions which are not supplied in the table for spur gears A, B, and C. Decimal dimensions must be correct to four places.

$$\text{Whole Tooth Depth} = \frac{2.157}{\text{Diametral Pitch}} \qquad \frac{\text{Pitch}}{\text{Diameter}} = \frac{\text{No. of Teeth}}{\text{Diametral Pitch}}$$

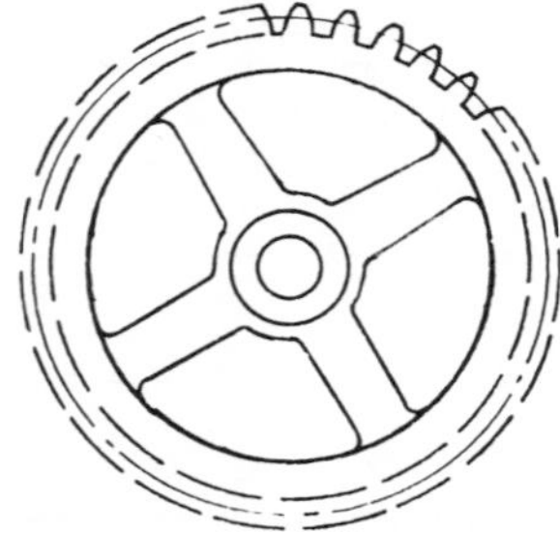

Gear	Number of Teeth	Pitch Diameter	Diametral Pitch	Whole Tooth Depth
A	48	6″		
B	32		6	
C		7.6666″		.1798″

Section 15

GEOMETRIC LINES AND SHAPES

Unit 70 THE CONCEPT OF LINES, ANGLES AND CIRCLES

Geometry is one of the oldest branches of mathematics. Applications were made of geometric constructions centuries before the mathematical principles on which the constructions were based were recorded.

Geometry is a mathematical study of points, lines, planes, closed flat shapes, and solids. Using any one of these alone, or in combination with others, it is possible to describe, design, and construct every visible object.

The purpose of this section is to provide a foundation of geometric principles and constructions on which many practical problems depend for solution.

PROPERTIES OF LINES

Lines are basic to all geometric shapes. There are two kinds of lines, the straight line and the curved line. A line is said to be of indefinite length when there are no fixed points to indicate a specific size.

Points are usually used to mark the *end points* of a line to show that it is a working line from which construction is started. The points are marked with letters or numbers to identify the working length of the line. This working length is sometimes referred to as a *line segment.*

The points lettered A and B on the straight line and numbered 1 and 2 on the curved line denote the end points. The line segment for the straight line is AB.

DIRECTION AND TYPES OF LINES

There are three general directions to lines.

- *Horizontal*, in which a level line goes from left to right or right to left.
- *Vertical*, in which the straight line is vertical or at 90° to a horizontal line or surface.
- *Slanted*, in which the line is inclined.

Lines may be parallel to one another, may touch at one or more points, or may intersect. In the first instance, when two lines are parallel, it means that they are always the same distance apart.

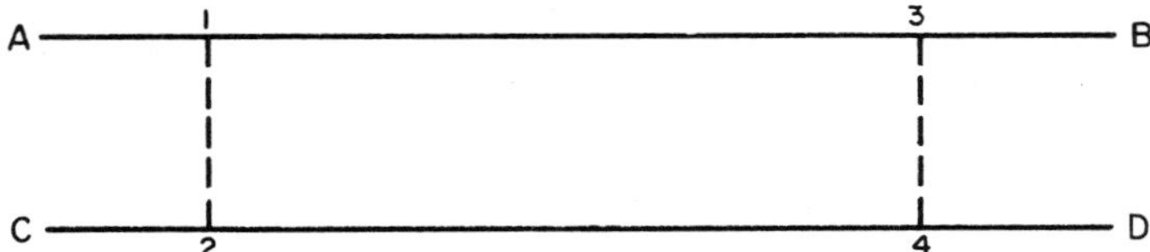

Straight lines AB and CD are parallel because they are the same distance apart. Measurements taken at lines 1-2 and 3-4, or at any other points, are equal.

When lines touch at one point, they are said to be *tangent* to one another. Two lines that cross each other are said to *intersect* or cut one another at a given point.

LINE TANGENT TO ARC

TANGENT ARCS

INTERSECTING LINES

TYPES OF ANGLES

As two straight lines come together (intersect) at a point, an angle is formed. In general, there are four common types of angles: straight, right, acute, and obtuse.

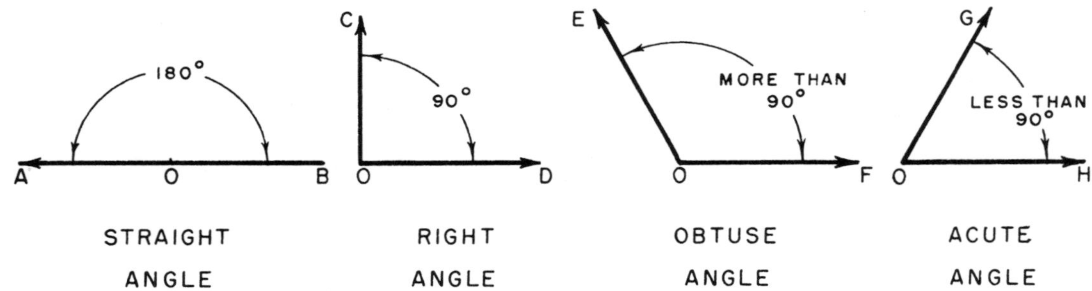

STRAIGHT ANGLE

RIGHT ANGLE

OBTUSE ANGLE

ACUTE ANGLE

In each illustration, three letters are used to describe each angle. One letter (O in each case) is placed at the point where the two lines intersect. This point is called the *vertex*.

The first illustration shows a straight angle of 180°. This angle may be identified as angle AOB. The symbol ∠ is sometimes used in place of the word angle. ∠ AOB has the same meaning as angle AOB.

A right angle has two sides, CO and OD, that form an angle of 90°. Occasionally, a 90° angle is denoted on a drawing by a square symbol (∟) placed in the corner of the 90° angle. The right angle in the illustration is ∟ COD.

When an angle formed by two intersecting lines is greater than 90° and smaller than 180°, the angle is known as an *obtuse* angle. Angle EOF is an obtuse angle. An *acute* angle is less than 90°, as shown by ∠ GOH.

CIRCLES AND PARTS OF CIRCLES

While many objects are represented by straight lines, others require the use of curved lines. Such parts of the circle as the center, diameter, radius, and chord are used.

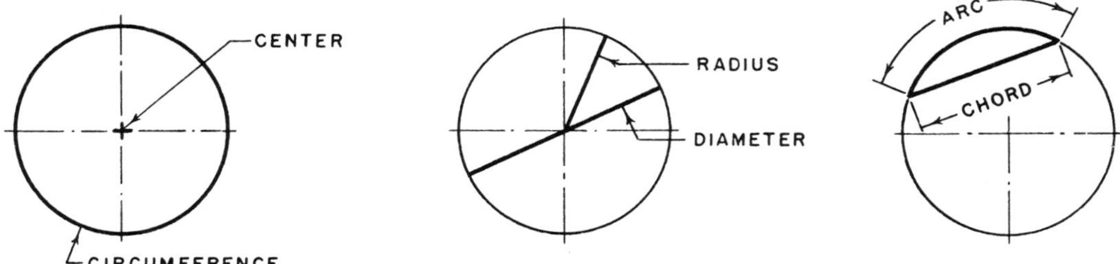

PARTS OF A CIRCLE

Each of these parts may be redefined in simple geometric terms. A *circle* is a closed curve on which all points are the same distance from a point (center) inside the circle. A straight line extending from the center to the closed curve line is the *radius.*

The straight line that passes through the center of the circle and ends at opposite sides of the closed curved line is the *diameter.*

An *arc* is a portion of the curved line or circle. A *chord* refers to the straight line segment between the end points of an arc. These are the terms relating to the circle that are most generally used in solving practical problems.

ASSIGNMENT UNIT 70

A. THE CONCEPT OF LINES

1. Lay out the lines to the lengths and in the directions indicated in the table. Label the end points of each line.

Line	Direction and Length		
	Horizontal	Vertical	Inclined 45°
A-B	3″		
A-C		4″	
A-D		3 1/2″	
XY			6″
XZ			5 1/8″

2. Identify each pair or combination of lines by name. Then indicate the characteristics of each.

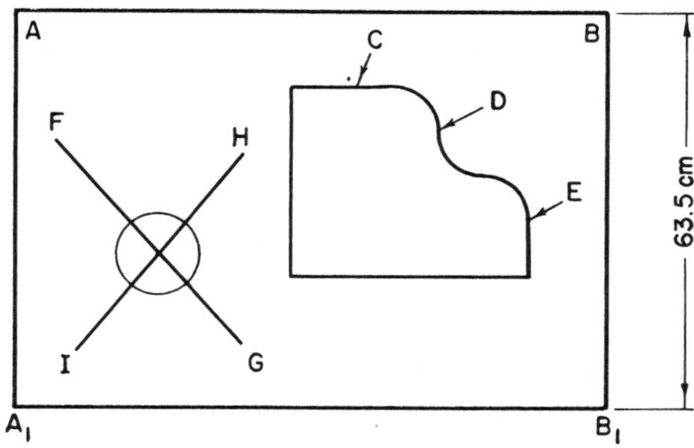

B. PROPERTIES OF ANGLES

1. Name the type of angle used in the cases shown.

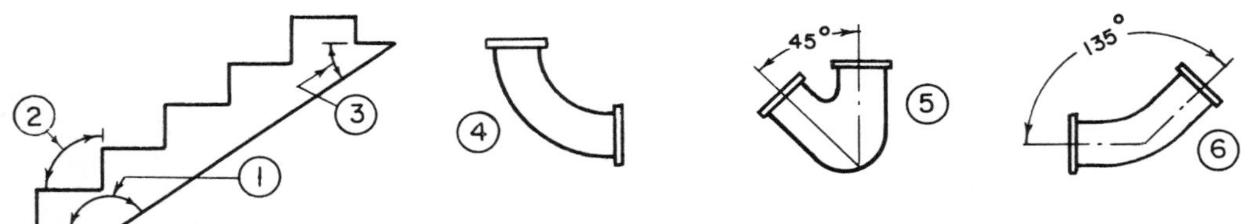

2. Draw the angles with sides and included angles equal to the sizes indicated in the table. Use a flat protractor to measure the angle.
   a. Label each angle for identification.
   b. Name the type of angle in each case.

Angle	Length of Sides				Included ∠
AOB	AO	2″	OB	3″	180°
AOC	AO	2″	OC	2″	90°
AOD	AO	3 1/2″	OD	3″	60°
XOY	XO	4″	OY	3 1/4″	28 1/2°
YOZ	YO	2″	OZ	1 7/8″	127°

3. Give the number of degrees in the layout angles A through E.

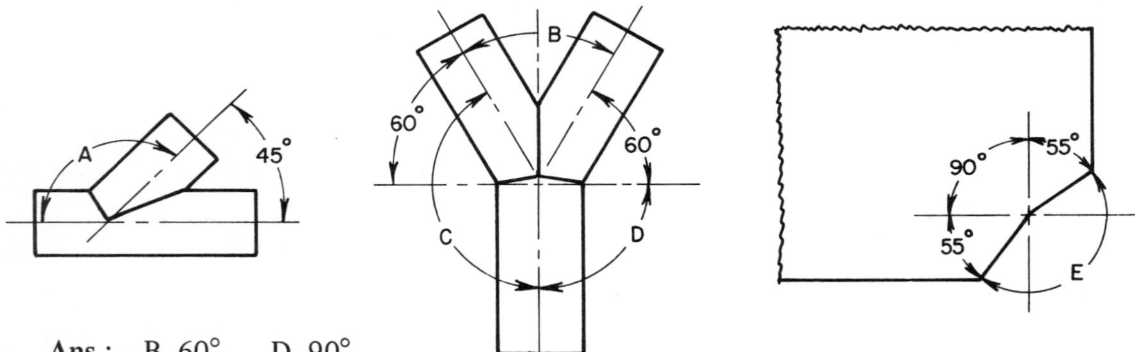

Ans.: B. 60° D. 90°

C. PROPERTIES OF CIRCLES AND PARTS OF A CIRCLE

1. Name and determine the value of each missing dimension.

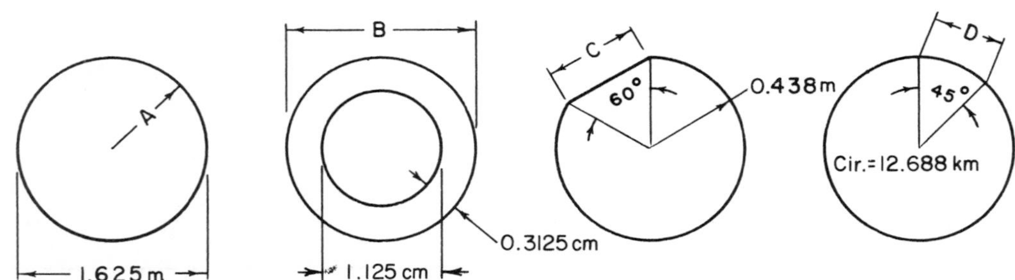

Ans.: B. 1.75 cm D. arc, 1.586 km

Unit 71 BASIC FLAT SHAPES

The terms and properties of lines, angles, and circles may be applied in the layout, design, development, and construction of closed flat shapes. A new term, *plane*, must be understood in order to visualize a closed flat shape accurately. A *plane* refers to a flat surface on which a straight line connecting any two points lies. In the illustration, the flat shape is in one plane because any straight line connecting any two lines or points on the lines lies in the plane.

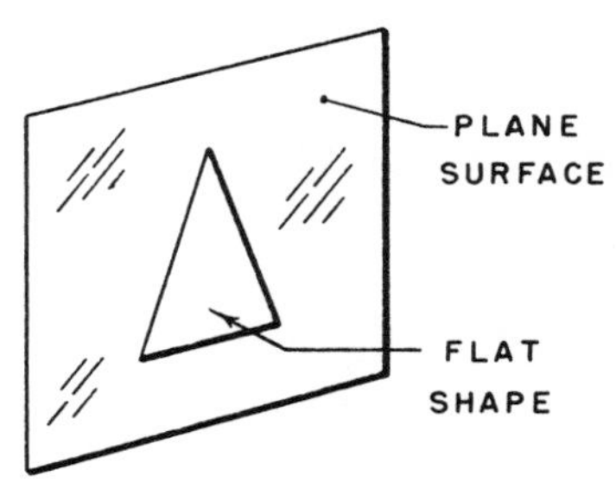

Fundamental to most design and construction are the three flat shapes of the triangle, rectangle, and circle.

CHARACTERISTICS OF TRIANGLES

A triangle consists of three line segments which are joined at the end points to form a closed flat shape. The line segments are called *sides*, and the angles formed, *inside angles.*

There are three broad classes of triangles: *equilateral*, *isosceles*, and *scalene*. As the name equilateral implies, the three sides of this type of triangle are the same length. The isosceles triangle has two sides of the same length. In the scalene triangle, all three sides are of different lengths.

TYPES ⇨ / ⇩	EQUILATERAL	ISOSCELES	SCALENE
RIGHT TRIANGLE	—		
ACUTE TRIANGLE			
OBTUSE TRIANGLE	—		

Each of these triangles is illustrated in table form. Note that a short line appears ($\triangle$) on those sides of the triangle that are equal. A short curved line indicates the angles of the triangle that are equal. ($\triangle$).

In each type of triangle the word *base* usually refers to the horizontal or lower side. Opposite this base is the *vertex* angle. The point at which the two sides of an angle come together is the *vertex*.

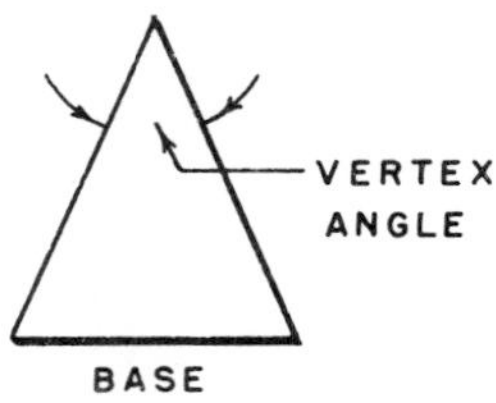

Triangles are further described by their included angles. The most commonly used triangle is the *right* triangle in which one angle is a right angle. An *acute* triangle has three acute angles. An *obtuse* triangle has one angle greater than 90°.

CHARACTERISTICS OF RECTANGLES

The second basic flat shape is the *rectangle*. A rectangle has four closed sides with four right angles. When the two pairs of sides are of equal length, the object is a rectangle. When all four sides are equal and the four angles are 90°, the shape is called *square.*

The base of the rectangle is usually the horizontal side at the bottom. The altitude or height is the vertical side. The diagonal of a rectangle is a straight line which connects the opposite corners.

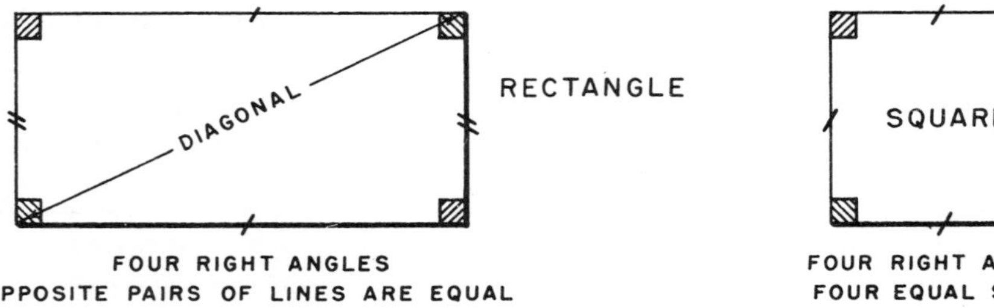

CHARACTERISTICS OF CIRCLES

The third basic flat shape is the circle. Three types of circles are used constantly in design. The circle where all parts on the curve are equidistant from a fixed center is the type used most widely. Round parts that have more than one diameter are usually machined or designed *concentric*. Concentric means that all points on each circle are equidistant from the same center. Occasionally, the centers of the circles on a part or mechanism are off-center. Circles drawn in the same plane from the different centers of a part are *eccentric.* The characteristics of the regular, concentric, and eccentric circles are shown graphically.

All three of the basic flat shapes may be modified, thus making possible a limitless number of layout constructions.

OTHER COMMON FLAT SHAPES

The next group of flat shapes that is used by craftspersons and others include the parallelogram, trapezoid, and hexagon. Sometimes, these shapes are broadly classified as *polygons.* A "polygon" is any closed flat shape of three or more sides. When all the sides are the same size, the polygon is *regular.*

A *parallelogram* has four sides consisting of two pairs of lines which are parallel and the same length and two opposite pairs of angles that are equal. The altitude of the parallelogram is the distance from the base to the opposite parallel line.

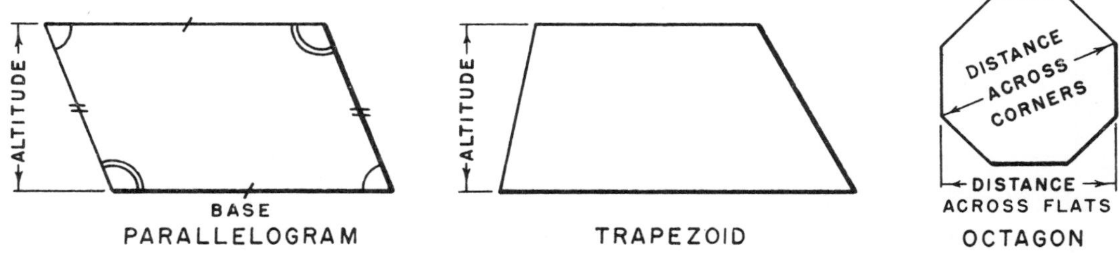

A *trapezoid* has four sides, two of which are parallel. The altitude, as illustrated, is the vertical distance between the two parallel sides.

The *hexagon* and *octagon* are common. As each name implies, the hexagon is a six-sided figure and the octagon, an eight-sided figure. The hexagon and octagon are regular polygons when each side of the hexagon is equal to every other side and the same holds true for the octagon. Two dimensions are referred to with the hexagon and octagon. The *distance across flats* is the measurement across any set of parallel sides. The *distance across corners* is the measurement from the vertex of one pair of sides to the vertex of the opposite pair of sides.

ASSIGNMENT UNIT 71

A. PROPERTIES OF TRIANGLES

1. Classify each triangle as to the group in which it falls.

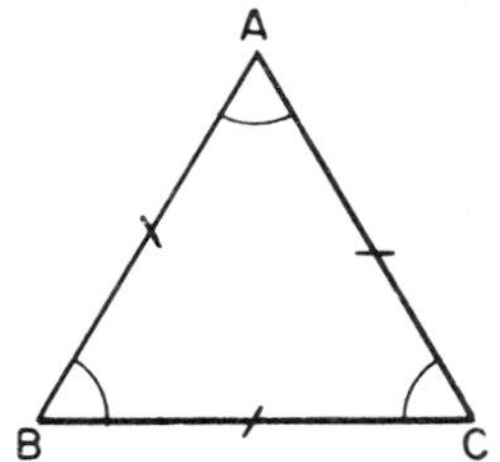

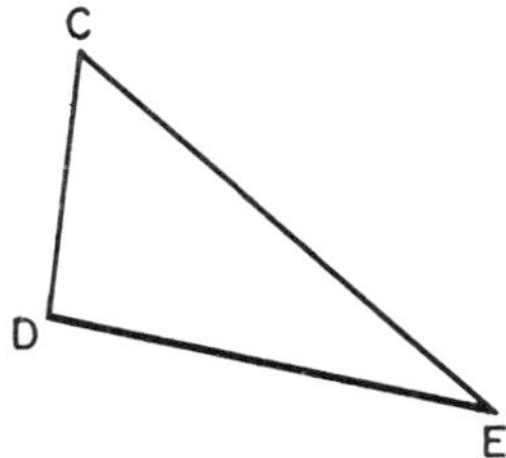

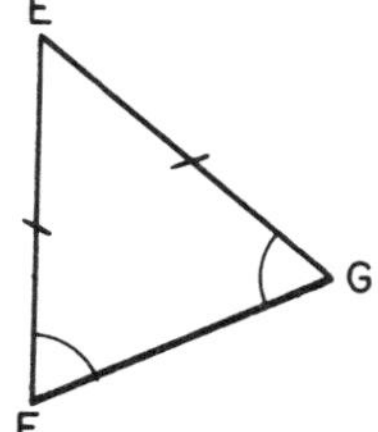

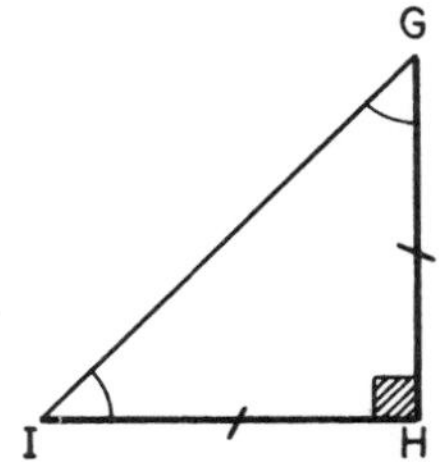

2. Sketch triangles 1, 2, 3, and 4, freehand.
   a. Label the sides and angles.
   b. Mark the sides or angles in each triangle that may be equal.

Triangle	Type
1	Right Triangle
2	Acute Triangle
3	Equilateral Triangle
4	Obtuse Triangle

B. PROPERTIES OF RECTANGLES

1. Sketch rectangles 1, 2, 3, and 4 and mark each line and angle for identification.

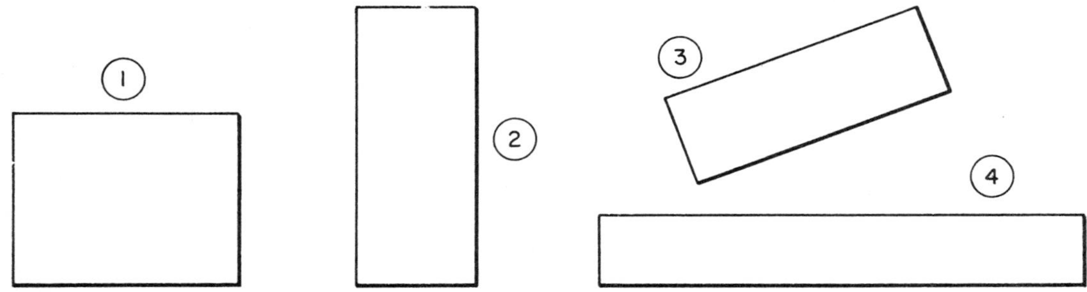

2. Identify all sides and angles in each rectangle that should be equal.
3. Draw a diagonal in each rectangle.

C. PROPERTIES OF CIRCLES

1. Identify the types of circles used in parts 1, 2, and 3.

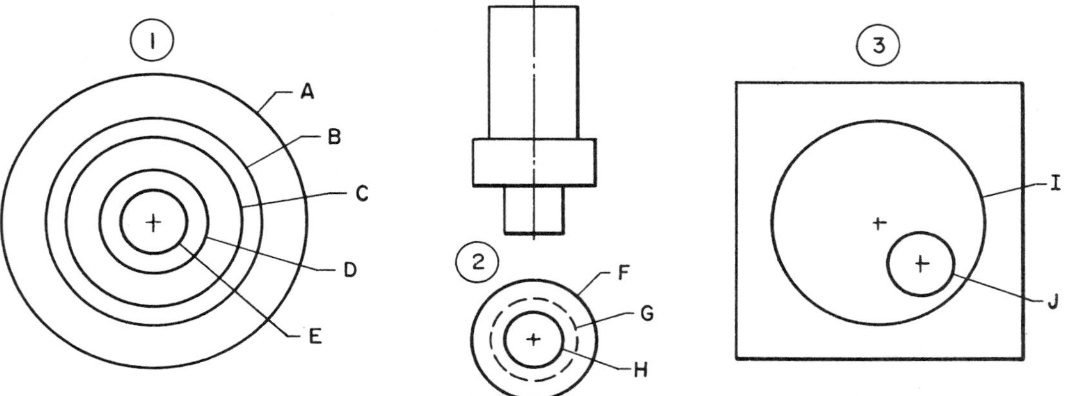

D. PROPERTIES OF OTHER COMMON FLAT SHAPES

1. Name parts 1, 2, 3, and 4.

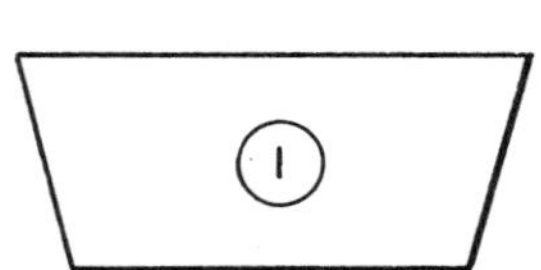

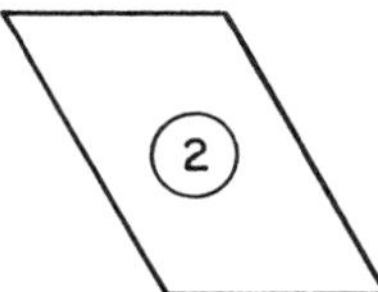

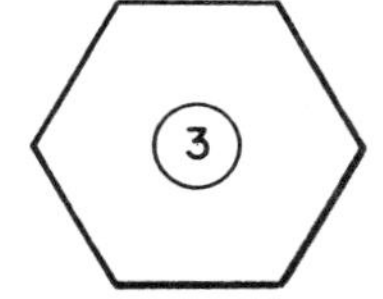

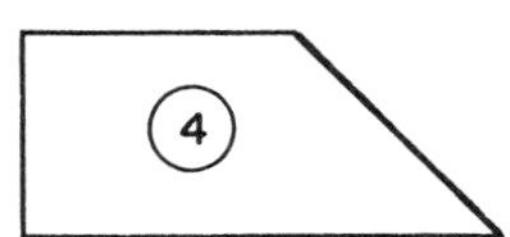

2. Sketch each part (1, 2, 3, and 4) freehand. Show either the altitude and base or the distance across flats, as may apply.
3. Use a drafting protractor and lay out the four shapes A, B, C, and D in the table.

Required Shape		Description
A	Square	Sides are 2″
B	Parallelogram	1. Inclined sides are 2″ long 2. Horizontal sides are 3″ long 3. Included angle is 60°
C	Hexagon	Distance across flats is 2 1/4″
D	Octagon	Distance across corners is 2 1/2″

Unit 72 BASIC SOLID SHAPES

A. THE THREE BASIC SOLIDS

The three flat shapes of the triangle, rectangle, and circle may be changed into solids by adding the third dimension of depth. The triangle becomes a prism; the rectangle, a rectangular solid; and the circle, a cylinder.

	TRIANGLE	RECTANGLE	CIRCLE
FLAT SHAPES			
SOLID SHAPES			
	PRISM	RECTANGULAR SOLID	CYLINDER

The word *base* has a somewhat different meaning with solids in that it usually refers to the surface on which the solid rests. Each circular end of the cylinder may be referred to as its base. The altitude of the prism is the perpendicular line segment which joins the point at which the triangular faces come together with the base. The altitude of the rectangular solid is the same as for the rectangle. The altitude or height of the cylinder is the distance between the two bases measured along the axis. The *axis* is the imaginary line that passes through the center of each base circle. A solid object that is cut by a plane at an angle to the base is said to be *truncated*.

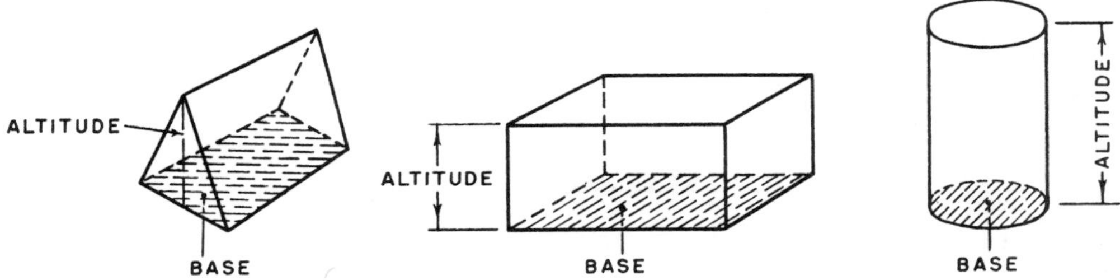

B. SOLIDS OF REVOLUTION

Solids are also formed by revolving a flat form and tracing the shape that the outside line or lines take during revolution. Such solid shapes are known as *solids of revolution.* The simplest solid of revolution to visualize is the sphere that is formed by revolving a circle completely around an axis.

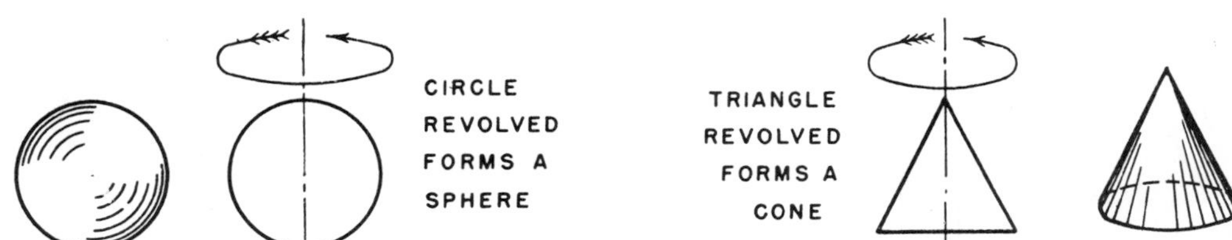

In like manner, if an isosceles triangle is revolved about its axis, a cone is formed. The shape of the solid of revolution is governed by the original flat shape.

OTHER COMMON SOLID SHAPES

Right prisms, pyramids, and segments of spheres are used in science and industry. A *right prism* is a solid formed by visualizing the shape that a flat form takes as it moves perpendicular to its base to a predetermined height known as the altitude. Right prisms are named according to the shape of the bases. A triangular base produces a *triangular prism*; an octagonal base, an *octagonal prism*.

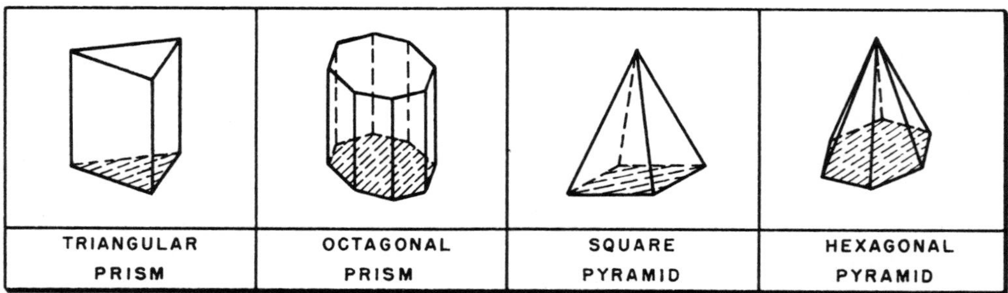

A *pyramid* is formed by connecting each corner of the base of a flat shape with a point outside the base. Each triangular face thus formed meets at the vertex. The name of the pyramid thus formed depends on the shape of the base. A six-sided base (hexagon) produces a hexagonal pyramid.

If a sphere is cut in two, or the circle is revolved through only 180°, half a sphere, or a *hemisphere*, is formed.

While there are many other basic and common solid shapes, those that have been described are the ones that have greatest daily application in the science, occupational and technical fields, and in everyday living.

ASSIGNMENT UNIT 72

A. PROPERTIES OF PRISMS, RECTANGULAR SOLIDS, AND CYLINDERS

1. Identify each solid shape or object as lettered on the pictorial drawings.

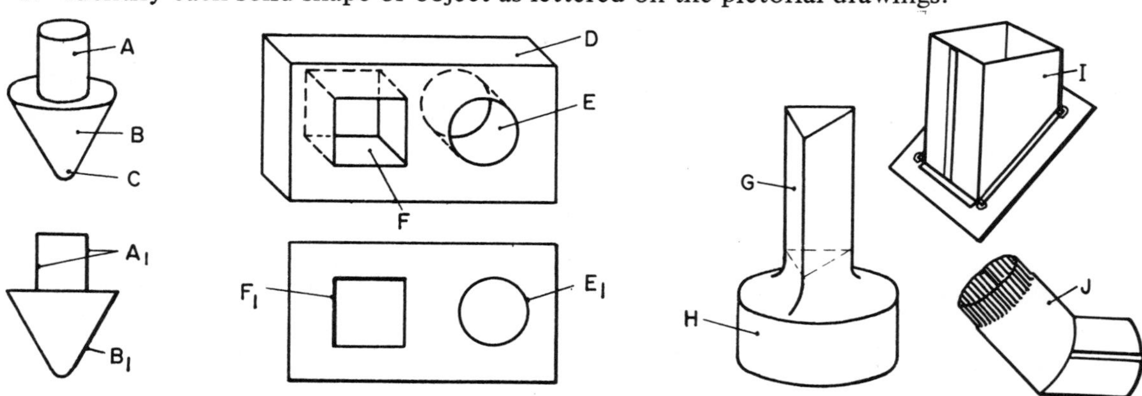

2. Name the type line or lines that describe the two parts shown on the mechanical drawings (i.e., A_1, B_1, E_1, F_1).
3. Sketch each of the following solid shapes.
   a. A cube
   b. A rectangular solid
   c. A triangular prism
   d. A cylinder
4. Compare each solid shape with the flat shape given in each case.
   a. A cube with a square
   b. A rectangular solid with a rectangle
   c. A triangular prism with a triangle
   d. A cylinder with a circle

B. PROPERTIES OF SOLIDS OF REVOLUTION

1. Sketch and name the solid shape that develops as each basic flat shape is revolved on the given axis.

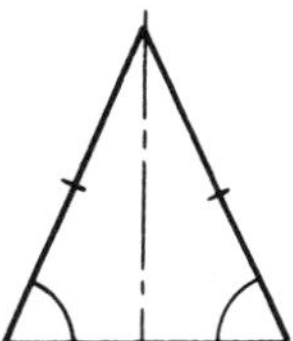
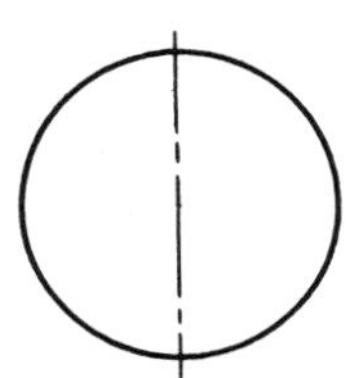
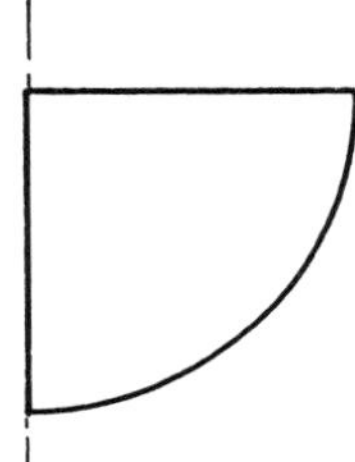

C. OTHER COMMON SOLID SHAPES

1. Sketch a square and a triangular pyramid.
   a. Show the base and altitude of each by a dotted line.
2. What two solid shapes are combined in A and B to form the two different types of bolt heads?

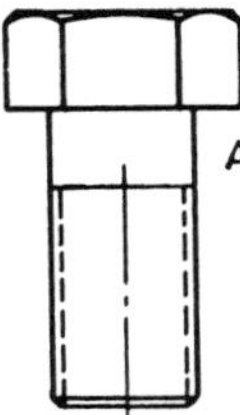

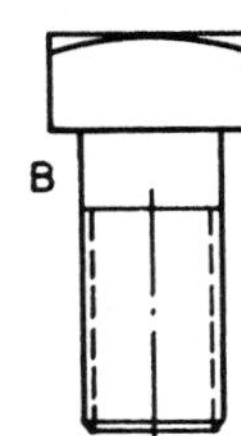

Unit 73 CONGRUENT AND SYMMETRICAL FLAT AND SOLID SHAPES

The production of identical shapes and interchangeable parts and mechanisms in modern manufacturing is based on congruence. *Congruence* is a geometric term which means that all the physical properties of size and shape in one part are duplicated in another. All bolts of the same size in a box or the patterns in a cloth are congruent when each one is an exact copy of the other.

The characteristics of congruent flat and solid shapes are covered in this unit. In proving the congruence of two shapes, the sides that fit, or are compared, or are constructed, are called *corresponding sides.* In the case of angles, they are known as *corresponding angles.* When a side is equal to its corresponding side, the sides are said to *coincide.* The same holds true when an angle is identical with its corresponding angle. The corresponding sides are located opposite the angles to which they correspond.

A. CONGRUENCE OF FLAT SHAPES

RULE FOR DETERMINING CONGRUENCE OF TRIANGLES

- Draw or place the triangles to be compared on a plane or flat surface.
- Compare the length of each corresponding side.
- Compare each corresponding angle to see if they coincide.
- Triangles are congruent

  When two corresponding angles and a corresponding side are equal.
  When two corresponding sides and the corresponding included angle are equal.
  When the three sides are equal.

EXAMPLE: Determine which of the three triangles are congruent.

I
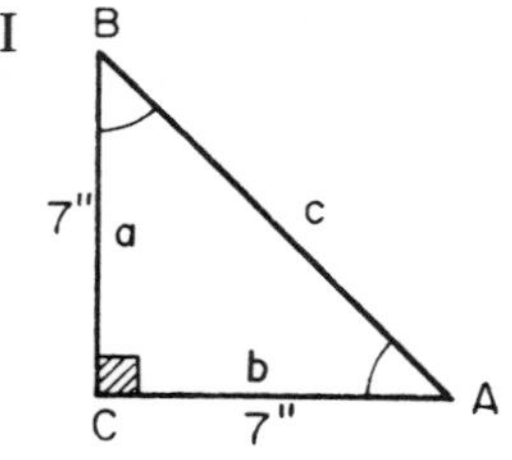

II
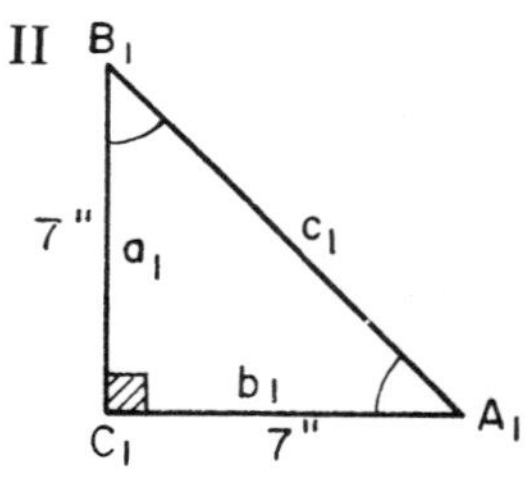

III
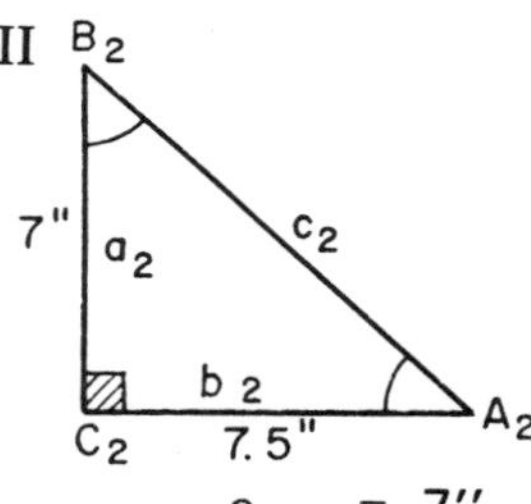

Step 1 Check the length of the corresponding sides a, a_1, and a_2. Note that all are equal.

$a = 7''$
$a_1 = 7''$
$a_2 = 7''$

Step 2 Compare the largest angle in triangles I, II, and III.

$\angle BCA = 90°$
$\angle B_1C_1A_1 = 90°$
$\angle B_2C_2A_2 = 90°$

Step 3 Determine the length of corresponding sides b, b_1, and b_2.

$b = 7''$
$b_1 = 7''$
$b_2 = 7.5''$

Step 4 Compare the values of the two sets of corresponding sides and the corresponding included angle. Triangles I and II are congruent. Triangle III is not because the side b_2 is larger than both b and b_1.

This same problem may be checked by taking any other combination of corresponding sides and corresponding angles.

RULE FOR DETERMINING THE CONGRUENCE OF POLYGONS

- Check each side of the polygons for congruence.
- Check each angle of the polygons against each corresponding angle.

NOTE: Plane polygons are similar when all the corresponding angles are equal.

RULE FOR DETERMINING CONGRUENCE OF PLANE CIRCLES

- Check the diameter of each circle. When the diameters are equal, the circles are congruent.

B. CONGRUENCE OF SOLID SHAPES

Solids are congruent when every point, face, edge, and vertex of one solid is equal to the corresponding part of the other.

RULE FOR DETERMINING THE CONGRUENCE OF SOLIDS

- Place solids in the same relative position to each other.
- Measure or test the length of each corresponding edge.
- Check each corresponding angle.

NOTE: When every part of one solid is equal to the corresponding part of the other, the solids are congruent.

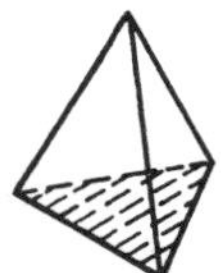
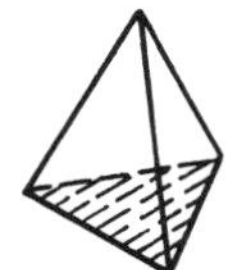
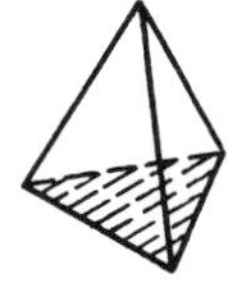

CONGRUENT SOLIDS

C. SYMMETRICAL FLAT SHAPES

Symmetry is important in production and design. Symmetrical parts are balanced, prevent undue wear and destructive vibration, and simplify manufacturing. A flat shape is symmetrical when corresponding points on each side of an axis are equidistant from the axis.

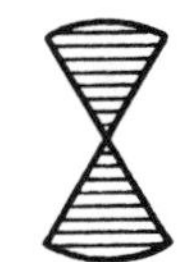

SYMMETRICAL FLAT SHAPES

The axis that cuts the part in two symmetrical halves is known as the *axis of symmetry* or the *line of symmetry.*

D. SYMMETRICAL SOLID SHAPES

A solid shape is symmetrical when all corresponding parts are equal but in an opposite position. This idea of symmetry is extremely valuable in drafting and sketching. It is the geometric principle on which many types of section drawings are made. On symmetrical objects fewer views are needed and considerable drafting time is saved.

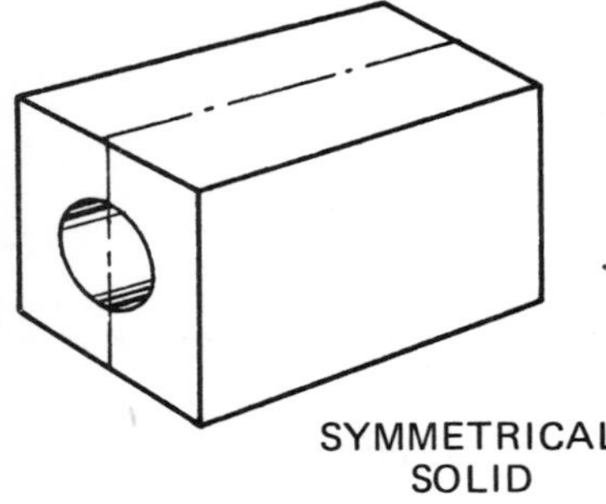

SYMMETRICAL SOLID

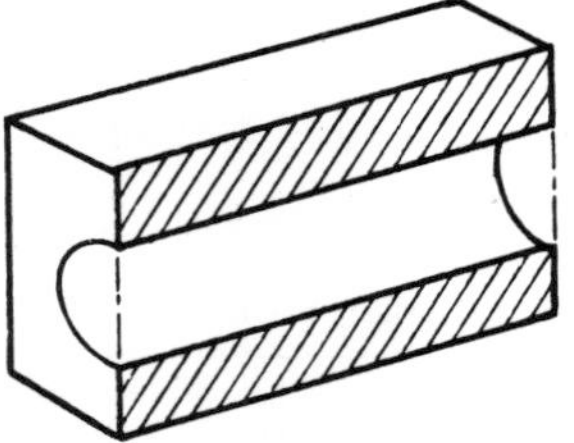

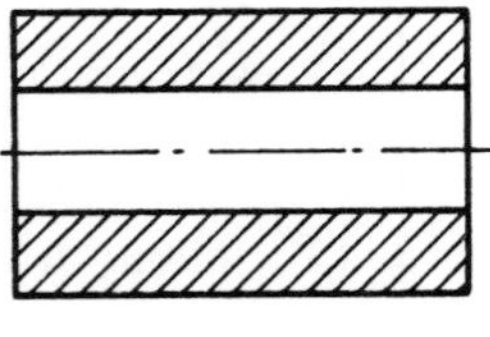

ONE HALF SYMMETRICAL SOLID

ASSIGNMENT UNIT 73

A. CONGRUENT FLAT SHAPES

1. Prepare a table similar to the one with places for the two sides and the included angle of a triangle.

   a. Complete the missing information by referring to the triangle.

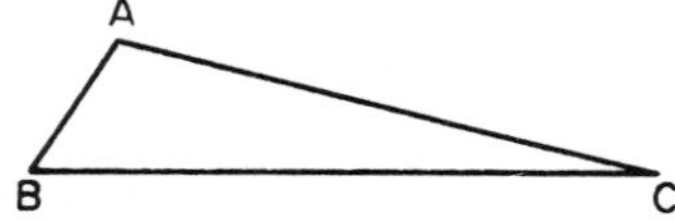

Side	Included Angle	Side
A-B		
	∠C	
		B-A
		B-C
	∠A	
B-C		

2. Use a protractor, rule, and compass to lay out triangles A, B, and C.

Triangle	Side	Angle	Side
A	3″	45°	3 1/2″
B	4″	60°	2 3/4″
C	2 1/2″	75°	4 1/8″

B. CONGRUENT SOLID SHAPES

1. Ten pieces of hexagon stock are all cut 2 cm long from a bar of stock. Are the ten pieces congruent to each other? Why?

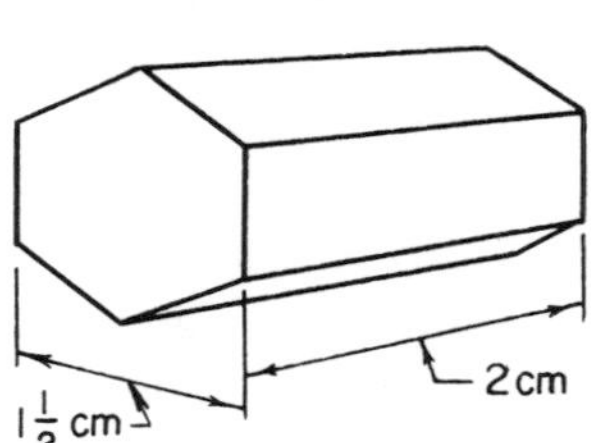

2. A plastic strip, triangular in shape, is formed by extrusion. If the strip is cut into 1/2″ lengths, is each piece congruent? Why?

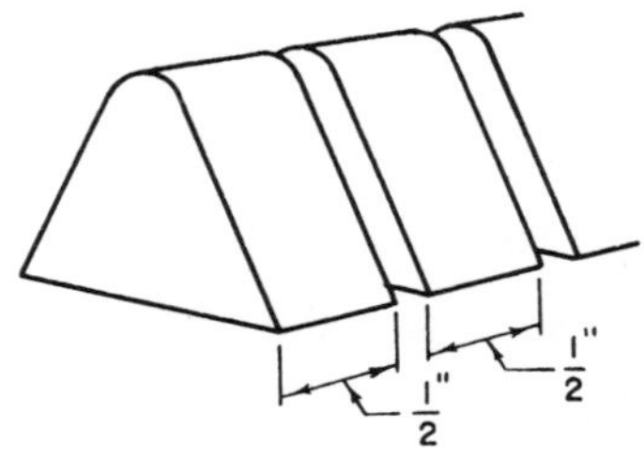

3. Pentagon-shaped plugs are to be stamped from 3.175 mm thick brass. If stock 2.778 mm is used instead of 3.175 mm, will the parts be congruent with those 3.175 mm thick? Why?

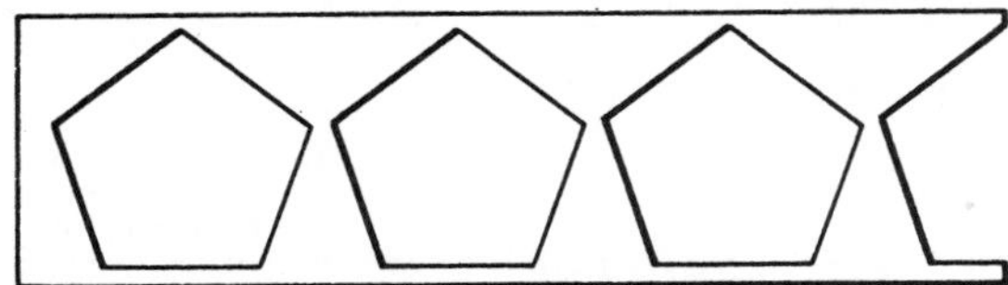

C. SYMMETRICAL FLAT SHAPES

1. Give three reasons why symmetry is essential in designing for production.
2. Sketch three flat shapes that are symmetrical. Label the axis in each case.

D. SYMMETRICAL SOLID SHAPES

1. Make a sketch of a simple part that is symmetrical.
   a. Pass an imaginary plane through the part.
   b. Sketch how the exterior and interior shape of the part look.
2. Explain the conditions under which each of the following machined parts is congruent.
   a. A pair of spur gears
   b. A set of pistons
   c. Precision ground threaded shafts

Unit 74 ACHIEVEMENT REVIEW ON GEOMETRIC LINES AND SHAPES

A. THE CONCEPT OF LINES, ANGLES, AND CIRCLES

1. Draw horizontal lines to the lengths indicated in the table.
   a. Connect the end point of each line with an inclined line drawn to the given length at the given angle.
   b. Name the type of angle formed in each case.

Line	Length of Sides		Included Angle
	Horizontal	Inclined	
A-B	4″	3 1/2″	90°
B-C	3 1/2″	3 1/2″	29°
C-D	3 1/2″	3 1/4″	120°
D-E	3 1/4″	3″	135°
E-F	2 7/8″	3 1/8″	59 1/2°

2. Refer to the sketch and name lines A, B, C, D, and E.
   a. Give the diameter of the outside cylindrical shape.
   b. What is the chordal dimension for the larger circle?

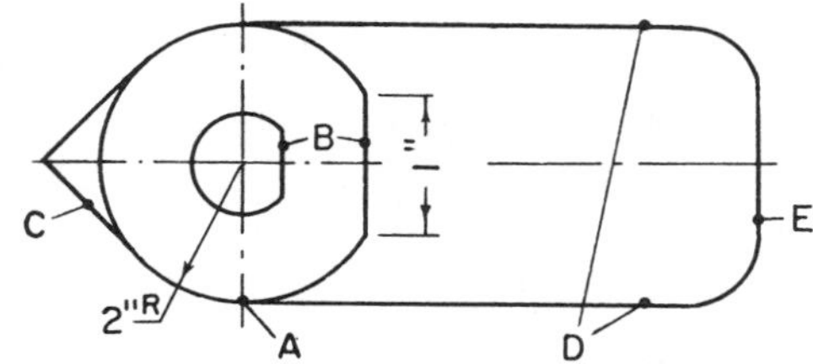

B. BASIC FLAT SHAPES

1. Draw the triangles indicated in each table. Label the base. Then show the altitude of each triangle by a dotted line.

△	Three Equal Sides
A	4″
B	3 1/4″
C	2 7/8″

△	Two Equal Sides	Incl. Angle
D	3″	90°
E	2″	120°
F	2 1/8″	60°

△	Base	Side	Side
G	4″	2 1/2″	3 1/2″
H	3 1/2″	2 1/4″	2 3/4″
I	2 11/16″	1 5/8″	3 1/16″

2. Name each flat shape and mark the sides and angles that are equal.

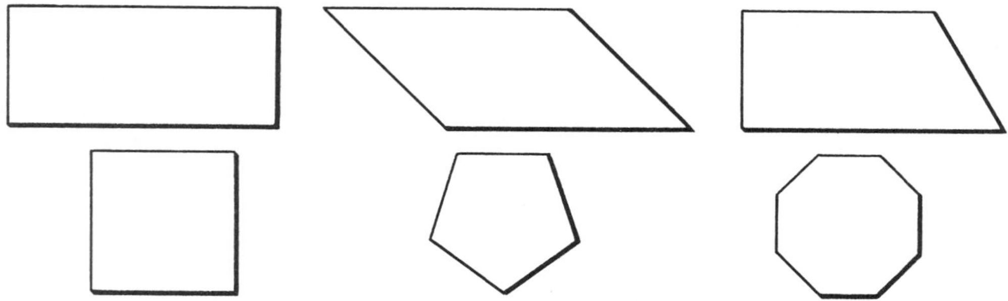

3. Sketch and label two simple round parts. The first should have all surfaces concentric; the second, eccentric.

C. BASIC SOLID SHAPES

1. Sketch the rectangular, cylindrical, and triangular parts to the sizes (approximately) given in the table. Draw either full size or to a reduced scale, if preferred.
   a. Use a ruled or graph sheet if available and indicate the scale to which the parts are sketched.
   b. Sketch freehand a cylindrical screw head that has a hexagonal prism shape formed in the head to receive a wrench.

	Rectangular			Cylindrical		Triangular
	Length	Height	Depth	Diam.	Height	3 Sides
A	4"	2"	3"	2"	2"	3"
B	3"	1 1/2"	2"	1 1/2"	2 1/2"	2 1/2"
C	2 1/8"	3"	5/8"	2 1/2"	3/4"	1 1/4"

D. CONGRUENT AND SIMILAR FLAT AND SOLID SHAPES

1. Lay out two congruent equilateral triangles and two congruent isosceles triangles.
   a. Mark the sides and the angles of each pair of corresponding sides or angles that are equal.
2. Which of the four pins are congruent? Why?

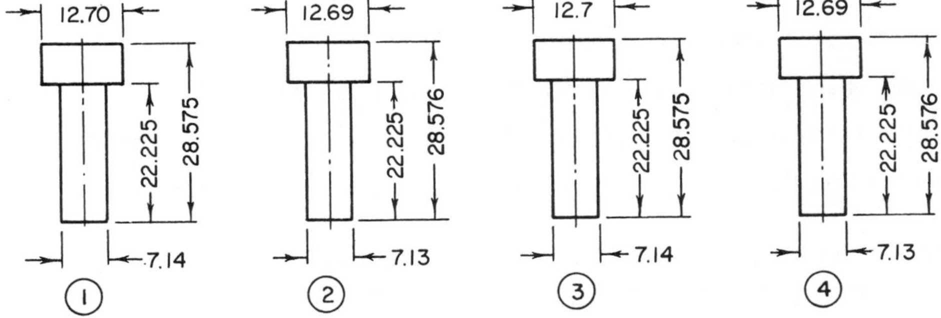

3. Are parts A and B similar or congruent? Why?

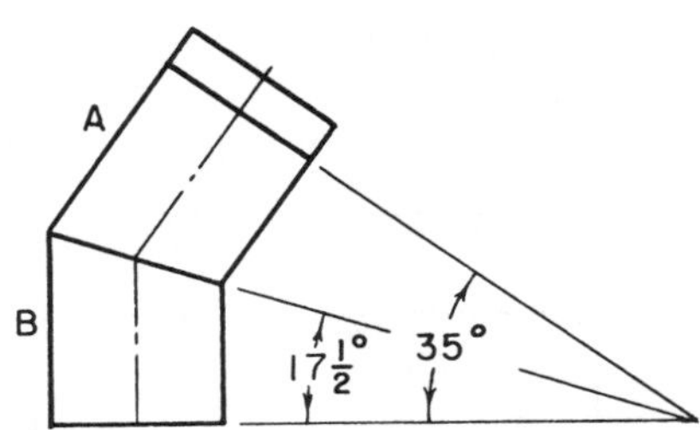

Section 16

COMMON GEOMETRIC CONSTRUCTIONS

Unit 75 BASIC GEOMETRIC CONSTRUCTIONS

The most practical applications of geometric principles are in the construction of parallel, perpendicular, and tangent lines, the dividing of straight and curved lines, and the bisecting of angles. These fundamental constructions are applied to closed flat shapes such as squares, rectangles, regular polygons, and circles. In advanced work, the constructions are used in drawing solid shapes which include cylinders, triangular prisms, and rectangular solids.

A. CONSTRUCTING PARALLEL LINES

Parallel lines are usually drawn at a specified distance apart. Regardless of the position of the parallel line, the steps used are the same.

RULE FOR CONSTRUCTING PARALLEL LINES

- Draw the first line.
- Set the compass the specified distance that the lines are to be drawn apart.
- Place the point end of the compass on the first line near one end of it.
- Swing an arc on the side on which the parallel line is required.
- Leave the compass set at the same distance and swing an arc at the other end of the line.
- Draw a line that touches the two arcs (is tangent). This line is parallel to the first line.

EXAMPLE: Draw a line parallel to the horizontal line AB and 1 inch away from it.

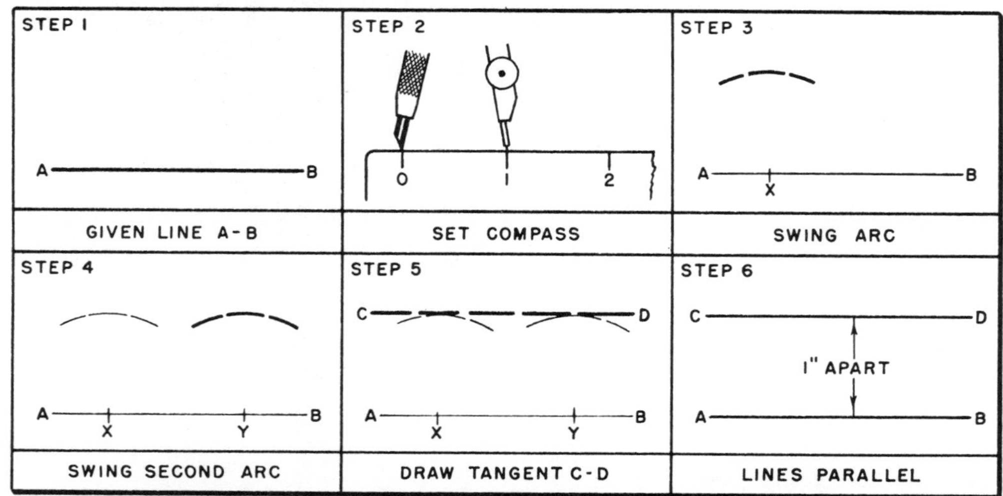

B. CONSTRUCTING ANGLES AND TRIANGLES

RULE FOR CONSTRUCTING AN ANGLE EQUAL TO A GIVEN ANGLE

- Draw the given angle.
- Lay out a line to be one side of the angle.
- Swing an arc, with the vertex of the angle as center, that intersects both sides.
- Transfer this arc, using the end point of the line as a center.
- Set the compass to the chordal distance between the two intersecting points of the arc and the sides of the original angle.
- Swing this same chordal distance (arc) from the point where the arc intersects the side of the new angle.
- Draw a line from the end point through the point of intersection of the arcs.
- The new angle thus formed is equal to the given angle.

EXAMPLE: Draw an angle equal to angle ABC.

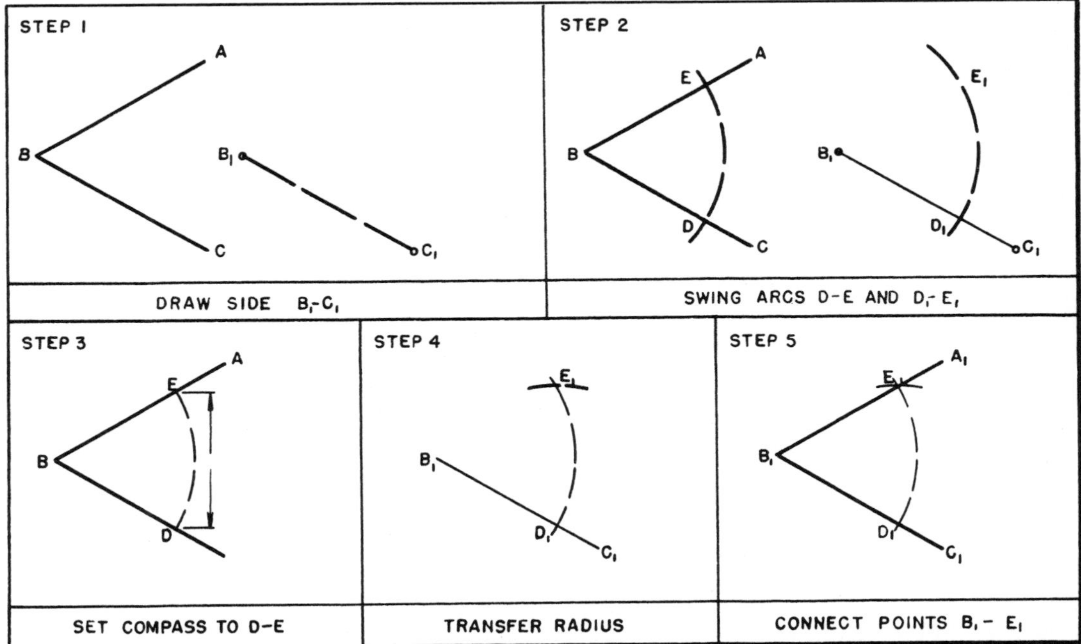

When constructing the sides of one angle equal to the sides of another angle and repeating the same steps to construct equal angles, it is possible to construct congruent angles, triangles, and other polygons.

C. DIVIDING A LINE

When a line of given length is bisected, it is divided into two equal parts. These are produced by swinging the same arc from both ends and drawing a line through the two points where the arcs intersect.

RULE FOR BISECTING A GIVEN LINE

- Set the compass at any radius greater than half the length of the given line.
- Place the point end of the compass at each of the end points of the line and swing an arc.
- Draw a light line through the points of intersection of the two arcs. The point where this line cuts the given line is the midpoint.

EXAMPLE: Lay out hole C the same distance from centers A and B in the plate illustrated.

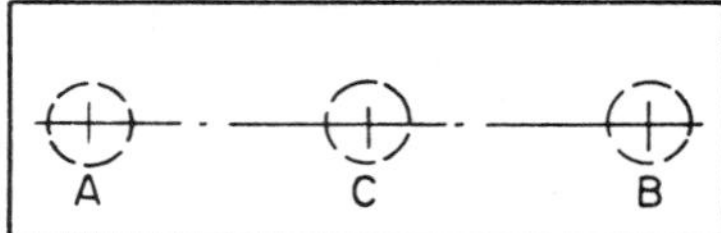

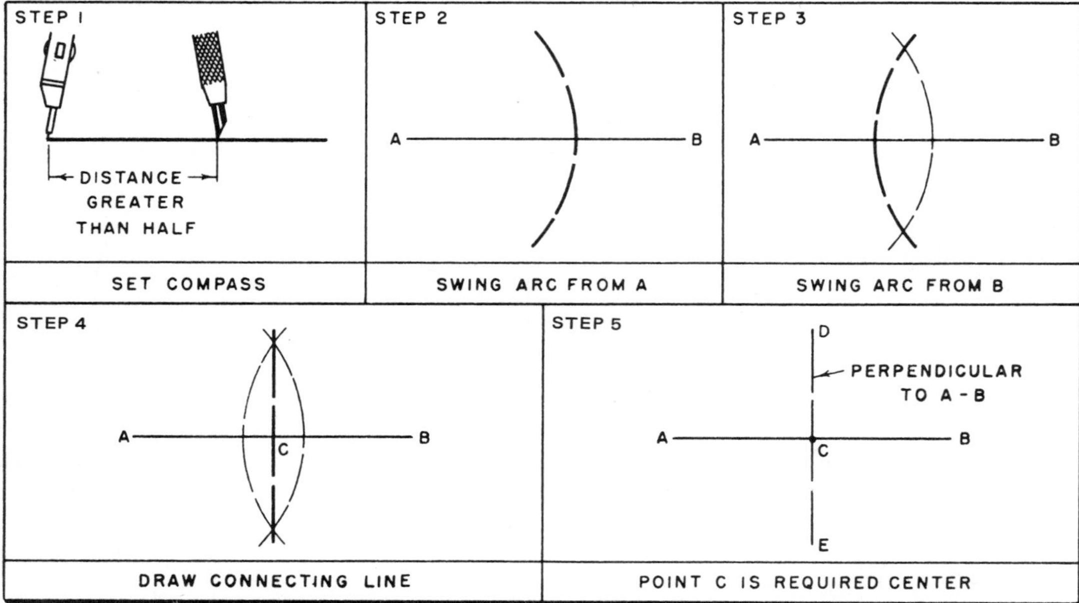

RULE FOR DIVIDING A LINE INTO A GIVEN NUMBER OF EQUAL PARTS

METHOD I

- Draw a line of given length.
- Draw another line at any angle and length to the given line from one end point.
- Step off on this angular line the number of equal spaces into which the line is to be divided.
- Connect the last point with the second end point on the given line.
- Draw lines parallel to this connecting line.

  Lay out angles equal to the last angle at each point on the angular line. These lines are parallel to the first line drawn.

EXAMPLE: Divide a line 3 5/16″ long into three equal parts.

METHOD I

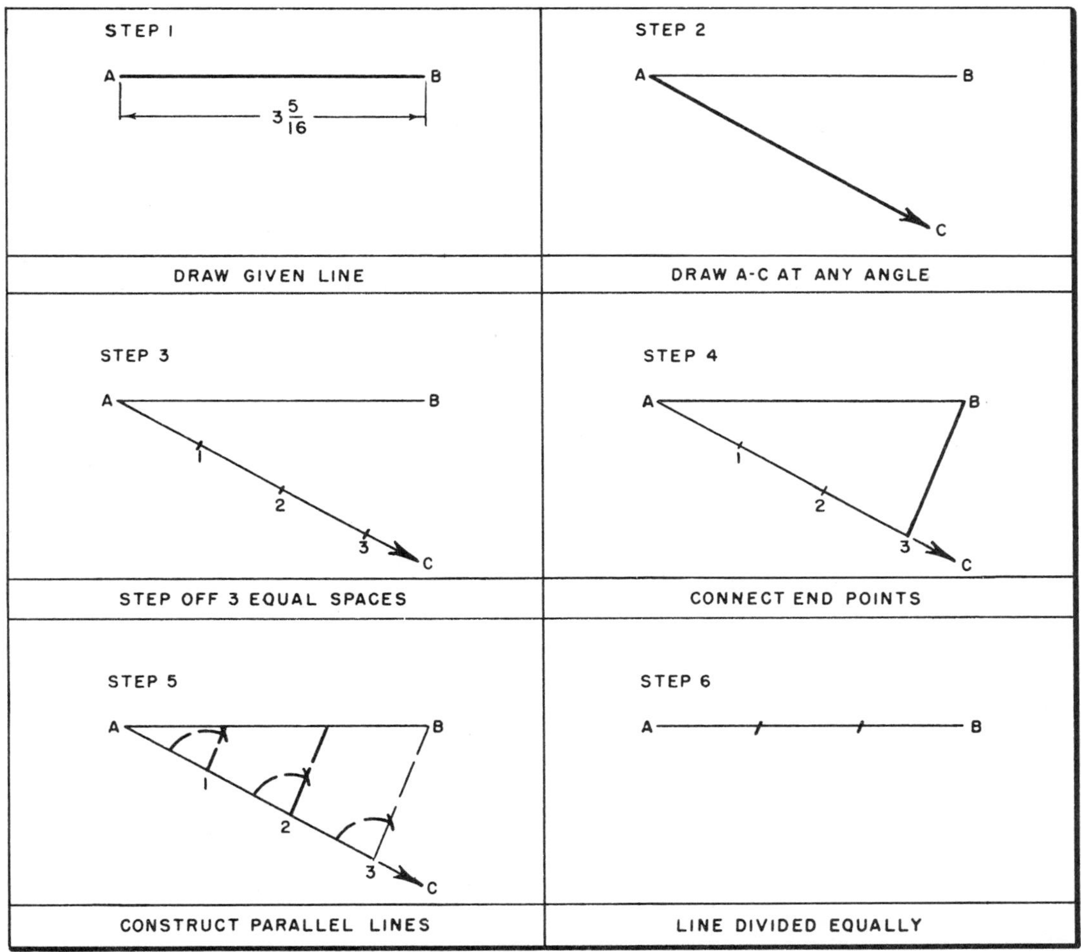

RULE FOR DIVIDING A LINE INTO A GIVEN NUMBER OF EQUAL PARTS

METHOD II

- Draw a line of a given length.
- From each end point, on the opposite sides of the line, construct equal angles to the given line.
- Step off on each angular line the number of equal spaces into which the original line is to be divided.
- Connect each end point of the original line with the last step-off point on the angular lines.
- Draw lines parallel to these connecting lines from the step-off points.

METHOD II

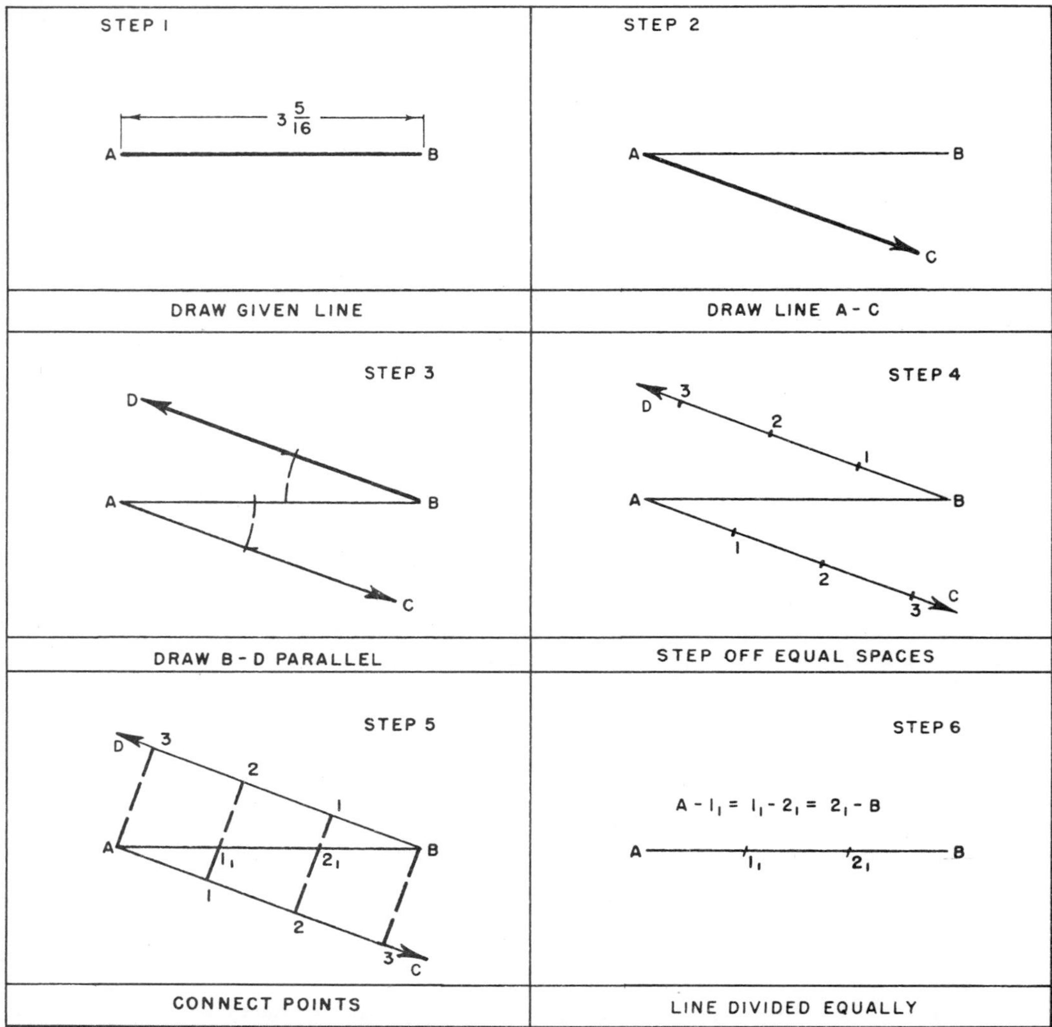

D. ERECTING A PERPENDICULAR

Two lines are perpendicular when they form an angle of 90° with each other. When a perpendicular is to be erected at the center of a line of given length, the same steps are followed as for bisecting a line. If a perpendicular is to be erected from any other point on a line, another procedure is used.

RULE FOR ERECTING A PERPENDICULAR (At a Given Point on a Line)

- Swing equal arcs from the given point to intersect the given line.
- Increase the size of the radius and swing equal arcs on the side of the line on which the perpendicular is to be erected. Use the intersecting points on the given line as centers.
- Draw a line from the point at which the two arcs intersect to the given point.
- This line is perpendicular at the given point to the given line.

EXAMPLE: Erect a perpendicular on line A-B at C.

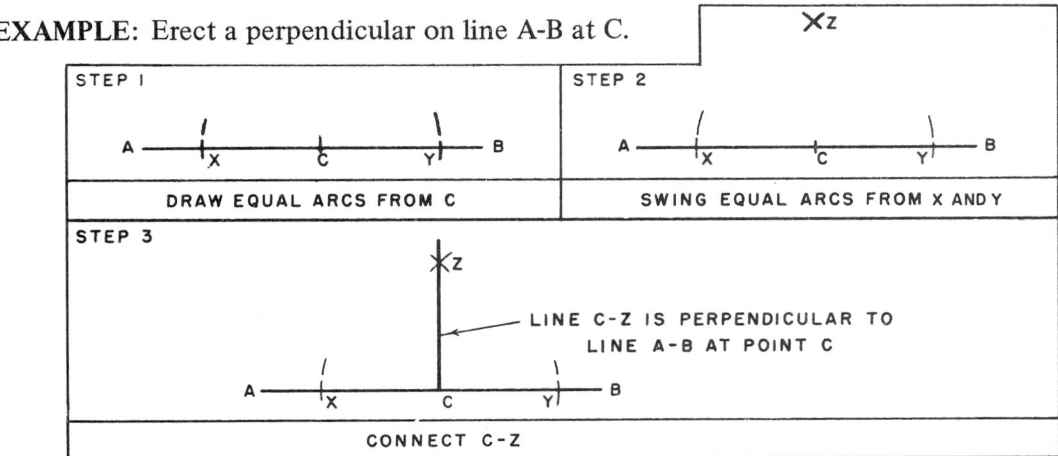

E. BISECTING A GIVEN ANGLE

RULE FOR BISECTING A GIVEN ANGLE

- Swing an arc (from the vertex of the angle) which intersects both sides.
- Use the intersecting points as centers and swing two more arcs.
- Draw a line which passes through the vertex and the point where the two arcs intersect.
- This line bisects the given angle into two equal angles.

EXAMPLE: Bisect angle ABC.

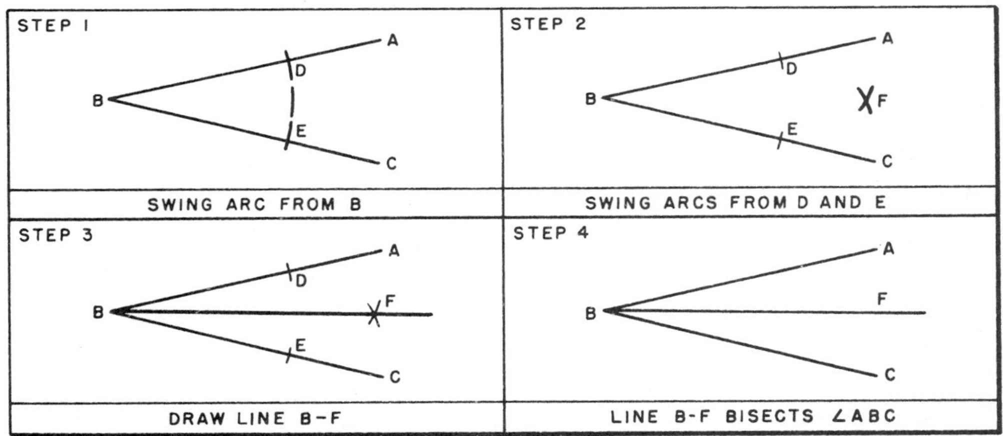

F. CONSTRUCTING TANGENTS TO A CIRCLE

The construction of tangents to circles, arcs, and straight lines is common in layout work. The drawing shows straight lines that are tangent to parts of circles and arcs that are tangent to other arcs. Two constructions are used widely in drawing tangents.

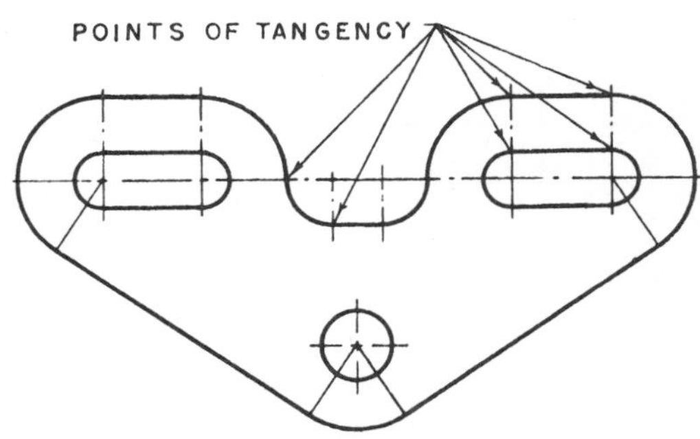

1. Constructing a tangent to a given circle at a given point.
2. Constructing a tangent to a circle from a given point outside the circle.

RULE FOR CONSTRUCTING A TANGENT (To a Given Circle at a Given Point)

- Draw the given circle and locate the given point on the circumference.
- Draw the radius from the center to the given point and extend it beyond the circle.
- Erect a perpendicular at the given point.
- The perpendicular is the tangent to the given circle at the given point.

EXAMPLE: Construct a tangent to circle O at point C.

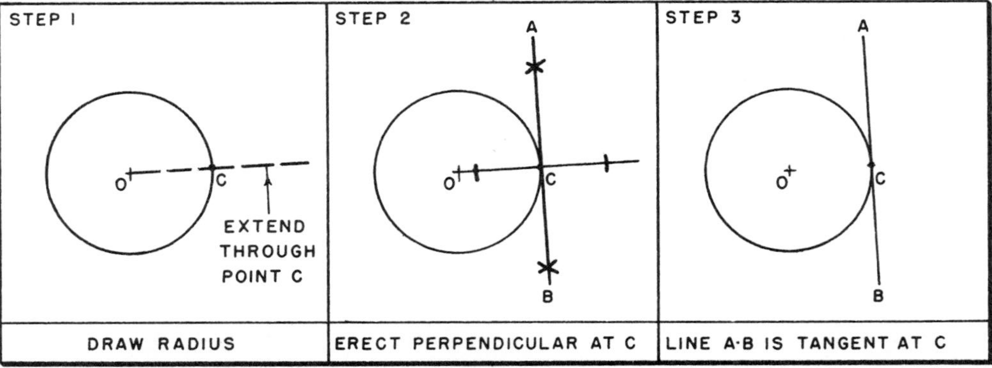

RULE FOR CONSTRUCTING A TANGENT
(To a Given Circle from a Point Outside the Circle)

- Draw a line connecting the given point outside the circle with the center.
- Bisect this line.
- Use the center point of the bisected line as a center. With a radius equal to the distance from this center point to the center of the circle, draw an arc that intersects the circle.
- Draw a line between the given point outside the circle and the point of intersection of the arc on the circle.
- This line is tangent to the given circle from a point outside the circle.

EXAMPLE: Construct a tangent to circle O from point X.

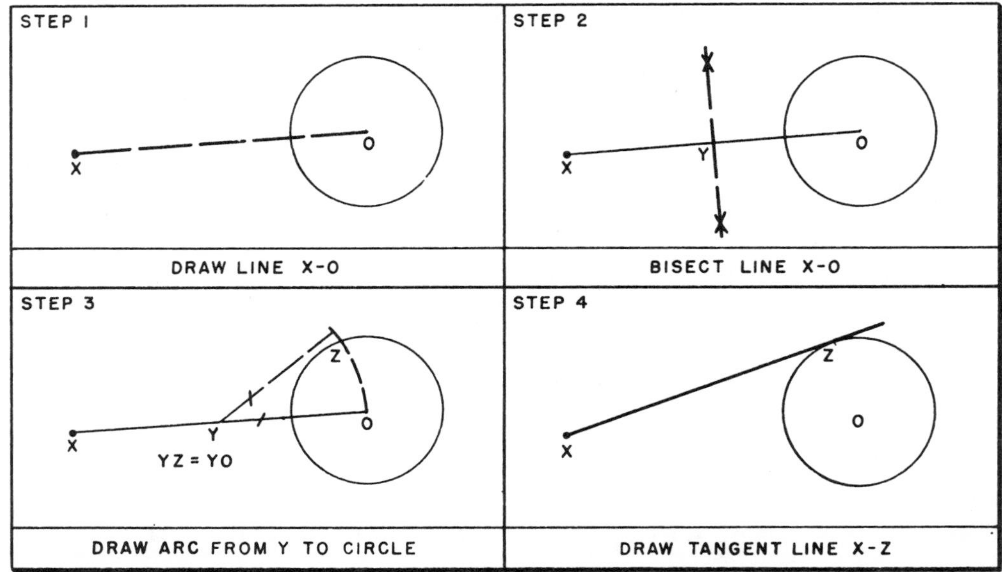

These basic constructions may be used alone or in combination as shown in the sketch.

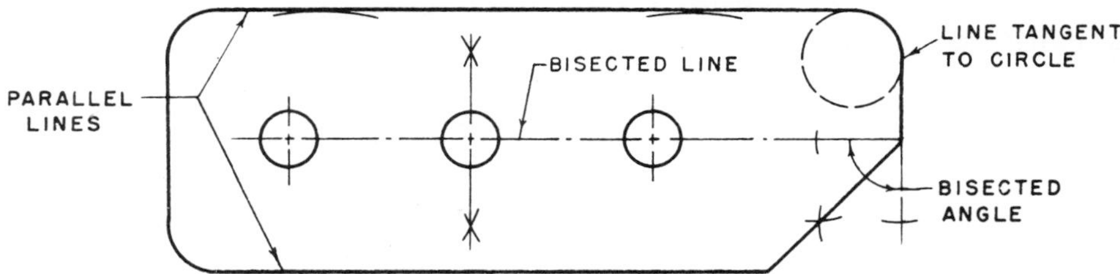

ASSIGNMENT UNIT 75

Note: Show all construction lines for all problems.

A. CONSTRUCTING PARALLEL LINES

1. Draw a parallel line for each line given in the table at the distance shown in each case.

Line	Length of Line	Distance
A-B	6″	2″
C-D	5″	1 1/2″
E-F	4″	1 1/4″
G-H	3″	2 1/8″
I-J	2″	1 7/16″

2. Draw two vertical lines of different lengths. Then draw the perpendicular bisector of each line. The perpendicular bisectors should be parallel to each other.

B. DIVIDING LINES

1. Bisect each line in the table.

Line	Length
A-B	4 1/2″
C-D	3 3/4″
E-F	2 7/8″
G-H	10.48 cm
I-J	119.1 mm

2. Lay out the centers for each of the five holes on the drill plate. Solve by geometric construction and draw to full size.

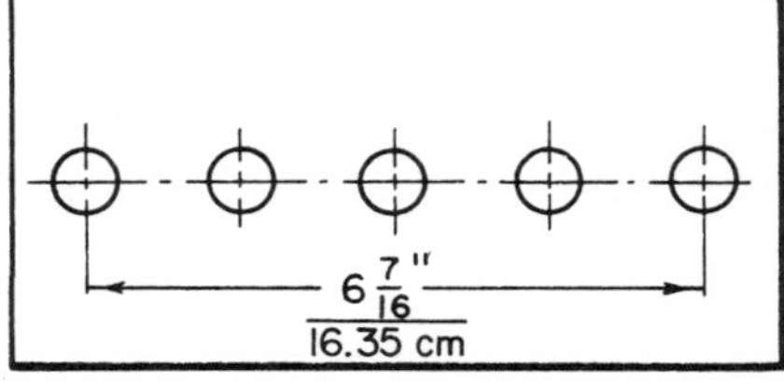

C. ERECTING PERPENDICULARS

1. Erect a perpendicular to each line given in the table at the point in the line as specified in each case.

Line	Length	Distance from End of Line
A-B	5″	2″
C-D	4 1/2″	1 1/2″
E-F	3 3/4″	1 1/4″
G-H	5 5/8″	2 3/8″
I-J	4 15/16″	1 11/16″

2. Erect a perpendicular to each given line from a point outside the line as indicated for each line in the table.

Line	Length and Point Outside Line
A - B	A B
C - D	C D

D. BISECTING ANGLES

1. Lay out the five angles given in the table with a protractor. Then bisect each angle.
2. Lay out an angle of 90° with a protractor.
   a. Bisect the angle.
   b. Construct two 22 1/2° angles by bisecting the 45° angle.

Angle	Number of Degrees
ABC	90°
CED	120°
DEF	75°
FGH	140°
IJK	29°

3. Show the construction used to lay out the centers of the 1/4″ circular slot.

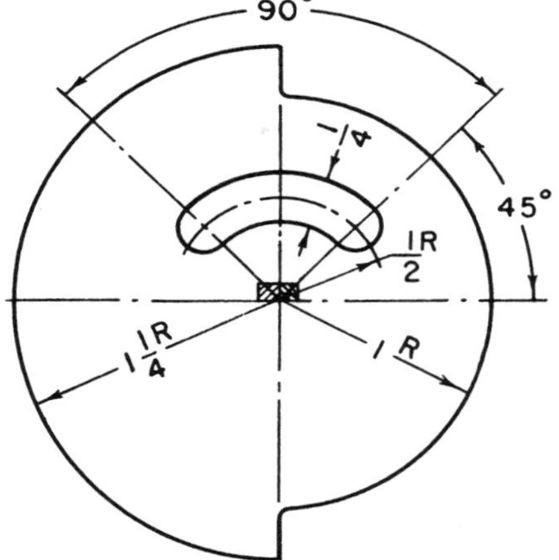

E. CONSTRUCTING TANGENTS

1. Construct tangents to circle O at points A, B, and C.

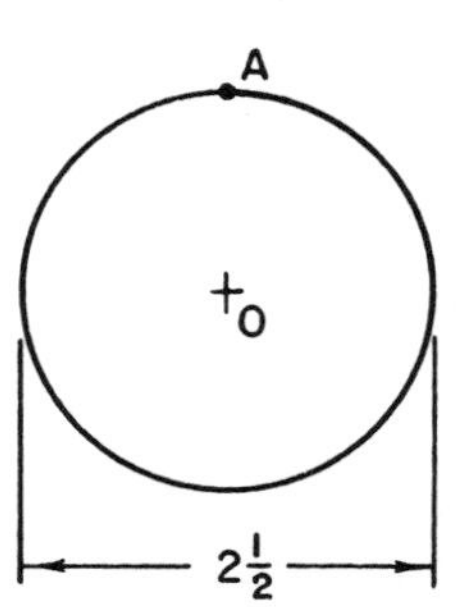

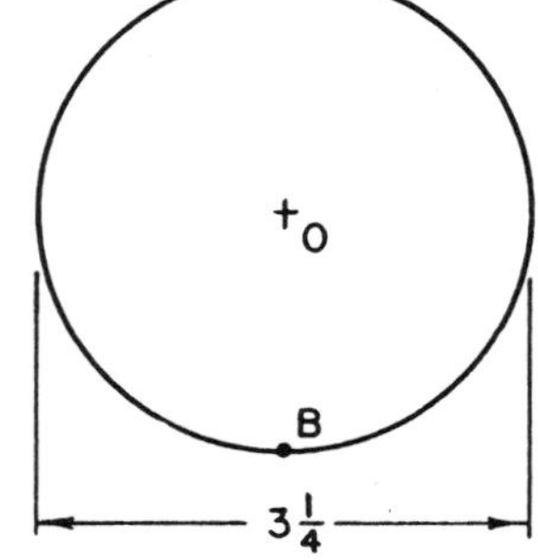

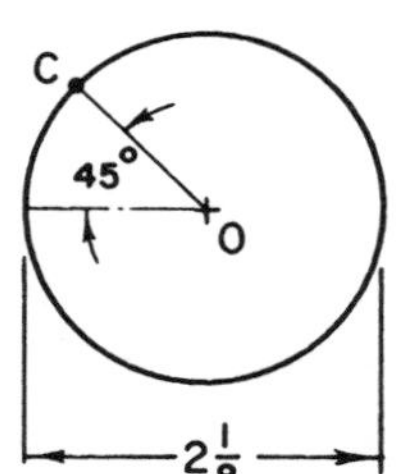

2. Construct tangents to circle X from points outside the circle at the distances given in the table.

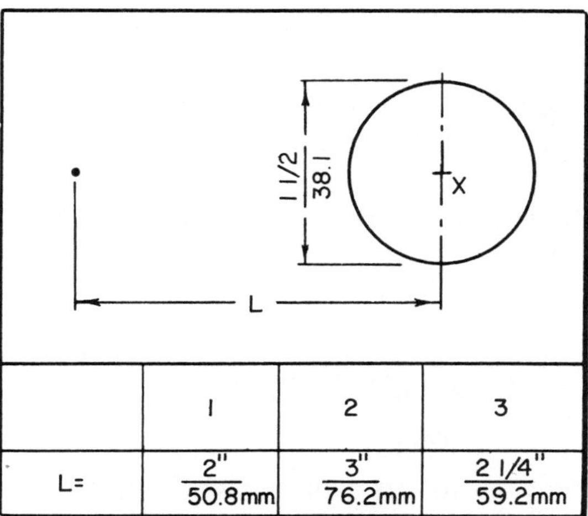

	1	2	3
L=	2" / 50.8mm	3" / 76.2mm	2 1/4" / 59.2mm

Unit 76 CONSTRUCTIONS APPLIED TO GEOMETRIC SHAPES

Geometry takes on increased value as more and more applications are made of the basic constructions in laying out geometric shapes. While the numbers become limitless, only a few of the most widely used constructions are described in this unit.

A. INSCRIBING SQUARES AND HEXAGONS IN A CIRCLE

A square is *inscribed* in a circle when all corners of the square lie within the circumference of the circle.

RULE FOR INSCRIBING A SQUARE IN A CIRCLE

- Draw any diameter in the given circle.
- Construct a perpendicular to this diameter which passes through the center of the circle.
- Extend the perpendicular so it becomes a second diameter.
- Connect the point at which the diameter intersects the circumference with the next corresponding point.
- Repeat this process to draw the next three sides of the square.
- The square thus formed is inscribed in a circle of given diameter.

EXAMPLE: Inscribe a square in a 2" diameter circle.

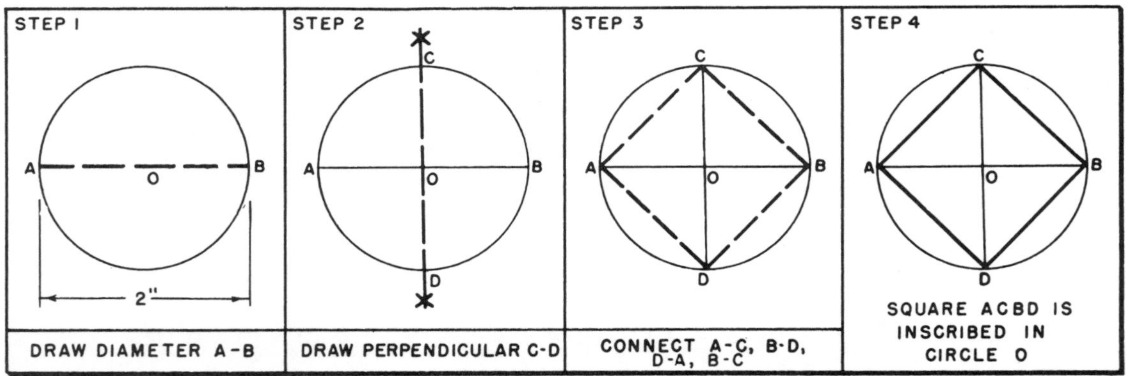

RULE FOR INSCRIBING A REGULAR HEXAGON IN A CIRCLE

- Take the radius of the circle and start at any point on the circumference to step off an arc.
- Use the point of intersection as a center and step off another arc of the same radius.
- Continue in the same way until the circle is divided into six equal parts.
- Connect each point of intersection with the next successive point until all points are connected.
- The six-sided figure inscribed in the circle is the required regular hexagon.

EXAMPLE: Construct a regular hexagon in a 1 1/2″ diameter circle.

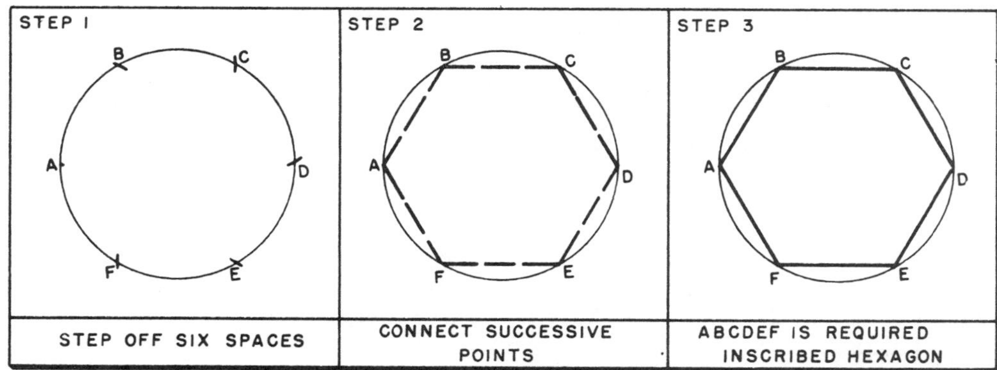

B. CIRCUMSCRIBING SQUARES AND HEXAGONS

Circumscribing a polygon about a given circle is a geometric expression. It means that a specially shaped figure is constructed outside a circle so that each line of the figure is tangent to the circle.

RULE FOR CIRCUMSCRIBING REGULAR POLYGONS

- Divide the circle into the number of desired parts the same as for inscribed shapes.
- Draw radii from the point of intersection to the center of the circle.
- Draw a tangent line perpendicular to each of the radii.
- The object formed by the intersecting lines is the circumscribed polygon.

EXAMPLE: Circumscribe a regular hexagon about a 2″ diameter circle.

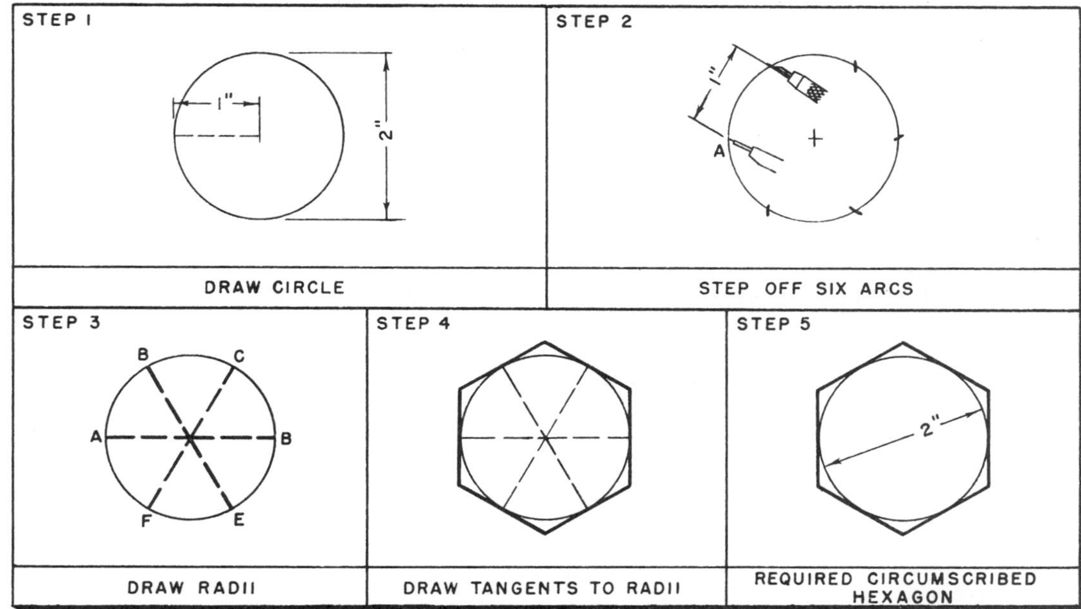

Steps similar to these may be followed in circumscribing other regular polygons about circles of known diameters.

ASSIGNMENT UNIT 76

NOTE: Show all construction lines for all problems, where used.

A. INSCRIBING POLYGONS IN CIRCLES

1. Construct each of the three polygons. Use a straightedge and compass.

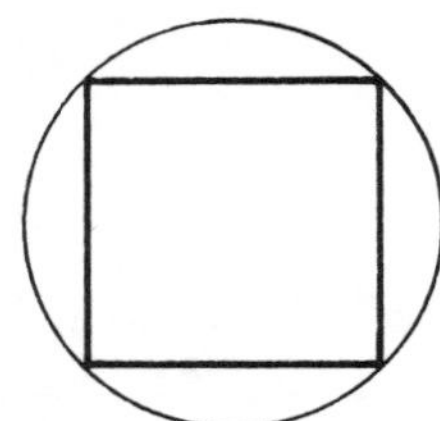
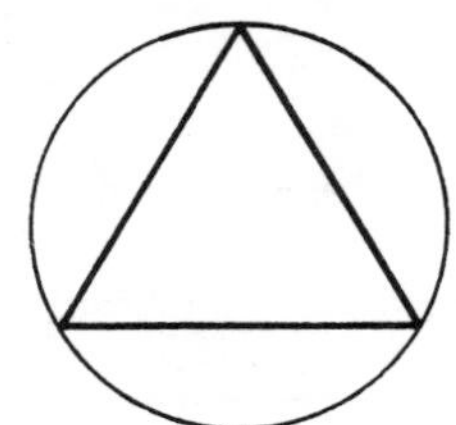
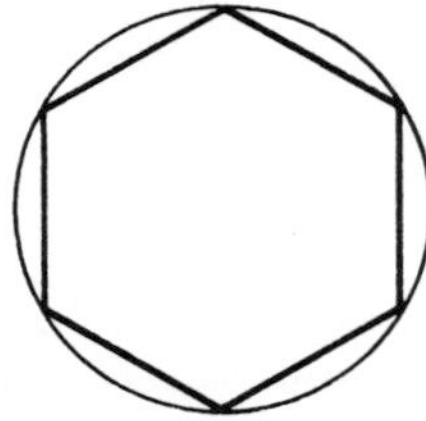

2. A piece of round stock is 2 1/2″ in diameter. Construct the largest square that can be machined at one end.
3. What is the largest hexagon that can be planed on a 6″ diameter post?

   a. What is the distance across flats for the hexagon?

   Ans.: 5.196″

B. CIRCUMSCRIBING REGULAR POLYGONS ABOUT CIRCLES

1. Circumscribe the square, equilateral triangle, and regular hexagon about the circles for the diameter given for each shape.

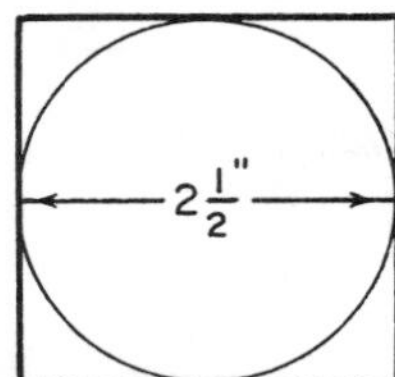

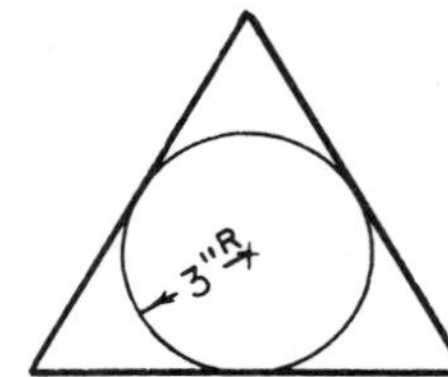

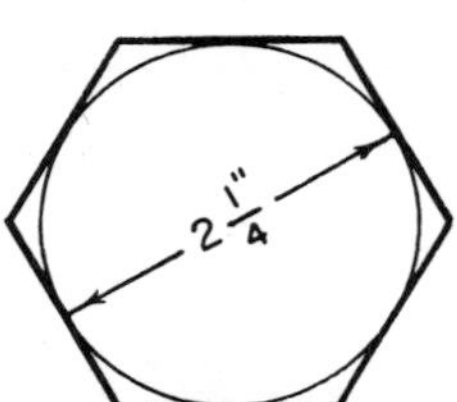

2. Circumscribe a regular hexagon about a 2″ diameter circle.

   a. Determine the distance (X) across corners by measuring.

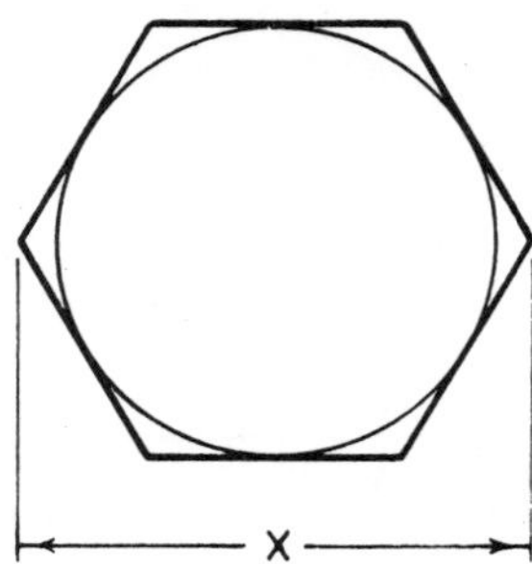

Unit 77 ACHIEVEMENT REVIEW ON GEOMETRIC CONSTRUCTIONS

A. BASIC CONSTRUCTIONS

1. Determine whether or not the dotted lines constructed with the framing square are parallel. Give reasons.

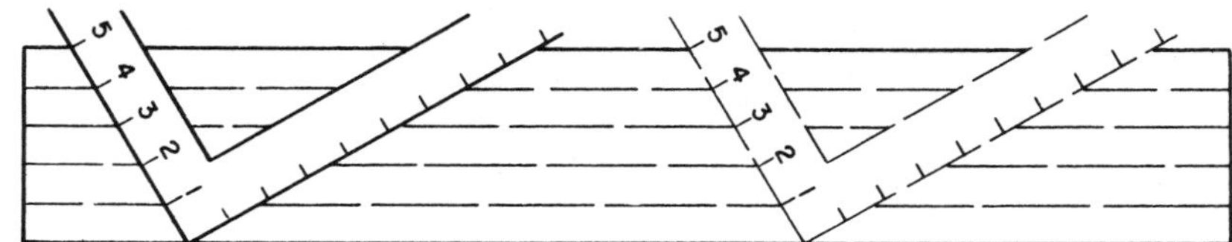

2. The value of angle A is 110° 30′. Lines 1-2 and 3-4 are parallel. Find the value of each angle (B through G).

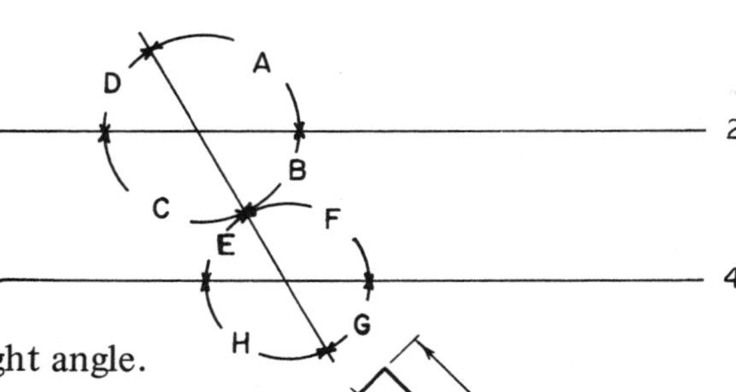

3. Lay out the 45° elbow. Start with a straight angle.
   a. Erect a perpendicular to the straight angle.
   b. Bisect the 90° angle formed.
   c. Draw lines parallel to the centerlines to form the sides, and perpendicular lines to form the ends.

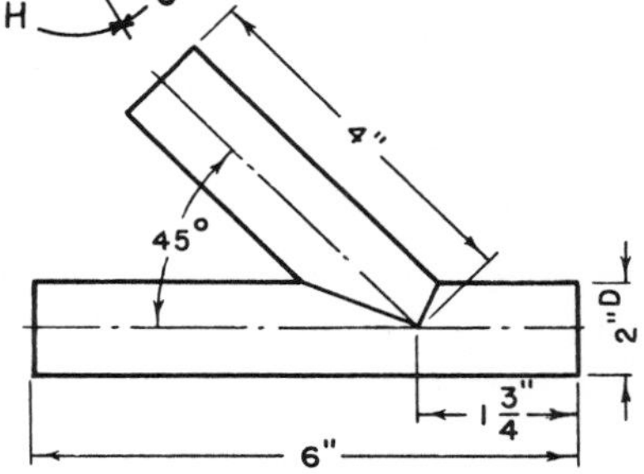

B. BASIC CONSTRUCTIONS APPLIED TO GEOMETRIC SHAPES

1. Construct the templet according to the dimensions as given.

   NOTE: Show all lines used for constructing parallel lines, erecting a perpendicular, bisecting an angle, and drawing tangents.

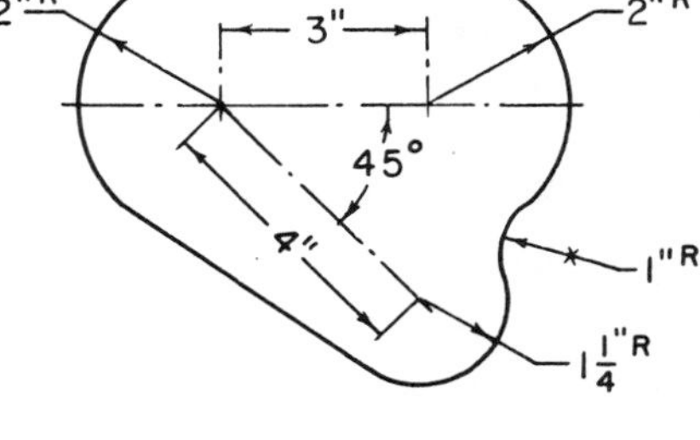

2. Construct the special plate with the circumscribed square and the inscribed portion of the regular hexagon. Show all construction lines.

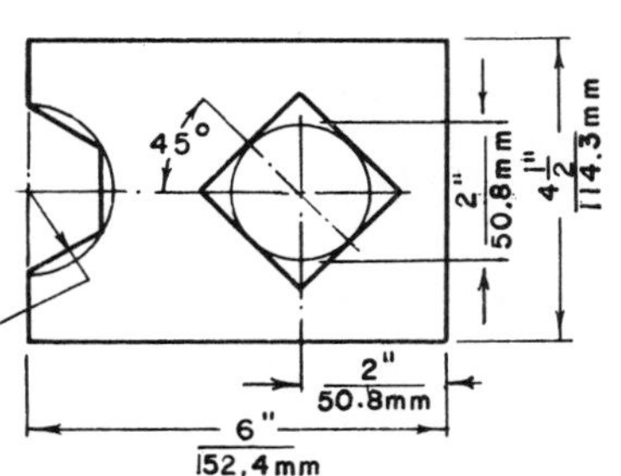

Section 17

RIGHT, ACUTE, AND OBLIQUE TRIANGLES

Unit 78 THE CONCEPT OF RIGHT TRIANGLE TRIGONOMETRY

The word trigonometry, as derived from the Greek, means two things: *triangle* and *measurement*. Trigonometry is a branch of mathematics which deals with the measurement of angles, triangles, and distances. A working knowledge of trigonometry requires an understanding of fundamental principles and constructions in geometry. Also, since symbols are used and algebraic equations are constructed, problems in trigonometry are solved by using algebra.

Trigonometry is preferred by many workers to other branches of mathematics. Trigonometry conserves time and effort, and simplifies the solution of common technical problems in different occupations and in consumer applications.

A. PARTS OF THE RIGHT TRIANGLE

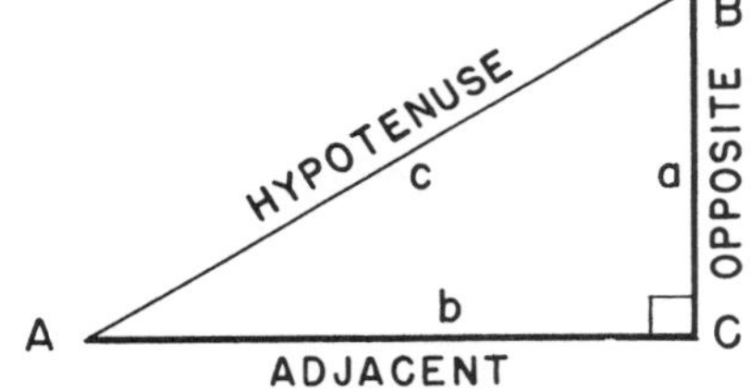

While trigonometry includes both the right triangle and the oblique triangle, the first named type is covered in this unit. A *right triangle,* as the name implies, is a triangle with one right angle. In the illustration of the right triangle ABC, the side opposite the right angle C is the *hypotenuse* (c). The side opposite the acute angle A is called the "side opposite" (a). Adjacent to angle A is the "side adjacent" (b). Note on the drawing and in the explanation that the angles are indicated by capital letters. The sides are denoted by either lowercase letters or the words opposite, adjacent, or hypotenuse.

B. TRIGONOMETRIC FUNCTIONS

There are six terms that are widely used in trigonometry to express the ratios between the sides. The terms and the abbreviation of each are *sine* (sin), *cosine* (cos), *tangent* (tan), *cotangent* (cot), *secant* (sec), and *cosecant* (csc).

The sine (sin) is the ratio of the side opposite to the hypotenuse. In triangle ABC, the

$$\sin A = \frac{\text{side opposite}}{\text{hypotenuse}} = \frac{a}{c}$$

SIN A = $\frac{a}{c}$

The cosine (cos) is the ratio of the side adjacent to the hypotenuse.

$$\cos A = \frac{\text{side adjacent}}{\text{hypotenuse}} = \frac{b}{c}$$

COS A = $\frac{b}{c}$

The tangent (tan) is the ratio of the side opposite to the side adjacent.

$$\tan A = \frac{\text{side opposite}}{\text{side adjacent}} = \frac{a}{b}$$

TAN A = $\frac{a}{b}$

A B C c a b

The cotangent (cot) is the ratio of the side adjacent to the side opposite.

$$\cot A = \frac{\text{side adjacent}}{\text{side opposite}} = \frac{b}{a}$$

The secant and cosecant of angle A may be expressed in algebraic form.

$$\sec A = \frac{\text{hypotenuse}}{\text{side adjacent}} = \frac{c}{b} \qquad \csc A = \frac{\text{hypotenuse}}{\text{side opposite}} = \frac{c}{a}$$

A comparison of the values of the six trigonometric functions shows two things. First, the sine and cosine, tangent and cotangent, and secant and cosecant may be grouped in pairs. Second, three of the trigonometric functions are reciprocals of the other three. Starting with the sine

$\sin A = \frac{a}{c}$ and the cosecant reciprocal, $\csc A = \frac{c}{a}$

$\cos A = \frac{b}{c}$ and the secant reciprocal, $\sec A = \frac{c}{b}$

$\tan A = \frac{a}{b}$ and the cotangent reciprocal, $\cot A = \frac{b}{a}$

C. FUNCTIONS AND COFUNCTIONS

In the right triangle ABC, angle A and angle B are *complementary* to each other and the sum of the two angles is 90°. The term *cofunction* refers to the function of the complementary angle.

The cofunction of the sine is the cosine which is a contraction of the phrase "the sine of the complement." The cofunction of the tangent is the cotangent; that of the secant, the cosecant.

- The sine of an acute angle is equal to the cosine of its complement.
- The tangent of an acute angle is equal to the cotangent of its complement.
- The secant of an acute angle is equal to the cosecant of its complement.

With the knowledge that the function of one acute angle in a right triangle is equal to the cofunction of the complement, it is possible to work with either acute angle. For instance, the tan of 30° = cot of 60°; the sin of 25° = cos 65°; the sec 75° = csc 15°.

ASSIGNMENT UNIT 78

A. PARTS OF THE RIGHT TRIANGLE

1. Letter the angles and name the side opposite, side adjacent and hypotenuse of each right triangle.

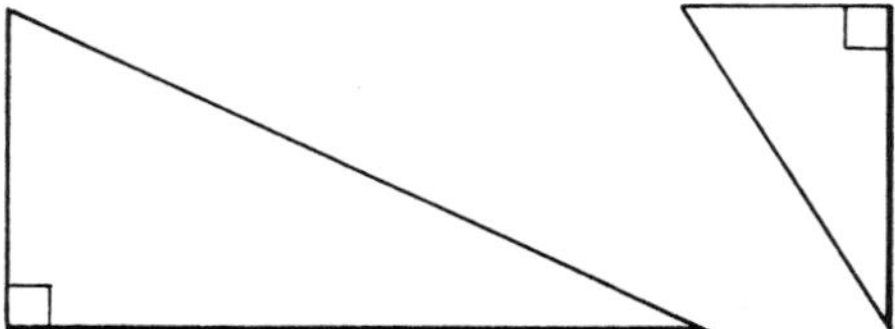

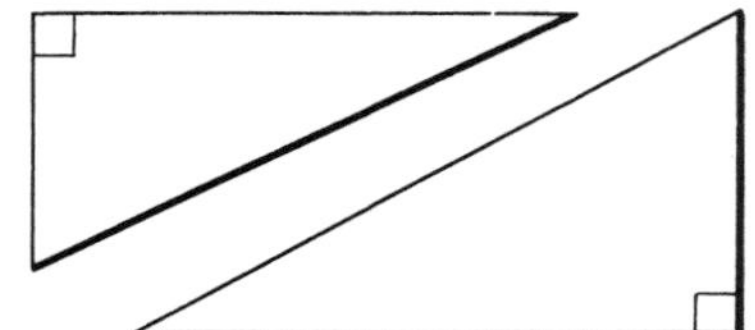

2. Draw each of the right triangles according to the dimensions given in the table. Label the angles and dimension the sides.

Triangle	Right Angle	Length of Side	
ABC	B	A	C
		3″	3″
LMN	N	L	M
		2 1/4″	3″
XYZ	X	Y	Z
		5.25″	4.50″

B. TRIGONOMETRIC FUNCTIONS

1. Prepare a table similar to the one shown. Complete the information called for in each column.

Function	Abbreviation	Trigonometry Ratios	
		Expressed as Sides	Sides Represented by Letters
Sine			
Cosine			
Tangent			
Cotangent			
Secant			
Cosecant			

2. The included angle of the National Form Thread is 60°. The crest and the root of the thread are each made flat for a depth of 1/8 the pitch. Sketch a single thread and show by dotted lines the trapezoid at the crest of the thread and the triangle at the root that are allowed for strength and clearance.

3. Determine the decimal value of each one of the six trigonometric ratios as they apply to angle D.

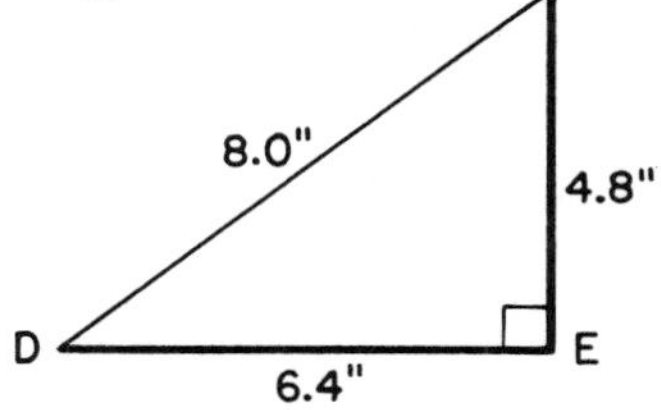

Ans.: $\sin \angle D = .600$ $\sec \angle D = 1.25$

4. Guidelines for laying up ceiling tiles on a job are checked for squareness. A measurement of 1.62 meters is marked on line AB and 2.46 meters on line AC. Determine measurement BC, correct to three decimal places.

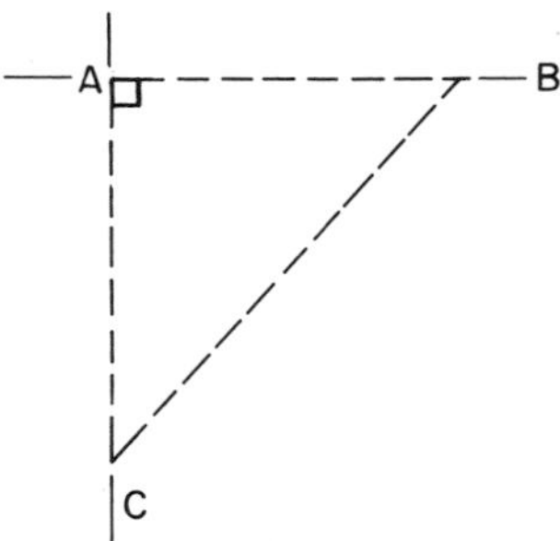

5. A derrick rig is 19.51 meters high. A guy wire is attached 1.83 meters from the top and 7.62 meters out from the base. Compute the length of the guy wire to two decimal places.

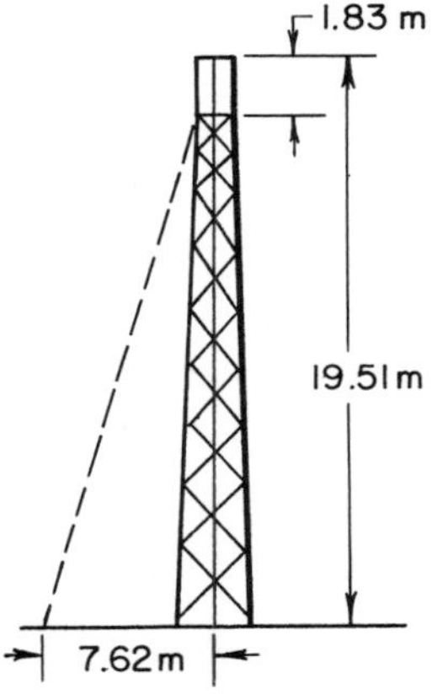

Ans.: 19.25 meters

C. FUNCTIONS AND COFUNCTIONS

1. Give the cofunction of each angle in a right triangle.

Ans: cot 70° is cofunction of tan 20°

Function	Cofunction
sin 45°	
tan 20°	
sec 29 1/2°	

2. a. Make a freehand sketch of each of the six right triangles given in the table. Label the angles with the given letters and the sides with corresponding lowercase letters.

   b. State the ratio of the sides for each function A through F.

   c. Give the cofunction of each of the six functions.

Ans.: B. $\tan \angle E = e/d$ $\cot \angle D = e/d$

	Right Triangle	Function
A	BAC	sin ∡A
B	DEF	tan ∡E
C	JKL	sec ∡K
D	MNO	sin 30°
E	STU	tan 25°
F	XYZ	sec 37 1/2°

Unit 79 APPLICATION OF TABLES OF TRIGONOMETRIC FUNCTIONS

The values of trigonometric functions may be found by construction and measurement or by tables. Of the two methods, the tables are more reliable where precision is necessary. The average accuracy where measuring rules and instruments are used is within two or three decimal places. Most tables of trigonometric functions are carried to four or more decimal places.

As long as the two acute angles in a right triangle remain the same, the trigonometric function of each angle is constant and does not change regardless of the size of the triangle. The sine of a 45° angle of a right triangle with 4-inch sides is the same as for one with 12-inch sides, or any other length sides.

A. CONSTRUCTION AND MEASUREMENT OF TRIGONOMETRIC FUNCTIONS

RULE FOR FINDING TRIGONOMETRIC FUNCTIONS
(By Construction and Measurement)

METHOD I Given an Angle

- Construct the desired angle.
- Measure a convenient even distance on the hypotenuse.
- Drop a perpendicular from the end point of the hypotenuse to the side adjacent.
- Measure the side opposite.
- Divide the two measurements. The quotient is the value of the sine of the angle.

The value of the other functions may be found by using the same steps and the actual measurements of the sides used.

METHOD II Given the Value of a Function

- Draw a horizontal line.
- Erect a perpendicular at the end of the line.
- Measure the given distance on the perpendicular.
- Swing a 1-inch arc from the end point of the perpendicular to intersect the horizontal line.
- Draw the hypotenuse through the end point and the intersecting point.
- Measure the acute angle formed with the horizontal line.

EXAMPLE: Given the sin D = .7071, find the angle by construction.

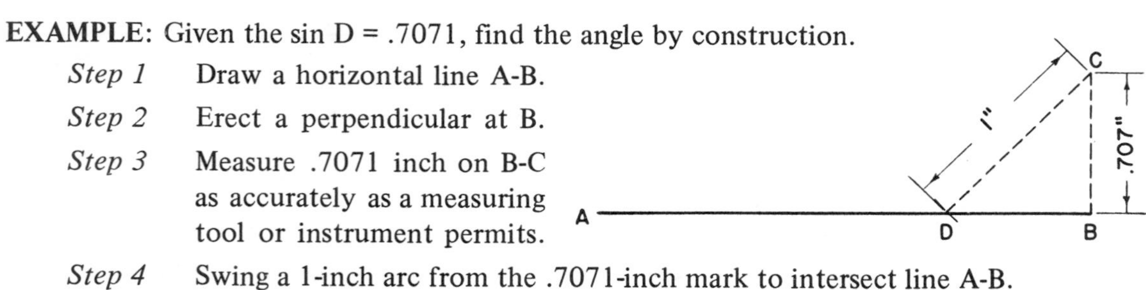

Step 1 Draw a horizontal line A-B.

Step 2 Erect a perpendicular at B.

Step 3 Measure .7071 inch on B-C as accurately as a measuring tool or instrument permits.

Step 4 Swing a 1-inch arc from the .7071-inch mark to intersect line A-B.

Step 5 Connect points D and C with a straight line.

Step 6 Measure angle D (=45°). Thus, the angle with the sine of .7071 is 45°.

B. READING TABLES OF NATURAL TRIGONOMETRIC FUNCTIONS

It is apparent that while the construction methods are interesting and practical for the layout of many jobs, precision is not possible. Since the value of the function of an angle is constant (once the value of angles is computed accurately) the results may be combined in table form. One of the simplest tables of natural trigonometric functions is illustrated. The more complicated tables give five or more decimal places for each degree and each minute in a degree.

Angle	Sine	Cosine	Tangent	Angle	Sine	Cosine	Tangent	Angle	Sine	Cosine	Tangent
1°	.0175	.9998	.0175	31°	.5150	.8572	.6009	61°	.8746	.4848	1.8040
2°	.0349	.9994	.0349	32°	.5299	.8480	.6249	62°	.8829	.4695	1.8807
3°	.0523	.9986	.0524	33°	.5446	.8387	.6494	63°	.8910	.4540	1.9626
4°	.0698	.9976	.0699	34°	.5592	.8290	.6745	64°	.8988	.4384	2.0503
5°	.0872	.9962	.0875	35°	.5736	.8192	.7002	65°	.9063	.4226	2.1445
6°	.1045	.9945	.1051	36°	.5878	.8090	.7265	66°	.9135	.4067	2.2460
7°	.1219	.9925	.1228	37°	.6018	.7986	.7536	67°	.9205	.3907	2.3559
8°	.1392	.9903	.1405	38°	.6157	.7880	.7813	68°	.9272	.3746	2.4751
9°	.1564	.9877	.1584	39°	.6293	.7771	.8098	69°	.9336	.3584	2.6051
10°	.1736	.9848	.1763	40°	.6428	.7660	.8391	70°	.9397	.3420	2.7475
11°	.1908	.9816	.1944	41°	.6561	.7547	.8693	71°	.9455	.3256	2.9042
12°	.2079	.9781	.2126	42°	.6691	.7431	.9004	72°	.9511	.3090	3.0777
13°	.2250	.9744	.2309	43°	.6820	.7314	.9325	73°	.9563	.2924	3.2709
14°	.2419	.9703	.2493	44°	.6947	.7193	.9657	74°	.9613	.2756	3.4874
15°	.2588	.9659	.2679	45°	.7071	.7071	1.0000	75°	.9659	.2588	3.7321
16°	.2756	.9613	.2867	46°	.7193	.6947	1.0355	76°	.9703	.2419	4.0108
17°	.2924	.9563	.3057	47°	.7314	.6820	1.0724	77°	.9744	.2250	4.3315
18°	.3090	.9511	.3249	48°	.7431	.6691	1.1106	78°	.9781	.2079	4.7046
19°	.3256	.9455	.3443	49°	.7547	.6561	1.1504	79°	.9816	.1908	5.1446
20°	.3420	.9397	.3640	50°	.7660	.6428	1.1918	80°	.9848	.1736	5.6713
21°	.3584	.9336	.3839	51°	.7771	.6293	1.2349	81°	.9877	.1564	6.3138
22°	.3746	.9272	.4040	52°	.7880	.6157	1.2799	82°	.9903	.1392	7.1154
23°	.3907	.9205	.4245	53°	.7986	.6018	1.3270	83°	.9925	.1219	8.1443
24°	.4067	.9135	.4452	54°	.8090	.5878	1.3764	84°	.9945	.1045	9.5144
25°	.4226	.9063	.4663	55°	.8192	.5736	1.4281	85°	.9962	.0872	11.4301
26°	.4384	.8988	.4877	56°	.8290	.5592	1.4826	86°	.9976	.0698	14.3007
27°	.4540	.8910	.5095	57°	.8387	.5446	1.5399	87°	.9986	.0523	19.0811
28°	.4695	.8829	.5317	58°	.8480	.5299	1.6003	88°	.9994	.0349	28.6363
29°	.4848	.8746	.5543	59°	.8572	.5150	1.6643	89°	.9998	.0175	57.2900
30°	.5000	.8660	.5774	60°	.8660	.5000	1.7321	90°	1.0000	.0000	

RULE FOR READING A TABLE

- Solve for one of the trigonometric functions.
- Locate the function in the appropriate column of a table of trigonometric functions.
- Read the degree equivalent to the closest value of the function.

NOTE: Where a larger table is used, the reading of the angle may be in degrees and minutes.

EXAMPLE: Find the two acute angles in triangle ABC whose sides are 3″, 4″, and 5″.

A, 5″, 4″, C, B, 3″

Step 1 Determine the value of the functions sin C and sin A.

$\sin C = \frac{4}{5} = .8000$

$\sin A = \frac{3}{5} = .6000$

Step 2 Find the angle closest to .8000 in the sine column of a table of trigonometric functions.

$\sin 53° = .7986$

Step 3 Repeat the step for the .6000 value.

$\sin 37° = .6018$

Step 4 Check to see that the complementary angles equal 90°.

$\angle C = 53°$
$\angle A = \underline{37°}$
Check $90°$

C. INTERPOLATION OF TABLES OF TRIGONOMETRIC FUNCTIONS

Angles that are given in degrees or trigonometric ratios of whole degrees may be read directly on all tables of trigonometric functions. The longer tables make it possible to read degrees and minutes directly from the table.

When such tables are not available, or when degrees, minutes, and seconds are needed and direct values are not accessible in table form, the values are *interpolated. Interpolation* is the process of finding an exact value between two consecutive values in a series. For instance, if the sine of an angle of 45° 30′ 25″ is needed, and a table is available reading in minutes, the desired reading falls between sin 45° 30′ and sin 45° 31′. To be exact, the numerical value is 25/60 of the difference between 30′ and 31′ more than the sin 45° 30′ value.

RULE FOR INTERPOLATING TABLES OF TRIGONOMETRIC FUNCTIONS

- Find the numerical difference in a table of trigonometric functions between the function of the given number of minutes and the next larger number.
- Place the given number of seconds over 60.
- Multiply the numerical difference by the fraction.

1. *Sine, Tangent, and Secant Functions*

- Add the product to the function of the given number of minutes.

  The sum is the value of the sine, tangent, or secant function of an angle in degrees, minutes, and seconds.

2. *Cosine, Cotangent, and Cosecant*

- Subtract the product from the function of the given number of minutes.

  The difference is the value of the cosine, cotangent, and cosecant functions.

EXAMPLE: Determine the sine value of angle A.

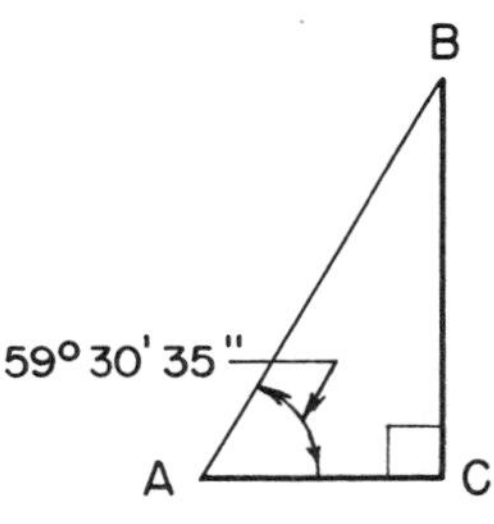

Step 1	Locate two numbers in the sine column of a table of trigonometric functions, one 1′ smaller and one 1′ larger.	sin 59°31′ = .86178 sin 59°30′ = .86163 Difference = .00015
Step 2	Subtract. Then take 35/60 of the difference (.00015).	35/60 (.00015) =
Step 3	Add the difference to the function of the smaller angle. The sum .86172 is the numerical value of the sin 59 ° 30′ 35″. NOTE: If the value of the function is decreasing, subtract rather than add the computed amount.	.00009 + .86163 .86172

ASSIGNMENT UNIT 79

A. CONSTRUCTION AND MEASUREMENT OF TRIGONOMETRIC FUNCTIONS

1. Find sin A by constructing the given angle, measuring the given distance on the hypotenuse, dropping and measuring a perpendicular, and apply the sine ratio.

Angle	Length of Hypotenuse
30°	4″
60°	2 1/2″
29 1/2°	3 1/4″

2. Find by construction each angle whose sin value is given in the table.

Value of Sine (Angle D)			
.5000	.8660	.4226	.6947

B. READING AND INTERPOLATING TABLES OF TRIGONOMETRIC FUNCTIONS

1. Find dimensions A and B correct to three decimal places. Solve by using trigonometric ratios and a table of trigonometric functions.

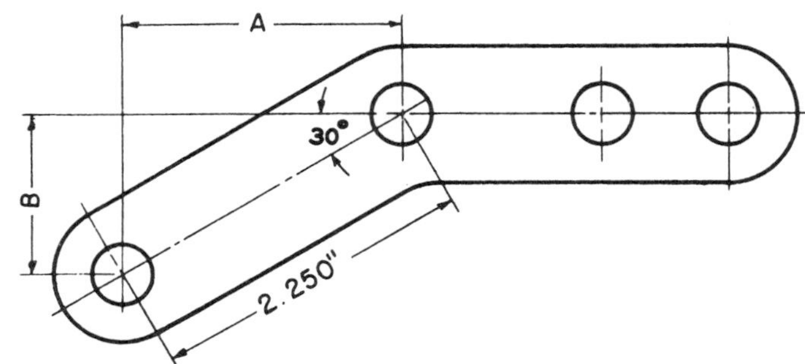

Ans: B = 1.125″

2. Determine each missing dimension in the table. Use trigonometric ratios and a table of trigonometric functions. Round off linear dimensions to three places and each angular dimension to degrees, minutes, and/or seconds as the case may be.

Triangle	Angles			Sides		
ABC	A	B	C	a	b	c
	45°	90°		1.414		1.414
DEF	D	E	F	d	e	f
	90°	30°			2.500	
XYZ	X	Y	Z	x	y	z
			90°	1.420		4.280

Ans.: b = 2″ ∡F = 60° Y = 4.038″

3. Compute the value of the included angle for the tapered cylinder. Round off the angle to the nearest minute.

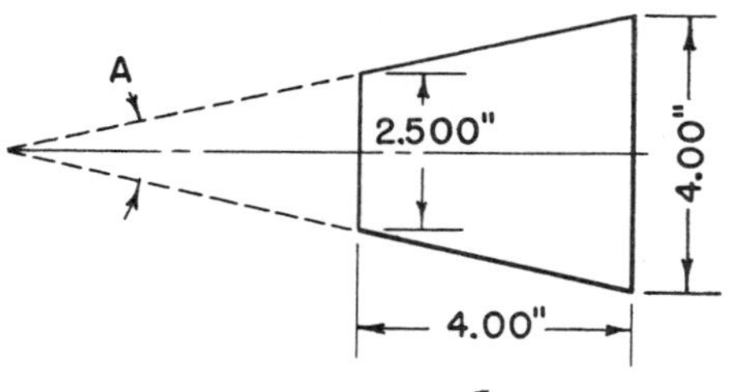

4. Compute the power output of the electrical circuit to a two decimal place accuracy.

   E = 208 volts
   I = 8.25 amperes

   Ans.: W = 1486.06 watts

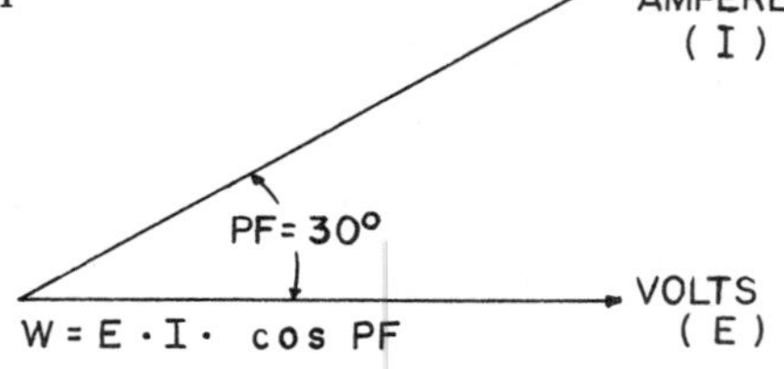

5. Solve for angle A of the cowl cover.

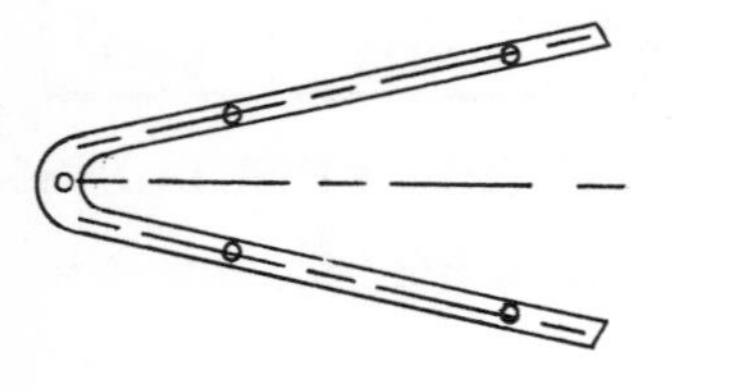

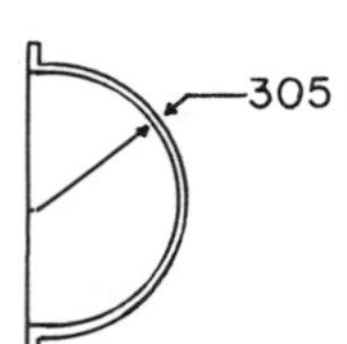

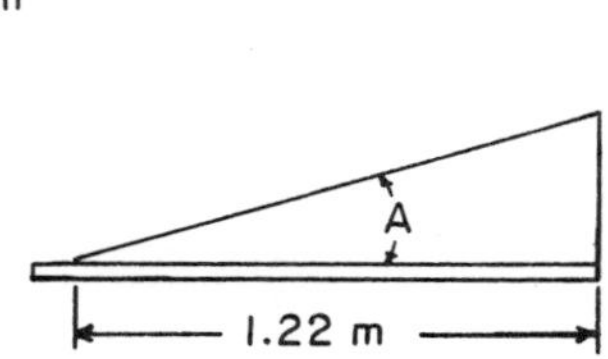

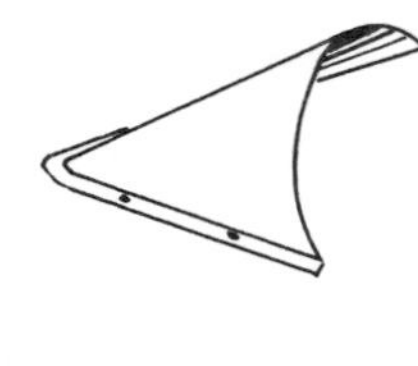

Unit 80 ACUTE TRIANGLES

The sides or angles of isosceles and equilateral triangles may be computed by right triangle trigonometry. In these triangles, a perpendicular is erected to form two right triangles. The ratios which apply to sides and angles are used to solve problems for a missing angle or dimension.

A. APPLICATION OF TRIGONOMETRIC RATIOS TO EQUILATERAL TRIANGLES

By definition, the equilateral triangle has three equal sides and three equal angles. Thus, if the total of all angles in a triangle is 180°, each angle equals 60°. The altitude of an equilateral triangle divides it into two congruent triangles having angles of 30°, 60°, and 90°.

RULE FOR FINDING THE SIDES OF EQUILATERAL TRIANGLES
(Given the Altitude)

- Sketch an equilateral triangle. Label the sides and angles.
- Drop a perpendicular from the vertex to the base for the altitude. Thus, two triangles are formed having angles of 30°, 60°, and 90°.
- Substitute the given value of the altitude as the side opposite the 60° angle.
- Determine the value of sin 60° in a table of trigonometric functions. Then substitute the value in the sine ratio.
- Use a letter to represent the hypotenuse as the missing side and solve the equation for the hypotenuse.

EXAMPLE: The altitude of an equilateral triangle is 20 inches. What is the length of each side?

Step 1 Sketch an equilateral triangle and label the sides, angles, and altitude.

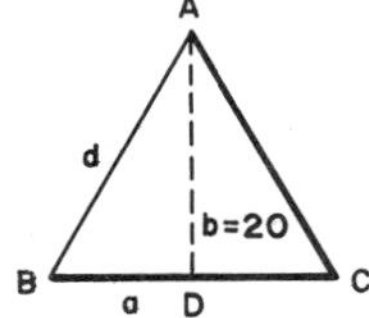

Step 2 Write the sine ratio.

$$\sin B = \frac{\text{side opposite}}{\text{hypotenuse}} = \frac{b}{d}$$

Step 3 Substitute known values in the equation.

$$\sin 60° = \frac{20}{d}$$

Step 4 Determine the value of sin 60° in a table of natural trigonometric functions. Then substitute this value in the equation.

$$\sin 60° = 0.8660$$

$$.866 = \frac{20}{d}$$

Step 5 Solve the equation. The value of (d) is the length of the hypotenuse.

$$d = 23.09''$$

B. APPLICATION OF TRIGONOMETRIC RATIOS TO ISOSCELES TRIANGLES

The isosceles triangle has two equal sides and two equal angles. Like the equilateral triangle, the value of any side or angle may be found by erecting a perpendicular and applying any one of the six trigonometric ratios. The perpendicular divides the triangle into two congruent triangles.

RULE FOR COMPUTING SIDES OR ANGLES OF ISOSCELES TRIANGLES

- Make a rough sketch of the triangle.
- Erect a perpendicular to the base from the vertex. The perpendicular divides the triangle into two congruent right triangles.
- Determine what the known values are and which of the six trigonometric ratios is easiest to apply.
- Substitute the given values in the selected ratio.

  NOTE: When either the vertex angle and/or the angle opposite the altitude is given, locate the numerical value in a table of trigonometric functions. Then, substitute this value in the ratio.
- Solve the missing value. Where an angle is to be computed, determine the number of degrees by locating the ratio in a table of trigonometric functions.

EXAMPLE: Find the number of degrees in angle B when line A-A_1 is parallel to B-C and angle B = angle C.

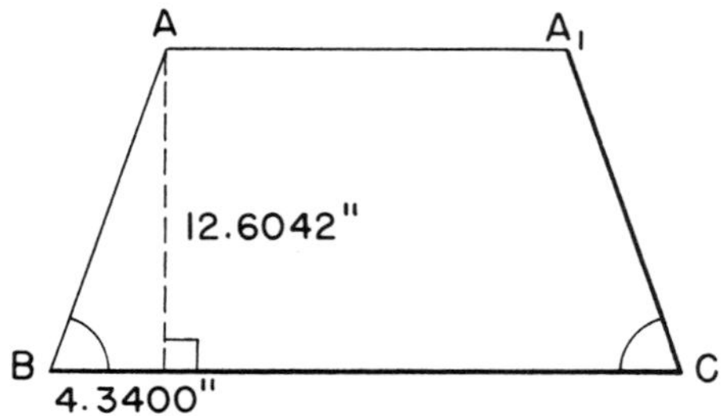

Step 1 Make a sketch of the isosceles triangle and label the given parts.

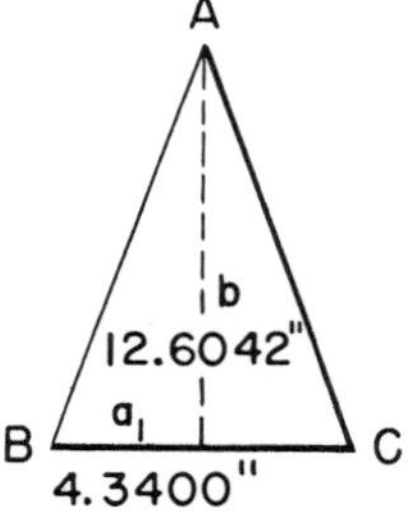

Step 2 Determine which trigonometry ratios may be used.

Step 3 Substitute the known value of the altitude (b = 12.6042") and side adjacent (a_1 = 4.3400") in the equation.

Step 4 Determine from a table of trigonometric functions how many degrees are in an angle whose tangent is 2.9042. The table gives 71° as the angle.

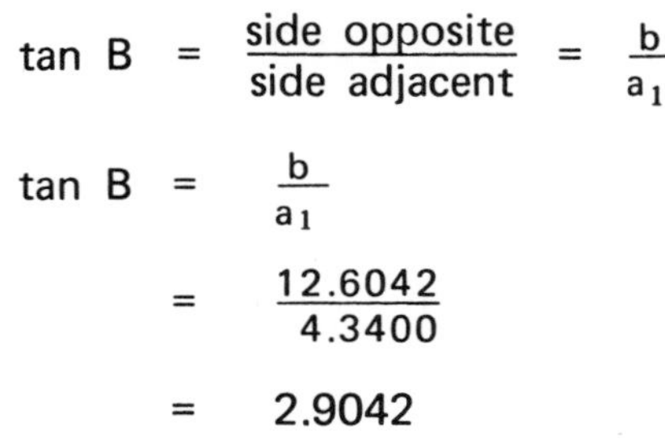

$$\tan B = \frac{\text{side opposite}}{\text{side adjacent}} = \frac{b}{a_1}$$

$$\tan B = \frac{b}{a_1} = \frac{12.6042}{4.3400} = 2.9042$$

$$\measuredangle B = 71°$$

In a similar manner, by selecting one of the six trigonometric ratios it is possible to determine the values of the other angles or sides.

ASSIGNMENT UNIT 80

A. APPLICATION OF TRIGONOMETRIC RATIOS TO EQUILATERAL TRIANGLES

1. Find dimensions O and altitude A for the plate illustrated.

   Ans.: A = 2.3815″

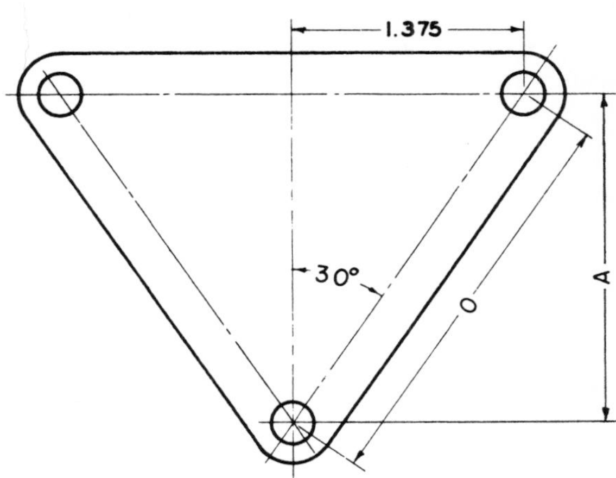

2. Compute the depth of a National Form (60°) screw thread according to the dimensions given on the drawing.

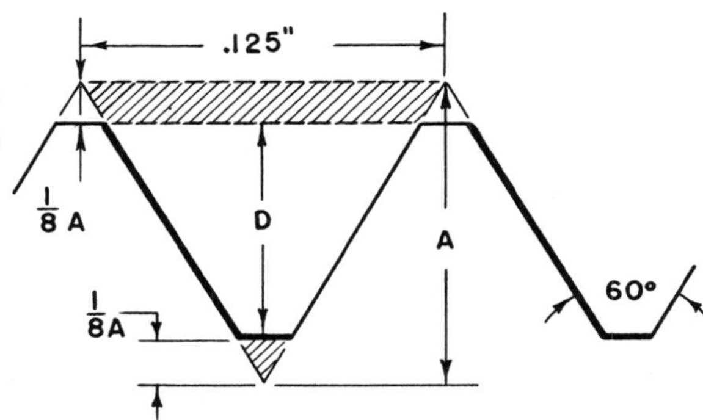

3. Calculate the following dimensions of the cylindrical shell.

   a. Height of cone
   b. Volume of cone
   c. Overall length

   Round off each dimension to two decimal places.

   Ans.: b. $V_c = 12.47\ m^3$

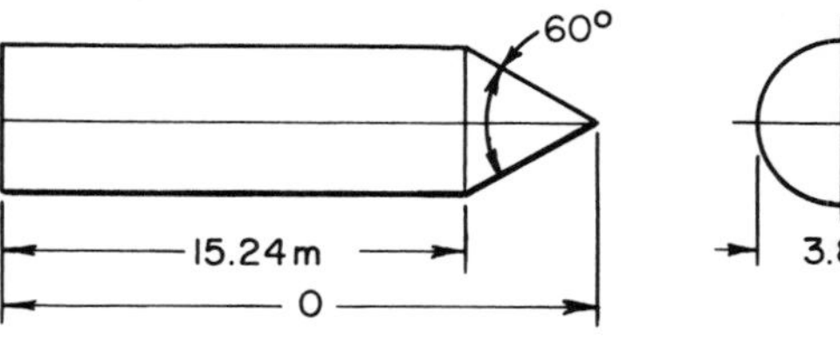

B. APPLICATION OF TRIGONOMETRIC RATIOS TO ISOSCELES TRIANGLES

1. Determine the length of the chord for two consecutive end points on a bolt circle 4 3/8-inches in diameter on which the centers of 14 holes are to be laid out.

2. Find the length of the perpendicular from the center to the chord connecting two consecutive centers.

   Ans.: 2.1326″

Unit 81 OBLIQUE TRIANGLES

Oblique triangles may be solved by drawing perpendiculars to make right triangles and using any combination of the six basic ratios of sides and angles. However, such a practice is time-consuming and there are easier ways to solve such problems. Two new laws, the Sine Law and the Cosine Law, simplify the solution of measurements of sides and angles in oblique triangles.

A. THE LAW OF SINES

The *Law of Sines* is a short way of saying that the sides of any triangle are proportional to the sines of the opposite angles. For instance, in triangle ABC, the acute angles are A and B; the altitude, h, and the sides, a, b, and c. In triangle ADC,

$$\sin \angle A = \frac{\text{side opposite}}{\text{hypotenuse}} = \frac{h}{b}$$

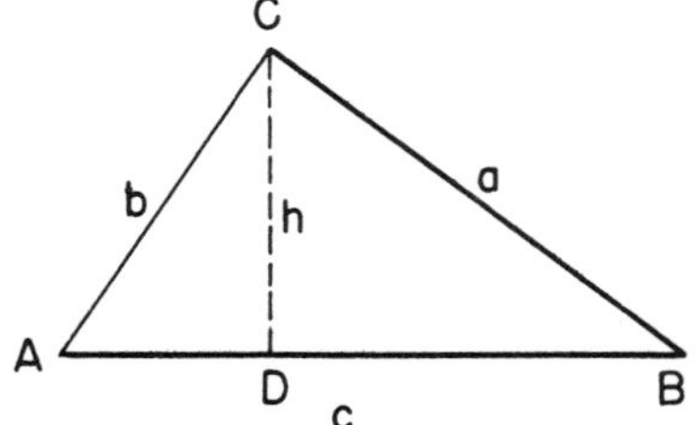

In triangle BCD,

$$\sin \angle B = \frac{\text{side opposite}}{\text{hypotenuse}} = \frac{h}{a}$$

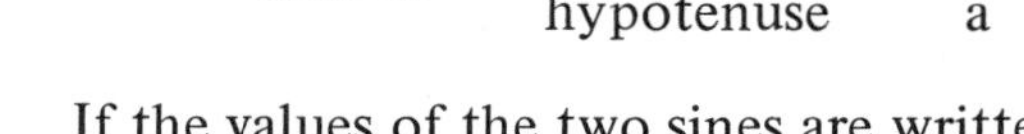

If the values of the two sines are written as a proportion, then

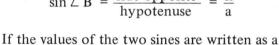

$$\sin A : \sin B = \frac{h}{b} : \frac{h}{a} \quad \text{or} \quad \frac{\sin A}{\sin B} = \frac{\frac{h}{b}}{\frac{h}{a}} = \frac{a}{b}$$

In a like manner, the relationship of any two sides is the same as that of the angles opposite the two sides. In the statement of such a relationship, there are four members. If three of these are known, the fourth may be found.

B. THE LAW OF COSINES

If, in setting up a proportion by the law of sines, two of the members are unknown, this law cannot be immediately applied. In such cases, the *Law of Cosines* can be used. This law states that in any triangle the square of any side is equal to the sum of the squares of the other sides minus twice the product of the two sides and the cosine of their included angle.

Hence, $a^2 = b^2 + c^2 - 2\,(bc \cos A)$ $\qquad$ $b^2 = a^2 + c^2 - 2\,(ac \cos B)$

$$c^2 = a^2 + b^2 - 2\,(ab \cos C)$$

Transposing these equations, the cosine values become:

$$\cos A = \frac{b^2 + c^2 - a^2}{2\,bc} \qquad \cos B = \frac{a^2 + c^2 - b^2}{2\,ac}$$

$$\cos C = \frac{a^2 + b^2 - c^2}{2\,ab}$$

C. APPLYING THE LAWS OF SINES AND COSINES

Problems in oblique triangles involve four types, depending on the data given:

Type I Any two angles and any one side are given.

Type II Any two sides and the angle opposite one of the sides are given.

Type III Any two sides and the included angle are given.

Type IV The three sides are given.

On Type I and Type II, the Law of Sines can be applied immediately. On Type III and Type IV, the Law of Cosines must be applied first. When the additional data is found, the Law of Sines can be used to complete the problem.

Type I

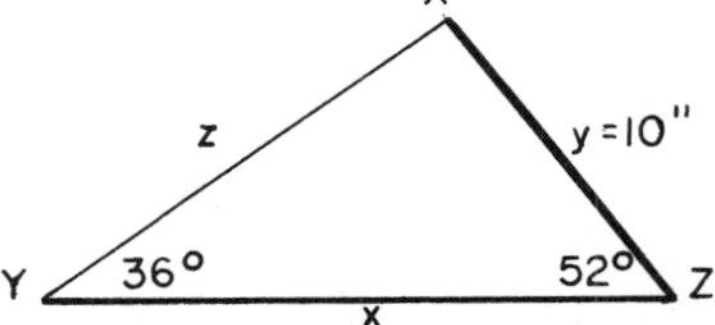

EXAMPLE: Find the missing sides and the third angle in triangle XYZ.

Step 1 The third angle can be found by using the fact that the sum of the angles of any triangle is 180°.

$$180° - (36° + 52°) = 92°$$

Step 2 Apply the Law of Sines.

$$\frac{\sin Y}{\sin Z} = \frac{y}{z} \qquad \frac{\sin 36°}{\sin 52°} = \frac{10}{z} \qquad \frac{.5878}{.7880} = \frac{10}{z} \qquad z = 13.4''$$

Also,

$$\frac{\sin X}{\sin Y} = \frac{x}{y} \qquad \frac{\sin 92°}{\sin 36°} = \frac{x}{10} \qquad \frac{.9994}{.5878} = \frac{x}{10} \qquad x = 17''$$

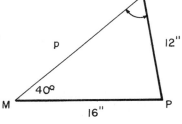

Type II

EXAMPLE: Find the missing side and the two missing angles.

Step 1 Select the sides and angle where three members will be known in the proportion.

$$\frac{\sin M}{\sin N} = \frac{12}{16} \qquad \sin 40° = .6428 \qquad \text{Therefore,} \quad \frac{.6428}{\sin N} = \frac{12}{16}$$

$N = 58° \, 59'$ (to nearest minute)

Step 2 $180° - (40° + 58° \, 59') = 81° \, 1' = \angle P$

Step 3

$$\frac{\sin M}{\sin P} = \frac{12}{p} \qquad \frac{.6428}{.9877} = \frac{12}{p} \qquad p = 18.44''$$

Type III

EXAMPLE: Find the missing side and the two missing angles.

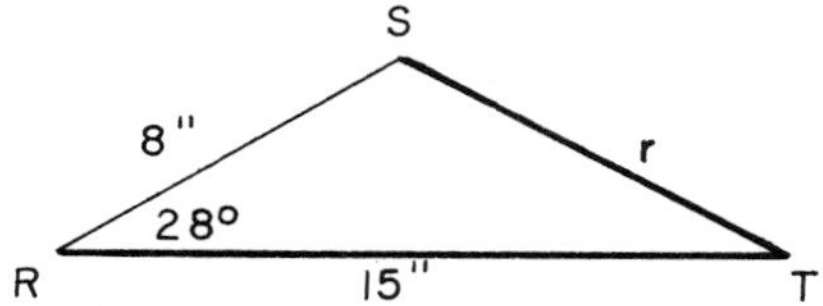

Step 1 As a proportion cannot be established in which three members are known, it is first necessary to apply the Law of Cosines.

$$r^2 = t^2 + s^2 - 2\text{ ts} \cos \angle R$$
$$r^2 = 64 + 225 - 2 \times 8 \times 15 \times .8829$$
$$r^2 = 289 - 211.896 = 77.104$$
$$r = \sqrt{77.104} = 8.781''$$

Step 2 Now apply the Law of Sines.

$$\frac{\sin 28^\circ}{\sin T} = \frac{8.781}{8}\ ;\quad \frac{.4695}{\sin\ T} = \frac{8.781}{8}\ ;\ \sin T = .4277; \angle T = 25^\circ\ 19'$$

(to nearest minute)

Step 3 $\angle S = 180^\circ - (28^\circ + 25^\circ\ 19')$

$\angle S = 126^\circ\ 41'$

Type IV

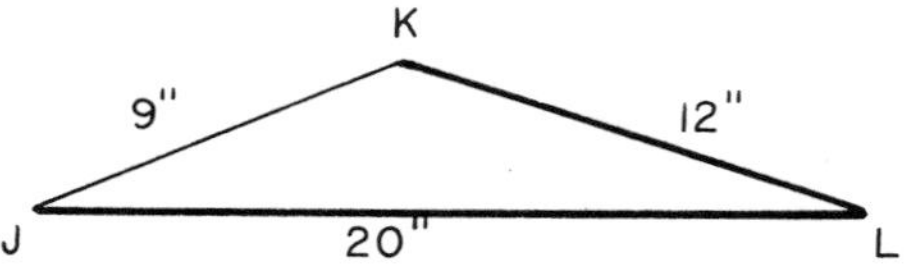

EXAMPLE: Find the three missing angles.

Step 1 Use the cosine form:

$$\cos J = \frac{l^2 + k^2 - j^2}{2\text{ lk}}$$

$$\cos J = \frac{81 + 400 - 144}{2 \times 9 \times 20}$$

$$\text{Cos } J = .9361$$

$$\angle\ J = 20^\circ\ 36' \text{ (to nearest minute)}$$

Step 2 Now, apply the Law of Sines.

$$\frac{\sin 20^\circ\ 36'}{\sin L} = \frac{12}{9}\ ;\quad \frac{.3518}{\sin L} = \frac{12}{9}\ ;\ \sin L = .2638$$

$$\angle L = 15^\circ\ 18'$$

Step 3 $\angle K = 180^\circ - (15^\circ\ 18' + 20^\circ\ 36') = 144^\circ\ 6'$

D. LAW OF SUPPLEMENTS

Problems in trigonometry are simplified by using supplements of angles. The sine or cosine of an angle between 90° and 180° is the sine or cosine of the difference between the angle and 180°. For cosines between 90° and 180°, the values are negative. When applied to the portion of the formula calling for -2ab cos C, if cos C is negative, the two negatives will make this value positive and necessitate adding it to the first part of the formula.

ASSIGNMENT UNIT 81

A. APPLICATION OF THE LAWS OF SINES AND COSINES

1. Find the missing sides and angles for the values given in the table. Round off decimal values to one place.

   Ans.: B. m = 2.867
   D. ∡O = 22° 22′

	Sides			Angles		
	m	n	o	M	N	O
A	4″		3″		100°	
B		3 1/2″	2″	55°		
C	5.6″		7.8″		61°	
D	4.2″		1.8″		95°	
E		4.6″	2.5″	57°		

2. Check the values of sides and angles of triangles A through E by first constructing the triangles and then measuring the angles with a protractor.

3. Determine the angle of slope (X) and the length (y) for the roof span as shown in drawing.

   Ans.: y = 21.6′

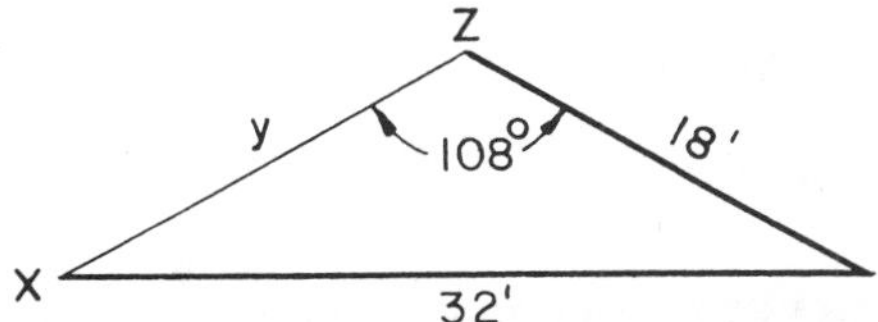

4. Find the number of degrees and minutes in all angles of triangles A through E.

   Ans.: B. ∡y = 27° 35′
   D. ∡y = 113° 45′

	Sides		
	X	Y	Z
A	5″	12″	9″
B	8 1/2″	8″	14 1/2″
C	17.6″	12.8″	8.8″
D	8.75″	12.25″	5.75″
E	9.82″	3.76″	7.54″

5. Determine angles X, Y, and Z with the Law of Cosines. Give angles correct to seconds.

   Ans.: ∡y = 118° 3′ 16″

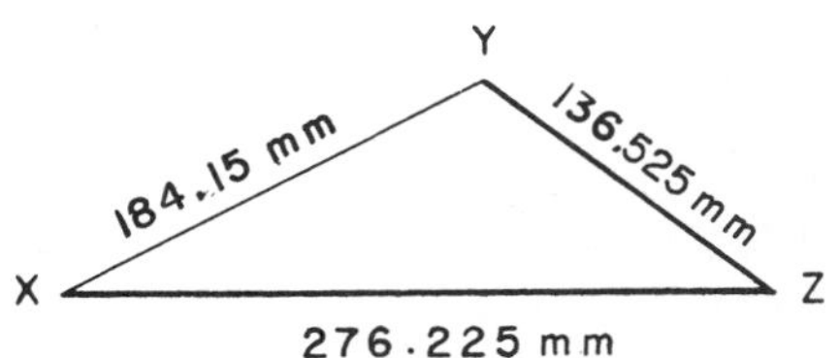

6. Find angles A, B, and C correct to minutes.

   Ans.: ∡ B = 95° 46′

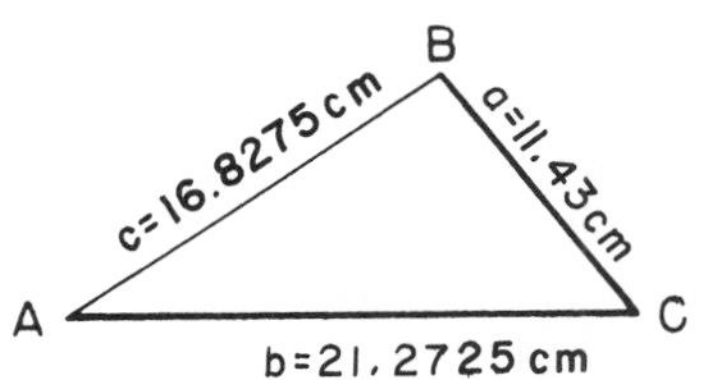

Unit 82 ACHIEVEMENT REVIEW ON APPLIED TRIGONOMETRY

A. THE CONCEPT OF RIGHT TRIANGLE TRIGONOMETRY

1. Sketch and label the sides and angles for the three right triangles given in the table.

Right Triangles	Sides			Angles			Trigonometric Function
ABC	a	b	c	A	B	C	$\frac{\text{side opposite}}{\text{hypotenuse}}$ = ____ A
LMN	l	m	n	L	M	N	$\frac{\text{side adjacent}}{\text{side opposite}}$ = ____ L
ZXY	z	x	y	Z	X	Y	$\frac{\text{side adjacent}}{\text{hypotenuse}}$ = ____ Y

2. Indicate the trigonometric function which each ratio of sides represents in the table.
3. Write each equation in the table using the letters for the sides as indicated in each case.

B. APPLICATION OF TABLES OF TRIGONOMETRIC FUNCTIONS

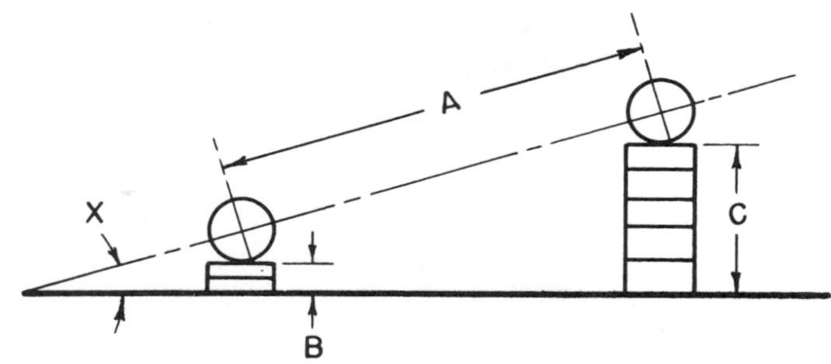

1. Determine either the height of gage blocks B or C, or angle X, whichever dimension is missing in the table. Give dimension B and C to the nearest ten-thousandth; angle X, to the nearest second.

Sine Bar Length A (inches)	Heights of Blocks (in.) B	Heights of Blocks (in.) C	Angle X
5.0000	1.2500	3.5000	
5.0000	1.0000	2.9375	
10.0000		4.3125	14° 30′
10.0000	1.5000		29° 1′ 30″

C. APPLICATION OF ACUTE TRIANGLES

1. Determine the distance across flats on hexagons inscribed in circles having diameters of 1 inch, 1 1/2 inches, 2 inches, and 3 inches.

2. Find chordal distance C, included angle A and distance H for the three circles given in the table.

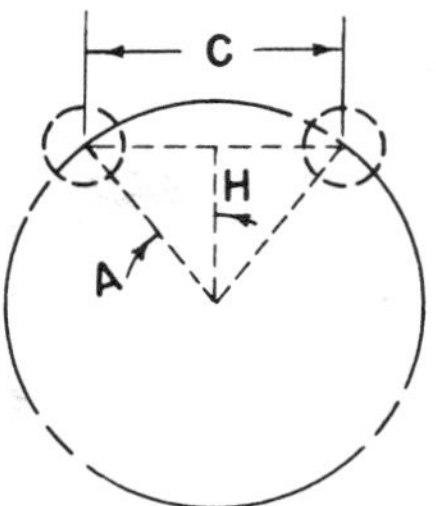

Diameter of Pitch Circle	No. of Holes on Pitch Circle
4″	6
3 1/2″	7
6.250″	5

D. APPLICATION OF OBLIQUE TRIANGLES

1. Find the missing sides and angles of the triangles that are given in the table, using the Law of Sines. Dimensions for sides are to be rounded off to two decimal places; dimensions of angles, to the nearest minute.

Triangle	Angles			Sides		
ABC	A	B	C	a	b	c
	45°		30°	12″		
DEF	D	E	F	d	e	f
		100°	60°		10 1/2″	
KLM	K	L	M	k	l	m
	29 1/2°	112 1/2°			20″	
XYZ	X	Y	Z	x	y	z
	59°30′		14°30′			12.50″

2. Determine the angle of slope (X) for the three roof spans indicated in the table. Use either the customary or the metric units.

S	32′ / 9.754 m	24′ / 7.315 m	36′ / 10.973 m
R	24′ / 7.315 m	16′-8″ / 5.08 m	22′ / 6.706 m

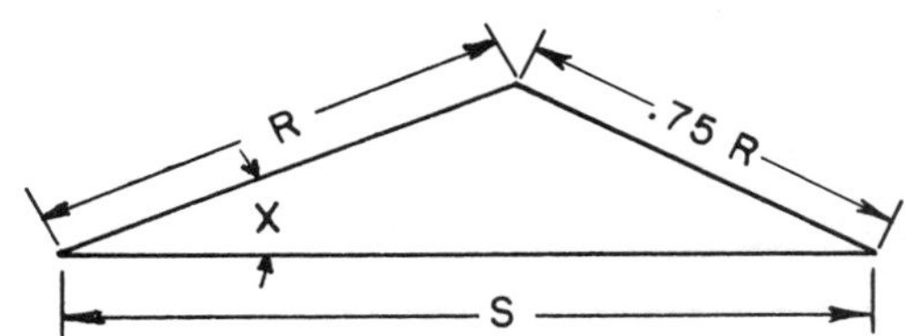

Section 18

THE SLIDE RULE

Unit 83 THE CONCEPT OF THE SLIDE RULE

The slide rule is a practical mechanical instrument which is used by craftspersons, technicians, and others to simplify the solution of many cumbersome and lengthy multiplication and division problems. The instrument uses what are called "logarithms" to change the mathematical processes of multiplication and division to simple addition and subtraction.

The slide rule is commonly used to:

1. multiply two or more numbers, or divide one number by another,
2. convert values from one unit of measurement to another,
3. square or cube a number, or find a number whose logarithm is unknown,
4. determine the logarithm of a number, or find a number whose logarithm is known,
5. calculate the sine, cosine or tangent of an angle, or to locate an angle whose sine, cosine or tangent is known, and
6. perform various combinations of these processes.

Two significant statements must be made regarding accuracy. First, the accuracy of the answer depends on care in making each setting and in taking readings on the slide rule. Second, the answer obtained by using the slide rule may not be an absolute one. Rather, the answer may be an extremely close approximation. The reasons become more apparent as slide rule settings are made and answers are read.

A. LOGARITHMS ARE FOUNDATIONAL TO SLIDE RULE USE

Numbers that are similar may be multiplied or divided by simply adding or subtracting their exponents. These same mathematical processes may be carried on with logarithms if the numbers are expressed in "powers of ten." Tables have been prepared by the use of higher mathematics, in which the value of any number may be expressed as a power of ten. Several examples taken from a four-decimal place logarithm table follow. The number 1 may be expressed as 10 to the 0.0000 power ($10^{0.0000}$) or the logarithm (log) of 1 = 0.0000. The log of 3 is 0.4771; the log of 6 is 0.7782; the log of 9 is 0.9542, and the log of 10 = 1.000.

Any real number from 1 to 10 has a log value between 0 and 1. The log of the real number 10 has a value of 1; 100, a value of 2; 1000, a value of 3. The intermediate real values fall between the log values. Logs are artificial, consistent, related values that may be substituted for real numbers.

Two simple examples are given to show how the use of logarithmic values simplify the processes of multiplication and division. For instance, if the real numbers of 10 and 100 are to be multiplied, all that needs to be done is to add the logarithmic values (10 = 1, 100 = 2). The real value of the log 3 is 1000.

On the other hand, if 100 is to be divided by 10, the log of the divisor 10 (= 1) is subtracted from the log of the dividend 100 (= 2). The log value 1 equals the real number 10. While these simple examples could have been done mentally, other more difficult problems involving complex real numbers may be solved just as easily by using logarithms and the slide rule. This brief explanation of logarithms is now related to the part they play in solving mathematical problems with the slide rule.

B. THE DEVELOPMENT OF SLIDE RULE GRADUATIONS AND SCALES

All slide rules consist of three basic parts: a stator, a sliding scale, and an indicator. The stator (stationary part) has a top bar and a bottom bar. Each bar has a series of graduated lines which comprise what are called scales. The slide also has graduations. The simple slide rule that is illustrated has four scales (A, B, C, and D). The A scale of the top bar has identical graduations to scale B. It can be seen, too, that the graduations on the C and D scales are identical. The indicator is movable along the stator and helps to align certain graduations when setting the instrument or reading an answer. There is a hairline on the indicator to assure greater accuracy. The C and D scales are used to demonstrate the system of reading all scales.

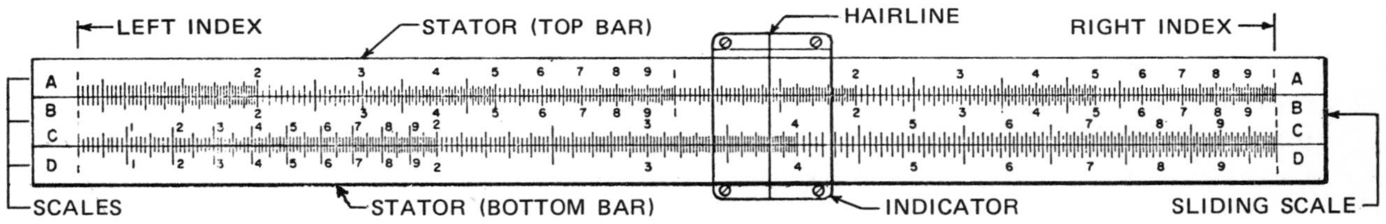

GRADUATIONS PROPORTIONATE TO LOGARITHMIC VALUES

Handling a slide rule should help explain two things to the student at this point. First, the slide rule scales are logarithmic. This means the distance between the graduations representing whole numbers is not uniform or proportionate to their real number values. Instead, the distances are proportionate to their log values.

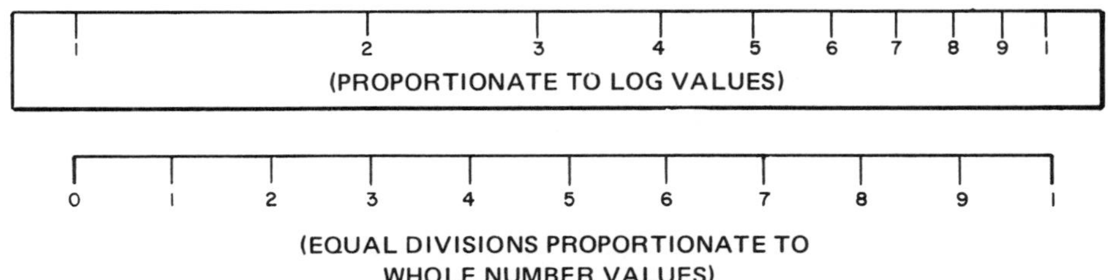

This is understandable if the slide rule is visualized as being divided into 1000 equal parts. The real number 2 would be located at the 301 graduation because this is the logarithmic value of 2; the real number 3, at graduation 477; 4 at 602; 5 at 699; 6 at 778; 7 at 845; 8 at 903; 9 at 945; and 10 at 1000. The real numbers 1 and 2 have log values which are spaced farther apart than 6 and 7 or 9 and 10.

C. PRIMARY, SECONDARY, AND TERTIARY DIVISIONS ON SCALES

Aside from the fact that the distances are proportionate to logarithmic values, there is also a variation in the number of graduations between the whole numbers from one end of the scale (1) to the other (1).

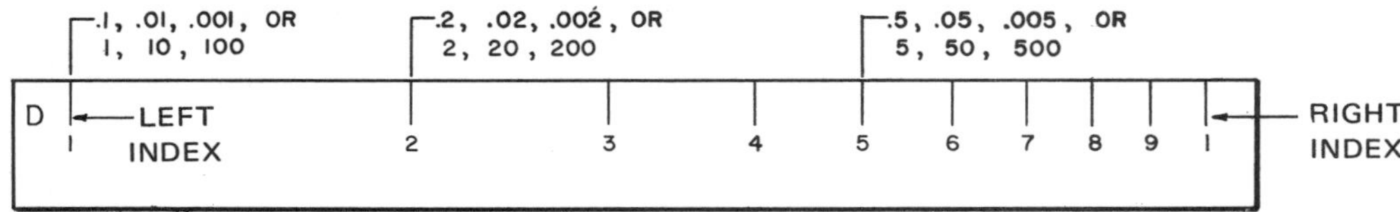

The C and D scales consist of ten primary divisions. These primary (main) divisions are numbered 1, 2, 3, 4, 5, 6, 7, 8, 9, and 1. The division representing 1 on the left is called the *left index*. The last graduation (1) on the right end of the scale is the *right index*. The ten numbered divisions may be used to represent many quantities. These may be whole numbers, decimals, or combinations of whole numbers and decimal values. For instance, either the first or last number 1 may represent .1, .01, .001, 1, 10, 100, 1000. Similarly, the graduation 3 may represent .3, .03, .003, 3, 30, 300, or 3000.

The spaces between the main divisions of 1 and 2 are further subdivided into ten spaces (tenths). Again, these are proportionate logarithmically and decrease in width from 1 to 2. These ten numbered spaces are called secondary divisions. These secondary divisions between 1 and 2 are divided again into ten spaces which represent tertiary divisions.

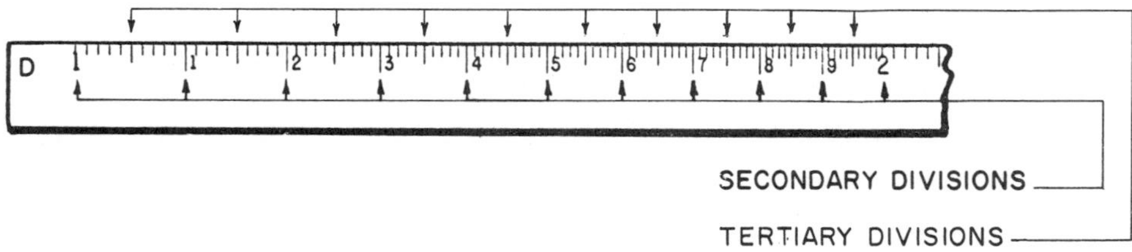

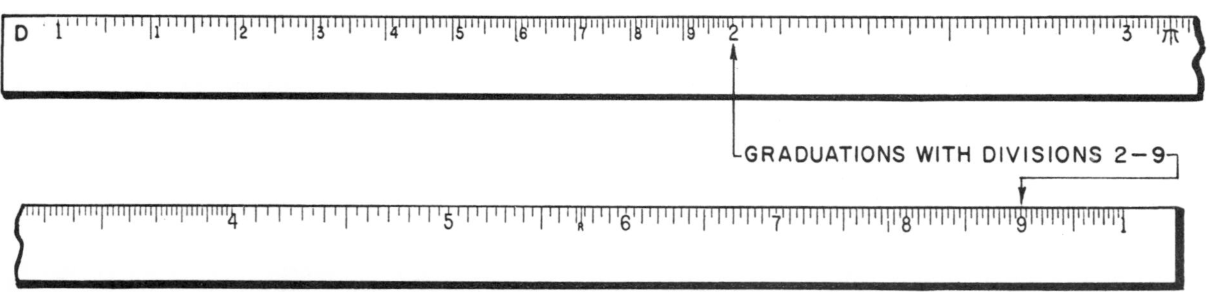

D. EXAMPLE OF SETTINGS OR READINGS

Four different line drawings are used to show various settings or readings on the D scale. The first drawing relates to settings that fall on the primary divisions. The further subdividing of the distance between 1 and 2 indicates that each subdivision is equal to 10. Between 2 and 4, the value of each subdivision equals 20. From 4 through 9 (1) each subdivision is equal to 50.

EXAMPLES OF PRIMARY DIVISION READINGS

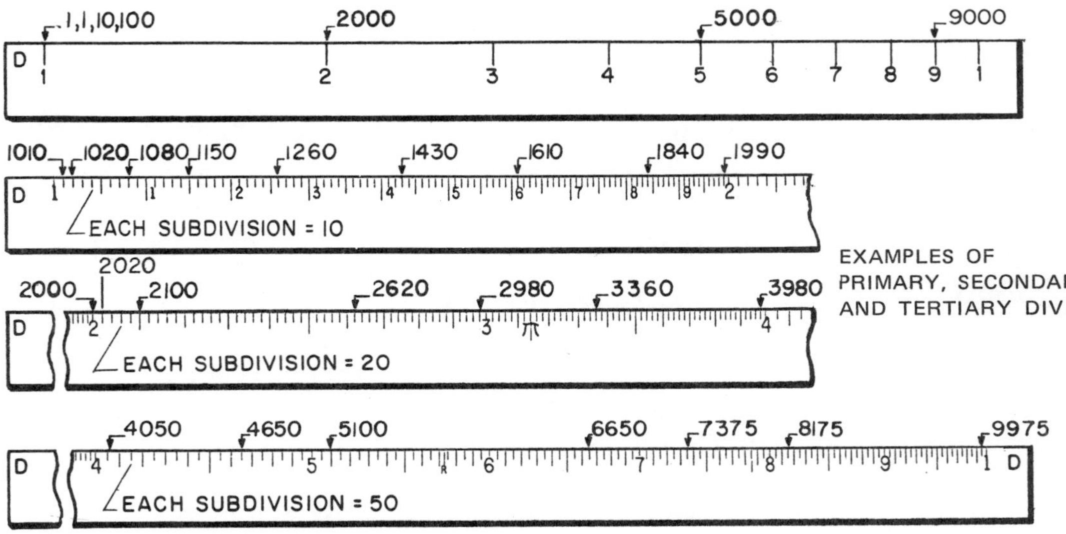

EXAMPLES OF PRIMARY, SECONDARY, AND TERTIARY DIVISIONS

E. SETTING AND READING VALUES ON THE SLIDE RULE

RULE FOR SETTING OR READING VALUES ON THE SLIDE RULE

- Determine the first numeral in the number that is not zero. This is the first significant figure.
- Locate the significant figure between the two primary divisions on the D scale to correspond with its value.
- Locate the second digit of the number on the appropriate secondary graduation.
- Locate the third digit of the number at the tertiary graduation.
- Locate any fourth digit number by estimating the distance between the last tertiary value and the next higher value.

NOTE: The last graduation or place on the scale indicates the setting for the original number. The indicator is used to locate and hold this position until the next number involved in the problem is located on another scale. Numbers with more than four digits may be rounded off to the fourth digit and set to the fourth place as the error in the final answer will be insignificant for most problems.

EXAMPLE: Locate the logarithmic value of 1865 on the D scale.

Step 1 Select the first significant figure (1) and establish that the final setting will be found between primary divisions 1 and 2 which may be considered as 1000 and 2000.

Step 2 Locate the second digit number 8 on the secondary division graduation 8 (1800).

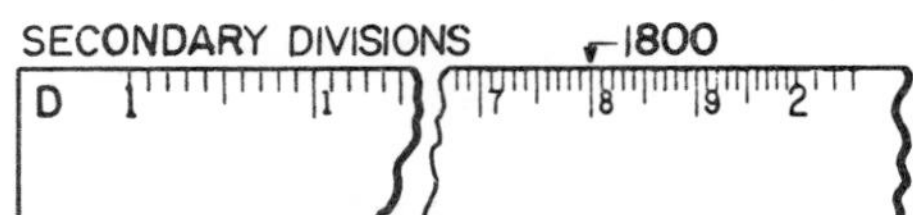

Step 3 Locate the third digit number 6 on the tertiary graduation (6) between secondary graduations 8 and 9.

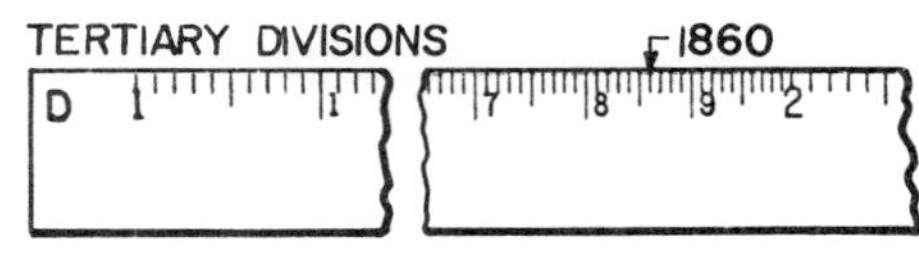

Step 4 Locate the fourth digit number 5 at the midpoint between tertiary graduations 6 and 7 (consider as 1865).

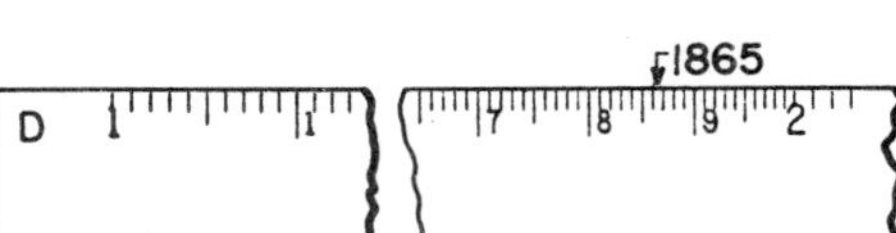

Step 5 Set the hairline of the indicator over this last position to indicate a setting of 1865.

Step 6 Recheck steps 1 through 5, particularly the last one where an approximation of a half division was made. Then, proceed with other processes.

All mathematical processes performed with the slide rule depend on accuracy in setting and reading primary, secondary, and tertiary graduations on the scales of the stator and the sliding scale. The problems which follow provide practice in developing facility to make accurate settings.

ASSIGNMENT UNIT 83

A. SLIDE RULE READINGS

1. Determine slide rule settings A-Z as illustrated on the D scale graduations of the stator.

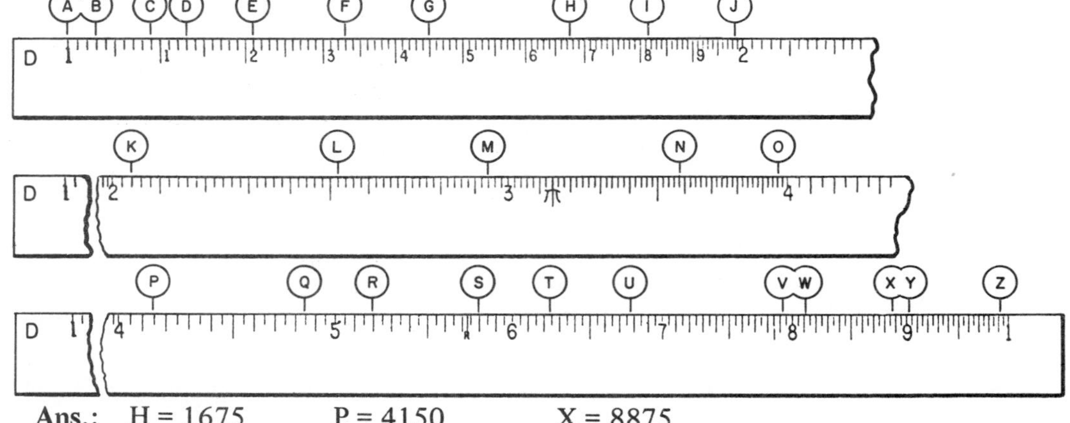

Ans.: H = 1675 P = 4150 X = 8875

B. SLIDE RULE SETTINGS ON THE D SCALE (STATOR)

1. Place the hairline of the indicator over the settings on the D scale for each value given in the table (A through X).

   NOTE: The sliding scale may be removed from the slide rule to avoid confusion in reading and setting the graduations.

Setting	Value	Setting	Value	Setting	Value	Setting	Value	Setting	Value	Setting	Value
A	1	E	11	I	31	M	615	Q	9375	U	3950
B	2	F	14	J	400	N	725	R	9925	V	2975
C	5	G	18	K	450	O	7750	S	950	W	1890
D	9	H	20	L	550	P	8125	T	825	X	1965

C. SLIDE RULE SETTINGS OF D AND C SCALES

NOTE: Replace the sliding scale, if necessary.

1. Place the left index over each graduation for the D scale readings given in the table for settings A through H; right index for I through N.
2. Locate the indicator hairline in each case (A through N) on the graduation which represents the C scale setting given in the table.

Left Index	Setting	A	B	C	D	E	F	G	H
	Scale D	2	3	4	12	17	22	290	320
	Scale C	2	2	2	3	4	4	3	22
Right Index	Setting	I	J	K	L	M	N		
	Scale D	455	675	715	875	925	9750		
	Scale C	40	53	720	339	1965	1455		

Unit 84 MULTIPLICATION WITH THE SLIDE RULE

Multiplication is a mathematical shortcut for adding numbers and values that may be expressed in letters and other terms. The solution of multiplication problems is simplified further and considerable time is saved when a slide rule is used.

The knowledge of what the different graduations mean on each scale must now be advanced. An understanding must be developed of how to determine the number of digits in an answer, the location of a decimal point (when decimals are required), and the rules and steps for multiplying two or more quantities (factors).

A. PLACING THE DECIMAL POINT AND DETERMINING THE NUMBER OF DIGITS

The placing of the decimal point and the number of digits in a final answer are obvious in many multiplication problems. However, when large, cumbersome numbers are multiplied (which contain whole and decimal parts) an accurate method must be followed to establish the number of digits in the answer. One logarithmic system requires the counting of digits and assigning a number to represent the digits in each factor.

RULE FOR DIGIT COUNTING IN MULTIPLICATION

- Assign a positive (+) digit count for each digit to the left of the decimal point for all numbers that are greater than 1.
- Assign a digit count of zero (0) for all numbers that are less than 1 (falling between .1 and 1).
- Assign a negative (–) digit count for decimal values by adding a – 1 for each zero after the decimal point and before the first number.

EXAMPLES: The table gives the digit count and rule for eight different factors.

	Factors	Digit Count	Rule
1	12,676.	+5	• Assign a + digit count for each digit to the left of the decimal point for all numbers that are greater than 1.
2	9,987.1	+4	
3	105.85	+3	
4	9.07	+1	
5	.163	0	• Assign a digit count of 0 for numbers between .1 and 1.
6	.099	-1	• Assign a -1 digit count for each zero after the decimal point.
7	.00329	-2	
8	.0000067	-5	

RULE FOR DETERMINING THE NUMBER OF DIGITS IN THE PRODUCT

Case 1 Estimating for simple number combinations

- Round off the numbers in each factor.
- Perform the multiplication processes mentally.
- Estimate the answer and compare this with the number of digits in the slide rule product.
- Adjust the slide rule product to conform to the number of digits obtained by estimating.

Case 2 Scale C, using the right index for multiplying

- Add the number of digits in all of the factors.
- Compare this sum with the slide rule product. Make adjustments in the product so that it contains the same number of digits as the sum of the digits for all factors.

Case 3 Scale C, using the left index for multiplying

- Add the number of digits in all of the factors.
- Subtract 1 from the sum of the digits. The difference represents the number of digits in the slide rule product and the placement of the decimal point, if required.

B. MULTIPLYING QUANTITIES WITH THE SLIDE RULE

The D scale on the stator and the C scale on the movable slide are used for multiplication. The hairline on the indicator is invaluable in locating graduations on the scales, saving intermediate answers, and in helping to establish the final answer. The indicator may be positioned very quickly and accurately by moving it into an approximate location. Further adjustment is then made by pressing from either side with the thumbnail.

RULE FOR MULTIPLYING TWO OR MORE FACTORS

- Move the indicator until the hairline is over the graduation on the D scale which corresponds to the value of the multiplicand.
- Move the slide until one of the index lines (1) is aligned with the multiplicand and is under the indicator hairline.

  NOTE: Whether the right- or left-index line is to be used can be determined by observing if the multiplier extends beyond the D scale. When this occurs, the opposite index line should be used. The problem can only be solved by using the correct index line.
- Locate the multiplier on the C scale.
- Move the indicator hairline to position it over the multiplier.
- Determine the product by reading the primary, secondary, tertiary, and estimated intermediate values on the D scale at the point covered by the hairline.

  NOTE: If there is more than one multiplier, place the appropriate index line over the product of the first two factors. Then, proceed to locate the second multiplier on the C scale. Repeat this process until all the factors in the problem have been multiplied.

- Establish the number of digits in the answer by adding the digit count for each of the factors.
- Apply the digit count to the slide rule reading, adjusting the reading to contain the right number of digits. The result is the answer.
- Recheck each of the steps to check the answer.

EXAMPLE: Case 1 Multiplying two factors   Multiply 179 by 47

Step 1 Set the left index of the C scale over the 179 graduation on the D scale.

Step 2 Move the indicator hairline to graduation 47 on the C scale.

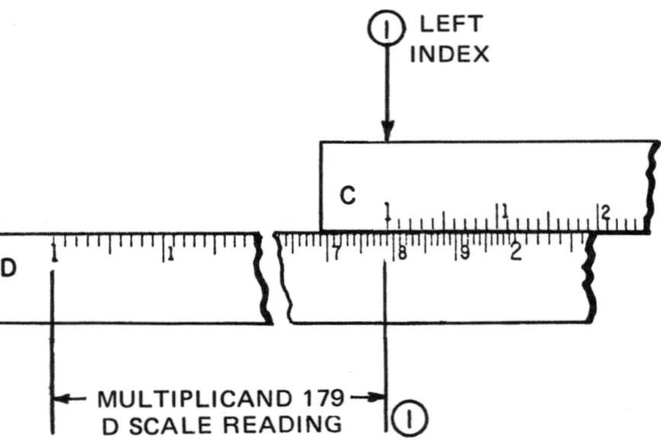

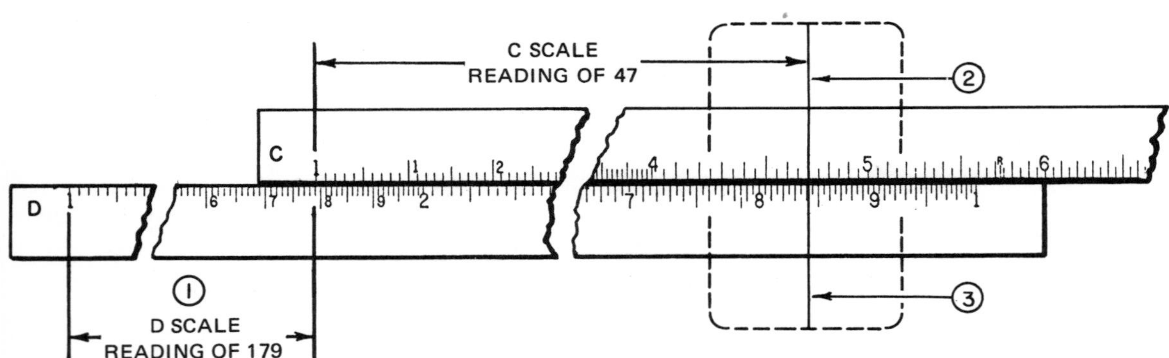

Step 3 Read the product under the indicator hairline on the D scale. 8 - 4 - 2

Step 4 Determine the digit count of both factors (+5). Since the left index was used, subtract 1.

(+5 – 1 = 4 digits in the product) (4)

179 = +3) digit
47 = +2) count
+5

Step 5 Adjust the slide rule reading (8 – 4 – 2) to obtain a four-digit product (8420).

8 - 4 - 2 reading
8420 adjusted product (5)

NOTE: The absolute product is 8413. Since many slide rule answers are close approximations, there may be slight variations between slide rule results and absolute answers.

EXAMPLE: Case 2 Multiplying more than two factors
Multiply 179 by 47 by 0.00078.

Step 1 Multiply the first two factors (179 by 47), repeating steps 1 and 2 as in case 1.

Step 2 Move the right index line until it is split by (directly under) the hairline.

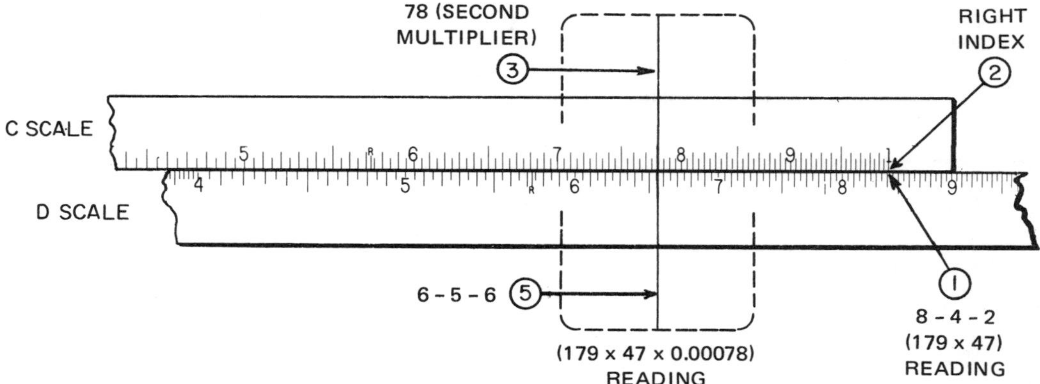

Step 3 Move the indicator to position the hairline over the 78 graduation on the C scale.

Step 4 Establish the digit count of each of the three factors by adding.

179 = +3) digit
47 = +2) count
0.00078 = −3)
all factors = +2

Step 5 Adjust the slide rule reading (6 − 5 − 6) to contain the correct number of digits in the product. The slide rule answer is 6.560.

NOTE: The absolute answer is 6.56214.

+2 digital count
−1 (left index used)
+1 digit in product

ASSIGNMENT UNIT 84

A. DETERMINING THE DIGITAL COUNT FOR DIFFERENT FACTORS

1. Establish the digital count for each of the factors given in the table (A through U).

A	22	H	22.09	O	0.179
B	176	I	176.07	P	·0.9994
C	2342	J	2342.03	Q	0.080
D	27564	K	27564.08	R	0.0014
E	10	L	10.006	S	0.00076
F	1	M	1.0009	T	0.000032
G	3.0	N	3.04273	U	0.096741

Ans.: E. +2 J. +4 O. 0 T. -4

B. MULTIPLICATION OF TWO OR MORE FACTORS WITH THE SLIDE RULE

1. Use the slide rule to compute the lengths of strip steel required to produce the quantities of stampings required for production A, B, and C. State answers to the nearest inch.

Stamping	Required Production	Hole (D) Diameter	Web (W) Thickness
A	125	0.750″	0.150″
B	275	2.063″	0.437″
C	5375	0.0813″	0.0162″

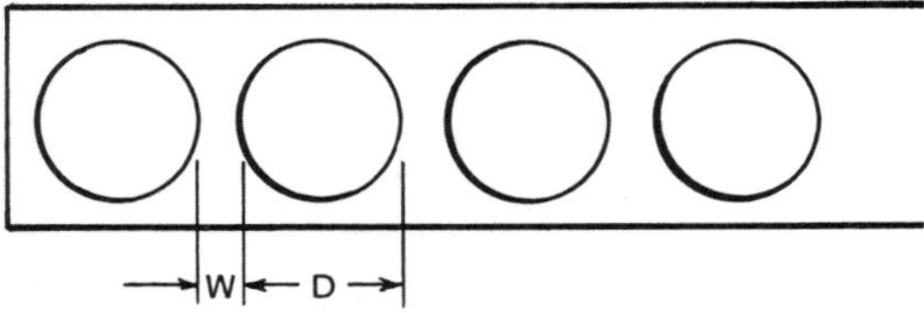

Ans.: B. 688 ± 5″

2. Refer to the specifications given in the table for parts A through F. Then, use a slide rule to determine:

   a. The number of parts produced daily (A-F) and

   Ans.: B. 2430 ± 30 D. 20,250 ± 50 F. 134,840 ± 100

   b. The lengths of bar stock (A, B, and C) and strip aluminum (D, E, and F) required in feet. Calculate the feet by long-hand division, rounded off to the nearest foot.

   Ans.: B. 471′ ± 3′ D. 1775′ ± 25′ F. 12,800 ± 25′

Part	Hourly Production Per Machine	Machine Hours Per Day	Length Per Piece: Finished Length (in ″)	Length Per Piece: Cut-off Allowance (in ″)	Required Part
A	15	16	6 1/2	1/2	LENGTH OF PLATE; ALLOWANCE FOR BLANKING; REQUIRED LENGTH; A
B	107	23	2.08	0.220	
C	229	106	1.063	0.250	
D	1125	18	0.990	0.06	B
E	1637	106	0.875	0.187	
F	2869	47	0.952	0.187	

Unit 85 DIVISION WITH THE SLIDE RULE

Division has been identified many times as a simplified, quick, and accurate way of subtracting numbers and quantities. The operation of division is the exact reverse of multiplication. Thus, determining the number of digits in a quotient, locating a decimal point, and setting and reading the slide rule must now be considered as reverse operations to those used in multiplication.

RULE FOR DIGIT COUNTING AND LOCATING THE DECIMAL POINT IN DIVISION

- Use the same rules as for multiplication for assigning a (+), (0), or (–) digit count for each factor.
- Subtract the digit count of the divisor(s) from the digit count of the dividend.

  NOTE: If the right index is used, the difference represents the number of digits in the quotient.

  The number of digits in the quotient is increased by 1 each time the left index is used.
- Apply the digit count to the slide rule reading to obtain the required number of digits in the answer. This may involve adding zeros (if necessary) and/or locating a decimal point to adjust the slide rule reading.

EXAMPLE: Case 1 Using the right index, divide 555 by 67.

Step 1 Assign a digit count to each factor.
555 = +3
67 = +2

Step 2 Subtract digit count of divisor from dividend.
(+3) – (+2) = +1

Step 3 Set the 67 on the C scale over the 555 on the D scale.

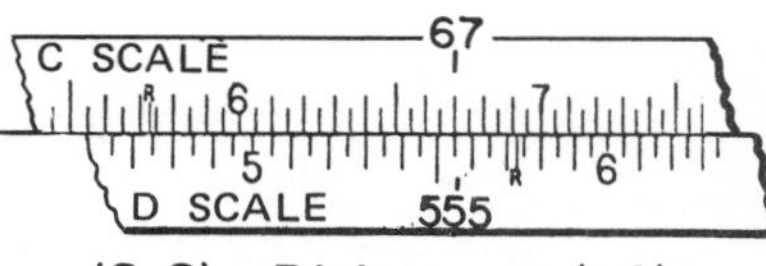

Step 4 Read the slide rule reading (8-3). Then, point off correct number of digits. The answer is 8.3.
(8–3). Digit count (+1).
(8–3) = 8.3

EXAMPLE: Case 2 Using the left index, divide 3080 by 0.0194.

Step 1 Assign a digit count to each factor.
3080 = +4
0.0194 = –1

Step 2 Subtract digit count of divisor from dividend.
(+4) – (–1) = +5

Step 3 Increase digit count by 1 for using left index.
(+5) + (1) = +6 digits

Step 4 Set the divisor (0.0194) on the C scale over the dividend (3080) on the D scale.

Step 5 Read the slide rule answer under the left index on the D scale.

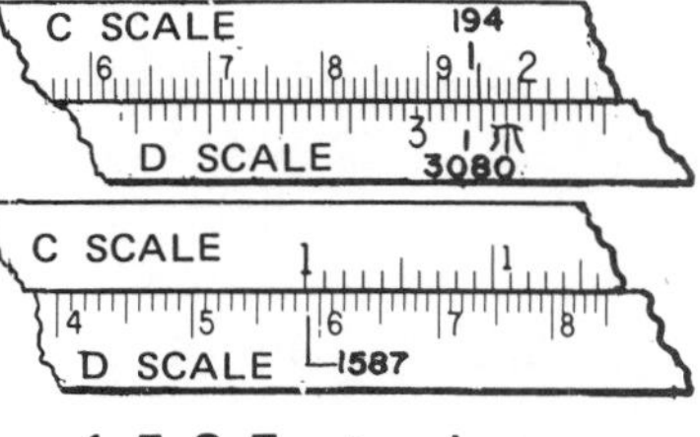

Step 6 Point off six digits (adding two zeros) to get the slide rule quotient answer of 158,700.
1–5–8–7 to six digits = 158,700

RULE FOR DIVIDING TWO OR MORE FACTORS WITH THE SLIDE RULE

- Use the rules for assigning a (+), (0), or (–) digit count for each factor.
- Subtract the digit count of the divisor(s) from the digit count of the dividend.
- Locate the place on the D scale which corresponds with the dividend. Move the indicator hairline over this position (graduation).
- Move the C scale until the graduation corresponding to the first divisor is aligned with the hairline (dividend).
- Place the indicator hairline over the appropriate index line.
- Read the quotient on the D scale. The value under the index line is the slide rule reading.

  NOTE: Repeat these steps if there is more than one divisor. The value of each new divisor is located on the C scale and is placed over each new intermediate reading on the D scale.
- Determine the number of digits in the answer.
- Adjust the slide rule reading so it contains the correct number of digits. The result is the slide rule quotient.

EXAMPLE: Dividing two or more factors with the slide rule.

Divide 136 by 14.2 by 0.000496.

Step 1 Locate the dividend (136) on the D scale.

Step 2 Move the sliding scale until the first divisor value (14.2) on the C scale is aligned with the dividend reading on the D scale.

Step 3 Slide the indicator hairline over the right index to locate and hold the position of the intermediate value (9-5-7-7).

Step 4 Move the slide until the second divisor value of (4-9-6) on the C scale is under the hairline at the intermediate position location.

Step 5 Position the hairline over the left index and take the slide rule reading (1-9-3).

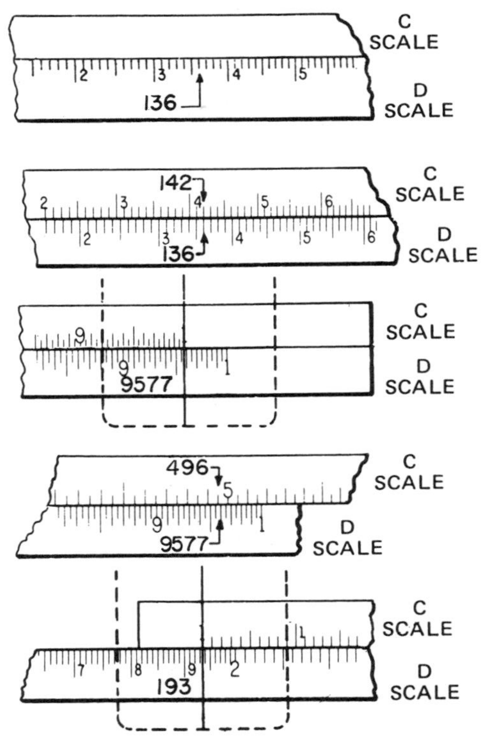

Step 6	Establish the digit count of each of the three factors. Add 1 because the left index is used once. The sum (5) indicates the number of digits in the answer.	Dividend 136 = +3 Divisor 14.2 = +2 Divisor 0.000496 = −3 +4

(+3 + 1 + 1 (left index) = 5 digit quotient

Step 7	Adjust the slide rule reading of (1-9-3) so it contains five digits. (1-9-3-0-0) is the slide rule answer. The absolute answer is 19,310 (rounded off to the nearest whole number). This indicates that there may be a (+) or (−) variation between the slide rule answer and the absolute answer.	1-9-3 represents 19,300

ASSIGNMENT UNIT 85

A. DETERMINING THE DIGITS COUNT AND LOCATION OF THE DECIMAL POINT

1. Show the digit count for each of the five sets of factors given in the table. Prepare a similar table and insert the correct count in each case.

   Ans.: Dividend B. +4 D. +2

   NOTE: Add additional sections to the table to insert the answers for problems 2 and 3.

	Sets of Factors				
	A	B	C	D	E
Dividend	488	6373	41,297	49.65	0.00964
Divisor(s)	55	251	769	2.57	0.065
		7	3.4	0.19	0.275
					0.0000782

2. Indicate the following:

   a. The total digit count in the divisor(s).

   Ans.: B. +4 D. +1

   b. The sum of the digit count of the dividend and divisors for each set of factors (A through E).

3. Determine the number of digits (and/or the location of the decimal point) in the final answers to the sets of factors (A through E).

   NOTE: Use a slide rule to establish the index line that may be used.

   Ans.: B. +1 D. +3

B. DIVISION OF TWO OR MORE FACTORS WITH THE SLIDE RULE

1. Determine dimensions W, T, F, and R for each of the values of P (diametral pitch) given in the table for gears A through E. State all dimensions in inches, rounded off to four decimal places.

Formulas for Required Dimensions (in inches)	Gear	Diametral Pitch (P)
Whole Depth (W) $W = \frac{2.157}{P}$	A	3
Tooth Thickness (T) $T = \frac{1.5708}{P}$	B	8
Rim Thickness (R)	C	12
$R = \frac{3.1416}{2P}$	D	16
Face Width (F) $F = \frac{9.4248}{P}$	E	1.5

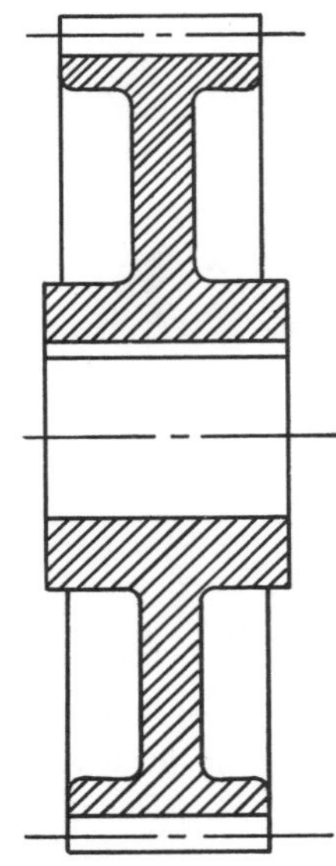

Ans.: B. W = .2696   T = .1964   F = 1.1781   R = .1964

2. Compute the slide rule values of each of the five different combinations of factors given in the table (A through E).

Combination	Factor 1 (Dividend)	Factors as Divisors		
		2	3	4
A	178	16	9	
B	2924	132	12	7
C	34,550	1675	149	15
D	4656	232.8	16.2	0.042
E	0.0965	0.00108	0.00022	0.915

Ans.: B. .2637 ± .0005   D. 29.37 ± .1

Unit 86 COMBINATIONS OF SLIDE RULE PROCESSES

The carrying out of multiplication and division processes with a slide rule was outlined in previous units. The principles will now be applied to using formulas, in finding squares and square roots, cubes and cube roots, to proportion, and in solving other problems. Scales, other than C and D, which further simplify some of the processes are described as they are needed.

A. COMBINATION MULTIPLICATION AND DIVISION PROCESSES

One of the simplified procedures that is used when multiplication and division processes are required in the same problem is to carry on one division between the first set of factors. Thus, the first factor in the numerator is divided by the first factor in the denominator. The other factors and processes are worked in alternately. Instead of reading each intermediate result, the process is a continuous one of setting the values on the C and D scales until all factors are used.

RULE FOR USING THE SLIDE RULE FOR COMBINATION PROCESSES

EXAMPLE: Find the value of X, when $X = \frac{(A) \cdot (C) \cdot (E)}{(B) \cdot (D) \cdot (F)}$

Step 1 Locate factor (A) on the D scale.

Step 2 Divide, using factor (B), by placing its value on the C scale over (A) on the D scale.

Step 3 Multiply the first intermediate result by factor (C) by locating its value on scale C and moving the indicator hairline over the value.

Step 4 Divide the result by factor (D) by locating the value of (D) on the C scale over the intermediate result.

Step 5 Multiply by factor (E) by moving the indicator hairline over the value of (E) on the C scale.

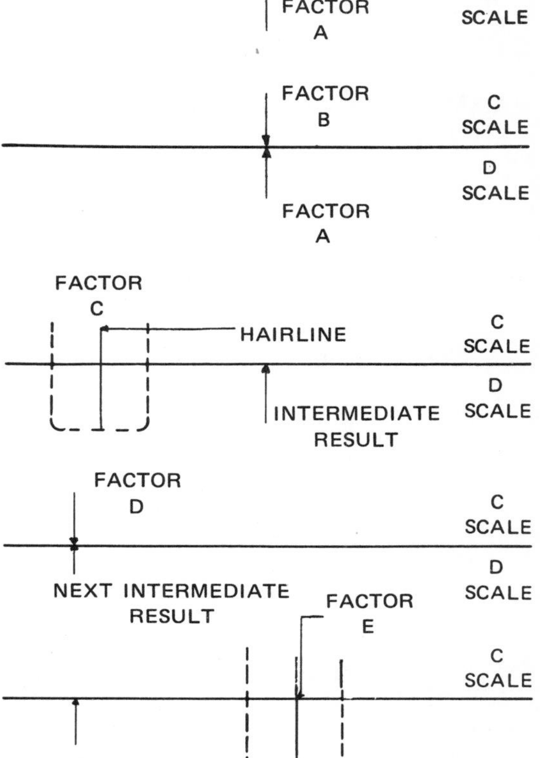

Step 6 Divide by factor (F) by locating the value of (F) on the C scale over the last intermediate result.

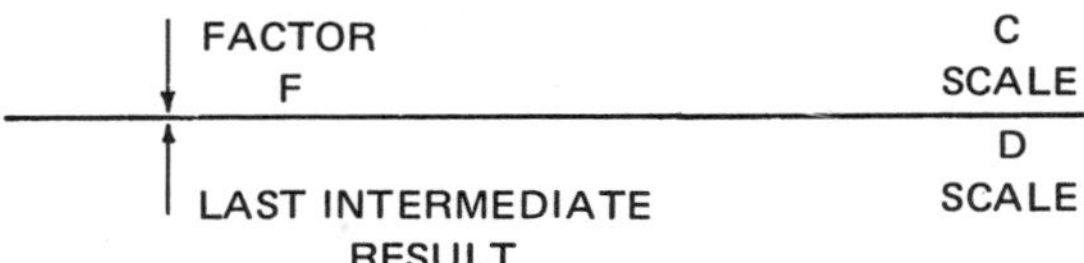

NOTE: The same steps are repeated when there are more multiplication and/or division processes to be completed.

Step 7 Read the slide rule reading under the appropriate index.

Step 8 Determine the number of digits in the answer.

Step 9 Adjust the slide rule result to contain the correct number of digits.

B. USING THE SLIDE RULE FOR PROPORTION PROBLEMS

Problems requiring the conversion of one value, measure or quantity to another are everyday examples of proportion. A proportion may be established by knowing how many units of a required measurement are contained in a basic unit of a known measurement. For instance, there are 2.54 centimeters in one inch. The 2.54 is called a "conversion factor."

These conversion factors are found in tables of technical data. However, they may be determined easily by referring for values to such standard tables as English and Metric linear, surface, volume, and mass measure.

The C and D scales of a slide rule are used for proportion problems because they combine multiplication and division processes.

RULE FOR SOLVING PROPORTION PROBLEMS WITH A SLIDE RULE

EXAMPLE: Determine how many millimeters there are in 14.25″.

Step 1 Set up the problem in the form of a proportion. (A):(B)::(C):(D)

Step 2 Check a table of metric measure and find the number of millimeters that are contained in one inch. 1″ = 25.40 mm

Step 3 Insert the values in the proportion. (A = 1″):(B = 25.40)::(C = 14.25):(D)

(1) (D) = (25.40) (14.25)

Step 4 Carry out the multiplication process on the slide rule.

1 | 1425 | C SCALE

254 | ANSWER 3-5-7 | D SCALE

Step 5 Determine the digit counts and the number of digits in the answer.

25.4	= +2	+4
14.25	= +2	
Left Index		−1
Digits in answer		+3

Step 6 Adjust the slide rule reading. Answer 14.25″ = 362 mm

C. USING THE SLIDE RULE FOR SQUARES AND SQUARE ROOTS

The A and D scales are used for problems which involve the squares and the square roots of numbers.

RULE FOR FINDING THE SQUARE OF A NUMBER

- Set the indicator hairline over the number on the D scale.
- Read the slide rule value of the square directly under the hairline on scale A.
- Determine the number of digits in the answer.
- Adjust the slide rule reading to contain the required number of digits.

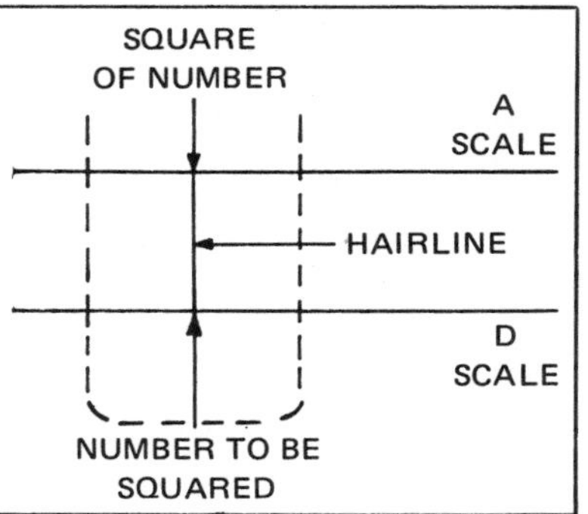

SQUARE ROOTS OF NUMBERS

Square roots of numbers are found in the exact opposite manner to determining the square of a number. Also, attention must now be paid to the different graduations on the A scale. Examination of the A scale shows that it contains two identical sections. Both sections are arranged logarithmically from 1 to 1.

RULE FOR DETERMINING WHICH SECTION OF SCALE A TO USE

EXAMPLE: Case 1 For numbers larger than 1

Step 1 Start at the decimal point, work to the left, and space off the digits in groups of two.

Step 2 Use the right section of scale A if the last group to the left has two digits.

Step 3 Use the left seciton of scale A if there is only one digit in the last group to the left.

Example

6|40|09

6 40 | 09

Last group has one digit

This rule applies

Step 4 Set the indicator hairline over the number (64009) on the left section of scale A.

Step 5 Read the squre root of the number on the D scale (2-5-3).

Step 6 Record the first digit of the answer under the first group. Record the second value for the second group, etc. and continue for each successive group of digits.

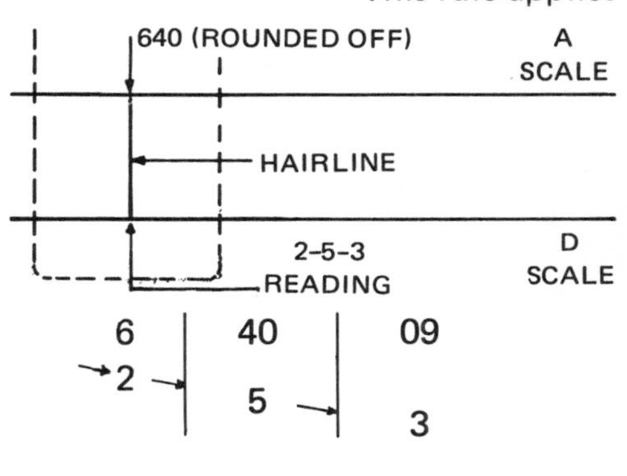

$\sqrt{64009} = 253$ Answer

It should be noted that the answer must contain a digit for each group of digits in the original group. A zero (or zeros) may need to be added to complete each group of digits which appear either before or following the decimal point.

EXAMPLE: Case 2 For numbers less than 1

Step 1 Start at the decimal point, work to the right, and pair off each set of two digits.

Step 2 Use the left section of scale A if the first group with a number to the right of the decimal point has one significant number.

Step 3 Use the right section if there are two significant numbers in the first group with a number.

Step 4 Proceed to find the square root according to the rules for numbers greater than 1.

$\sqrt{0.00016492} = .0128$

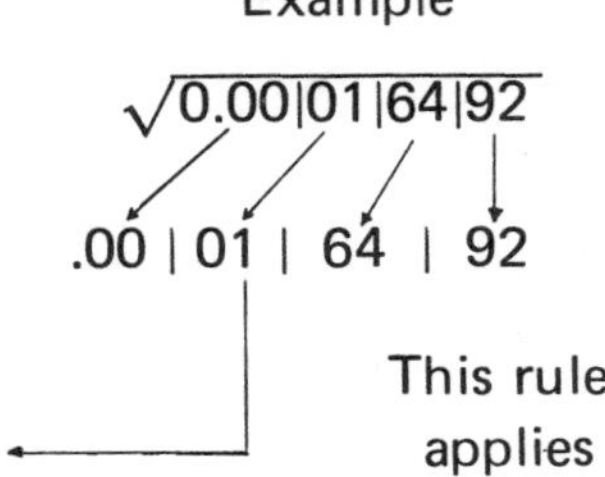

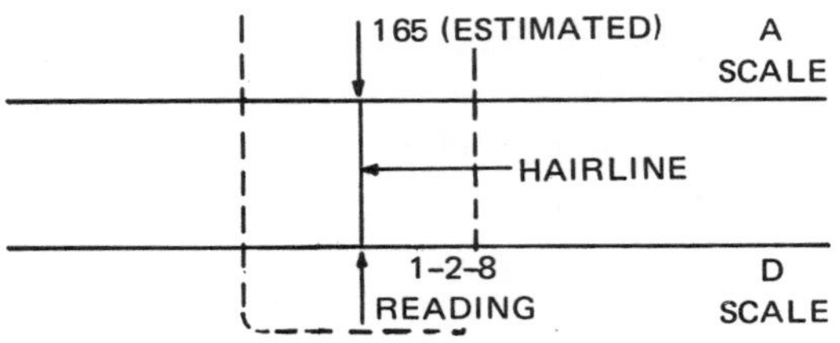

D. USING THE SLIDE RULE FOR FINDING CUBES AND CUBE ROOTS

The K and D scales of the slide rule are used to find the cubes and cube roots of numbers.

RULE FOR FINDING THE CUBE OF A NUMBER

- Set the indicator hairline over the number on the D scale.
- Read the slide rule value on the K scale directly under the hairline.
- Estimate the number of digits in the answer.
- Adjust the slide rule reading so it has the correct number of digits. The result is the cube of the original number.

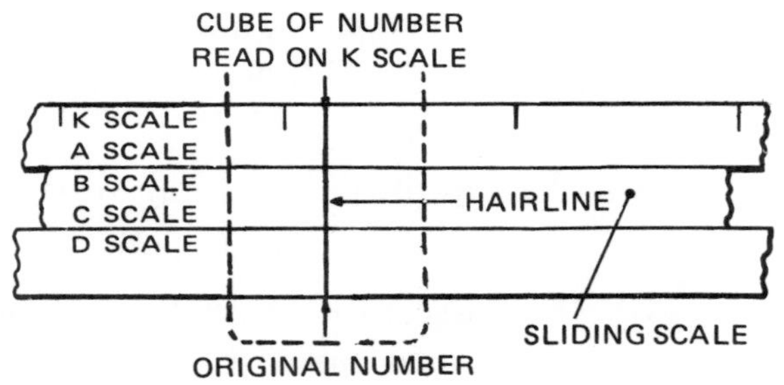

The graduations on the K scale are arranged logarithmically from 1 to 1 in three equal sections: left, middle, and right. Each section is used to accommodate a different number of digits for numbers that are larger than 1 or less than 1.

RULE FOR FINDING THE CUBE ROOT OF A NUMBER

EXAMPLE: Case 1 Finding the cube root of numbers larger than 1.

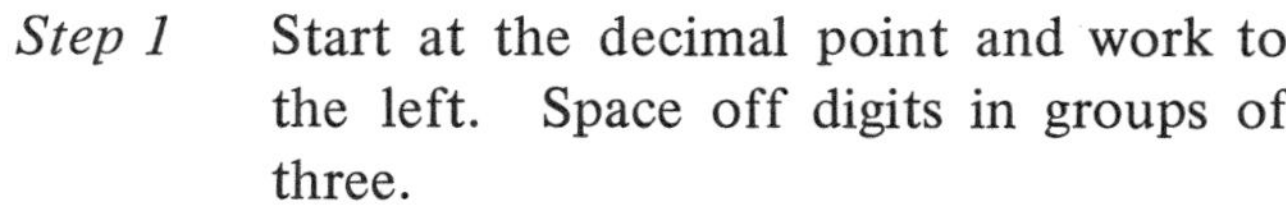

Step 1 Start at the decimal point and work to the left. Space off digits in groups of three.

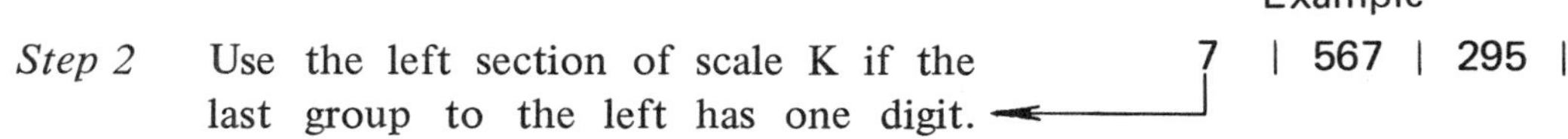

Step 2 Use the left section of scale K if the last group to the left has one digit.

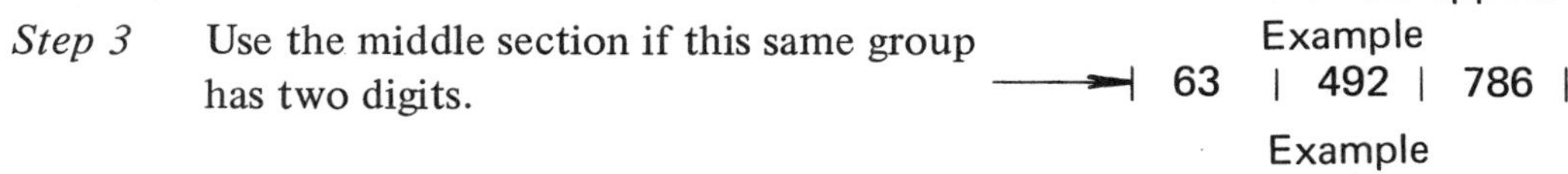

Step 3 Use the middle section if this same group has two digits.

Step 4 Use the right section if the first left group has three digits.

Example
351 | 568 | 943 |

Step 5 Set the hairline over the number on the K scale.

Step 6 Read the cube root of the number under the hairline on the D scale.

EXAMPLE: Case 2 Finding the cube root of numbers smaller than 1.

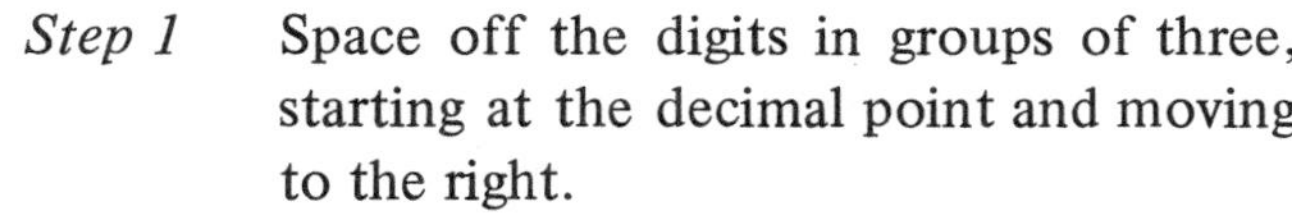

Step 1 Space off the digits in groups of three, starting at the decimal point and moving to the right.

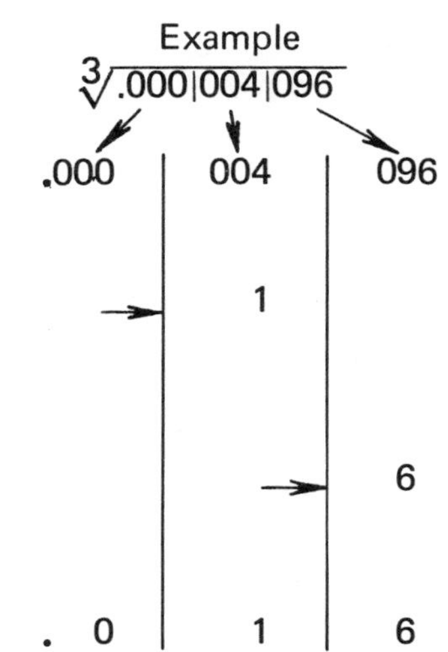

Step 2 Place the first digit in the answer under the first group containing a significant number.

Step 3 Place the second digit of the slide rule reading under the second group.

Step 4 Proceed in this manner with each successive group.

The final answer must contain one digit for each group of three digits in the original number. A zero may be added to represent a digit for each group where there is no expressed value.

ASSIGNMENT UNIT 86

A. PRACTICAL PROBLEMS IN PROPORTION AND CONVERSION

1. Convert each linear measurement in the English system to the metric equivalent as indicated in readings A through M. Round off answers to the nearest two decimal places.

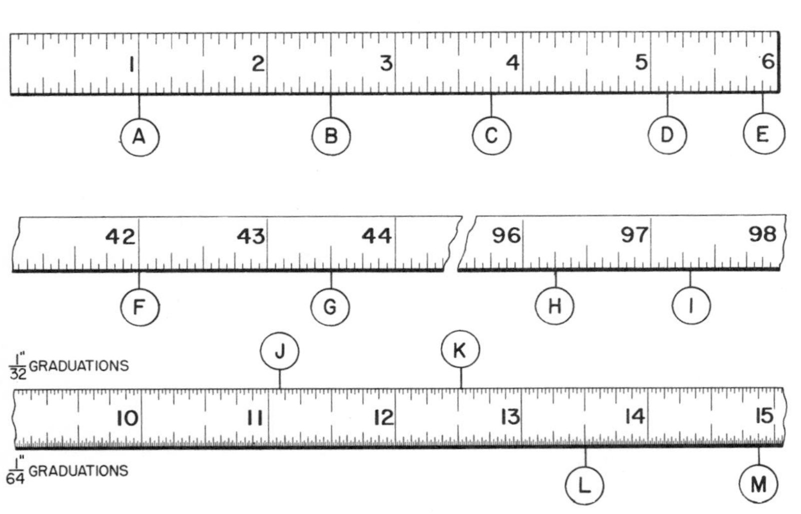

Linear Measurement		
	Given Unit	Required Unit
A	inches	millimeters
B	inches	centimeters
C	inches	millimeters
D	inches	centimeters
E	inches	millimeters
F	inches	meters
G	inches	meters
H	inches	meters
I	inches	meters
J	inches	millimeters
K	inches	centimeters
L	inches	meters
M	inches	meters

Ans.: D. 5 1/8″ = 12.99 cm H. 96 1/4″ = 2.44 m L. 13 33/64″ = .34 m

2. Check each converted measurement (A through M) by resetting the slide rule with the metric measurement and converting it to its equivalent English measurement.

B. APPLICATIONS OF SQUARES AND SQUARE ROOT, CUBES AND CUBE ROOT, AND PROPORTION

1. Compute the areas or volumes of sheet metal ducts A through L with a slide rule.

Use $\pi = 3.142$	Formulas		Given Values	Required Units of Measurement
	$A = \pi R^2$		R	A
		A	4″	square inches
		B	9.5 m	square meters
		C	0.0025 cm	square centimeters
	$R = \sqrt{\frac{A}{\pi}}$		A	R
		D	14 sq. cm	centimeters
		E	0.00672 sq. ft.	feet
		F	0.01967 sq. m	meters
	$V = S^3$		S	V
		G	12″	cubic inches
		H	9.82 cm	cubic centimeters
		I	0.067m	cubic meters
	$S = \sqrt[3]{V}$		V	S
		J	126 cu. yds	yards
		K	0.87 cu. mm	millimeters
		L	0.0288 cu. in.	inches

Ans.: B. 283.57 sq. m E. .046 ft. H. 947 cu. cm K. .95 mm

Unit 87 ACHIEVEMENT REVIEW ON THE SLIDE RULE

A. COMBINATION MULTIPLICATION AND DIVISION PROBLEMS

1. Compute the values of X, Y, and Z under conditions 1 through 6. Round off answers to one decimal place.

Formula	Condition	Value of Factors A	B	C	D	E	F
$X = \frac{A \times C}{B}$	1	6925	451	706			
	2	295.2	37.72	0.074			
$Y = \frac{(A) \times (C)}{(B) \times (D)}$	3	258.6	27.69	0.0051	0.0095		
	4	0.0458	0.0906	7.046	0.0382		
$Z = \frac{(A) \times (C) \times (E)}{(B) \times (D) \times (F)}$	5	37.53	0.00576	0.089	0.0656	122.5	10.32
	6	9.787	0.0259	0.00007	0.00455	0.00090	9.125

B. PRACTICAL PROBLEMS INVOLVING SQUARES AND SQUARE ROOTS, CUBES AND CUBE ROOTS, AND CONVERSION OF VALUES

1. Find (a) the volume of parts A, B, and C, (b) the diameter of parts D, E, and F, and (c) the volume of parts G, H, and I. Round off answers to one decimal place.

2. Determine the weight of the metal required to cast the quantities of parts A through I according to the values given in the table. Find the total weights for the quantity needed of each part A through I to the nearest pound.

Formula	Parts	Given Dimensions: Diameter (D)	Height (H)	Volume (V)	Weight (W)	Quantity
$V = .785\ D^2H$	A	10″	10″		.1 lb./cu. in.	10
	B	6.5″	12″		.12 lb./cu. in.	150
	C	4.25″	9.8″		.14 lb./cu. in.	276
$D = \sqrt{\frac{V}{.785\ (H)}}$	D		4″	256 cu. in.	.17 lb./cu. in.	20
	E		8′	476.2 cu. ft.	19.2 lbs./cu. ft.	163
	F		7.6′	29.7 cu. ft.	28.7 lbs./cu. ft.	1715
$V = S^3 + .785\ S^2$			Side (S)			
	G		11″		.156 lb./cu. in.	57
	H		16.4″		.096 lb./cu. in.	219
	I		3.28″		.0096 lb./cu. in.	1736

3. Convert the cube root value of D for parts A through D to the required units indicated in the table.

Formula	Parts	Value of V	Required Unit of Measure
$D = \sqrt[3]{V}$	A	81 cu. cm	inches
	B	9198.2 cu. m	yards and inches
	C	2752.66 liters	U.S. gallons
	D	172.98 kg /cu. m	kg /foot

4. Determine the volume of each sheet metal duct A through D from the dimensions given in the table.

	Formula		Given Values			Required Measurements
			(L)	(W)	(D)	(V)
L, W, D	$V = 2\,(L)\,(W)\,(D) + \frac{\pi L^2\,(W)}{4}$	A	3″	10″	32″	cu. in.
		B	3.5″	11.25″	28″	cu. in.
		C	0.63 m	4.95 m	12.25m	cu. meters
		D	0.09″	0.526″	0.00328″	cu. in.

Section 19

CALCULATORS: BASIC AND ADVANCED MATHEMATICAL PROCESSES

Unit 88 CALCULATORS AND BASIC MATHEMATICAL PROCESSES

A *calculator* is a computing machine which performs either basic arithmetical or advanced mathematical processes. All calculators may be used to compute the four basic processes of addition, subtraction, multiplication and division. There are, however, larger and more complicated calculators. These models are identified as engineering and scientific calculators, advanced business computers or electronic slide rules.

A. CHARACTERISTICS OF ELECTRONIC CALCULATORS AND TERMINOLOGY

Calculators that are small and pocket-sized are classified as "hand-held" or "pocket calculators." Larger calculators that are operated from a desk are called "desk-top" models. Some calculators are battery-operated; others depend on electric power, or a combination. Since calculators consist of modern, compact integrated electronic circuits which perform the mathematical operations, they are also called "electronic calculators." Modern electronic calculators have many advantages over the older forms of calculators, slide rules, adding and other business machines. These advantages include:

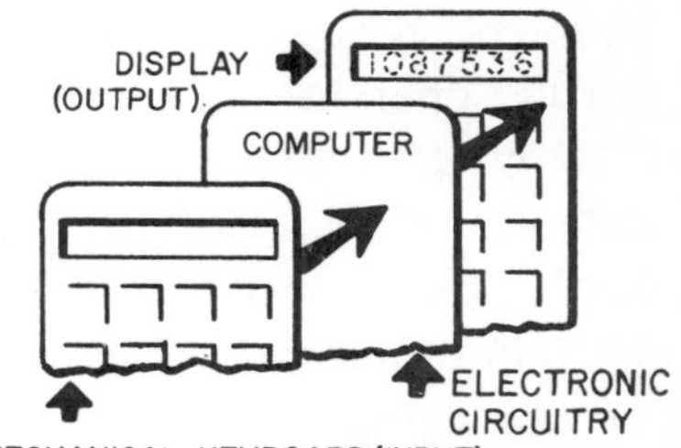

- Portability: lightweight, small size, comparative inexpensiveness
- Higher calculating speed and greater accuracy
- Performance in carrying out calculations and processes that are not possible by other machines.

Every calculator has a *"keyboard."* The keyboard consists of a number of keys. There are ten keys for the basic numerals: 0, 1, 2, 3, 4, 5, 6, 7, 8, and 9. In addition, there is a decimal point and another set of keys for instructions relating to mathematical processes. The numerical keys, when pressed, enter the values to be used in the computation. The mathematical keys indicate the processes (+, –, x, etc.) that are to be performed.

Four-Function Calculator (Battery and/or AC Power Operated)

The mechanical operations of the keys provide the *"input."* The computer component of the calculator performs the mathematical processes as directed by the input. The answer appears as an easy-to-read numerical value in the "*display.*"

The four basic arithmetical processes (functions) are addition, subtraction, multiplication, and division. These processes are required in over 90% of all calculations. The electronic calculator that performs these processes is identified as a "four-function" type. This four-function calculator can also be used to perform higher mathematical processes. This is accomplished by breaking down the problem into a form which requires the four basic processes. In addition, the four-function calculator usually includes a percent (%) key to perform this particular arithmetical process.

PROGRAMMABLE CALCULATORS

"*Programmable calculators*" contain a memory to store numbers and "instructions" for performing a sequence of operations. The sequence in which the instructions are to be executed on the numerical values forms a "*program*" for solving the problem.

The program is stored in the calculator. Problems are entered and all mathematical processes are performed electronically according to the specified sequence. The program may be repeated any number of times using different numerical values. At the completion of the problem the correct answer is displayed. There is no further operator input into the problem.

Programmable calculators perform other sophisticated processes such as "decision-making" and "branching." Under specified conditions quantities are analyzed. Certain numerical values are then automatically processed by branching through a different program. Programmable calculators have the capacity to execute a program which is stored in a memory in the calculator.

Hand-Held Engineering and Scientific Calculator

ALGEBRAIC ENTRY

The sequence in which the numerals of a problem are entered on the calculator is referred to as the "algebraic (logic) entry." This means that a problem is solved according to standard "algebraic rules of order." Thus, the calculator uses the same logical sequence in which an individual solves a problem. The keys on an algebraic calculator are identified as +, –, x, ÷ and =.

Numerical values and mathematical processes are entered on the calculator in the sequence in which they occur in the problem. Basic rules of order must be followed. For example, all of the multiplication and division processes in the problem must be performed first. Then, the addition and subtraction calculations are completed as required.

The advantages of this system are simplicity and consistency. Its disadvantages lie in the fact that the individual must arrange the sequence of processes, write down and remember intermediate results, and apply these values later in the solution of the problem.

Some of the more advanced calculators use another form of algebraic entry. Engineering calculators are able to perform a series of "hierarchy" operations. Internal storage registers eliminate intermediate storage as well as the need to remember the rules of order. Information is entered as an algebraic entry in the same sequence in which the problem is to be solved. The correct answer appears when the equals key is depressed.

ARITHMETIC ENTRY

Computations for addition and subtraction are carried on differently on the arithmetic calculator. The arithmetic calculator is distinguished by its += key and −= key. The += key is pressed after all positive numbers. The −= key is pressed after all negative numbers, or if the numbers are to be subtracted. For instance, if 27 is to be subtracted from 85, the key sequence on the arithmetic calculator is: 85 += 27 −= 58.

The procedures for multiplication and division are the same on both the algebraic and the arithmetic calculators.

TRUE-CREDIT BALANCE

A calculator is said to have a "true-credit balance" when the display indicates whether the resulting numerical value is positive or negative. Usually, a negative result or difference on a true-credit balance calculator is displayed with a minus sign.

REGISTERS

A *register* is a memory circuit. It is used to remember multi-digit numbers. Four-function calculators have at least three "operating registers." These registers are used to enter the numbers of a problem, display the numbers, and carry out the arithmetical processes. The most significant register is known as the "*accumulator*" or "display register." The numbers which the operator enters via the keyboard are stored in the accumulator register. The numbers appear on the display register.

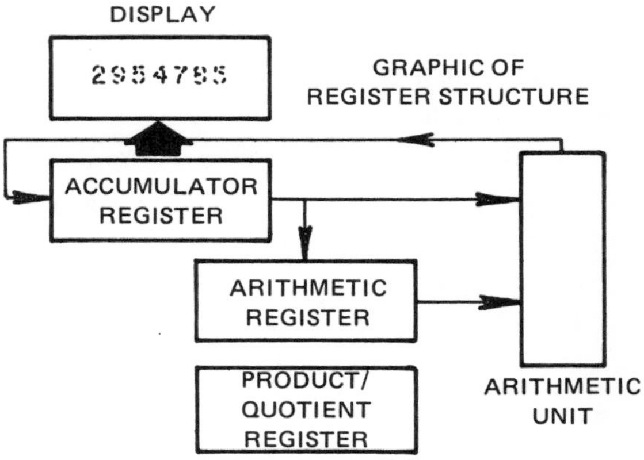

When the arithmetical process is entered on the keyboard, followed by the next value in the problem, the first number is transferred from the accumulator register into the arithmetic register. When the equals key is pressed, the numbers (which are stored in the accumulator register and the arithmetic register) are transmitted to the arithmetic unit. Here the values are added or subtracted. The addition or subtraction result is stored in the accumulator. It is also displayed.

DISPLAY
GRAPHIC OF REGISTER STRUCTURE
ACCUMULATOR REGISTER
ARITHMETIC REGISTER
PRODUCT/ QUOTIENT REGISTER
ARITHMETIC UNIT

Since multiplication and division processes are shortened methods of adding and subtracting, a third register known as the "product/quotient register" is used to give the calculator additional memory storage.

MEMORY

As just stated, all calculators have registers (memories) that store values to be used in a problem. The registers are fixed because they are permanently tied into the calculator circuitry. The registers are adequate for everyday applications.

Other calculators have greater capacity with long·multi-digit numbers which normally require complex calculations. Auxiliary memory is provided in such calculators to permit the storage and later recall of intermediate calculation results.

Separate keys are used to control the auxiliary memory features. A "CM" (or "MC") key clears all numbers from the memory register, returning to zero. Pressing the "RM" (or "MR") key recalls and transfers the value in memory to the accumulator register. The numerical value is displayed and is ready to be used in some computation without clearing or disturbing the memory accumulation.

The sum or difference of the memory content and the content of the accumulator register may be computed by pressing the appropriate "M+" or "M-" key. The sum or difference calculation is then contained in the memory. A number is stored in memory by first clearing the memory with the CM key. The M+ key is pressed to transfer the accumulator contents to the memory. The M- key subtracts numbers in display from memory. On some calculators, when memory is in use, a decimal place appears in the furthest left ("left-most") digit space.

While one model of memory system has been covered briefly, the methods of operation of different calculators are similar, even though the keys may not be the same.

CLEAR (C), CLEAR-ENTRY (CE), AND CLEAR DISPLAY (CD) KEY FUNCTIONS

These keys are used to clear or erase the results of previous calculations and to reset the calculator. The clear (C) key is pressed on many calculators to reset the contents of the accumulator display register and the arithmetic register to zero. In this state, the circuitry of the calculator is set to start a new calculation.

The clear-entry (CE) or clear-display (CD) key is used to correct number-entry errors without disturbing any previous part of the calculating sequence. The CE key is pressed to erase an error and to enter a correct new value. On some models the clear-error and total-erase processes are performed by a key marked "C/CE." An entry mistake is corrected by pressing the C/CE key once and entering the correct value. This action does not disturb any previously recorded data or calculations. The C/CE key is pressed twice to erase all previous data and to clear the machine completely.

CALCULATOR DISPLAY

The numerical readout on a calculator is found in a lighted "*display*." The display serves three main purposes.

- Answers to problems are presented as a series of numerical digits in a readout display.
- Intermediate numbers used in a calculation are entered on the keyboard and presented on the display as a visual check.
- Information is fed back to a calculator operator through the "display."

The number of digits in a calculator display varies. Six-digit displays are found in the less expensive models. Twenty or more digits are used in scientific calculators where greater precision is required. A practical common electronic calculator has an eight-digit display. This calculator has the capacity to display any number from 00 000 000 to 99 999 999. Fractional values are displayed by using a decimal point preceding the appropriate digit. Calculators are available in a variety of lighted color digit displays. The displays operate on extremely small quantities of power.

Some accounting, scientific and other business applications require a printed record. Calculators are designed with impact ribbon, heat-sensitive mechanical printers, ink injectors, and other mechanisms to meet such requirements and to produce a record tape.

B. SIGNIFICANT FIGURES, PRECISION AND ACCURACY

"*Precision*" refers to exactness in defining a quantity. Precision is determined by the smallest increment that can be distinguished in the change of a quantity. When a higher degree of precision is required, there must be greater "resolution" and number of "significant figures" in a problem result.

A linear dimension like 3.01″ may be measured directly on a steel rule to a precision of roughly one one-hundred part of one inch. If a precision of .001″, or 0.0001″, or 0.0254 mm, or 0.00254 mm is required, measuring instruments with capability to measure to these degrees of precision are needed. In either instance, the number of significant digits in a required dimension is determined by the required precision. In these two examples, the steel rule may not be used to resolve any shorter differences in length. Its limits of precision are reached at ± .01″. The micrometer, by comparison, has capacity to increase the precision from 10 (0.001″ or 0.0254 mm) to 100 (0.0001″ or 0.00254 mm) times. Precision is determined by the number of significant figures in a quantity, particularly those relating to decimal values.

The number of significant digits in whole numbers is determined by counting the number of digits with values from 0 through 9 that appear in the display to the left of the decimal point. For whole numbers and decimal values all of the digits are counted.

Significant Digits (Figures)	Examples	
1	0.000 005	
2	98.	or 0.098
3	268.	or 0.000 268
4	3.192	or 0.003 192
5	29 323	or 29.323
6	29.3230	or 0.293230

At this point a statement should be made about "accuracy" as contrasted with precision. "*Accuracy*" is associated with degree of closeness to precision. While a micrometer may be used to measure to a precision of 0.001″ or 0.0001″, the operator's handling of the instrument may cause an inaccurate measurement to be taken. Accuracy is the relationship between a computed measurement and any variance with the true required measurement. Accuracy is usually stated as a percent of the actual (or calculated) value to the true value. If a measurement is computed to be 7.65 meters and its true length is known to be 7.77 meters, the calculated value is 7.65/7.77 of 100%, or 98.5% accurate.

ROUNDING OFF VALUES

Regardless of whether a value is rounded off by conventional mathematical computing processes or on a calculator, error results. For most practical purposes dimensions and values that are rounded off to two, three and four decimal places are well within the usual range required. Parts produced within dimensional tolerances of 0.001″ and 0.0001″ are considered to be practical to measure and may be reproduced at reasonable cost. Movable units machined to such tolerance limits, will mesh and work properly.

The degree of required precision should be determined first, before the solution of a mathematical problem. The precision will then establish the number of significant figures in the answer and at what point the computed value may be rounded off.

The calculator also "*truncates*" values. For example, the display of the decimal value for 1/3 is "truncated." This means the display value on an eight-digit calculator reads .33333333, rounded off by eliminating the least significant digits. While this degree of accuracy in a final result is acceptable in most everyday problems, added care must be taken in making a long series of calculations. When values are rounded off after each calculation, the "cumulative" error may result in an inaccurate measurement.

OVERFLOW AND UNDERFLOW CALCULATOR CONDITIONS

When the numerical capacity of a calculator is exceeded, a condition of "overflow" exists. Overflow occurs when a quantity greater than the number of digits in the calculator is fed into it or when the result of a calculation exceeds the calculator capacity. This overflow condition is indicated in the display by the appearance of the letter "E" or "C" in the furthest left position of the display.

The overflow may be cleared by dividing by 10. This is repeated enough times to bring the decimal point into the display. Calculations are then continued. The result will be multiplied by 10^N. N represents the number of times the overflow was divided by ten.

"Underflow" denotes a condition where, again, the capacity of the calculator is exceeded. In this instance, the least significant digits may be lost. For example, in an eight-digit calculator, the display would register zero if the keys were pushed to record a value like .000 000 003 256.

C. BASIC MATHEMATICAL PROCESSES

As stated earlier, all calculators may be used for the four basic arithmetical processes of addition, subtraction, multiplication and division. To do this, an individual must know the basic arithmetic principles and their application. The calculator simplifies all of the basic processes, insures accurate results and conserves time.

ADDITION

The first of the processes to be discussed is that of addition. Two common methods of carrying on addition are described:

METHOD 1 Simulated Example: Add quantities $A_1 + A_2 + A_3 + A_4$

Step 1 Turn the calculator on.

Step 2 Press the numbered keys to enter the numerical value of A_1. Read the visual display to check that the correct number is recorded.

Step 3 Press the + key.

Step 4 Press the numbered keys to enter the second numerical value (A_2). Read the visual display for accuracy.

Step 5 Press the = key. This value is the sum of ($A_1 + A_2$).

Step 6 Press the + key.

Step 7 Press the numbered keys to enter the value of A_3. Read the visual display to check the entry.

Step 8 Press the = key. This is the sum of $(A_1 + A_2) + A_3$. The display shows this sum.

Step 9 Press the + key.

Step 10 Enter the value of A_4. Check this value on the display.

Step 11 Press the = key. The display total is the answer, representing the sum of $A_1 + A_2 + A_3 + A_4$.

NOTE: If whole numbers and decimal values are involved, the decimal key is used to enter the value. The "floating-decimal point" within the calculator automatically indicates the position of the decimal point in the answer.

METHOD 2 A number of key strokes may be eliminated by a second method.

Example: Add 1 763, (A_1) + 23 825, (A_2) + 197, (A_3) + 192 368, (A_4)

Step 1 Turn the calculator on.

Step 2 Press the numerical keys to enter the value of A_1 of 1 763. Check this number on the display.

Step 3 Press the + key.

Step 4 Press the numerical keys to enter the value of A_2 of 23 825. Check the display.

Step 5 Press the + key.

Step 6 Enter the value of A_3 of 197. Again, check this entry on the display.

Step 7 Press the + key.

Step 8 Enter the value of A_4 of 192 368. Check the display.

Step 9 Press the equals key. Read the answer (218 253) on the display. In this example, 1 763 + 23 825 + 197 + 192 368 = 218 153. Answer.

NOTE: All problems should be rechecked by repeating the steps and comparing the answers.

SUBTRACTION: The same two methods may be used to solve problems involving subtraction. Instead of pressing the + key, the – key is used.

CORRECTING AN ERROR

If a wrong numerical value is entered, two simple steps are required to correct the error.

- Press the C (or CE key on some models) key once. This removes the last entry.
- Enter the correct value on the keyboard. Check this value on the display. Then proceed with the remaining part of the problem.

EXAMPLE: Add 79 and 67

		The Display Reads
Step 1	Enter the 79.	79
Step 2	Press the + key. Check the display.	79
Step 3	Assume you enter 65 by mistake.	65
Step 4	Press the "C" key.	0
Step 5	Enter the 67. Check the display.	67
Step 6	Press the = key. The display quantity is the answer.	146

MULTIPLICATION AND DIVISION

In addition to regular multiplication and division problems, a number of calculators have what is called a "constant feature." Some calculators have a constant (K) panel switch to enter a required constant with the keyboard. This means that if a constant number is used in a series of multiplication or divison problems, the constant is entered once. For example, in the accompanying series of multiplications

12 x 12 12 x 16 12 x 47

12 is the constant. The table shows how each value is computed.

Step	Press	Display Reads	
1	CC (Press C key twice)	0	
2	12 (and the x key)	12	
3	=	144	(Ans. to 12 x 12)
4	16	16	
5	=	192	(Ans. to 12 x 16)
6	47	47	
7	=	564	(Ans. to 12 x 47)

A similar series of steps is following in division. For example, if -10 is to be divided three times by 3.2,

-10 ÷ 3.2 ÷ 3.2 ÷ 3.2,

the 3.2 would be a constant. If an answer to three significant digits is required, the -0.3051757 would be rounded off to -0.305.

Step	Press	Display Reads
1	CC	0
2	−10	−10
3	÷	−10
4	3.2	3.2
5	=	−3.125
6	=	0.9765625
7	=	−0.3051757

COMBINATION OR CHAIN ARITHMETICAL PROCESSES

Many practical problems require a series of mathematical processes. Such series are known as chain calculations. They may involve addition, subtraction, multiplication, and division in varying combinations. In chain processes one of the goals is to solve the problem without having to store or write down intermediate values. Another goal is to keep the number of key strokes to a minimum.

There are "rules of order" to follow in establishing a sequence for carrying out chain calculations.

- Multiplication and division calculations are completed before addition and subtraction.

  For example, to solve the problem 7 + 9 x 5 - 8 ÷ 4,

  carry out the multiplication (9 x 5 = 45) and division (8 ÷ 4 = 2) processes first. Add: 7 + 45 - 2 = 50 Answer

  NOTE: If the rules of order were not followed, an incorrect answer is obtained, like: (7 + 9 = 16; 16 x 5 = 80; 80 - 8 = 72; 72 ÷ 4 = 18). Answer

- Portions of the problem are grouped before any mathematical processes are started. In the example, the values may be grouped and enclosed in parentheses as follows:

  7 + (9 x 5) - (8 ÷ 4).

The correct order or sequence for more complicated problems may be clarified by using brackets and parentheses. The operations in the parentheses in the following example are performed first. Those within the brackets are carried out next. The division process (which refers to all items within the brackets) is last.

The keys, processes and display readouts for this problem are shown in chart form.

[27 x (19 + 17) + 68] ÷ 56

[27 x (36) + 68] ÷ 56

[972 + 68] ÷ 56

1040 ÷ 56 = 18.571428 Answer

Step	Press	Display Reads
1	CC	0
2	19	19
3	+	19
4	17	17
5	x	36
6	27	27
7	+	972
8	68	68
9	÷	1040
10	56	56
11	=	18.571428

CONVERSIONS OF FRACTIONS AND DECIMALS

Calculators are used with whole numbers or decimal parts. Sometimes, it is necessary to convert a fractional quantity to its equivalent decimal value. This process is easily accomplished by dividing the numerator by the denominator. Where the floating decimal is incorporated in the calculator, the decimal is automatically located. For instance to convert the fraction 7/64 to the equivalent decimal value, divide the numerator 7 by 64 = 0.109375.

To convert a decimal quantity to its fractional value, determine the number of decimal digits in the fractional part. A quantity like 1.104 indicates that there are 104 thousandths in the fractional part. So, the 1.104 quantity, expressed as a mixed number = 1 104/1 000. The fraction is further reduced by dividing by the greatest common divisor (8). Expressed in its lowest terms, the 1 104/1 000 = 1 13/125.

DOUBLE-PRECISION CALCULATIONS

Occasionally, it is necessary to add numbers that have more significant digits than the capacity of the calculator. Two numbers like

140 569 074 279. and
9 435 829 308 695. can be added on an eight-digit

calculator by following these steps.

Step 1 Align the decimal points.

Step 2 Split each number into two parts: most significant digits and least significant digits. Keep each set of digits properly aligned. The number of least significant digits should be one less than the number of digits in the calculator display.

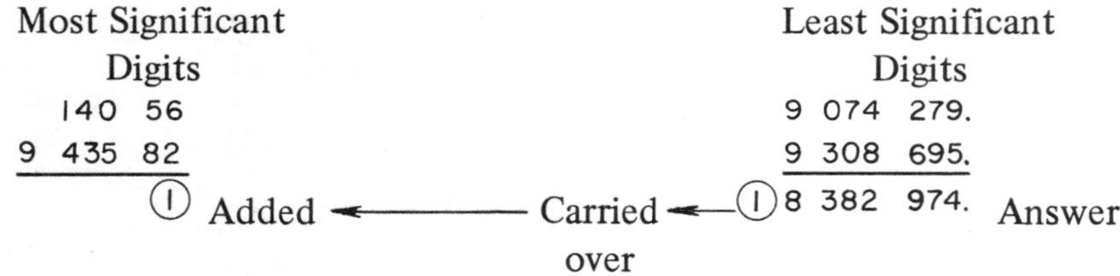

Step 3 Add the least significant digit values. Record the answer. Note that there are eight digits in this answer. The eighth place digit value ① is carried over and added to the most significant digit value in the furthest right digit column.

```
   140 56
+9 435 82
+       ①  (carryover)
 9 576 39
```

Step 4 Combine the sums of the two parts. The sum of the two combined display readings of 9576398382974 may be more easily read and accurately used when it is written as 9, 576, 398, 382, 974. In SI Metrics, the sum is given in this form: 9 576 398 382 974. This form is used in this section.

Large quantities may be subtracted in a similar manner. The decimal points are aligned. The values are placed in two columns: (1) the most significant part and (2) the least significant part. There must be one less number of digits than the capacity of the calculator. The values (1) and (2) are then subtracted.

It should be noted that if the top number is less than the lower number, one (1) must be "borrowed" the same as in simple arithmetic. When (1) is borrowed in the last (left) digit position of the least significant part, the right (and first) digit in the most significant part is reduced by (1). After the two parts are subtracted, they are combined to obtain the answer.

EXAMPLE:

```
                     1 549 075 239.983 1
                   -   752 365 841.994 2
                   ---------------------
            4
  1 549 075 (Reduce by (1)) ------> Add 1 -> (1) 239.983 1
  - 752 365                                    - 841.994 2
  ---------                                    ---------
    796 709                                      397.988 9
                 796 709 397.988 9   Answer
```

As stated earlier, most practical problems involve the four basic mathematical processes covered in this unit. The pocket model four-function calculator with eight-digit display is uniquely adapted to handle common everyday computing needs. The next unit describes algorithms. These procedures for solving problems which involve higher mathematical processes may be used on any four-function calculator.

ASSIGNMENT UNIT 88

A. CHARACTERISTICS OF ELECTRONIC CALCULATORS

Indicate the one process in column II which correctly relates to each machine or function (column I)

Column I

Calculator or Function

1. Four-function calculator
2. Display
3. Programmable calculator
4. Program
5. Algebraic entry

Column II

Process

a. Contains memory and instructions capability.
b. Problem solving in the same logical sequence a person usually follows.
c. Performs addition, subtraction, multiplication and division processes only.
d. Total-erase process.
e. Visible colored entry or problem solution.
f. Registers that store problem values.
g. Corrects a number entry error.
h. Sequence for executing instructions entered in a computer.

Ans. 2. (e) 4. (h)

6. State the functions performed by the (a) CM, (b) RM, and (c) M+ memory keys.

Ans.: (b) RM (MR) key recalls a value in a memory registor . . . and/or transfers a memory register value to the accumulator register.

7. Indicate (a) how a calculator may be reset to zero and (b) a method of correcting an entry error.

   Ans.: (b) The CE or CD key is pressed to erase an error, followed by the entry of the correct new value.

8. (a) Describe what an eight-digit display means. (b) Give a numerical example of the capacity of this model calculator.

   Ans.: (a) An eight-digit display means that a calculator has a numerical capacity of eight digits that may be displayed at one time.

B. SIGNIFICANT FIGURES, PRECISION AND ACCURACY

1. Give four examples of whole quantities and four of mixed number quantities. The quantities must contain the required significant digits given in the table for A, B, C and D.

	Required Significant Digits	Quantity Examples: Whole Number Values	Quantity Examples: Mixed Number Values
A	1		
B	3		
C	5		
D	7		

2. Define (a) precision and (b) accuracy.

   Ans.: (b) Accuracy relates to the degree of closeness to precision.

3. State how rounding off errors in high precision calculations result from truncated display values.

4. Define (a) overflow and (b) underflow. Give a numerical example in each case.

   Ans.: (a) Overflow denotes a condition where the numerical capacity of the calculator is exceeded.

C. BASIC ARITHMETICAL PROCESSES . . . ADDITION, SUBTRACTION, MULTIPLICATION, DIVISION

1. Add the linear measurements given in the table with a calculator. List (a) the sequence of steps, (b) the key(s) and values to be entered, and (c) the display readings. Mark the answer with the appropriate unit of measurement.

Problem (Add):

29 375. Kilometers (km)
7 645.2 km
987.96 km
1 969.7 km

Step (a)	Keyboard Entry (b)	Display Reads (c)

2. Add the following numerical quantities with a calculator having fewer digits than any of the three quantities. (a) Arrange the quantities into two columns of most significant digits and least significant digits. Then proceed to find the sum. (b) State the answer in megahertz (MHz) to four decimal places (least significant digits).

765 372 987.37	Hz
8 849 235.967 89	Hz
26 795 869.758 7	Hz

Ans.: (b) 801.018 1 MHz

3. Add the four quantities given in the table with a calculator. Indicate (a) the sequence of steps, (b) keys to be pressed or value to be entered, and (c) the display reading.

   Between the second and third quantity introduce an error. Include the steps to show the wrong entry, the display, and how the error is corrected.

Problem (Add)	797.75 rpm 8 756.90 rpm + 95 682. rpm 439.6 rpm	
Step (a)	**Press (Keyboard) (b)**	**Display Reads (c)**

4. Subtract the three given quantities which follow. Use a calculator. State the answer correct to three decimal places. Label the answer.

$$736.5\ \text{cm}^3 - 287.75\ \text{cm}^3 - 67.475\ \text{cm}^3 - 92.895\,6\ \text{cm}^3$$

Ans.: 288.379 cm^3

5. Subtract the three numerical quantities listed, using either a six- or eight-digit calculator. Label the answer, rounding off the metric measurement to five significant digits.

	8 957.625	mm
-	2 868.732 9	mm
-	4 927.843 42	mm

Ans.: 1 161.0 mm

6. Set up a problem with a quantity that is to be divided three times by a constant value. State the problem, the keyboard inputs, and the display readout for each step.

Problem		
Step	**Keyboard Input**	**Display Readout**

7. Solve the following problem, using the rules of order. Round off the decimal value to two significant places.

$$27 + 19.2 \times 31.3 \div 7.9$$

Ans.: 103.071

Unit 89 FOUR-FUNCTION CALCULATORS AND ADVANCED MATHEMATICAL PROCESSES

Persons who regularly deal with financial, business, engineering, scientific, slide rule, or other advanced mathematical processes usually perform them on more expensive, special calculators. The electronic circuitry is more complex in these special calculators and there is additional built-in capacity and accuracy. Also, additional keys are included in order to carry on many combinations of mathematical functions.

It is possible, however, to perform higher mathematical processes involving algebraic, trigonometric, or geometric calculations, using the four-function calculator. Step-by-step procedures are described in this unit for performing these mathematical functions.

ALGORITHMS

An *algorithm* is a step-by-step routine used in solving a problem. It is this same routine that is used internally in calculators. The electronic circuitry within a calculator performs three basic processes to solve or implement any mathematical problem. The circuitry can perform only addition, subtraction and shifting. The term *shifting* means moving a number one or more digits to the right or left in relation to another number. As stated many times, multiplication and division processes require successive addition and subtraction, respectively.

In summary, an algorithm is a set of mathematical rules, numerical procedures, or logical decisions. It provides variable input data to a calculator. Once an algorithm is mastered, advanced problems that would involve a single key on a sophisticated calculator may be easily performed on the four-function calculator.

A. ALGEBRAIC PROCESSES WITH THE FOUR-FUNCTION CALCULATOR

RECIPROCALS

The *reciprocal* interchanges a numerator and denominator. This interchanging is a valuable technique in chain processes. Since division is involved in finding a reciprocal, the value (1) is divided by a designated value. For instance, the reciprocal of 16 is 1 divided by 16 = 0.0625. Another procedure for finding the reciprocal of 16 is illustrated by the five steps shown in the table.

Step	Keyboard Entry	Display Readout
1	CC	0
2	16	16
3	÷	16
4	=	1
5	=	0.0625

When used in a chain process, the following algorithm applies.

Example: Find the reciprocal of (275.392 75 ÷ 17.687)

Step	Keyboard Entry	Display Readout
1	CC	0
2	275.392 75	275.392 75
3	÷	275.392 75
4	17.687	17.687
5	=	15.570 348
6	÷	15.570 348
7	=	1
8	=	0.064 224 6

RAISING NUMERICAL VALUES TO HIGHER POWERS

One of the simplest problems of raising a number to a higher power is squaring the number. This process requires the use of the exponent (^{2}) with the number. Squaring problems are computed on the calculator the same as in ordinary multiplication. The square of 6.7 is 6.7 x 6.7 = 44.89.

There are two common algorithms that may be used when a number (N) must be raised to a higher power like the (nth) power. The first sequence is practical when the value of the power is smaller than ten. The number to be raised to a given power is entered on the keyboard. Then the multiplication (X) key is pressed. This step is followed by pressing the (=) key one less time than the required power. The final value represents N^n, the quantity (N) raised to the required (^{n}) power.

If there is a chain calculation involving the raising of a quantity to a power, the problem should be restated in the sequence in which the combined mathematical processes are performed. The following method eliminates going back to parts of a problem.

EXAMPLE: $$\frac{(17.96 + 8.53)\ 6.2^3}{(7.23 \times 3.45)}$$

Restated as (17.96 + 8.53) x 6.2 x 6.2 x 6.2 ÷ (7.23 x 3.45) the problem is keyed as a chain process into a calculator.

RAISING A NUMBER TO A VERY HIGH POWER

Raising a quantity to a very high power by using the first method is cumbersome and subject to possible error of a lost count. A simple algorithm to follow requires the breaking down of the high power into smaller factors. Assuming a quantity N is to be raised to the 180th power $(N)^{180}$, the 180 is broken down into smaller factors, like 3 x 3 x 4 x 5.

EXAMPLE:

Raise N (value 1.3) to the 45th power.
$(1.3)^{45} = (1.3^3)^3)^5$

- Enter N (1.3)
- Press x key
- Press = key one less time than the value of first power
- Press x key
- Press = key one less time than the value of the second power
- Press x key
- Press = key one less time than the value of the third power
- Read the display.

Step	Keyboard Entry	Display Readout
1	CC	0
2	1.3	1.3
3	x	1.3
4, 5	=, =	1.69 2.197
6	x	2.197
7, 8	=, =	4.826 809 10.604 499
9	x	10.604 499
10	=	112.455 539
11	=	1 192.533
12	=	12 646.215
13	=	134 106.77

The thirteen steps shown in the table may be reduced if the calculator has a key for squaring (X^2). After the required power has been factored, each factor may be further broken down. For example, $N^4 = N^2 \times N^2$; $N^3 = N^2 \times N$; $N^8 = N^2 \times N^2 \times N^2$, etc. The required quantity is factored by using the X^2 key in combination with the X key to produce the equivalent exponential factor value.

SQUARE ROOT

Square root problems are easily solved on calculators that have a square root function key. The required quantity for which the square root is needed is entered on the keyboard. The $\sqrt{\ }$ key is pressed. The display readout is the answer.

The process is more complicated on the four-function calculator because a trial-and-error procedure known as "iterative approximation" and a formula are used. An estimate is made of the square root of the required quantity. Suppose the square root of 97 is required. An estimate of 10 is made. Substitute the first estimate (10) for E, and 97 for N in the formula.

$$\sqrt{R} = [(N \div E) + E] \div 2$$
$$= [(97 \div 10) + 10] \div 2$$
$$= 9.85$$

$\sqrt{R}$ = square root value

N = number for which the square root is required

E = estimated square root of N

The approximate root (9.85) is now squared. The result of 97.022 5 is too inaccurate. So, the process is repeated. This time the second estimated new root of 9.85 is substituted.

$$\sqrt{R} = [(N \div E) + E] \div 2$$
$$= [(97 \div 9.85) + 9.85] \div 2$$
$$= 9.848\ 857\ 5$$

Again, squaring the resulting third estimating root of 9.848 857 5 gives a product of 96.999 994. With this degree of precision, the third estimate is accepted as the answer. Normally, a four-place decimal value is sufficiently accurate.

If the last estimate does not produce a product within the limits of accuracy required in the problem, the estimating procedure is repeated one or more times. When still higher degrees of accuracy are needed, a calculator with a greater number of digits or built-in square root capacity should be used.

The percent of error may be calculated by using a formula and substituting values.

$$\frac{(N) - (R)^2}{(N)} \times 100 = \text{Percent Error}$$

For example, if the second estimated root of 9.85 is squared and the product (97.022 5) is substituted for R^2,

$$\frac{97 - 97.022\ 5}{97} \times 100 = -0.023\ 19\%\ \text{error.}$$

CUBE ROOT AND HIGHER ROOTS

Another algorithm is needed to obtain the cube and higher roots. While a similar procedure is followed as for determining square root, a different formula is used.

$$R^x = [(N \div A^{n-1}) + (n-1)A] \div n$$

R^x = cube root or higher root
N = quantity for which root is to be computed
n = order of the root
A = approximate value of the nth root

As an example of the steps and entries that are made on a calculator, assume the cube root of 500 is required. The root value should be within .001% of accuracy. The estimated value (A) of the nth (^{3}) root is 8.

Formula		Step	Keyboard Entry	Display Readout
Item	Quantity			
		1	CC	0
[N	500	2	500	500
÷		3	÷	500
(A^{n-1})	(8^{3-1})	4	64	7.8125
+		5	+	7.8125
(n-1)A]	(3–1) 8	6	16	23.8125
÷		7	÷	23.8125
n	(3)	8	3	3
=	R^x	9	=	7.9375

The cube of 7.937 5 = 500.093 5. If the error of .093 5 is too great, the process may be repeated. In this case, the second estimated root value should be slightly smaller. For closer precision, an estimated value smaller than the first estimate of 7.9375 (like 7.937) may be used. $(7.937)^3 = 499.999$. This value is accurate to within 0.0002%.

While a cube root example was used to show the steps involved with a four-function calculator, higher root values may be computed using the same formula and processes.

FACTORIAL FUNCTION

Another common function in higher mathematical calculations is *factorial*. *Factorial* denotes that a product is to be established for all possible integers of a value. The symbol (!) identifies the process. A designation like 7! means "seven factorial." The value is computed by finding the product of

1 x 2; 2 x 3; 6 x 4; 24 x 5; 120 x 6; 720 x 7 = 5 040

This problem is a continuous series of multiplication steps. The calculator entries would be 2 x 3 x 4 x 5 x 6 x 7 = 5 040. Other factorial problem are solved using this same process.

PI (π) AND EPSILON (ϵ) VALUES

Throughout the text, pi (π) has been used in many different types of practical mathematical problems. *Pi* is an "irrational number" whose value is 3.141 592 653 589 793 . . . It is obvious that most calculations are not this precise. So, the exact value is rounded off to a required number of decimal places. Values of 3.1416, 3.142 and 3.14, and the fractional value 22/7 are widely used for most everyday problems.

The highest degree of precision possible on an eight-digit calculator is to round the value of π to eight decimal places: 3.141 592 7.

Another important value is designated by the Greek letter, *epsilon* (ϵ). The value of ϵ is also an irrational number with a value of 2.718 281 828 459 045 . . . The number of decimal places that are entered on the calculator depends on the machine limits and the degree of accuracy required.

The value of epsilon is important as it is the base of a system of natural logarithms. Calculator operations, using an epsilon (ϵ) value and an exponent, are carried on as a simple multiplication process. For example, if the value of ϵ^3 is needed, the ϵ quantity 2.718 281 8 is entered on an eight-digit calculator. The x key is pressed twice (for the third power) to obtain 20.085 536 as the value of ϵ^3.

B. TRIGONOMETRIC FUNCTIONS WITH THE FOUR-DIGIT CALCULATOR

In review, it may be stated that trigonometry is a study of the properties, applications and solutions related to three-sided (triangular) shapes. Trigonometry incorporates basic mathematical processes which establish the relationships among the sides and angles. The names and the ratios between the sides and angles of right, acute and oblique triangles, and the application of trigonometric function tables were covered in earlier units of this text.

At this time, algorithms are illustrated for calculating sine, cosine, tangent and cotangent values.

CALCULATING SINE VALUES

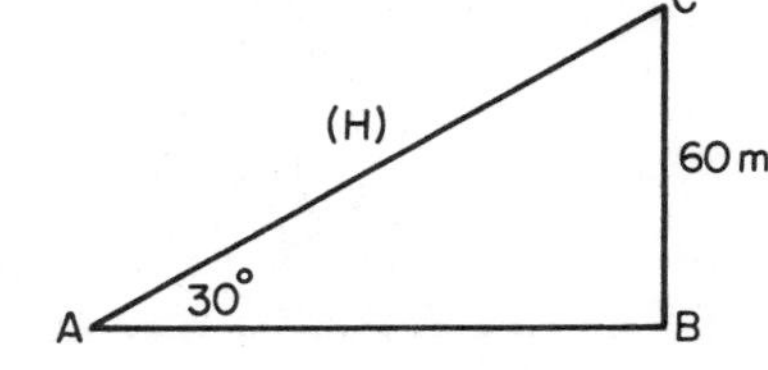

Problem. The length (H) of a laminated timber truss must be determined to meet the construction requirements specified on the drawing.

The sine of angle A may be found be using the algorithm

$$\text{Sin A} = 1.745\,\alpha\,[1 + 0.508\,\alpha^2\ (0.15\,\alpha^2 - 1)]$$

$$\alpha = \frac{\angle A}{100} = \frac{30}{100} = 0.30$$

To eliminate the need for setting down an intermediate value for the square of angle A, the sequence in the chart may be used:

Step	Keyboard Entry	
	Numerical Value	Process
1	0.30	x
2	0.30	x
3	0.15	–
4	1	x
5	0.30	x
6	0.30	x
7	0.508	+
8	1	x
9	0.30	x
10	1.745	=
Display readout 0.4998885 = sin A		

If the sine value of 30° as produced by the calculator (0.499 888 5) is checked against a table of natural trigonometric functions (0.500 000 0) the calculator result is in error. Thus, a word of caution is in order. When this algorithm is used, a possible small error is introduced.

Continuing with the problem, the length of the laminated wooden truss is found by the sine formula: $\sin A = \frac{\text{opposite side (60)}}{\text{hypotenuse (H)}}$; Transposing, $H = \frac{60}{\sin A = (.499\ 888\ 5)}$

$= 120.026$ meters long. Ans.

When calculated by conventional trigonometric methods the truss would be exactly 120 meters long. Using this algorithm and a calculator an error of + 0.026 meters, or 1.024" is introduced. This degree of tolerance may not be acceptable. With engineering problems such as this one, the calculator may be used to supplement the conventional computation method (using table values for natural trigonometric functions). In this instance, the table value of the 30° angle of .500 000 would have produced the exact 120 meter measurement.

CALCULATING COSINE VALUES

A different formula and algorithm is used for determining cosine values.

$$\cos A = 1 - 1.523\ \alpha^2\ [1 + 0.254\ \alpha^2\ (0.1\ \alpha^2 - 1)]$$

The numerical value and process entries on the keyboard are similar to the steps followed with the sine calculations. Again α = angle A ÷ 100.

Problem. Determine the distance (D) a surveyor is to locate a construction bench mark, according to the drawing dimensions.

$$\cos A = \frac{\text{side adjacent}}{\text{hypotenuse}}$$

$\cos 40^\circ = D/3$

$D = \cos 40^\circ \times 3$

Using rules of order for solving internal parentheses values first, and substituting known values,

$$\cos A = 1 - 1.523\ (.4)^2\ [1 + (0.254 \times .4^2)\ (0.1 \times (.4^2) - 1)] = .766\ 064\ 8$$

Substituting this value for cos A, D = .766 064 8 x 3 = 2.298 194 4 kilometers. Again, it should be noted that this quantity varies from the exact dimension of 2.298 kilometers.

CALCULATING SECANT VALUES

The secant is the ratio of the hypotenuse divided by the side adjacent. The value of the secant of an angle is the reciprocal of its cosine. Thus, the secant may be found by computing the reciprocal.

$$\sec A = \frac{1}{\cos A}$$

CALCULATING TANGENT VALUES

A tangent value may be computed with a calculator using the following algorithm.

$$\tan A = 1.745\ \alpha\left(\frac{1.015\ \alpha^2 - 5}{6.092\ \alpha^2 - 5}\right) \qquad \alpha = \frac{\angle A}{100}$$

In setting up the procedure to follow, it is necessary to carry on the numerator and denominator computations first and to record the display readouts of the intermediate values.

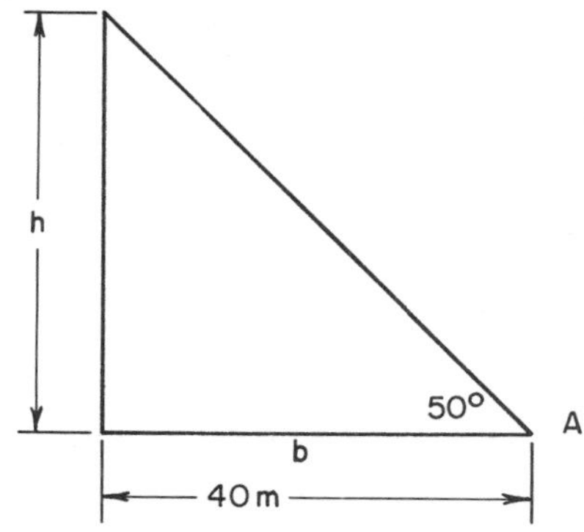

Problem. The distance from a vertical beam to a mooring post is 40 meters. The angle of a connecting brace is 50 degrees. Determine the height (h) of the vertical beam.

Using the formula and substituting the value 0.50 for α,

$$\tan A = 1.745\,\alpha \left(\frac{1.015\,\alpha^2 - 5}{6.092\,\alpha^2 - 5} \right)$$

$$= \underbrace{1.745\,(.5)}_{\text{STEP 4}} \left(\frac{\boxed{1.015\,(.25) - 5}}{\boxed{6.092\,(.25) - 5}} \right)$$

STEP 1: $\boxed{= -4.746\ 25}$

STEP 2: $\boxed{= -3.477}$

STEP 4: $\boxed{0.8725}$

STEP 3: $\boxed{\dfrac{-4.746\ 25}{-3.477}} \;—\; \boxed{= 1.365\ 041\ 7}$

$$= \underbrace{0.8725 \times 1.365\ 041\ 7}_{\text{STEP 5}} = 1.190\ 998\ 8$$

$$\tan A = \frac{\text{side opposite (h)}}{\text{side adjacent (b)}}$$

$$\begin{aligned} (h) &= \tan A\,(b) \\ &= 1.190\ 998\ 8\,(40) \\ &= 47.639\ 952 \text{ meters (m)} \quad \text{Answer.} \end{aligned}$$

NOTE: The conventional trigonometric method of solving this problem is simpler and does not have the built-in error of this algorithm. The correct (error-free) height of the vertical beam is 47.62 meters. This height is calculated by using the tangent formula, a four-place decimal natural trigonometric function value for the 60° tangent (1.1918), and substituting quantities.

$$\begin{aligned} \text{Since (h)} &= \tan A\,(b) \\ &= 1.1918\,(40) \\ &= 47.62 \text{ meters (m). Answer} \end{aligned}$$

The solving of this type of problem by the conventional method, supplemented by the calculator for carrying out the multiplication process is simple, conserves time, and produces an accurate measurement.

CALCULATING COTANGENT VALUES

The cotangent denotes the relationship between the side adjacent to an angle and the side opposite to the same angle. Thus, the cotangent is the inverted tangent ratio.

$$\cot A = \frac{1}{\tan A}$$

The cotangent may be determined by calculating the reciprocal of the tangent.

OTHER TRIGONOMETRIC ALGORITHMS

A number of other algorithms have been developed to solve additional trigonometric functions. Since each algorithm produces a small error, it is recommended that the conventional computational methods previously described in the trigonometry units be used. The calculator is invaluable in carrying out the actual computations that otherwise would be done by hand or with a slide rule.

C. GEOMETRIC CALCULATIONS WITH THE FOUR-DIGIT CALCULATOR

The importance of geometry in the construction of every visible part, component, mechanism, and object was described in Part 4. Some descriptions and measurements related to closed flat surfaces on a plane. Triangles, circles, squares, parallelograms, trapezoids and combinations of these shapes are examples of everyday common applications.

Adaptations of these flat shapes are found in cones, pyramids, prisms, spheres, and other combinations. These shapes are identified as solids. Measurements apply to both plane and solid shapes. Direct measurements are taken with measuring instruments, others are computed. Thus, geometric figures require computations for linear, circular, area, and volume measurements.

An analysis of the formulas used to compute such quantities reveals that they incorporate the four basic mathematical processes, higher powers, and roots of numerical values. Table XIV in the Appendix lists calculator processes which relate to measurements of common geometric constructions. This information simplifies computations for dimensions and other values for flat and solid shapes.

ASSIGNMENT UNIT 89

A. ALGEBRAIC PROCESSES WITH THE FOUR-FUNCTION CALCULATOR

1. Describe briefly the importance of an algorithm in using a calculator.

2. a. Calculate the reciprocal of the four quantities given in the table. List the display readouts.
   b. State the answer, rounding each decimal value to four significant digits.

   Ans.: (b) B. 7.4000 D. 2.0840

	Quantity	RECIPROCAL VALUE	
		Display Readout (a)	Rounded Answer (b)
A	18		
B	$\frac{1}{7.4}$		
C	$\frac{176.33}{16\ 206.4}$		
D	$\frac{422.17 \times 16.7}{14\ 692.9}$		

3. a. Raise each quantity (A through H) to the required power. Record the display readout.
   b. Indicate each measurement by rounding off the decimal display values to two significant digits, unless otherwise indicated.

   Ans.: (b) B. 373.25
   E. 12855.00
   H. 403.445

	Quantity	Power Value: Display Readout (a)	Power Value: Measurement (b)
A	8^6		
B	7.2^3		
C	$8.4^2 \times 10.6^2$		
D	$10.04^3 \times 16.2^2$		
E	2.2^{12}		
F	0.46^{15}		
G	π^4 Use $\pi = 3.1416$		
H	α^6 Use $\alpha = 2.7183$		

4. Compute the square root and the higher roots for quantities A, B, C, and D. Note the required degree of precision.
   a. Give the display readout of each final root value.
   b. Round each root value to four decimal places.

   Ans.: (b) B. 5.6629
   D. 2.9916

	Quantity	Required Precision	Root Value: Display Readout (a)	Root Value: Required Dimension (b)
A	$\sqrt{86}$	±.001		
B	$\sqrt{\frac{(6.2 \times 9)}{1.74}}$	±.01		
C	$\sqrt[3]{(5.07 \times 4.02)^2}$	±.02		
D	$\sqrt[6]{716.88}$	±.005		

B. TRIGONOMETRIC FUNCTIONS WITH THE FOUR-DIGIT CALCULATOR

1. Calculate the structural steel beam lengths for four different trusses, according to the dimensions given in the table.
   a. Give the display readout of each measurement.
   b. Convert the display readouts to feet-inch dimensions. Use the sine algorithm and a calculator.

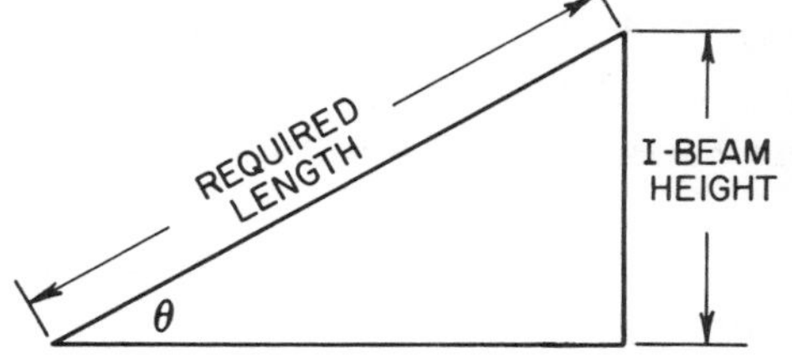

	Truss Angle	I-Beam Height	Required Beam Length: 1. Calculator/Algorithm Method — Display Readout	1. Calculator/Algorithm Method — Dimension (feet/inches)	2. Conventional Method — Computed Value	2. Conventional Method — Dimension (feet/inches)	3. Dimensional Variation
A	30°	20′					
B	45°	24′					
C	60°	32′					
D	22°30′	16′-6″					

Ans.: (a) B. 33.95 D. 43.125

2. Check the structural steel length dimensions in problem 1 by the conventional method. Use four-place decimal values for the natural trigonometric functions.
   a. Compute and record the lengths, rounding off the measurements to two decimal places.
   b. Convert these values to the closest 1/8″ dimension.

   Ans.: (b) B. 33′-11 1/4″ D. 43′-1 3/8″

3. Compare each structural steel beam length as computed by the two methods. Indicate any dimensional variation in the last right column of the table.

   Ans.: B. 1/8″ D. 1/8″

C. GEOMETRIC APPLICATIONS USING THE CALCULATOR

1. The dimensions of three rectangular cold air return ducts for a heating system are given in the table. Determine the volume of air each duct will hold in both British and metric units of measure. Round off the final calculated volumes to two decimal places and record. Use

   $1 \text{ m}^3 = \text{ft}^3 \times .02832$

   $1 \text{ ft}^3 = \text{m}^3 \times 35.3147$

Dimensions				Calculated Volume	
Duct	Height	Width	Length	m^3	ft^3
A	9″	1′-6″	20′		
B	.305 m	.610 m	9.144 m		
C	.406 m	.762 m	14.021 m		

2. A fluid system has a rectangular reservoir and two round feeder pipes of different diameters.
   a. Use a calculator to compute the cubic meter volume in the system to the nearest whole number.
   b. Convert the volume m^3 to ft^3, correct to the nearest whole number.

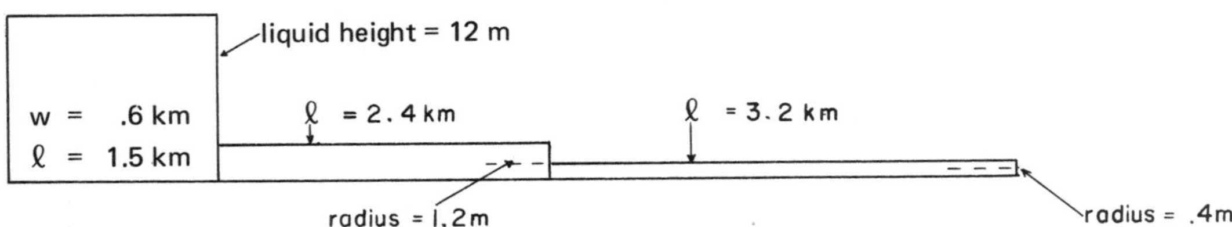

Unit 90 ACHIEVEMENT REVIEW ON CALCULATORS

A. CHARACTERISTICS OF ELECTRONIC CALCULATORS

1. State four advantages of modern electronic calculators over older calculating machines and devices.
2. a. Describe the purpose served by the registers of a calculator.
   b. State the function of three operating registers in a four-process calculator.
3. Cite two purposes that are served by the calculator display.

B. SIGNIFICANT FIGURES, PRECISION AND ACCURACY

1. Tell and illustrate how the number of digits in a least significant decimal value indicates the precision of a quantity.
2. State a problem with three mixed numbers having an overall total of 12 digits and requiring addition and subtraction processes. Show how the three quantities may be grouped for an eight-digit calculator for double-precision calculations.

C. THE CALCULATOR AND BASIC ARITHMETICAL PROCESSES

1. Solve the problem given in the table. (a) Number the steps and indicate the (b) keyboard entries and (c) display readings. Round the answer to six significant digits and mark the answer with the appropriate unit of measurement.

Problem	Step (a)	Keyboard Entry (b)	Display Readout (c)
865.7 volts +1 720. volts - 440.80 volts - 720.095 volts			

2. Add and subtract the quantities given in the problem. Use a six- or eight-digit calculator.
   a. Show how the quantities are arranged in two columns.
   b. Label and give the answer corrected to eight significant digits.

	4 3 5 8 7 2 . 5	cycles
+	8 9 4 2 5 . 7 6	"
+	4 9 8 7 . 5 3 7	"
–	2 0 9 . 6 7 9 6	"
–	3 2 6 8 . 7 8 2 5	"

3. Multiply the quantity of 208 volts by the constant value 2.67 for three times. Use a hand calculator and give the answer correct to three decimal places.

D. ALGEBRAIC PROCESSES WITH THE FOUR-DIGIT CALCULATOR

1. Determine the ignition pulse (distributor point) frequency (ipf) for the two- and four-stroke cycle engine specifications given in the table.

   Use the formula, $\text{ipf} = \frac{(n) \times (\text{rpm})}{(X)}$

   n = number of cylinders
   X = 120 for 4-stroke cycle engines
   = 60 for 2-stroke cycle engines

   NOTE: Round off the pulses per second (ips) to one decimal place.

Engine			Specifications		
	Cylinders (n)	**Crankshaft (rpm)**	**Stroke Cycle**	**Distributor Point Frequency (ipf)**
A	8	2 000	4	
B	12	1 625	4	
C	6	1 375	2	
D	4	1 840	2	

2. The rise time (t_r) and the cutoff frequency (f_2) of a circuit may be computed by the following formulas.

$$t_r = \sqrt{(c^2) - (a^2 + b^2)} \qquad f_2 = \frac{0.35}{t_r}$$

Rise Time (in nanoseconds)					Upper Cutoff Frequency (f_2 in megahertz MHz)
Circuit	**Oscilloscope (a)**	**Square Wave (b)**	**Pulse (c)**	**Circuit (t_r)**	
A	40	20	110		
B	32	18	90		

Use a calculator to compute the t_r and f_2 values for the A and B circuit conditions given in the table. Round off megahertz values to two decimal places.

3. Determine the liquid volume capacity of containers A, B, and C with a calculator, correct to two decimal places. $V = 0.7854\,(D^2)\,h$

Container			Volume Capacity
	D	h	
A	2″	4″	
B	2.54 cm	15.24 cm	
C	6.62 m	5.2 m	

E. TRIGONOMETRIC APPLICATIONS USING THE FOUR-DIGIT CALCULATOR

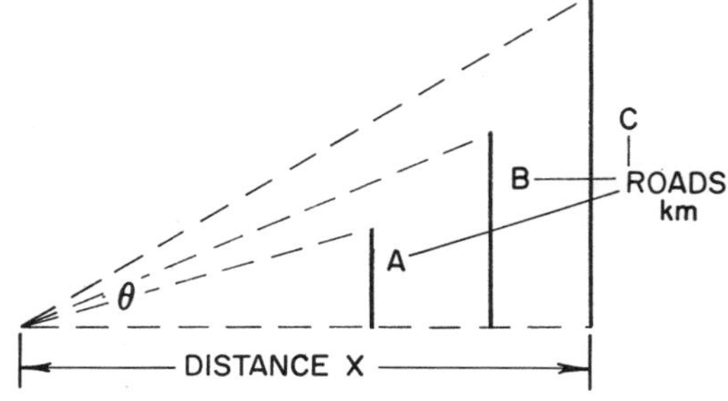

1. Compute the lengths of highway that must be paved for roads A, B, and C. The table indicates the angles of the feeder roads and the distance (X). Use the following formula and a calculator.

$$\tan\theta = 1.745\,\alpha\left(\frac{1.015\,\alpha^2 - 5}{6.092\,\alpha^2 - 5}\right)$$

$\alpha = \theta \div 100$ Side A = $\tan\theta$ (X)

   a. Show the display readout for the value of $\tan\theta$ and (b) the new highway distances in kilometers.

Apex to			Calculator-Algorithm Method			Trigonometric Function Method			Accuracy of Computations (Variations)	
Road	Angle θ	Crossroad Distance (kilometers) (km)	Display Readout $\tan\theta$ 1(a)	New Highway Distances (km) 1(b)	New Highway Distances (miles) (2)	$\tan\theta$ 3(a)	New Highway Distances (km) (b)	New Highway Distances (miles) (c)	(km) 4(a)	(miles) (b)
A	20°	5.5								
B	25°	12.25								
C	32° 30′	16.375								

2. Convert each kilometer distance to its mile equivalent. Use 1 km = 0.6214 mi. Round the mileage values to four decimal places.

3. Check the highway lengths by conventional trigonometric methods, using natural trigonometric functions. Record (a) the natural function of $\tan\theta$ and (b) the kilometer and (c) equivalent mile quantities.

4. Compare the calculator and the conventional method results. Indicate any variations in computations for road lengths A, B, or C. Express the variations (a) in decimal kilometer quantities and (b) equivalent mileage quantities.

F. GEOMETRIC APPLICATIONS USING THE FOUR-DIGIT CALCULATOR

1. a. Determine the volume of liquid contained in the conical, cylindrical and rectangular tank illustrated. Round off the answer to two decimal places. Use these formulas.

   Cylinder $V = 0.7854\ D^2\ (\ell)$

   Cone $V = 0.2618\ h\ (D^2 + D\ d + d^2)$

   b. Convert the cubic feet volume to a metric volume measurement, correct to two decimal places. Use:

   $1\ ft^3 = 0.028\ 32\ m^3$

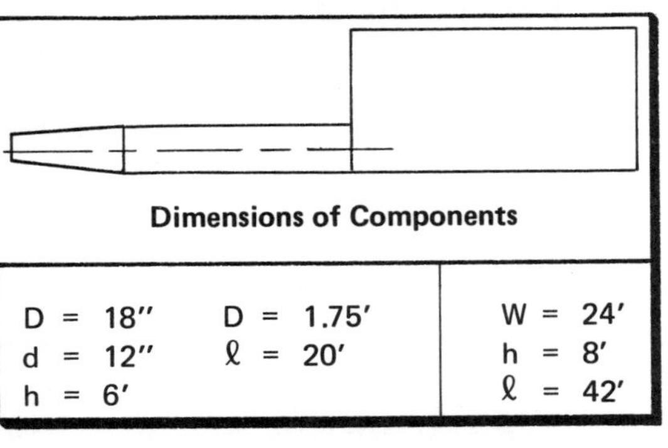

2. Find the liquid volume capacity of cylindrical vessels A, B, and C with a calculator. Round the values to two decimal places.

	Container Dimensions	Volume Capacity
A	2″ diameter, 4″ high	
B	2.54 cm diam. 15.24 cm high	
C	11.4 m diam. .875 m high	

Section 20

APPLICATION OF MATHEMATICS TO CONSUMER AND CAREER NEEDS

Unit 91 CONSUMER APPLICATIONS OF MATHEMATICS

Every individual has a financial responsibility to himself, his family, and the community. Students with limited income from work experience or other employment, young adults planning marriage and home responsibilities, adults and older persons with family and other obligations, all represent different levels of earning and income capacity, needs, and expenditures.

A. MATHEMATICS APPLIED IN MONEY MANAGEMENT AND BUDGETING

The plan for money management is commonly referred to as a "*budget.*" A budget is an intelligent way of making long-term judgments. These decisions prevent overspending. They help to methodically save to meet specific needs for later or accumulating expenses. A budget helps the individual to:

- Determine the purpose for which money will be used.
- Distribute and spend income for essential items according to established priorities. This practice eliminates wasteful habits.
- Achieve long-range goals for investing and building assets.
- Avoid unnecessary borrowing which, normally requires the borrower to produce a greater income to pay off charges for the use of other people's money.

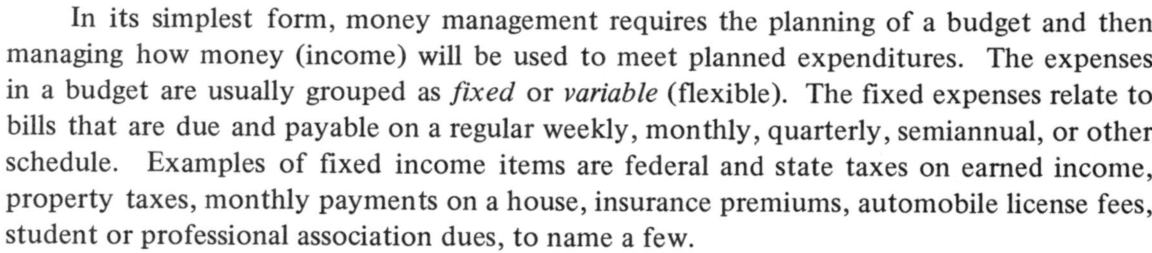

In its simplest form, money management requires the planning of a budget and then managing how money (income) will be used to meet planned expenditures. The expenses in a budget are usually grouped as *fixed* or *variable* (flexible). The fixed expenses relate to bills that are due and payable on a regular weekly, monthly, quarterly, semiannual, or other schedule. Examples of fixed income items are federal and state taxes on earned income, property taxes, monthly payments on a house, insurance premiums, automobile license fees, student or professional association dues, to name a few.

Variable (flexible) expenses represent those that may be changed. Such expenses permit flexibility in adjusting a budget to meet emergency conditions or other changes in earnings or expenses. Expenditures for flexible items cover recreation and hobbies, gifts, entertainment, nonessential clothing, additional furniture, dining out, and any items that may be included, changed, or dropped from a budget.

Expertise in budget preparation requires setting up a trial budget, adjusting the budget, and learning to live within the plan of a working budget. The trial budget starts with a listing of both fixed and flexible day-to-day expenses. Expenses should be grouped under main categories: personal expenses (food and clothing), housing and household expenses, transportation expenses, taxes, and other items such as medical services. These items require expenditures that are actual or estimated by the day and week and are totalled for the month and year.

Larger items that are paid monthly, quarterly, or annually should be identified under a proper category and then combined with related day-to-day items. Monthly mortgage payments, estimated costs of utilities, insurance premiums, automobile or boat payments, installment payments for furniture and equipment. . . each is a significant expenditure and should be listed.

The trial plan should include a list of all sources of income: wages, scholarships, dividends, interest, gifts. The income part is then matched with the estimated expenditures to determine what adjustments must be made. Since it is difficult to anticipate all expenditures, especially when a budget is prepared in advance, provision should be made for emergency situations.

To bring a budget in balance requires making decisions about the importance of one item in relation to another. Once priorties have been established and the income is balanced with the expenditures, a new breakdown of the budget should be made according to a monthly and weekly schedule. There will be peaks and valleys in money management since all bills are not due according to a regular pattern. Expenditures will not be made at the same level each week and month.

Effective money management requires the setting up of a system of records, maintaining them in a regular and orderly manner, controlling and managing income and expenses through a budget. All essential information such as bills, payments, receipts, and cancelled checks, should be recorded in a book or ledger and kept in properly labelled envelopes or files. This requires putting valuable papers, bonds, saving and checking account passbooks, insurance policies, tax records, and other valuable documents, in a safe deposit box at a bank or in a fireproof container.

The budget must be realistic and convenient to use systematically. Additional information on money management is available through teachers and courses in basic economics and consumer education, extension services, government publications and banks. In larger corporations persons are usually assigned to deal with personal employee problems.

SETTING UP A BUDGET FOR A MONEY MANAGEMENT PLAN

√ PREPARING THE INCOME PART OF A TRIAL BUDGET

Step 1 Rule a worksheet and list the main categories for all items of income.

Step 2 Set up "amount" and "schedule" columns to indicate how much and when the income items are payable.

Step 3 Compute the monthly and annual income for each item.

Step 4 Rule monthly blocks for recording the monthly and annual totals on the worksheet. Record the computed amount.

Step 1 — Step 2 — Steps 3 and 4

Income Item Categories	Amount	Schedule: Period	Schedule: Date (Examples)	Income: Monthly: January	February	March	Annually
1. Wages	$	Biweekly	First & Fifteenth				
2. Dividends	$	Semiannual	January 1 & July 1				
3. Interest	$	Quarterly	Jan. 1, Apr. 1, July 1, Oct. 1				
4. Gifts	$	Semiannual	May 15 & Sept. 15				
5. Other	$						
			Total				

Note: • The total wage, salary, or other income should be recorded without payroll deductions. These will be recorded as expenditures.

• Monthly costs/payments may be averaged by multiplying the weekly amount by 4 1/3.

√ PREPARING THE EXPENDITURE PART OF A TRIAL BUDGET

Step 1 Set up a worksheet listing major categories of expenditures under the two headings of "fixed" and "variable," or "flexible," expenditures.

Step 2 List the major categories and the main items under each category in a vertical column.

Step 3 Rule a series of vertical "month" columns and an "annual" column and horizontal blocks for each month and the annual total.

Step 4 Total the weekly fixed expenses for each item in a category for each month.

Step 5 Record (post) the amount of each fixed item for each month.

EXAMPLE:

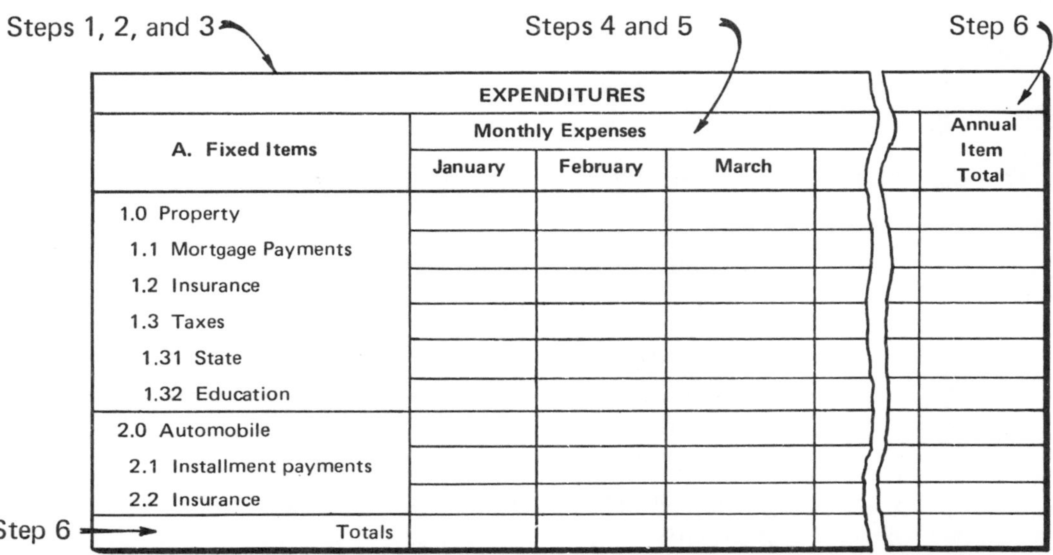

A. Fixed Items	EXPENDITURES: Monthly Expenses: January	February	March		Annual Item Total
1.0 Property					
1.1 Mortgage Payments					
1.2 Insurance					
1.3 Taxes					
1.31 State					
1.32 Education					
2.0 Automobile					
2.1 Installment payments					
2.2 Insurance					
Totals					

Step 6 Total the monthly columns horizontally to get the annual expenditures for each major item. Add the columns vertically to determine the monthly expenses and the grand total for the year.

Step 7 Continue to list the major categories and main items for the variable expenses for each week. Total these by the month and for the year. Record these expenses in the trial budget.

Step 8 Determine the grand totals for fixed and variable expenses. Record these amounts by the month and as the overall gross amount.

Step 7

B. Variable Items	Monthly Expenses					Annual Item Total
	January	February	March			
7.0 Entertainment 7.1 7.2						
8.0 Hobbies 8.1 Athletics 8.2 Boating						
9.0 Investments 9.1 Savings 9.2 Bonds						
Totals of Variable Items						
Grand Totals Fixed/Variable Items						

Step 8

Gross Amount

√ SETTING UP THE ACTUAL BUDGET

Step 1 Compare the grand totals of income and expenses. Establish priorities and reduce the variable expenditures first if the income is less than the anticipated expenses.

Step 2 Prepare the actual budget after all adjustments have been made and the income and expenses are in balance.

Note:
- The budget should be reviewed periodically and adjusted to meet changing needs, income, and expenses.
- If the income for a period of three months, six months, or a year is less than the fixed expenses, and future income will be adequate to cover the budget needs plus payments on a loan, it may be necessary to borrow money. Under these conditions, the budget should be reworked to cover a longer period to include loan payments.

√ MANAGING THE BUDGET: CONTROL SYSTEM

Step 1 Develop weekly income/expense control cards for the year. These cards should include three parts: balances, income, and expenses.

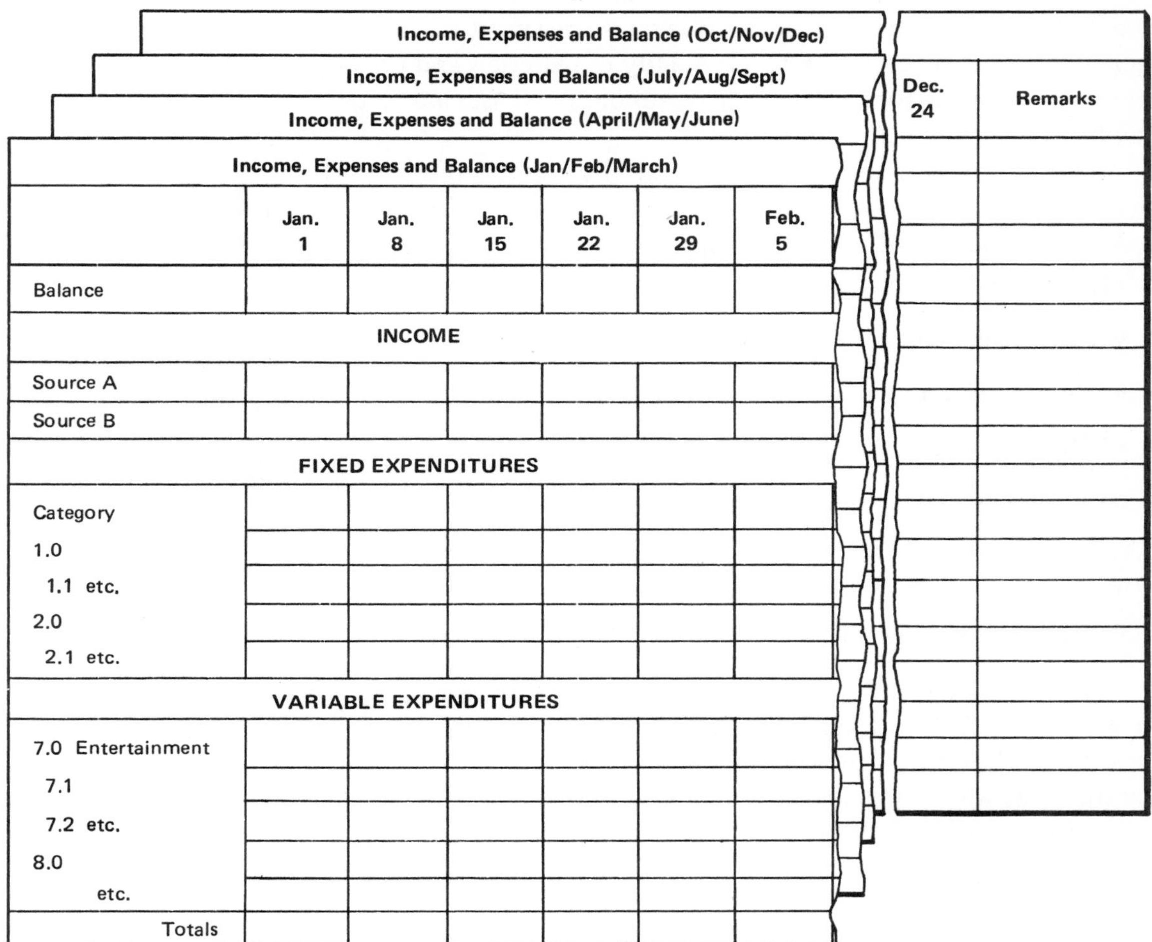

Income, Expenses and Balance (Oct/Nov/Dec)

Income, Expenses and Balance (July/Aug/Sept)

Income, Expenses and Balance (April/May/June)

Income, Expenses and Balance (Jan/Feb/March)

	Jan. 1	Jan. 8	Jan. 15	Jan. 22	Jan. 29	Feb. 5
Balance						
INCOME						
Source A						
Source B						
FIXED EXPENDITURES						
Category						
1.0						
1.1 etc.						
2.0						
2.1 etc.						
VARIABLE EXPENDITURES						
7.0 Entertainment						
7.1						
7.2 etc.						
8.0						
etc.						
Totals						

Dec. 24	Remarks

Step 2 Total the weekly income and weekly expenditures. Add the income to the starting balance. Then subtract the expenditures and record this difference as the "new balance."

Note:
- This should be done at least a month in advance. This practice establishes whether an adequate reserve has been built to take care of bills at the time they become payable.
- If the expenses exceed the balance, record the amount as a negative one (for example, -$50 or $-50.00).

Step 3 Review, recompute and adjust the budget whenever there is any significant change in either income or expenditures.

Money management also includes a plan for building assets. These will be covered later. At this point in budgeting, assets (or investments) are recorded as a major expenditure category.

B. MATHEMATICS APPLIED IN THE BUYING OF GOODS AND SERVICES

A long-range budget gives direction and helps to establish values in money management. Wise use of a budget can save precious dollars through planned, intelligent, and effective purchasing. Since money is limited, the consumer must continuously make judgments. This means paying close attention to the quality of materials and possible maintenance or operating costs. Comparisons must be made so that purchases are made based on effective buying habits.

One of the first steps in planning to buy goods and services requires that a priority be established based on needs and the availablity of immediate and future money. Consideration must be given to such factors as

- The nature and amount of use.
- How durable the item must be in quality.
- The cost of various qualities of the merchandise.
- A comparison of the cost and quality of well-known brands and retail store brands with unknown brands.

CONSUMER PROTECTION AND MISREPRESENTATION

The consumer is being protected more and more against misrepresentation and acts or words that may mislead, deceive, or exploit a person into buying a misrepresented article or service. However, proving fraud may be costly and time consuming. The federal and state governments are trying to protect the consumer through such laws as *truth-in-purchasing* and *truth-in-lending.* However, it is up to the consumer to carefully study the product and the producer. The consumer must examine the costs to maintain or operate an item, and any "hidden" extra charges.

Frauds are common in short measuring, confusing labels for weights and contents, and misrepresentation. There are frauds in food, clothing, home furnishings, appliances and other essential goods. Frauds may also take place in the purchasing, financing, and maintaining of homes, property insurance, car buying, as well as such services as automotive and machinery repairs. Some dealers use the technique of having the potential customer sign a purchase order before all additional costs and conditions of financing are known. These are just a few examples of possible misrepresentation of a material, product, commodity or service.

The consumer must, therefore, be able to make a decision in which as many facts as possible are known about an item. These facts may relate to material, workmanship and design, safety features, cost of operating the product, and the pricing of similar models. Advertising must be scrutinized for "baited items:" the consumer is told that the lesser priced item is "sold out;" or the product may be "talked down" as an inferior one in favor of a higher priced item; or the consumer is told that long delays are involved in getting the required item. All of these are techniques by which the consumer is fradulently misled.

DEPRECIATION, MAINTENANCE AND OPERATING COSTS

Most consumable products, when once purchased, depreciate in value. Automobiles, television sets, sound reproduction systems, furniture, appliances, and thousands of similar items, lose value due to age, use, wear, and changing styles. This loss is known as *depreciation.* In addition to depreciation, the consumer must consider the cost of maintaining and operating the equipment or appliance. All of these costs must be included in a budget.

Intelligent buying involves a study of each product. When all facts are known, the consumer must determine whether an article that initially costs less may be more expensive. Repair, operating, and depreciation costs must be considered over the period an item is used.

PERSONAL CREDIT AND INSTALLMENT BUYING

Credit and installment buying is the foundation upon which a great percent of the business of this nation is conducted. Credit means that for the exchange of goods, services, or money, there is an agreement to pay at a future date. Credit also requires that the person who agrees to pay has the earning capacity and meets each obligation at the time it becomes due. Credit must be earned through demonstrated performance in using credit wisely. The capacity to repay a loan and having sufficient possessions (which may be set aside as *collateral* to guarantee the payment of a debt) are required.

Credit is used by individuals, business, industry, agricultural organizations, government, and others. Credit is necessary to purchase materials, enlarge a plant, carry on exploration for new sources of energy, purchase land and property, improve state and national waterways and other transportation systems. Credit applies as well to such person needs as clothing, gasoline purchases, or appliances.

Three common types of credit as used by an individual include: (1) service, (2) charge account, and (3) installment credit. *Service credit* relates to such credits as a utility makes when its services for gas, water, telephone, fuel, or electricity are first provided and later billed to the consumer for payment.

Charge account credits deal with the purchases of such items as hotel and motel lodging and food charges, gasoline purchases, and clothing. Charges are made against *credit cards* which are issued by special banks and finance organizations or other businesses. These are issued upon application to individuals who have established that they are a good "credit risk."

The accumulated charges are billed at regular periods. When paid within specified time limits, there is no additional finance charge to the individual. However, it must be understood that there is no "free" use of money. The organization that uses the charge account credit system (which guarantees payment on all of its active credit card holders) pays the credit organization a percent on all such transactions. This additional charge, indirectly, is paid by the consumer because the cost of the goods or services includes all the costs of doing business.

Installment credit is a third form of credit. It is a personal loan that may be negotiated through a bank, credit union, loan company, personal finance organization, automobile agency or manufacturer organization, department store, business and other retail establishment. Every person seeking installment credit is entitled to know what the total cost of a loan will be and that the interest rates are within the maximum set by the laws of a state. Although there is *truth-in-lending* legislation in effect, the consumer must still be cautious in reading a contract. Comparisons must be made of the initial cost, carrying charges, cost of credit and other finance charges, and the total cost; before making a judgment on what is the best buy.

PRECAUTIONS WHEN BUYING ON CREDIT

Step 1 Determine the total amount an item will cost, including credit and other charges.

Step 2 Compare the interest rates of a bank, credit union, the retailer, or other financial organization, if money is to be borrowed.

Step 3 Purchase only needed and wanted items, not those a salesman has "talked you into" buying.

Step 4 Avoid having any item left for you to "try out" if you do not want the item.

Step 5 Make your personal decision without being influenced by the pressure of a salesperson.

Step 6 Make a written contract for all sales which require financing.

CONSUMER PRECAUTIONS BEFORE SIGNING A CONTRACT

Step 1 Read each page of the contract. Establish that the contract includes what the salesperson says and what the price tag includes.

Step 2 Compute the total cost from the actual price plus (a) carrying charges, (b) cost of credit, and (c) other finance charges.

Step 3 Check for additional costs for delivery and service contracts, installation charges, and availability of repair parts.

Step 4 Compare total costs from actual product/cost analysis in different stores.

Step 5 Contact legal services or governmental consumer fraud services if there was a mistake in contract and the consumer is asked to "sign again."

DISCOUNT, DISCOUNT RATES, AND SUCCESSIVE DISCOUNTS

Many items are sold at a reduction from the original or the regular price. To repeat, this deduction is called a *discount.* Discounts are common when businesses have clearance sales for a product that may be discontinued, end-of-season sales, and anniversary sales. Sometimes the discounts are expressed as a markdown in price. In other instances, discounts are stated as a percent reduction (regular price less 20% discount) or as a fraction (1/2 off the list price).

A series of discounts is sometimes given on large purchases because each sale can be made at less expense to the retailer. Also, if cash payments are made, money is readily available for reinvestment. To reemphasize the procedures that were covered in an earlier unit, in *successive discounts*, the first discount rate applies on the list price. The second discount rate applies on the amount remaining after the first discount has been deducted; the third, after the second. It should be noted that two or more successive discount rates cannot be added to give an equivalent discount rate.

C. MATHEMATICS APPLIED IN CREDIT FINANCING

Buying on an investment plan means that the purchaser is actually using a product or service before completely owning it. In a free enterprise system, many sellers provide credit for customers in order to stimulate and maintain sales. Some have open charge accounts with a grace period, after receipt of the bill, to pay it without credit charges. Others may require the customer to cover the payments by financing through some type of finance organization.

THE COST OF CREDIT

EXAMPLE: The cost of lumber, panelling and hardware totals $1500. The lumber yard requires a 20% down payment and 12 monthly installment payments at the rate of 1 1/2% of the unpaid balance. Determine the additional expense of making installment payments.

Step 1 Subtract the 20% down payment from the total cost of $1500 to find the amount subject to installment charges.

$1500 Total cost
x .20 Down payment (%)
$ 300 Down payment ($)
$1500 – 300 = $1200

Step 2 Compute the credit charge on the beginning balance of $1200. The first month credit charge is $18.

12)1200 = $100 Monthly payment
$1200 x .015 = $18 first credit charge

Step 3 Subtract the monthly payment on the principal for the second month ($1200 – 100 = $1100). Multiply the new principal ($1100) by the installment charge rate of 1 1/2%. The second monthly credit charge is $16.50.

$1100 x .015 = $16.50 second credit charge

Step 4 Repeat step 3 until all the monthly payments are computed.

Step 5 Total the installment charges for the 12-month period. These equal $117.00.

Step 6 Divide the installment charges by the original principal. The quotient is the percent charged annually for buying the hardware items on the installment plan of the dealer. (.0975 = 9 3/4%)

Credit Charge

Month	Principal	Charge
1	1200	$18.00
2	1100	16.50
3	1000	15.00
4	900	13.50
5	800	12.00
6	700	10.50
7	600	9.00
8	500	7.50
9	400	6.00
10	300	4.50
11	200	3.00
12	100	1.50
		$117.00 Total Charges

1200)117.0000 = .0975 Ans.

The example shows that the principal (loan total) changes each month as a payment is made and the cost of buying the construction materials on the installment plan is $117.00 or 9.75%. Before buying, the consumer should not hesitate to get the rates from several sources of installment credit. These costs should be compared.

As stated earlier, the consumer must compare the benefits of buying the item on credit and paying additional finance costs. The benefits may relate to increased earning power, emergency situations which might result in a greater loss if the purchase is not made, leaving savings and other investments intact, or better living conditions brought about by purchases of labor-saving devices. The importance of the loan, the ease and time it takes to make the loan, and the collection methods are additional considerations.

COMPARISON OF TYPICAL CREDIT CHARGES

EXAMPLE 1: Repayment of a loan where the credit charge is added to the beginning balance and the total is repaid in 12 equal monthly payments.

Specified Rate		Actual Annual Rate
Per $100	% Per Year	
$ 4.00	4%	7.4%
6.00	6%	11.1%
8.00	8%	14.8%
10.00	10%	18.5%
12.00	12% (or 1% per month)	22.2%

EXAMPLE 2: Repayment of a loan where the credit rate is applied against the total amount of the loan and payments are made monthly.

Rate Per Month On Unpaid Balance	Actual Annual Rate
1/2 of 1%	6%
5/6 of 1%	10%
1%	12%
1 1/2%	18%
2%	24%
3%	36%

Example 2 shows a high actual annual rate because the rate of the loan is being charged against the total amount of the loan (principal) instead of the true balance. The true balance changes each month as payments on principal and other charges are made.

CALCULATING THE ACTUAL CREDIT RATE

A formula may be used to determine how much a consumer is paying on installment purchases in terms of the annual percent rate for credit.

ESTABLISHING CREDIT RATE

Use the formula: $R = \dfrac{2(I \times F)}{U(n+1)}$

R denotes installment credit as a percent

I is the number of installment payments in one year.

F represents the amount of the finance charges.

U is the unpaid balance.

n equals the number of payments in the contract.

EXAMPLE: The unpaid cost of tools and equipment is $600. This amount is to be paid in 12 equal installments of $58 each. Determine the rate for the installment credit at an annual percent.

Step 1 Substitute given or computed values in the formula.

I = 12

F = (12 x $58) - $600 = $96

U = $600

n = 12

$$R = \frac{2\,(I \times F)}{U\,(n + 1)}$$

$$R = \frac{2\,(12 \times 96)}{600\,(13)} = .295$$

Step 2 Carry out the indicated mathematical processes.

Step 3 Convert the decimal value (.295) to a percent. .295 = 29.5% Ans.

As the number and value of installment purchases increase, merchants incur greater losses due to unpaid bills, added administrative and bookkeeping expenses, and the loss of interest on substantial amounts of money that are outstanding. Installment costs must reflect these conditions. The extra charge for credit may be called a "service, carrying, or interest finance charge." Different finance patterns and charges on a $400 credit purchase are illustrated in the following table.

Finance Items	Financing Patterns				
	Dealer	Mail Order Company	Bank	Loan Company	Credit Union
Amount of Credit	$400.00	$400.00	$400.00	$400.00	$400.00
Monthly Payments	36.66	37.50	37.84	44.66	36.60
Total Payments (12 months)	440.00	450.00	454.00	500.00	439.00
Service Charge	40.00	50.00	54.00	100.00	39.00
Rate	10%	12.5%	13.5%	30% on first $300; 10% on all over $300	1 1/2% per month on unpaid balance

CREDIT SYSTEMS

BANKS

Banks provide one of the common systems for making personal loans. The following describes three types of personal loans.

- An individual may sign a promissory note for an amount to be borrowed, plus the interest which is deducted in advance, when there is no security risk involved.
- The borrower and a co-signer may be required to sign a promissory note when the bank needs additional assurance that the loan will be repaid.
- The borrower makes a "collateral loan" by leaving a savings account passbook or other "collateral item" (which may be sold if there is a default in the repayment of the loan) as security. The selling value of the security must be equal in value to the loan.

In each instance the rate for the kind of loan may differ, depending on the amount being borrowed and the security risk.

CREDIT UNIONS

Credit unions are found among professional groups (like a Teacher's Credit Union for a large system), Civil Service Systems, business and industry organizations, and the like. The credit unions provide an easy way for members to obtain loans and make payments. Normally, a credit charge of 1% per month is charged against the unpaid balance.

LOAN COMPANIES

Loan companies provide the borrower with cash. Many advertise to suggest that loans are available to consolidate many debts and to extend payments over a longer period of time. As in all other cases of borrowing money, careful comparisons should be made of interest, finance, insurance, bookkeeping, and other charges. Rates may start at 3% a month (36% per year) for the first $300 borrowed and then drop as the loan amount increases.

INSTALLMENT LOANS

Many retail establishments carry on installment credit contracts, requiring security agreements. The consumer enters into agreement with the business firm to buy certain merchandise, supplies, tools, or equipment. The order indicates (1) the cash price, (2) the amount to be financed, (3) the finance charge (as well as the finance percentage rate), and (4) the total payments. The consumer agrees to pay a fixed amount each month over a stated number of months until the total of payments for the credit that is extended is reached. In addition, the agreement provides that ownership of the purchased items remains with the business organization until all payments are made. The buyer must also protect the company against loss, damage, sale, or transfer of the property.

A major area of installment loans is for the purchase of automobiles. As with any other installment loan, the buyer should first check all conditions and charges which are included in the total purchase price. Then, another check should be made of such conditions and charges as security of the loan, interest rates, insurance costs, penalties, and payment information.

REVOLVING CHARGE ACCOUNTS

Another popular form of consumer credit is the revolving charge account plan. This plan is offered by department stores, mail order houses, charge-card organizations, gasoline companies, retailers, and others. The consumer may pay the account as a 30-day account without credit charges or have the payments extended according to a monthly plan which includes a charge for financing.

A security and revolving charge account agreement is signed by the customer in advance. Information must be furnished about employment and income and other resources and financial obligations so that a credit rating may be established. The printed form must contain information about interest and additonal charges, purchases, payments, and other conditions agreed upon by both parties. Here, again, while state laws regulate interest rates, a number permit "add-on" rates which may reach 20% a year.

PROPERTY (HOME) LOANS

The purchase of a home usually requires a long-term loan. Such loans must meet the real estate laws of the state. Financial groups like private investors; insurance, building, loan, and mortgage companies; and banks offer housing loans under a contract (*mortgage*). In each instance a down payment is required. Also, the security of the loan is guaranteed either by an insured mortgage loan (war veterans or other insurer) and/or the value of the property. In the event of default of payments the loan organization, after giving due notice, may sell the property. Any balance resulting from this sale over the unpaid mortgage and legal expenses is returned to the second mortgage parties, or the contracting party.

Before a home loan is made, the loan organization requires a series of searches. These are made to establish what judgments, liens or defects there are in the property and to determine its resale value. When the credit of the buyer is established and other loan conditions are fulfilled, the loan organization and buyer legally record their transactions. A duplicate of the property papers is filed in the legal public office of the municipality. The bank secures a mortgage and is the owner of the property until all conditions are met by the buyer.

The budget for home ownership and management must include items for both fixed expenditures for housing (mortgage payments, property taxes, and continuous insurance on the property) and variable expenditures (maintenance, furnishings, and heating/cooling the home). Before purchasing a home, a long-term budget extending over a number of years should be prepared. The budget establishes that there will be adequate resources to meet ownership obligations. It is important that an attorney be employed to handle all legal aspects of the transaction, to provide advice and counsel, and to see that all papers and records are in order and are legally filed.

D. MATHEMATICS APPLIED TO BANKING SERVICES

Banks are authorized by a state or federal government to perform the following listed services:

- Receive money from depositors.
- Permit withdrawals by depositors.
- Arrange for the transfer of money and credit.
- Invest money.
- Arrange credits to business, industry, and governments.
- Pay earnings (interest) to depositors.
- Make loans.

A bank may be classified as a *savings bank*, or a *commercial bank*, or a *trust company* which administers trust funds and estates. National banks are corporations that are chartered by the federal government. They must conform to federal banking laws and are regulated by the Federal Reserve System.

The sign in a state or national bank | Member of FDIC | means that the account of an individual depositor is protected against loss up to the amount specified. All banks pay for the use of the depositor's savings. The return on money is often referred to as *interest* or *dividend.* The interest rates governing the use of money vary. Some banks pay interest from the day-of-deposit to the day-of-withdrawal; others, from the day-of-deposit to the end of a quarterly period. Money placed in a savings account on a long-term plan (two, three, four, or more years) yields the highest dividend (interest) rate. However, there is a financial penalty on the amount of a "term deposit" that must be withdrawn before the term expires.

A savings account may be opened by completing a simple application and signature form. A *passbook* is issued to record deposits and withdrawals and to post the interest at the end of each quarterly period. The interest depends upon the *principal* (amount in the account), the rate of interest per year, and the length of time the money remains on deposit. The interest, then, represents a payment for the use of money since the bank receives a return on the depositors' money that it invests or loans.

Interest may be simple or compounded. *Compounded* means that the principal increases continuously because the rate of interest at each interest posting date is applied to the previously accumulated interest and principal.

RULE FOR SIMPLE INTEREST

- Simple interest is equal to the product of the principal (P), yearly interest rate (R), and the length of deposit (T) in years.
- $I = (P) \times (R) \times (T)$

EXAMPLE: Compute the simple interest on $300 at 6% interest for six months.

$$I = (P) \times (R) \times (T)$$

$$I = (\$300) \times (.06) \times (1/2) = \$9.00 \text{ Ans.}$$

NOTE: The formula may be used to determine the principal, rate, or time when any of the three other factors are known and substituted in the formula.

COMPOUND INTEREST

Instead of computing mathematically the amount of interest that may be compounded, a simplified formula may be used to find the accumulated principal.

$$A = (P) \times (1 + R)^n$$

A = Accumulated principal
P = Principal
R = Annual rate of interest
n = Number of (year) periods

NOTE: If interest is compounded semiannually, the (R) becomes (R/2) and (n) becomes (n) (2). Similarly, for interest that is compounded quarterly, (R) becomes (R/4) and (n), (n) (4).

EXAMPLE: Compute the accumulated principal on $500 at 6% interest compounded annually for four years.

$$\begin{aligned} A &= (P) \times (1 + R)^n \\ &= (\$500) \times (1 + .06)^4 \\ &= \$631.24 \text{ Accumulated principal Ans.} \end{aligned}$$

The use of the formula may be simplified further by the use of a "Compound Interest Table." (Appendix, Table XIV) The value of $(1 + R)^n$ is located in the appropriate interest column which corresponds to the number of years (n). Using a table, the value of $(1.06)^4$ equals 1.262 477.

CHECKING ACCOUNT SERVICES AND BANK STATEMENTS

Another practical form of substitute money is a *personal check.* A checking account has these advantages:

- Security in making payments; money need not be sent in the mail.
- Smaller amounts of ready cash are needed; protection against loss and robbery.
- Cancelled checks represent a receipt of payment.
- The checkbook stub (ledger) provides a quick record of available funds.

Money is deposited in a checking account by completing a *deposit slip.* This slip is prepared in the name of the depositor, using a special form on which the account number is usually récorded. The deposits are posted in a checking account passbook.

Withdrawals or payments are made with checks prepared in the name of the individual or organization (or even the depositor) to whom money is to be paid. All withdrawals are posted automatically at the bank. The depositor keeps a control on the checking account by noting and adding the amount of every deposit and subtracting the value of each withdrawal. These transactions are recorded on the check "stub."

A bank statement is sent to the depositor at regular intervals. These include cancelled checks that have been "cleared" and returned to the bank by the last date recorded on the statement. The bank statement usually shows the account number and date and has an entry for each check and other debits (like a service charge) and deposits. The balance shown for the previous period $(B)_p$ and the deposits (D) should equal the sum of the closing balance $(B)_c$ and all withdrawals (W).

RULE FOR CHECKING THE BALANCE OF A BANK STATEMENT

- $(B)_p + (D) = (B)_c + (W)$

EXAMPLE: The closing balance reported on the bank statement of a checking account is \$324.22. Deposits total \$217.64 and cancelled checks and other debits total \$284.89. The previous balance was \$391.47. The total of uncashed checks recorded on the checkbook stubs is \$57.29; deposits, \$46.65. Determine the actual balance at a specified date.

Step 1 Examine all cancelled checks and debit entries to establish that all are chargeable against the account.

Step 2 Check all items against entries on the bank statement and in the checkbook ledger (stub). List any checks that were not cashed.

Step 3 Check the deposits noted in the checkbook with those posted on the statement. List any unposted deposits.

Step 4 Check the balance as shown on the previous statement against a similar notation in the checkbook ledger.

Step 5 Use the formula to check the bank statement.

$$(B)_p + (D) = (B)_c + (W)$$
$$(\$391.47) + (217.64) = (324.22) + (284.89)$$
$$\$609.11 = \$609.11$$

Step 6 Add the total of the unposted deposits ($46.65) to the reported closing balance ($324.22).

$324.22	$(B)_c$
+ 46.65	(D)
$370.87	New balance

Step 7 Subtract from the new balance ($370.87) the total of the unposted withdrawals ($57.29). This difference represents the actual balance on the date the checkbook is "balanced."

$370.87	New balance
- 57.29	(W)
$313.58	Actual balance

Interest or dividends are not normally paid on checking accounts. Many banks provide checking services "without charge" (when a minimum balance is maintained) in exchange for the earnings on a depositor's money. Any special service charge (SC) is identified on the bank statement as a debit and is accompanied by a form explaining the service.

Personal checks are accepted on condition that they will be "cleared," that is, there is an adequate balance to cover the amount of the check. Since this processing takes time, payments on some large checks must be made by a *certified* or a *cashier's check* issued by a bank as a guaranteed payment. Other forms of money that are readily accepted include Western Union Telegraphic Money Orders, traveller's checks, postal and recognized company money orders, and bank card services. A charge is made for each of these money exchange services.

E. MATHEMATICS APPLIED TO INVESTMENTS

INVESTMENTS IN STOCKS

The income earned by working at an occupation may be supplemented by income from investments. Large corporations, governments (local, state, and federal), and other businesses depend on the availability of outside money to operate or to expand. These organizations issue stocks in exchange for money. Through the ownership of stocks, an individual becomes a stockholder and a part owner of a corporation.

A stock issuance is no guarantee that the corporation will make a profit or that it will continue in business. Thus, money diverted to stocks carries an element of gamble, with possible loss in part or in total of the money invested. Usually, the corporation holds an annual business meeting. Stockholders attend these meetings. Voting is carried on in person or by proxy. Specific policy matters and other items brought up at the business meeting are acted upon. The assets and liabilities, management, conditions of growth or decline in the organization, and its products and services are reviewed. A decision is made about profits and how much is to be distributed among the stockholders. The stocks are classified as *preferred* or *common*. The holders of preferred stocks receive a fixed earning (*dividend*) if there is a profit and a dividend is declared.

The holders of shares of common stock may receive a larger or smaller dividend per share.

Stocks may be purchased through a broker or agent for a smaller company. Large organizations purchase a "seat" on the stock exchange. Stocks and bonds are "traded" on the stock exchange. Stocks are purchased or sold by placing an order with a stockbroker to buy or sell so many shares of a stock at a designated price. The accumulation of orders is "bid" in at the appropriate stock exchange like the New York Stock Exchange, the American Stock Exchange, or other exchange.

There is a brokerage charge for buying and selling stocks. Therefore, the original cost of stocks equals the purchase price plus the commission charge. The net return from the sale of stocks equals the original cost minus the sum of the selling price and sales commission.

Varying commission rates are charged by brokers. The table illustrates sample rates for purchases or sales of stocks in multiples of 100. The rate on "odd lots" of less than 100 is higher.

Dollar Value Per 100 Shares	Commission
\$ 100 to \$1999.99	1% + \$5
\$2000 to \$4999.99	1/2% + \$15
\$5000 and above	1/10% + \$35

Some stockholders invest in corporations that have high potential for growth so that at a later date the stocks may be sold at a higher price than the one at which they were purchased. Other investors are concerned with immediate yields in terms of a high dividend return.

Stock transactions are summarized throughout each day that the Exchange is open. The transactions are printed in newspapers in at least three different versions: at the opening of the business day, midday, and as final or closing market prices. A portion of a typical closing stock table is illustrated to show "quotations" (prices) and other important information.

READING STOCK MARKET INFORMATION

- Start at the two left columns. Use the Exxon Corporation common stock as an example.
- Note the high-low range of prices during the year: High (99 3/4), Low (69 7/8).
- Move to the next column on the right. The current dividend follows the identification of the Company. The expected stock yield (annual dividend) is \$4.55 per share.
- The P/E column is an index of earning capability.
- The next column (Sales in 100's) shows that (2191) (100) shares (219,100) were sold on this day.

Current Year High	Low	Stocks and Div in Dollars		P/E	Sales 100s	High	Low	Close	Net Chg
28	22 1/8	EltraCp	1.50	5	69	23 5/8	22 1/4	23 5/8	+1 1/2
45 3/8	37 1/4	EmerEl	.70	24	1936	41 3/8	38 5/8	40 1/4	+ 3/4
59 1/2	46 1/4	EmeryA	.96	39	519	58	53 7/8	57 7/8	+4 3/8
22	16 7/8	Emhrt	1.30	5	86	18 1/2	17 1/8	18	+1 1/8
16 3/4	11	EmpDE	1.28	8	98	13 1/4	11 3/8	13 1/8	+1 3/4
21 5/8	16	EnglhdM	.50	7	895	18 5/8	16 1/2	18	+1 1/4
7	5 1/4	EnnisB	.18	6	351	6 1/2	6	6 1/2	+ 1/8
35	12	Envirotech		10	204	16 3/4	12 1/8	16	+4
28	19 1/2	ESBInc	1.40	8	144	22 1/4	19 1/2	21 3/4	-2
7	5 1/4	Esquire	.32	3	19	5 7/8	5 3/8	5 7/8	- 1/8
99 3/4	69 7/8	Exxon	4.55	6	2191	79	72 1/2	77 3/4	+5 1/4
				-F	-F	-F-			
14 3/8	9 3/8	FinSanB	.28	8	15	12 5/8	12 3/8	12 3/8	.....
26	21 1/4	Firestn	1.10	11	363	23	22 7/8	22 7/8	- 1/8
30	22 5/8	FstNBo	1.88	9	248	27 3/8	26 1/2	27	+ 1/2
17 1/8	14 5/8	FstPa	1.32	12	83	15	14 7/8	14 7/8	- 1/8
33 7/8	23 1/8	FischM	1.10	9	16	30	30	30	+ 1/4
18 1/8	13 1/4	Fleming	.80	8	8	15 1/4	14 7/8	15 1/8	- 1/8
29 5/8	25	Flin	2.25	...	1	27 3/4	27 3/4	27 3/4	.....
30 3/8	25 1/8	FlaPow	2.10	7	120	26 1/2	25 1/8	26 3/8	+ 3/8
39 1/8	29 5/8	FluorCp	.62	12	748	38 3/4	38 1/4	38 3/4	+ 1/8
27 1/4	19 7/8	FMC		1	23	22 5/8	22 1/8	22 1/4	+ 1/8
6 1/2	4 1/2	FdFair	.20	...	19	5 3/8	5 1/4	5 1/2	.....
60 7/8	43 5/8	FordM	2.40	7	731	58 1/8	56	58	+ 1/8
40 1/4	28 5/8	FtHowP	.64	10	99	30 7/8	30 1/2	30 7/8	+ 1/2
43 1/4	27 1/2	Foxboro	.80	11	181	42 1/2	41 1/2	40	+1
28 1/2	21 1/2	FreepM	1.60	14	51	26 1/8	25 3/4	26	+ 5/8
27 3/4	18 3/4	Fruehf	1.80	8	87	25 3/4	25 1/2	25 3/4	- 1/4

- The next four columns show the market price action on the stock during the day. Throughout the day the highest price paid was \$79; the lowest, \$72.50; and at the close, the price was \$77.75.
- The final right column gives the "net change." This value (+5 1/4) reflects a variation of \$5.25 in the price of the last sale for the day as compared with the last sale of the previous business day.

  Some quotation prices end in a fraction which is a multiple of 1/8. A quotation of 71 1/8 means \$71.125; 71 3/8, \$71.375; 71 3/4, \$71.75.

RULE FOR COMPUTING THE YIELD ON STOCKS

- Use the formula

$$Y = \frac{D}{P}$$

Y = Yield or interest rate for one year
D = Yearly dividend
P = Price of one share of stock

EXAMPLE: One share of stock in Corporation X sells for \$60 a share. An annual dividend of \$4.20 is paid. Find the yield.

$$Y = \frac{D}{P} \qquad Y = \frac{4.20}{60} = 7\% \text{ Ans.}$$

INVESTMENTS IN BONDS

A *bond* is a document by which federal, state, or local governments, and business, industrial, agricultural, or other establishments promise to repay money by a stated date and to pay a fixed amount of interest according to a schedule of payments. Three common terms are used with bonds. (1) The *face value* is the amount stated on the bond, usually as a multiple of \$1,000. (2) The *market value* is the price at which the bond is sold. (3) *Par value* is used when the market and face values of a bond are the same.

Corporation bonds are also purchased through brokers who charge a commission. The interest on a bond is paid on the face value. A section of a daily bond market quotation is used to interpret the nature of the information that is published in newspapers. The entry for Nabisco is used as an example.

- The two left columns show that the bonds sold for a high of \$100.50 and a low of \$90.00 during the current year. These amounts constitute the numerators of fractions with a denominator of \$100.
- The notation "Nabisco 7 3/4 s03" indicates that these bonds pay 7 3/4% interest annually and the face value of the bonds will be paid in 2003.
- The sales in 1,000 indicates that (30) (1,000) or 30,000 in bonds were exchanged that day.

Current Year High	Current Year Low			Sales in \$1,000	High	Low	Last	Net Chg
87 1/8	71 3/8	Medus	5 3/4 88	10	80	80	80	+2
99 7/8	88 3/8	Mellon	6s 89	16	99 5/8	99 1/2	99 5/8	. . . .
89 3/8	72	Melvl	4 7/8s 96	14	81 1/2	81	81	-1 1/4
93 1/8	81 1/8	MGM	10s 93	11	88	88	88	+1
71	60 1/2	MileL	5 1/4 94	3	66 3/4	65 1/2	65 7/8	- 1/4
53 1/2	41 7/8	MPac	4 1/4 05	8	48 1/4	47 3/4	48 1/8	+ 1/8
23 1/8	9 3/8	MrE	3 1/2 00	3	12 3/4	12 1/8	12 3/4	-1 1/4
86 3/8	79 1/2	MonyM	7s 90	10	79 7/8	79 7/8	79 7/8	- 3/4
100 1/2	90	Nabisco	7 3/4s 03	30	93	90	93	-2
74 1/2	66	NatBisc	4 3/4 87	4	70 1/8	69 5/8	70	+ 7/8
94 1/2	85	NatCash	7 1/2 93	10	87 7/8	87 1/8	87 1/8	+ 7/8
69	52 5/8	NCtyL	6 1/2 91	5	54 3/4	54 1/2	54 3/4	+1 3/4
72 1/8	62 1/4	NDist	4 1/4 94	29	67 1/2	66 7/8	66 7/8	- 1/8
39 1/2	26 1/8	NHom	4 3/4 96	175	29 1/2	27 1/2	29 1/2	+1
72 1/4	56 5/8	NatLead	4 3/8 88	26	57 1/8	56 5/8	57 5/8	+ 1/4
62	57 1/8	NatTea	3 1/2s 99	14	59 7/8	58 7/8	59	+ 1/8

- The remaining columns compare the bond market action during the day. The highest amount paid was 93/$100 or $93.00; lowest 90/100 or $90.00; last 93/100 or $93.00.
- The net change shows that the price of the last sale was (-2) or $2.00 less than the last sale the preceding business day.

RULE FOR COMPUTING THE YIELD ON A BOND

- Divide the interest on the face value by the cost of the bond.

$$Y = \frac{\text{Interest on Face Value}}{\text{Cost of Bond}}$$

UNITED STATES GOVERNMENT SAVINGS BONDS

Two common forms of U.S. Government Savings Bonds are the Series E and the Series H bonds. The *Series E bonds* provide a system of investing by which the interest accumulates during the life of the bond and the face value may be automatically reinvested at maturity. The income may be declared when the bond is "cashed." This is an important feature for persons who want to reduce income taxes during high earning years by cashing the bonds during periods of low income. Series E bonds are popular; employees and others invest regularly through a payroll savings and other plans. These bonds are sold in denominations of $25, $50, $75, $100, $200, $500, and $1,000 at issue cost prices of $18.75, $37.50, $56.25, $75, $150, $375, and $750, respectively.

The value of series E bonds is printed on each bond. There is a penalty (no interest) for redeeming a bond before it is held for six months. Interest is accrued at the beginning of each successive half-year period with the rate increasing gradually until at maturity the yield reaches the percent declared from the issue date to maturity. The yield on U.S. Government Savings Bonds has steadily increased over the years to remain competitive with other investments. Increases have been applied automatically on these bond holdings and are reflected in the increased value which is received when such a bond is cashed.

Series H bonds are issued in denominations of $500, $1,000, and $5,000. Semiannual interest is mailed regularly to bondholders. This income must be included as part of the ongoing income. These bonds have an expiration date at which time they may be reinvested.

Municipality bonds and other special bonds have tax-exempt provisions. These permit local governments and other privileged organizations to obtain money for public use and projects at low interest rates. In return, the holders of such bonds (which yield a lower interest) receive a tax break because the yield is tax free.

INVESTMENTS IN REAL ESTATE

Real estate investments are another source of income. Unlike bonds, income from property may not follow a uniform yield on the money invested. Income may result from purchasing at one amount and selling at a higher price, or through renting. The cost of the property is the sum of the purchase price and the closing fees. When property is to be sold, consideration must be given to maintenance and other construction improvement costs, assessment payments (for sewers and roads), amount of taxes and insurance premiums, and the income that the dollars invested in property would have produced from savings or bonds. The real profit from the sale or rental of property should be based on all of these factors.

Property ownership resides with the *mortgagee* (moneylender) until all repayment conditions are fulfilled. The home loan is secured by a legal document known as a *mortgage*, a bond and schedule of payments, a home property insurance policy as a guarantee against possible loss, and (sometimes) the payment of all taxes by the mortgagor.

Some banks and home loan companies include a property package. A single monthly payment is made which includes the interest, payment on principal, and advance tax and insurance payments which are accumulated to pay such bills when they are due. These institutions charge a "fixed" interest rate on the unpaid principal, subject to a periodic review when the rate may be increased or decreased depending on economic and banking conditions.

Property taxes provide one source of revenue for local and state government expenditures. The state sets a ceiling on the property tax rate. Within this limitation, the local community prepares its budget and determines the amount of property taxes that must be collected. The tax rate is applied on the *assesed valuation*, which is the amount a selected group of qualified people (*assessors*) estimate the property to be worth in relation to other property in the community.

Mathematics problems in relation to property involve the interpretation of graphs on sources of income and expenditures; budgeting for fixed and variable expenses for purchasing property, taxes, insurance, maintenance, and other household items; and many simple computations for comparing the effect of different interest rates and payment schedules on income, expenditures, and investments.

F. MATHEMATICS APPLIED TO SOCIAL SECURITY AND INSURANCE

Social Security is associated with the personal protection of the worker, the family, and heirs under certain conditions. This plan provides either financial payments at retirement, benefits to survivors in the event of death, or disability benefits. In addition, health insurance and medical care are available to persons 65 years of age and over. This protection package is administered by the Social Security Administration, U.S. Department of Health, Education and Welfare. Other medical and health insurance plans are provided through bargaining agreements with employers, unions, and members, or through other arrangements. In some instances, the employee or employer pays the total cost; sometimes both employee and employer contribute in prearranged proportions.

Many workers also contribute to pension plans that are admininstered for a local government, state government, or a business organization. Such participation provides a pension at retirement under qualifying conditions of years of service and payments into the system. This earned pension may be in addition to the Social Security payments.

Social Security payments are paid as taxes by workers and employers. Payments into the system are uniformly applied across the nation against a stated maximum on earnings in "covered employment." This refers to a definite period of time worked each year. Self-employed persons are also eligible. Tax payments for Social Security are deposited in separate trust funds in the United States Treasury: (1) retirement and survivors insurance, (2) disability insurance, (3) hospital insurance, and (4) medical insurance.

SOCIAL SECURITY COVERAGE

DISABILITY PROTECTION AND SURVIVORS INSURANCE

Monthly benefit payments for disability may be made to:

- A worker under 65 years of age and the family, when the worker becomes disabled.
- A person, disabled before 22 years of age, who has a continuing disability and whose parent receives Social Security retirement of disability benefits or dies.
- Disabled widows, disabled dependent widowers, and others who were insured at the time of the death of insured worker; payable at age 50.

Disability is paid when the worker has contributed into the system for at least five years within the ten-year-period ending when the disability begins. Conditions for establishing eligibility for disability payments are defined in publications of the Social Security Administration. These are obtainable locally at a U.S. Post Office or other U.S. Government Office. Charts are available to show monthly retirement and disability insurance benefits and survivor insurance benefits.

SOCIAL SECURITY RETIREMENT INSURANCE

An insured worker who qualifies under the Social Security System is eligible for monthly retirement income upon retiring at age 65 (a reduced amount is paid on early retirement, age 62-65). Certain dependents of qualified persons are also eligible to receive benefits upon the retirement, disability, or death of the insured. Included are such dependents as the insured's spouse at age 62 years or a wife at any age if caring for a child.

The continuously expanding Social Security payments and services and the effect of inflation are reflected in a comparison of cost for such insurance. In 1957 the worker and the employer each paid 2 1/2 percent on the first $4200 earned income. By 1975 the tax had been increased to a combined deduction of 11.7 percent on the first $14,100. The self-employed worker's tax increased from 3 3/8 to 7.9 percent on the same amounts.

The premiums the worker pays into the Social Security Insurance Fund are deducted from wages and are considered federal government taxes. These amounts together with the contributions of the employer are paid regularly to the federal government. The contributions are recorded as covered periods of employment in a social security account for the employee. All transactions with a state or the federal government are identified by this number.

The amount to include in a budget as a fixed expenditure for Social Security tax payments may be computed as the product of wages (up to the maximum specified) and the annual percent contribution by the worker. The employer contributes the same amount.

Case 1 Determine the Social Security taxes to be paid by the employee and employer on $3200 wages. The employee and employer tax rates are the same, (6%).

Employee's contribution =	($3200) x (.06)	= $192.00
Employer's contribution =	($3200) x (.06)	= 192.00
	Total taxes	= $384.00 Ans.

Case 2 Compute the total Social Security taxes that are to be paid by a self-employed person whose annual wages were $16,000. The rate of taxes is 7.9%; the maximum taxable income is $14,100.

Step 1 Multiply the maximum taxable income by the tax rate.

Self-employed person's contribution = ($14,100) x (.079) = $1,113.90

UNEMPLOYMENT INSURANCE

Unemployment insurance provides an income for a worker whose employment is seasonal or who is laid off for long periods of time due to production, retooling, cutbacks, and other employment factors. Unemployment insurance helps to stabilize the economy by moving money back into circulation when unemployment is high.

The unemployment system is administered jointly by the unemployment insurance agency in each state and the U.S. Department of Labor, Manpower Administration, Unemployment and Insurance Service. Each state establishes maximum weekly benefit amounts and the maximum time over which payments will be made. Payments stop before the maximum time if the recipient becomes employed.

Payments for unemployment insurance are made by employers in most states at a standard rate applied on the taxable payroll. An added-on fractional percent is paid to the federal government for administration of the program. While most workers are covered by unemployment insurance, certain occupations and groups (agricultural labor, some municipal and local government employees, for example) are excluded.

WORKMEN'S COMPENSATION

Workmen's Compensation is a form of insurance that protects the worker and family from loss of income suffered as a result of an accident or other occupational hazard. In addition to income, states provide programs of rehabilitation in order to assist the disabled worker to develop new skills and to re-enter employment as a productive citizen. Health and medical payments, corrective devices, added transportation, and other related services become part of the costs that may be paid to rehabilitate an injured or disabled person.

PROBABILITY AND PERSONAL INSURANCE

Another form of insurance for family security is *life insurance*. Insurance is a cooperative plan of sharing a risk. An insurance *policy* is the agreement or contract each participant receives. The policy has a *face amount* that is payable in the event of loss. A *premium* is the money paid at regular dates for the insurance protection.

The premium for a specified face amount of insurance is determined by using *mortality tables* and the mathematics of probability. The mortality tables represent years of accumulating data on life conditions and life spans. Mortality tables usually start with 1,000,000 births and trace the death per 1,000 each year from age 1 through 100 years.

RULE FOR DETERMINING PROBABILITY

- The probability (P) of an event occurring may be stated as

$$P = \frac{(N)_o}{(N)_o + (N)_f}$$

$(N)_o$ = The number of ways the event can occur.
$(N)_f$ = The number of ways the event can fail to occur.

EXAMPLE: What is the probability that an 18-year-old worker of today will be alive 25 years from now?

Step 1 Check the mortality tables for expected life spans.

Of the original 1,000,000, there will be 971,397 who will be alive at 18 years of age. It is expected that 917,338 will be living 25 years later at age 43.

Step 2 Compute the probability. The probability is that .944 or 94.4% of the 18-year-olds will be alive 25 years from now.

$$P = \frac{917{,}338}{971{,}397} \text{ or } .944 \text{ Ans.}$$

Insurance companies use the mortality tables, the mathematics of probability, administrative and operating costs, reserves as required by state insurance laws to insure there will be adequate sums to meet emergency and other contingencies, and a profit margin, to establish the different premiums for different coverages under state laws.

RULE ESTABLISHING PROBABILITY OF TWO OR MORE EVENTS OCCURRING

- The probability that two or more independent events $(P)_1$ and $(P)_2$ will occur is the product of the respective probabilities.

$$P = (P)_1 \times (P)_2$$

EXAMPLE: Determine the probability of students age 18 and students age 23 being alive 20 years later. (Correct to three decimal places).

Step 1 Determine the probability of survival of the 18-year-old students 20 years later, using a mortality table. $(P)_1 = \frac{932{,}559}{971{,}397} = .9602$

Step 2 Repeat this step for the 23-year-old students. $(P)_2 = \frac{917{,}338}{963{,}004} = .9515$

Step 3 Apply the rule: $(P) = (P)_1 \times (P)_2$.

$(P) = (.9602) \times (.9515) = .914$ (rounded to three decimal places)
$(P) = .914$ or 91.4% Ans.

It should be noted that there are a number of different mortality tables. These reflect the several factors that affect mortality: the life span that varies between the sexes, health and nutrition conditions that vary among nations, and others. Mortality tables and premiums are revised continously on new and term policies to more accurately reflect actual conditions.

TYPES OF LIFE INSURANCE PROTECTION AND COST FACTORS

Life insurance may be *term insurance* which covers the insured for a specified time or term. The premiums are paid for the limited period of insurance coverage. For example, Miss X buys a $5,000 ten-year insurance policy.

Straight life or *ordinary life* insurance offers lifetime protection. On, for example, a $5,000 straight life insurance policy, the premiums are paid as long as the insured lives. The face value ($5,000) is paid to the *beneficiary* who is designated to receive this money upon the death of the insured.

Limited payment life insurance offers protection for life. However, the premiums are paid for a fixed number of years only. A $5,000 20-year limited payment life insurance policy means that the insured in this case pays premiums for 20 years.

Endowment life insurance offers insurance protection for the life of the policy. The face value of the policy is paid if the insured lives to that date.

The amount and kind of life insurance to take out should be determined after the particular needs for insurance are established and the different types of coverage, premiums, and income are studied and compared with income and budgeted expenses. Insurance companies have tables of premiums per $1,000 of face value and age. Note in the four examples of premiums for different types of insurance that in each instance the cost of the premiums if paid monthly is the highest. The total premium costs are lowest when paid annually.

REGULAR PREMIUMS FOR SELECTED AGES

Ten-Year Term $1,000					Straight Life $1,000					Twenty-Payment Life $1,000					Twenty-Year Endowment, $1,000				
Age	A	S	Q	M	Age	A	S	Q	M	Age	A	S	Q	M	Age	A	S	Q	M
15	6.86	3.53	1.80	.61	15	16.42	8.46	4.31	1.46	15	27.41	14.12	7.20	2.43	5	49.10	25.29	12.89	4.36
16	6.94	3.57	1.82	.62	16	16.76	8.63	4.40	1.49	16	27.87	14.35	7.32	2.47	10	49.05	25.26	12.88	4.35
17	7.03	3.62	1.85	.62	17	17.12	8.82	4.49	1.52	17	28.35	14.60	7.44	2.52	15	49.28	25.35	12.94	4.37
18	7.13	3.67	1.87	.63	18	17.50	9.01	4.59	1.55	18	28.84	14.85	7.57	2.56	20	49.61	25.55	13.02	4.40
19	7.24	3.73	1.90	.64	19	17.89	9.21	4.70	1.59	19	29.32	15.11	7.70	2.60	25	50.11	25.88	13.15	4.45
20	7.36	3.79	1.93	.65	20	18.30	9.42	4.80	1.62	20	29.85	15.37	7.84	2.65	30	50.87	26.20	13.35	4.51
21	7.49	3.86	1.97	.66	21	18.74	9.65	4.92	1.66	25	32.67	16.83	8.58	2.90	35	52.05	26.81	13.66	4.62
22	7.64	3.93	2.01	.68	22	19.19	9.88	5.04	1.70	30	35.93	18.50	9.43	3.19					
23	7.79	4.01	2.04	.69	23	19.66	10.12	5.16	1.74										
24	7.96	4.10	2.09	.71	24	20.16	10.38	5.29	1.79										
25	8.14	4.19	2.14	.72	25	20.68	10.65	5.43	1.84										
26	8.34	4.30	2.19	.74	26	21.23	10.93	5.57	1.88										
27	8.56	4.41	2.25	.76	27	21.80	11.23	5.72	1.93										
28	8.79	4.53	2.31	.78	28	22.40	11.54	5.88	1.99										
29	9.05	4.66	2.38	.80	29	23.03	11.86	6.05	2.04										
30	9.33	4.80	2.45	.83	30	23.69	12.20	6.22	2.10										

A life insurance policy also provides other benefits. A policyholder may borrow money against the policy. After premiums are paid a number of years, some policies have a cash surrender value, or the policy may continue in force for an extended period. Tables are included with the insurance policy to show the benefits.

AUTOMOBILE INSURANCE

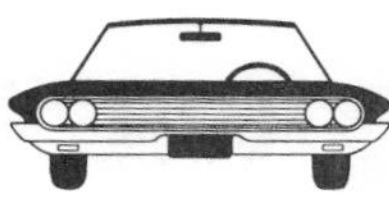

Automobile insurance provides protection in case of personal losses to the driver(s) and occupant(s) of the vehicle, property losses, and claims resulting from injury, death, or other factors related to an accident.

Each automobile insurance has a *limits code.* Premiums are based on the code, the age and make of the automobile(s), the drivers and their ages, and the use and geographic area in which most driving takes place. The following table shows the major categories of automobile insurance coverage with limits and other qualifying conditions.

(A) Bodily Injury	(B) Property Damage	(C) Automobile Medical Payments	(J) Uninsured Motorists
Limits Code	Limits Code	Limits Code	Limits Code
1 $ 5,000/10,000	1 $ 5,000	2 $ 500	1 $ 5,000/10,000
2 10,000/20,000	2 10,000	3 1,000	2 10,000/20,000
3 20,000/20,000	3 15,000	4 2,000	3 20,000/20,000
4 15,000/30,000	4 20,000	5 3,000	4 15,000/30,000
5 20,000/40,000	5 25,000	6 4,000	5 20,000/40,000
6 25,000/50,000	6 50,000	7 5,000	6 12,500/25,000
7 50,000/100,000	7 100,000	9 7,500	E 25,000/50,000
8 100,000/200,000		1 10,000	F 50,000/100,000
9 100,000/300,000			
O 300,000/300,000			
E 300,000/500,000			
F 500,000/500,000			

Personal Effects	(H) Comprehensive Fire, Theft, etc.	(D) Fire, Lightning, Transportation, Theft and Combined Additional
Coverage Code	Limits Code	Coverage Code
3 Fire, Lightning Combined Additional	1 or 5 Full Coverage	3 Yes
9 Fire Lightning	2 or 7 $50 Deductible	4 Fire, Lightning Transportation and Theft only

(E) Collision or Upset	(I) Towing and Labor Costs
Limits Code	Limits Code
1 $ 25 Deductible	2 $25 Per Disablement
4 50 Deductible	
5 100 Deductible	
8 150 Deductible	
6 250 Deductible	

The person desiring automobile insurance determines the amount and coverage needed, provided these are not less than state laws require. The cost of each item of coverage is added to make up the total annual premium. Again, while some insurers provide for quarterly and semiannual premium payments, these are always more than a single annual payment. Automobile insurance companies are required in most states to provide the insured with a notice of insurance. This must be available if requested for checking and for the renewal of the automobile registration.

PROPERTY INSURANCE

Homeowner's insurance provides protection for the insured against losses to dwelling and household possessions resulting from fire and other causes and/or for personal liability related to homeownership. Each policy includes the limits of liability and the conditions of insurance. The normal coverages in such a policy relate to (1) dwelling, (2) personal property in the home or in possession of persons covered by the policy, and (3) additional living expenses. The personal section covers (1) personal liability and (2) medical payments.

Some homeowner policies extend for three years; other policies are written for a one-year period. It is important to continuously study the nature and amounts of coverage to be sure that these are adequate for the period of the insurance and that there is no lapse between the expiration date and the new policy effective (*inception*) date. Insurance inventory forms are available to serve as worksheets for recording amounts of insurance needed for each major category.

There are other kinds of special property insurance, such as policies covering boats and boating. A number of insurance companies are now handling a "package" of insurance which includes personal insurance as well as homeowners, automobile and boating, and other property and liability insurance.

G. MATHEMATICS APPLIED TO TAXES

State and local governments use many different forms of taxes to produce adequate revenue to meet expenditures. There are state income taxes, state and local sales taxes, gasoline and highway taxes, payroll and business taxes (on partnerships and corporations), inheritance taxes, property taxes, and others.

The United States Government imposes a federal income tax on practically all workers who earn wages. Returns from individual income taxes, corporation income taxes, and taxes for Social Security insurance and retirement, account for approximately two-thirds of the national budget. This budget, like a personal budget, represents proposed programs and services to meet the needs of the United States.

When the income for a year equals expenditures, the budget is said to be *balanced*. If the anticipated expenditures exceed the income, money is borrowed up to a national debt ceiling that Congress establishes. All "money bills" are acted on by both Congress and the Presidents of the United States.

THE FEDERAL INCOME TAX "PACKAGE"

Annually, each person who previously filed a federal income tax receives a package called *Federal Income Tax Forms.* Actually, the mailing includes duplicates of blank U.S. Individual Income Tax Returns, schedules for further description, reporting and computations, specific directions to clarify every item on the forms and schedules; various tax tables and other processing information.

EMPLOYEES WITHHOLDING EXEMPTION CERTIFICATE

Since taxes are withheld by an employer each payroll period, a worker who is employed for the first time by a company, or whose family status is changed, completes an "Employees Withholding Exemption Certificate." The employee is identified by full name and Social Security number. The employee indicates the number of exemptions, theoretically the number of persons who are dependent on the wage earner. The exemptions and allowances and any additional withholding payments per pay period the employee wants to be deducted from wages, are totaled on this form (W-4). The amounts withheld are credited to the employees federal account with the Internal Revenue Service as income tax payments. An adjustment is made before April 15 for taxable income earned to December 31 of the previous year. This is done by filing a Federal Income Tax Return.

FORM W-4 (Rev. Jan. 1967)
U.S. Treasury Department
Internal Revenue Service

EMPLOYEE'S WITHHOLDING EXEMPTION CERTIFICATE

Type or print full name .... Social Security Number ....

Home address .... City .... State .... ZIP code ....

EMPLOYEE: File this form with your employer. Otherwise, he must withhold U.S. Income tax from your wages without exemption.

EMPLOYER: Keep this certificate with your records. If the employee is believed to have claimed too many exemptions, the District Director should be so advised.

HOW TO CLAIM YOUR WITHHOLDING EXEMPTIONS

1. If SINGLE (or if married and wish withholding as single person), write "1." If you claim no exemptions, write "0" . . . .
2. If MARRIED, one exemption each is allowable for husband and wife if not claimed on another certificate.
   (a) If you claim both of these exemptions, write "2"; (b) If you claim one of these exemptions, write "1"; (c) If you claim neither of these exemptions, write "0" . . . .
3. Exemptions for age and blindness (applicable only to you and your wife but not to dependents):
   (a) If you or your wife will be 65 years of age or older at the end of the year, and you claim this exemption, write "1"; if both will be 65 or older, and you claim both of these exemptions, write "2" . . . .
   (b) If you or your wife are blind, and you claim this exemption, write "1"; if both are blind, and you claim both of these exemptions, write "2" . . . .
4. If you claim exemptions for one or more dependents, write the number of such exemptions. (Do not claim exemption for a dependent unless you are qualified under Instruction 4 on other side.) . . . .
5. If you claim additional withholding allowances for itemized deductions fill out and attach Schedule A (Form W-4), and enter the number of allowances claimed (if claimed file new Form W-4 each year) . . . .
6. Add the exemptions and allowances (if any) which you have claimed above and write total . . . . [ ]
7. Additional withholding per pay period under agreement with employer. (See Instruction 1.) . . . . $

I CERTIFY that the number of withholding exemptions claimed on this certificate does not exceed the number to which I am entitled. c48—16—79061-1

(Date) ...., 19...... (Signed) ....

WAGE AND TAX STATEMENT

Each employer is required to withhold Social Security tax (F.I.C.A. – Federal Insurance Contributions Act) payments on wages up to a stated amount. The employer must also contribute an equal amount as a tax. The Federal income tax withheld, the total wages,

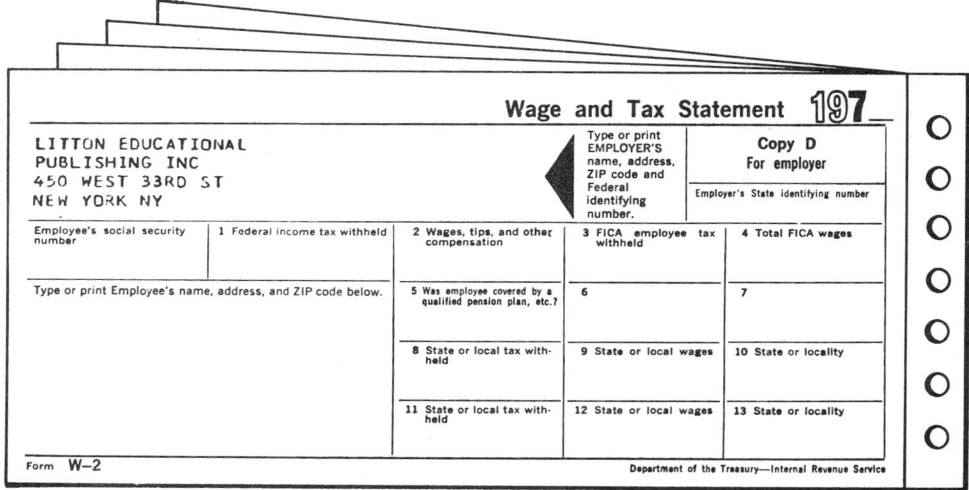

Wage and Tax Statement 197_

LITTON EDUCATIONAL
PUBLISHING INC
450 WEST 33RD ST
NEW YORK NY

Type or print EMPLOYER'S name, address, ZIP code and Federal identifying number.

Copy D
For employer

Employer's State identifying number

Employee's social security number	1 Federal income tax withheld	2 Wages, tips, and other compensation	3 FICA employee tax withheld	4 Total FICA wages
Type or print Employee's name, address, and ZIP code below.		5 Was employee covered by a qualified pension plan, etc.?	6	7
		8 State or local tax withheld	9 State or local wages	10 State or locality
		11 State or local tax withheld	12 State or local wages	13 State or locality

Form W–2 Department of the Treasury—Internal Revenue Service

F.I.C.A. tax, and state and city taxes that are withheld are all summarized by the employer on a "Wage and Tax Statement" (W-2). Multiple copies of this form are given to the employee, who attaches them to Federal and State Income Tax Returns, retaining the "Employee's copy."

FEDERAL INCOME TAX RETURNS

Any individual with a prescribed minimum gross income must file an income tax return annually. This return, when accurately completed and accepted, shows the conditions and qualification for each entry and how the final tax computations were determined. If the total withholding payments made by one or more companies for income tax and Social Security tax were larger than the one computed on the income tax return, the difference will either be returned to the wage earner or credited on the next year's tax, depending on the block the wage earner checks.

STEPS IN PREPARING AN INCOME TAX RETURN

Step 1 Gather together all income tax records, including Form W-2.

197_
Instructions for Form 1040
AND for Schedules
A,
R,

SCHEDULE B

SCHEDULE A

1040 — U.S. Individual

197_ Tax Rate Schedules

If you do not use one of the Tax Tables, figure your tax on the amount on Form 1040, line 47, by using the appropriate Tax Rate Schedule on this page. Enter tax on Form 1040, line 16a.

SCHEDULE X—Single Taxpayers Not Qualifying for Rates in Schedule Y or Z

Use this schedule if you checked the box on Form 1040, line 1—

If the amount on Form 1040, line 47, is: / Enter on Form 1040, line 16a:

Not over $500 **14% of the amount on line 47.**

Over—	But not over—		of the amount over—
$500	$1,000	$70+15%	$500
$1,000	$1,500	$145+16%	$1,000
$1,500	$2,000	$225+17%	$1,500
$2,000	$4,000	$310+19%	$2,000
$4,000	$6,000	$690+21%	$4,000
$6,000	$8,000	$1,110+24%	$6,000
$8,000	$10,000	$1,590+25%	$8,000
$10,000	$12,000	$2,090+27%	$10,000
$12,000	$14,000	$2,630+29%	$12,000
$14,000	$16,000	$3,210+31%	$14,000
$16,000	$18,000	$3,830+34%	$16,000
$18,000	$20,000	$4,510+36%	$18,000
$20,000	$22,000	$5,230+38%	$20,000
$22,000	$26,000	$5,990+40%	$22,000
$26,000	$32,000	$7,590+45%	$26,000
$32,000	$38,000	$10,290+50%	$32,000
$38,000	$44,000	$13,290+55%	$38,000
$44,000	$50,000	$16,590+60%	$44,000
$50,000	$60,000	$20,190+62%	$50,000
$60,000	$70,000	$26,390+64%	$60,000
$70,000	$80,000	$32,790+66%	$70,000
$80,000	$90,000	$39,390+68%	$80,000
$90,000	$100,000	$46,190+69%	$90,000
$100,000	......	$53,090+70%	$100,000

SCHEDULE Y—Married Taxpayers and Qualifying Widows and Widowers
If you are a married person living apart from your spouse, see page 5 of the instructions to see if you can be considered to be "unmarried" for purposes of using Schedule X or Z.

Use this schedule if you checked the box on Form 1040, line 2 or 5—

Married Taxpayers Filing Joint Returns and Qualifying Widows and Widowers (See page 5)

If the amount on Form 1040, line 47, is: / Enter on Form 1040, line 16a:

Not over $1,000 **14% of the amount on line 47.**

Over—	But not over—		of the amount over—
$1,000	$2,000	$140+15%	$1,000
$2,000	$3,000	$290+16%	$2,000
$3,000	$4,000	$450+17%	$3,000
$4,000	$8,000	$620+19%	$4,000
$8,000	$12,000	$1,380+22%	$8,000
$12,000	$16,000	$2,260+25%	$12,000
$16,000	$20,000	$3,260+28%	$16,000
$20,000	$24,000	$4,380+32%	$20,000
$24,000	$28,000	$5,660+36%	$24,000
$28,000	$32,000	$7,100+39%	$28,000
$32,000	$36,000	$8,660+42%	$32,000
$36,000	$40,000	$10,340+45%	$36,000
$40,000	$44,000	$12,140+48%	$40,000
$44,000	$52,000	$14,060+50%	$44,000
$52,000	$64,000	$18,060+53%	$52,000
$64,000	$76,000	$24,420+55%	$64,000
$76,000	$88,000	$31,020+58%	$76,000
$88,000	$100,000	$37,980+60%	$88,000
$100,000	$120,000	$45,180+62%	$100,000
$120,000	$140,000	$57,580+64%	$120,000
$140,000	$160,000	$70,380+66%	$140,000
$160,000	$180,000	$83,580+68%	$160,000
$180,000	$200,000	$97,180+69%	$180,000
$200,000	...	$110,980+70%	$200,000

Use this schedule if you checked the box on Form 1040, line 3—

Married Taxpayers Filing Separate Returns

If the amount on Form 1040, line 47, is: / Enter on Form 1040, line 16a:

Not over $500 **14% of the amount on line 47.**

Over—	But not over—		of the amount over—
$500	$1,000	$70+15%	$500
$1,000	$1,500	$145+16%	$1,000
$1,500	$2,000	$225+17%	$1,500
$2,000	$4,000	$310+19%	$2,000
$4,000	$6,000	$690+22%	$4,000
$6,000	$8,000	$1,130+25%	$6,000
$8,000	$10,000	$1,630+28%	$8,000
$10,000	$12,000	$2,190+32%	$10,000
$12,000	$14,000	$2,830+36%	$12,000
$14,000	$16,000	$3,550+39%	$14,000
$16,000	$18,000	$4,330+42%	$16,000
$18,000	$20,000	$5,170+45%	$18,000
$20,000	$22,000	$6,070+48%	$20,000
$22,000	$26,000	$7,030+50%	$22,000
$26,000	$32,000	$9,030+53%	$26,000
$32,000	$38,000	$12,210+55%	$32,000
$38,000	$44,000	$15,510+58%	$38,000
$44,000	$50,000	$18,990+60%	$44,000
$50,000	$60,000	$22,590+62%	$50,000
$60,000	$70,000	$28,790+64%	$60,000
$70,000	$80,000	$35,190+66%	$70,000
$80,000	$90,000	$41,790+68%	$80,000
$90,000	$100,000	$48,590+69%	$90,000
$100,000		$55,490+70%	$100,000

SCHEDULE Z—Unmarried (or legally separated) Taxpayers Who Qualify as Heads of Household (See page 5)

Use this schedule if you checked the box on Form 1040, line 4—

If the amount on Form 1040, line 47, is: / Enter on Form 1040, line 16a:

Not over $1,000 **14% of the amount on line 47.**

Over—	But not over—		of the amount over—
$1,000	$2,000	$140+16%	$1,000
$2,000	$4,000	$300+18%	$2,000
$4,000	$6,000	$660+19%	$4,000
$6,000	$8,000	$1,040+22%	$6,000
$8,000	$10,000	$1,480+23%	$8,000
$10,000	$12,000	$1,940+25%	$10,000
$12,000	$14,000	$2,440+27%	$12,000
$14,000	$16,000	$2,980+28%	$14,000
$16,000	$18,000	$3,540+31%	$16,000
$18,000	$20,000	$4,160+32%	$18,000
$20,000	$22,000	$4,800+35%	$20,000
$22,000	$24,000	$5,500+36%	$22,000
$24,000	$26,000	$6,220+38%	$24,000
$26,000	$28,000	$6,980+41%	$26,000
$28,000	$32,000	$7,800+42%	$28,000
$32,000	$36,000	$9,480+45%	$32,000
$36,000	$38,000	$11,280+48%	$36,000
$38,000	$40,000	$12,240+51%	$38,000
$40,000	$44,000	$13,260+52%	$40,000
$44,000	$50,000	$15,340+55%	$44,000
$50,000	$52,000	$18,640+56%	$50,000
$52,000	$64,000	$19,760+58%	$52,000
$64,000	$70,000	$26,720+59%	$64,000
$70,000	$76,000	$30,260+61%	$70,000
$76,000	$80,000	$33,920+62%	$76,000
$80,000	$88,000	$36,400+63%	$80,000
$88,000	$100,000	$41,440+64%	$88,000
$100,000	$120,000	$49,120+66%	$100,000
$120,000	$140,000	$62,320+67%	$120,000
$140,000	$160,000	$75,720+68%	$140,000
$160,000	$180,000	$89,320+69%	$160,000
$180,000		$103,120+70%	$180,000

Step 2 Collect all expense records if deductions are to be itemized.

Step 3 Secure the necessary "Package" of forms, tax tables, and directions.

Step 4 Fill in the personal information and check one block for *filing status.*

Step 5 Indicate number of exemptions.

Step 6 Review quickly all lines. These are numbered consecutively and the directions relate to these numbers.

Step 7 Fill in the Gross Income.

Step 8 Determine whether to use the standard deduction or to itemize deductions (if there is a possibility of a tax saving).

Step 9 Check the appropriate tax tables to establish the tax. If the income was less than $10,000 and the deductions are not itemized, use the tables which include the standard deduction, depending on the number of exemptions claimed.

Step 10 Compute the tax if the income was more than $10,000 and the deductions are itemized. In this case, the tax rate schedules for single and married taxpayers, and others, show the dollar amounts and percent to use in computing the tax.

Step 11 Check the appropriate lines and report any credits or other taxes and payments.

Step 12 Prepare brief supplemental statements to justify expenses and/or other deductions.

Step 13 Enclose a check or money order for any amount that may be due. This is to be attached on the front of Form 1040.

Step 14 Indicate if there is a refund for overpayment and whether all or part should be credited to the next year's tax, or be refunded.

Step 15 Attach Form W-2 or W-2P to the front of Form 1040. Any applicable schedules, arranged in alphabetical order, follow Form 1040.

Step 16 Make certain that a duplicate of all forms and worksheets are kept as a record.

STATE INCOME TAX FORMS

Many states provide taxpayers with a packet of materials that is similar to the U.S. Internal Revenue Service mailing. The State forms are comparatively simple to prepare provided the U.S. Individual Income Tax Return Form 1040 and supplemental schedules are prepared first. Much of the information on the federal form can be transferred. There are differences between the two forms, however. The allowances for taxes, state pensions, exemption amounts, and the tax rate schedule are different, for example.

Computations involved in the preparation of income tax returns are usually simple applications of the four basic arithmetical processes of addition, subtraction, multiplication and division.

Unit 92 ACHIEVEMENT REVIEW ON CONSUMER APPLICATIONS OF MATHEMATICS

A. MATHEMATICS APPLIED TO MONEY MANAGEMENT AND BUDGETING

NOTE: Problems 1 through 6 relate to (a) the preparation of a trial budget, (b) an actual or simulated working budget, and (c) a system for controlling and managing the budget.

1. Prepare a worksheet for listing major categories of (a) income and (b) fixed and variable expenditure items that are to be included in an actual or a simulated trial budget.
2. Add columns for both income and expenses. Then, record (a) the amounts for exact or anticipated income and expenses and (b) prepare a schedule showing when each item is due and payable.
3. Add still other columns to show monthly and annual income for each item. (a) Compute and record monthly income and expenditures. (b) Add the monthly totals and post the yearly amounts. (c) Add and record the gross annual totals.
4. Develop a balanced budget by establishing priorities and making adjustments until the income and expenditures are equal. Then, prepare the working budget.

   NOTE: If a loan is needed to supplement the income in order to cover expenditures, justify this decision.
5. Develop a system for the control and management of the one year budget.
6. Compute the percent of the total annual income that each major category of (a) income and (b) expenditures constitutes. Add another column on the budget forms and record these percents.

B. MATHEMATICS APPLIED IN THE BUYING OF GOODS AND SERVICES

CONSUMER JUDGMENT IN BUYING GOODS AND SERVICES

1. Locate a consumer publication of an organization like the U.S. Department of Agriculture or *Consumers Digest.*
   a. Select (1) a food product, (2) an appliance, and (3) a major piece of equipment.
   b. State the factors that the consumer must compare in order to reach an intelligent decision on what is the best value for each of the three items.
   c. Recommend which (1) food product, (2) appliance, and (3) major piece of equipment to purchase, stating the reasons for your selection.

SERVICE, CHARGE ACCOUNT AND INSTALLMENT CREDIT

2. Secure a copy of a monthly utility energy service bill.
   a. Determine how much service credit has been granted.
   b. Compute the monthly percent interest rate the utility company charges on the amount of the bill if it is not paid before a specified date.

3. Secure a copy of a "charge account" application.
   a. Study the nature of the information an applicant must supply to establish credit.
   b. List the purposes for which the credit card (charge account) may be used.
   c. State what the monthly and annual carrying charges are if the account is paid in installments and the amount due is spread out over a number of months.

4. Secure a copy of an "installment credit" application.
   a. Establish the purposes for which credit may be used.
   b. List the interest, carrying, and other charges which the business organization applies against installment buying.

LIST PRIÇE, SALES PRICE, SINGLE AND SUCCESSIVE DISCOUNTS

5. Calculate (a) the amount of discount, (b) the sales price, (c) the total savings, and (d) the total cost of construction units A through E.

Construction Unit	List Price	Rate of Discount	Discount (a)	Sales Price (b)
A	$250.00	40%		
B	$199.50	10%		
C	$150.00	12 1/2%		
D	$126.12	1/2 off		
E	$ 85.02	1/6 off		
		Total	(c)	(d)

6. Compute (a) the rate of discount, (b) total cost of the material for the number of required units, (c) the total savings on each material, (d) the grand total cost of all materials, and (e) the grand savings on the whole order, for materials A through E and for the quantities as indicated in the table.

Material	List Price Per Unit	Sale Price Per Unit	Number of Units Required	Rate of Discount (a)	Total Cost of Units (b)	Total Savings on Units (c)
A	$ 10.00	$ 8.00	3			
B	$ 15.00	$12.00	6			
C	$ 18.98	$16.13	10			
D	$ 21.76	$19.04	12			
E	$119.58	$79.72	37			
				Grand Total	(d)	(e)

C. MATHEMATICS APPLIED IN CREDIT FINANCING

1. Compute (a) the total cost, (b) amount of carrying charges, and (c) the percent of the finance charge on the loan principal for Parts A through D.

Part	Cost (Loan Principal)	Down Payment	Number of Payments	Amount of Each Payment	Total Cost (a)	Carrying Charge (b)	Percent Finance Charge (c)
A	$ 100	$ 20	4	$24.00			
B	$ 620	$120	8	$80.00			
C	$ 480	1/3	12	$32.00			
D	$2440	10%	12	$221.25			

2. Secure and read a loan payment schedule and installment purchase plan from three sources: a bank, a retailer, and another loan organization.
   a. Prepare a table for materials A through E. The following items may be stated and compared: (1) the conditions under which an installment credit loan is made, (2) the rates for credit charges, (3) number of payments, (4) the amount of each payment, (5) the total amounts of payments, and (6) the total cost of installment buying.
   b. Determine which financial organization to use. State the reasons for the decision.

Materials	Principal of Loan ($ Cost)	Period of Financing (Months)	LOAN ORGANIZATIONS				
			Rates for Credit	Payment Number	Amount Each Payment	Total of Payments	Total Cost of Service
A	200	6	(B) (R) (O)	(B) (R) (O)	(B) (R) (O)	(B) (R) (O)	(B) (R) (O)
B	500	12	(B) (R) (O)	(B) (R) (O)	(B) (R) (O)	(B) (R) (O)	(B) (R) (O)
C	1200	18	(B) (R) (O)	(B) (R) (O)	(B) (R) (O)	(B) (R) (O)	(B) (R) (O)
D	1650	24	(B) (R) (O)	(B) (R) (O)	(B) (R) (O)	(B) (R) (O)	(B) (R) (O)
E	3480	30	(B) (R) (O)	(B) (R) (O)	(B) (R) (O)	(B) (R) (O)	(B) (R) (O)

Conditions of Installment Loan

Bank (B) ____________________

Retailer (R) ____________________

Other Service (O) ____________________

3. Establish the credit rate for equipment items A through E. Use the formula:

$$R = \frac{2\,(I \times F)}{U\,(n + 1)}$$

State the credit rate as a percent, rounded to one decimal place.

Equipment	Principal (Unpaid Balance) (U)	Installment Payments in One Year (I)	Number of Payments in Contract (n)	Finance Charges (F)	Credit Rate (%) (R)
A	$ 500	12	12	$ 50	
B	$ 1,200	6	18	$ 144	
C	$ 2,400	12	18	$ 288	
D	$ 3,050	6	24	$ 568	
E	$10,400	4	16	$2,528	

4. Review a loan application from a bank, credit union or other loan organization.
   a. List the conditions under which a loan may be made.
   b. Determine the percent of the total charge that is paid for a specified amount of a loan.
   c. Compare the two finance organizations in terms of making an installment loan.

5. Secure a copy of an installment credit contract and security agreement from an automobile dealer or a retail establishment.
   a. Read and state the kind of information that is needed for security and to establish credit.
   b. List the conditions relating to (1) a purchase, (2) installment buying terms for a 30-day no-charge account and a revolving charge account, and (3) ownership of the property/merchandise.

6. Prepare a list of items that a homeowner should include as (a) "closing" expenses when purchasing a home, and (b) fixed and variable continuing expenditure items in a budget.

D. MATHEMATICS APPLIED TO BANKING SERVICES

1. State the formula for computing simple interest. Then, compute the missing values for accounts A through F.

Formula:				
Account	**Simple Interest**	**Principal**	**Rate of Interest**	**Time**
A		$ 400	6%	1 year
B	$ 31.05		5 3/4%	1 year
C	$ 97.50	$ 750		2 years
D		$1200	5 1/4%	6 months
E	$139.50		7 3/4%	8 months
F	$191.25	$3600		10 months

2. Compute the accumulated principal for accounts A through D, applying both compound and simple interest.
   a. State the formulas for computing simple and compound interest.
   b. Use a compound interest table and/or formula and compute the accumulated principal.
   c. Compute the simple interest, using the same annual interest rate and length of deposit.

Account Information				Formula:	Formula:
				Accumulated Principal	
Account	Original Principal	Rate of Interest	Number of Periods	Compound Interest (b)	Simple Interest (c)
A	$ 500	6%/year compounded annually	2 years		
B	$ 750	6%/year compounded semiannually	1 1/2 years		
C	$2400	6%/year compounded quarterly	15 years		
D	$1500	8%/year compounded quarterly	4 years		

3. Compute each amount that is not recorded on the checkbook stubs for accounts A, B, C, and D.

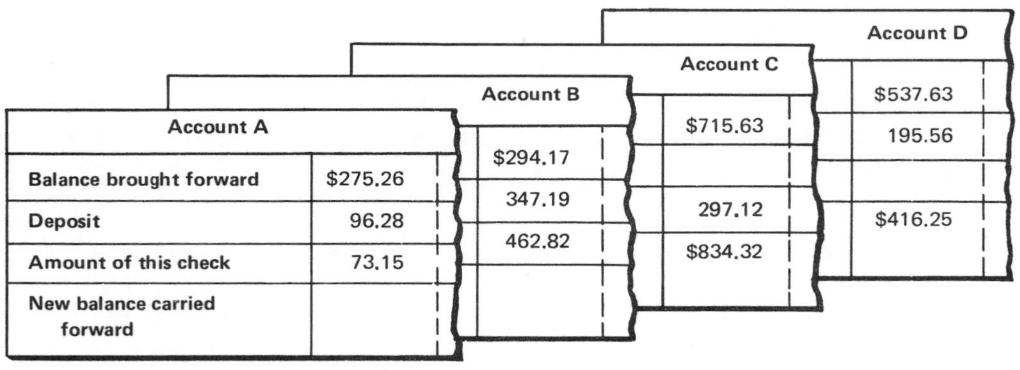

	Account A	Account B	Account C	Account D
Balance brought forward	$275.26	$294.17	$715.63	$537.63
Deposit	96.28	347.19		195.56
Amount of this check	73.15	462.82	297.12	
New balance carried forward			$834.32	$416.25

4. Determine the amount of the uncashed checks for the accounts in Problem 3, using the following closing balances from the bank statements of the four accounts.

Account	A	B	C	D
Closing balance	$426.72	$1923.61	$1022.28	$637.64
Uncashed Checks				

E. MATHEMATICS APPLIED TO INVESTMENTS

INVESTMENTS IN COMMON AND PREFERRED STOCKS

1. Locate and clip a section of a detailed daily stock quotation from a newspaper.
   a. Select and name one common stock.
   b. Start with the left column and describe the meaning and values for each entry in each column.

2. Select another common or preferred stock. Locate a schedule of a broker's commissions.
   a. Name the stock.
   b. Record the "high" price for the stock.
   c. Record the current dividend.
   d. Compute the book values of the stock (250 shares), commissions, and profit or loss according to the three conditions given in the table. Assume the original purchase price was based on the high quotation of the day.

Common or Preferred Stock Identification	Number of Shares in Transaction	Conditions	Market Price	Broker Com-mission	Gross Profit or Loss	Net Profit or Loss
"High" price on business day		1	Day of Quotation (low)			
	250	2	Sale at *High* of Year			
Current dividend		3	Sale at *Low* of Year			

3. Find quotations and market prices on bonds in the financial pages of a newspaper.
   a. Select one bond from the table.
   b. Start with the left column and describe the meaning and values found in each column.

4. Take the market information on the bond in problem 3.
   a. State the corporation name, the percent interest, face value, and redemptive (maturity) date.
   b. Compute (1) the broker commission on the 375 shares and (2) the profit or loss if the bonds were sold (a) at the "high" for the year, (b) the "low" for the year, and (c) the high on the day of the quotation. Assume the purchase price was at the "low" for the business day.

Bond Identification	Number of Shares	Conditions	Market Price	Broker Com-mission	Gross Profit/ Loss	Net Profit/ Loss
Face Value $______		1	High for the year			
Percent Interest ______ % Maturity Date	375	2	Low for the year			
______ Purchase Price $______		3	Day of Quotation			

5. Review the payment schedule of a current issue of a U.S. Government Savings Bond, Series E.

   a. State the value of holding such a bond to maturity.
   b. Compare the yield on the bond with the interest that would accrue on the same investment if it were placed in a savings bank account. Show the yield in dollars and percent at the end of 1/2 year, 1 year, 5 years, and 9 years.

Amount Invested	Source	Condition of Investment		Comparison of Income			
		Rate	Period	1/2 year	1 year	5 years	9 years
$_____	Savings Bank						
	U. S. Gov't. Bond						

REAL ESTATE INVESTMENTS

6. The sum of $200 per month has been budgeted for the reduction of principal and the payment of interest on real estate. The purchase price of the property (including all closing and other expenses) is $25,000. A 20% down payment is made. The balance is covered by a binder and a schedule of payments. The interest rate is 8% per year on the unpaid balance.

   a. Prepare a schedule of payments for the first two years.
   b. Determine the remaining balance on principal beginning the third year, the total interest paid in the two years, and the amount that has been paid on the principal of the loan.

Month	Balance (Principal)	Interest Paid	Amount Applied on Reduction of Principal
1	$20,000		
2			
24			
Principal at beginning of third year $_____		_____ Total Interest Paid	_____ Total Amount Paid on Principal

F. MATHEMATICS APPLIED TO SOCIAL SECURITY, PERSONAL AND PROPERTY INSURANCES

DISABILITY, SURVIVORS, UNEMPLOYMENT AND RETIREMENT INSURANCE

1. Secure a Social Security Administration "Retirement and Disability Insurance Benefit" and a "Monthly Survivors Insurance Benefit" chart.

   a. Find and record the retirement benefits payable beginning three months from this date, for (1) workers A, B, and C, (2) their spouses (D, E, and F); and (3) compute the total worker-spouse retirement income at ages 65 and 62.

Average Yearly Earnings	Worker Retirement Benefits			Benefits of Spouse			Total Income of Worker and Spouse	
		65	62		65	62	65	62
$ 4,200	A			D				
$ 8,400	B			E				
$12,600	C			F				

b. State the amount of monthly survivors insurance benefits that are payable, beginning two months from this date, to (1) widows A, B, and C, and (2) disabled widows D, E, and F.

Average Yearly Earnings	Widow (40 years of age, one child)		Disabled Widow (40 years of age, no child)	
$ 4,200	A		D	
$ 8,400	B		E	
$12,600	C		F	

SOCIAL SECURITY TAXES

2. Compute the amount of taxes for selected years from 1957 through 1975-76 that were
   a. Deducted from the wages of workers, with equal contributions from employers. Record these for both employee and employer. Then show the total percent and total taxes paid on the wage base.
   b. Record in a similar way the amount of Social Security taxes paid by a self-employed person over these same years.

   NOTE: Use the percents and maximum taxable amounts given in the table.

Selected Years	Wage Base for Computing Tax	Worker-Employer Taxes				Total Taxes		Self-Employed Taxes	
		Worker		Employer					
		Percent	Taxes	Percent	Taxes	Percent	Taxes	Percent	Taxes
1957-58	$ 4,200	2.25%		2.25%				3.375%	
1963-65	$ 5,400	3.625%		3.625%				5.4%	
1970	$ 7,800	5.2%		5.2%				7.2%	
1973	$10,800	5.85%		5.85%				7.5%	
1974	$13,200	5.85%		5.85%				7.9%	
1975	$14,100	5.85%		5.85%				7.9%	

PERSONAL INSURANCE

3. Use the premium tables for four different types of life insurance.
   a. Compute the premiums for a $10,000 (face value) policy for a person 25 years of age.
   b. Determine how much the policyholder will save each five years if the premiums are paid annually instead of monthly.

Face Value ($10,000)	Type of Insurance (Age of Insured. . .25)			
Payment Schedule	5-Year Term	Straight Life	20-Payment Life	20-Year Endowment
Annually				
Semiannually				
Quarterly				
Monthly				
Savings				

PROPERTY AND PERSONAL LIABILITY INSURANCE: AUTOMOBILE AND HOMEOWNERS

4. Secure a copy of an automobile insurance policy, a premium notice on which charges for different coverages are noted, and a rate schedule.
   a. Explain the meaning of each category of insurable item.
   b. Select a limit code for each category. Justify your decision.
   c. Compute the total cost of the policy, using the premium quotation for each category.

5. Examine a Homeowners Insurance policy and secure a worksheet.
   a. Indicate the coverages that relate to property and those to personal losses and payments.
   b. Prepare an inventory of major categories of items that should be included in a homeowners policy.
   c. Explain how a homeowner should establish the policy limits of liability for each category covered.

G. MATHEMATICS APPLIED TO INCOME TAXES

PREPARING WAGE AND TAX STATEMENTS AND INCOME TAX RETURNS

1. Secure a copy of a *Wage and Tax Statement* (Form W-2), and *Employees Withholding Exemption Certificate* (Form W-4), and an *Application for Social Security Identification* (Form SS-5).
   a. Read the information that is required on each form.
   b. Prepare as a simulated exercise (1) a Form W-2, (2) Form W-4, and (3) Form SS-5.

2. Secure a package which includes the *U.S. Individual Income Tax Return* (Form 1040), schedules, tax tables, and directions. Then prepare the federal income tax return as a simulation exercise.
   a. List the steps to follow (using the numbered lines on the forms as a guide) in preparing the return.

Assume:		
	Income from wages and other taxable compensation	$12,600
	Dividends from stocks	220
	Interest on savings accounts	120
	Federal income tax withheld from wages	1,800
	Credit on overpayment from previous year	150
	Estimated payments made during the year	200

   b. Prepare a U.S. Individual Income Tax Return (Form 1040). Use Schedule A to itemize some assumed deductions.
   c. Compute the taxes and record any balance due the Internal Revenue Service or any overpayment.

3. Secure a packet of state income tax materials, including the individual income tax return, schedules, tax table and the information brochure.
   a. Repeat the simulation exercise in problem 2. Prepare the individual state income tax return and schedule(s).

Unit 93 MATHEMATICS ESSENTIAL TO CAREERS, CAREER PLANNING AND DEVELOPMENT

Each nation is built on a concept of work, called a "work ethic." In turn, the well-being of each individual depends on productivity in producing goods and services. Individual development is also based on the freedom to make career choices for serving and growing in an occupation that is personally fulfilling.

A. FOUNDATIONS FOR CAREERS AND CAREER PLANNING

Productive work is recognized as the foundation for wealth . . . human, social, economic, cultural, spiritual and moral. Importantly, work is essential to national survival.

In this nation, full employment is a continuing goal. The maximum development of each person, consistent with his or her capabilities and desires and the needs of society, are centered around the work ethic. Unemployment, underemployment, idleness and separation from work are recognized as wasteful of human resources.

Finally, in the work ethic each person finds meaning and purpose, ideals, values and happiness as a contributing member of society. This means preparation for entry into the "work force." Once employed, provision must be made for retraining or occupational upgrading. Since the skills and technology (theory and related knowledge) change over a period of years, the parallel development of the individual takes place throughout a life span.

Some of the new knowledge and skills may be obtained through on-the-job, in-plant or business training. Other personal development takes place through what are called extension and special training courses in schools and institutions. This pyramiding of school and business/industry experience is intended to continuously develop employee capability. This is necessary for the individual to remain employable, to deal with life problems, and to progress to other satisfying levels of occupational competency and responsibility.

Each person and each occupation requires a different degree of skill in language communication; making computations; interpreting environmental, social, natural and other sciences; reading drawings, sketches and diagrams, and the like. The mathematics that is especially important at the level of the worker is identified as "related mathematics."

This book is based on analyses of many occupations. The selection of mathematics principles and the order in which each is presented follow a definite organization pattern. The fundamentals are intended to develop individual capability to relate principles to practical occupational problems. Other principles are included to meet the needs of the worker as a consumer.

The importance of mathematics in career planning may be better understood by relating it to the characteristics of the work force. This approach provides an overall view of "work" within the different economic sectors. These sectors comprise the labor market and the "work force" of the society. The work force indicates potential levels of employment, possible worker mobility, and further need for career planning and development.

CAREER PLANNING AND MANPOWER NEEDS IN THE ECONOMIC SECTORS

The world of work consists of a series of "economic sectors." The economic sectors refer to major groupings of occupations within which people work. The most common economic sectors include:

- agricultural
- health
- business/banking
- home and institutional
- distribution
- trades and industrial
- public services

The occupations that relate to each economic sector may be grouped in "occupational constellations." For instance, all the job titles in the health and medical sector may be identified within the health and allied industries occupations constellation.

JOB FAMILIES AND MAJOR OCCUPATIONAL FIELDS

There are, also, "job families" in each constellation. In the industry sector alone, the constellation includes at least 75 major "occupational clusters" ("job families"). These cover jobs that are classified as trades, industries, industrial services, and industrial-technical occupations.

Sample occupational clusters in the trade and industry occupations are: building industries occupations, textile and clothing manufacturing industries occupations, food industries occupations, automotive industries occupations, machine industries occupations, graphic arts industries occupations, to name a few.

Each of the occupational clusters includes other job clusters. Examination of the building industries occupations cluster reveals that it consists of such trades or fields as:

architectural drafting and design, masonry and trowel trades, electrical installation and servicing trades, plumbing and pipefitting trades, carpentry trades, millwork and cabinetmaking trades, and others.

JOB LEVELS AND CAREER PLANNING

Another dimension is that of work levels. Work within each occupational field is performed by workers at many different levels. Some workers perform within a narrow range of job skills, requiring a limited amount of simple arithmetics and other related subjects. This level is unskilled; sometimes called limited operative level.

Other jobs beyond this basic level require a higher degree of manipulative (performance) skills, the ability to make decisions and apply related mathematics, science, and other technical knowledge. Clusters of jobs range from semiskilled to skilled craftspersons and technicians, including middle management and supervisory titles.

Other job levels in each field reach up to semiprofessional and professional. Career development is obviously a lifetime process. It involves career planning and a number of job changes at different times. "Job mobility" must be considered to advance vertically to successively higher job levels. Mobility means, also, lateral movement into a supplementary or related job cluster. For example, many craftspersons in the building industries occupations move into positions dealing with finance and business related to the building industries.

To summarize up to this point, career planning and development begin with an understanding of the work ethic. Analyses of the work world reveal that job titles may be clustered according to economic sectors (occupational constellations). Within each constellation there are occupational fields. Each field contains other clusters of jobs ranging from unskilled and limited skill levels to highly qualified technologists and professional worker levels. Job mobility may be vertical or lateral, involving the mastery of advanced skills and the technology for the job level.

B. MATHEMATICS APPLIED TO CAREERS AND CAREER PLANNING

Many workers perform successfully and derive personal job satisfaction as laborers and unskilled workers. Some persons seek to enter employment at the earliest possible legal age. Once employed, a number develop a career plan for continuing study or to prepare for the next level position.

Sizable numbers of students prefer to plan careers starting with the selection of a vocation at an early age. Preparation for the labor market takes place through a secondary school vocational education curriculum. Others delay this decision until postsecondary school, or enter into a cooperative industry/school training program. The first occupational preparation for still others is through occupational specialty training in the military. These are common pathways to occupational preparation and employment.

Training programs are usually developed from occupational, trade, job, and task analyses. The analyses reveal the skill and technology, related, and general education requirements essential for successful job performance. The sequential order in which the learning units are grouped into courses and other less formal learning experiences is called a "curriculum." Thus, a curriculum in carpentry includes all the skills and technology, related and general education necessary to achieve the career objective of preparing for employment. Another different curriculum is required for workers who may need retraining. Still another curriculum is needed to extend the work skills of a highly competent worker.

Occupational analyses are used, too, by labor market analyses to describe the work specifications for each job title. These include the educational requirements based on what the worker needs to know and be able to do on the job.

EDUCATIONAL CAREER DEVELOPMENT LADDER: OCCUPATIONAL AWARENESS, ORIENTATION AND EXPLORATION

Many school systems are attempting to develop a general curriculum which has elements for career development. The earlier mentioned needs for communication skills, social, science, health and other basic understandings are integral parts of the curriculum. The development of computational skills is included.

Beginning in the elementary grades, the subject areas in the curriculum are interrelated to develop an "awareness" of the economic sectors. Learning experiences center around simple activities that develop an awareness to the world of work.

Orientation and exploratory experiences are essential parts of the middle and junior high school curriculum. Further exploratory experiences are provided in general senior high schools. Thus, school curriculums provide increasingly higher degrees of experiences from the awareness stage to orientation and exploration.

These three stages are part of the common core or foundational skills and knowledge of all youth and young adults. Since society includes many economic sectors, these experiences should relate broadly across all of the practical arts. The learning experiences deal with health and allied industries, home and institutional arts, business and banking industries, distribution, agricultural and industrial arts.

The underlying purpose of exploratory experiences is to guide a person in a career decision and career planning. Once a vocation is selected, the appropriate curriculum may be pursued in a quality secondary or postsecondary vocational education and manpower training program. The objective is preparation for entrance into an economic sector as an advanced learner. Additional highly specialized skills that are needed in a particular business, office, or industry are developed on the job.

The four arithmetic processes of addition, subtraction, multiplication and division are basic learning experiences. These basics comprise the computational skills needed daily by every individual. Mathematical awareness is threaded throughout the elementary school grades. Orientation to mathematics takes on a more formal approach in the context of orientation to vocations.

At the middle school, junior high or lower secondary school levels, the emphasis on teaching and learning changes to exploration. The student is rotated among different laboratories, shops and related subjects.

The learning experiences are "coordinated" so the student may explore many different avenues of development by sampling activities. Thus, exploration is interwoven throughout the general education curriculum. Mathematics is treated as a subject. At the same time it is linked with exploratory experiences in the practical arts, fine arts, sciences, and all other subject areas.

Out of the broad-based experiences of the practical arts some youth plan their occupational careers. At this stage the student is knowledgeable about the mathematics needed as an individual, the needs as a citizen, and the essential place mathematics occupies in occupational preparation and employment. Thus, work-bound students elect to pursue vocational education as preparation for employment.

MATHEMATICAL COMPETENCIES TO MEET VARYING OCCUPATIONAL NEEDS

Mathematics is related within each vocational-technical curriculum. This means that out of each occupational analysis a body of mathematics is identified which is very specific for an occupation. This content differs for each occupational group and for each level within an occupation. As examples, the related mathematics requirements are different in each of these curricula: licensed practical nurse, dietary technician, secretarial and office practice, marketing and merchandising, ornamental horticulture, and machine trades.

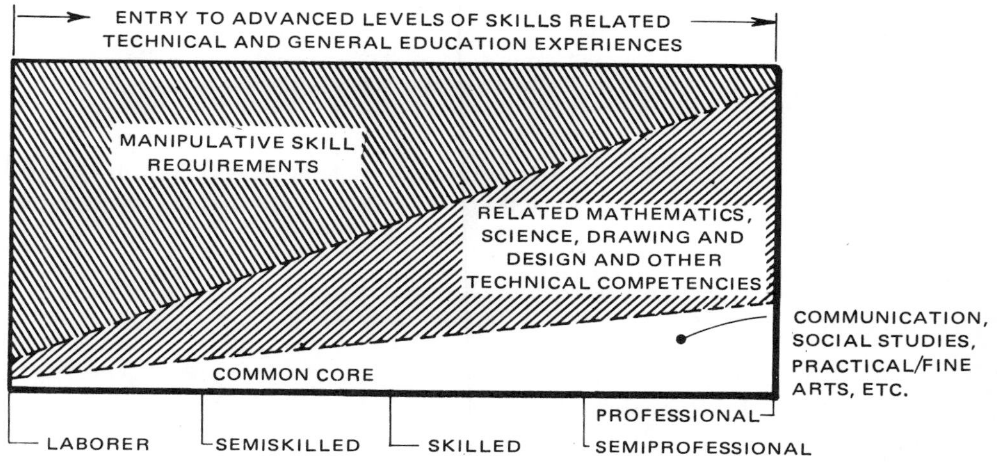

Mathematical Needs for Different Careers

The nature and depth of mathematics is influenced, also, by the objectives of the curriculum. Vocational-technical education has three prime objectives; to prepare an individual for initial entry or reentry into employment, to advance in employment, and to be occupationally upgraded.

In the work force there are job opportunities for individuals which cut across the full range of abilities. Some jobs require the ability to apply just the four basic arithmetic processes. At the next stage of development and level of employment, other fundamentals relating to common fractions, decimal fractions and direct and indirect measurements are required.

There is a growing need to deal with customary units, the conventional metric units and the SI Metrics. At still higher levels of employment the worker must apply mathematics to graphs and statistics, finance, and problems of percents and averages.

Up to and including the skilled craftsperson and technician levels, the individual must use fundamentals of algebra, geometry and trigonometry appropriate to the occupational group. In algebra, the four basic arithmetic processes must be applied to the solution of practical problems requiring symbols and equations. Principles that relate to ratio and proportion, exponents and radicals must be interpreted in terms of daily occupational problems.

Occupational skills depend on the worker's ability to accurately interpret and apply formulas. Selected geometric lines, shapes and constructions are dealt with in descriptions and measurements of plane and solid articles, parts and mechanisms. Practical applications of right, acute and oblique triangles are required by many skilled workers.

A number of occupational problems require expertise in the use of the slide rule to simplify and speed up mathematical computations. Skill in the use of an electronic calculator is needed. This is in addition to the capability to solve problems "long-hand" by conventional methods.

C. MATHEMATICS NEEDED FOR CONTINUING CAREER DEVELOPMENT

As a person advances career-wise, each higher level requires further development. This development relates to skills, technology, and related mathematics, science, blueprint reading, sketching and circuitry, and the like. To repeat, the mathematics units in this book are based on occupational analyses. They were selected as being essential to developing occupational competency through the level of craftsperson and technician and to meet consumer needs.

For semiprofessional and professional levels, more advanced principles must be mastered and applied in solving complex problems. These levels require greater depth and concentration in pure and applied higher mathematics.

TEAM INPUT INTO CAREER PLANNING

Other team input into career planning is provided by persons who have special preparation to accurately interpret individual abilities, matched against required occupational specifications. These deal with physical requirements, educational achievement, special skills development and other conditions.

Based on practical and realistic testing, students are screened and referred to a planned performance-based training program. Completion of training, or termination of training and education, requires placement and follow-up on-the-job services. The schools, industry and other community agencies participate. There is continuous recycling of these services for upgrading and retraining.

Business and industry personnel serve to interpret skill requirements for different employment. Local, state and national units of government are involved in manpower training activities. Other manpower and human resource services are available. An individual may have a team input to determine the many pathways and opportunities to employment and development.

Such a publication as the "Occupational Outlook Handbook," labor market analyses and manpower demand brochures are available in most schools. Other guides are available for recommending credit for military occupational specialty training toward particular career goals.

MATHEMATICS AS PREREQUISITE FOR CAREERS AT ALL OCCUPATIONAL LEVELS

Regardless of geographic locality in which employed, mathematics (like science and drawing interpretation) is part of the universal technical language of the occupation. Achievement in mathematics must parallel understandings that are developed in related science, as well as the theory (technology) around which each process or skill is developed.

The point being reemphasized is that computational skills are essential at every job level and in everyday living. Occupational progress is interwoven with the individual's ability to comprehend a problem and set up practical mathematical guidelines for solving it. The individual must be able to perform the processes, estimate a probable answer, and check each solution for technical accuracy. Mathematics is interlocked with career planning, career development and a successful career.

Unit 94 ACHIEVEMENT REVIEW ON MATHEMATICS IN CAREERS

ESSENTIAL TO CAREERS, CAREER PLANNING AND DEVELOPMENT

A. FOUNDATIONS FOR CAREERS AND CAREER PLANNING

1. State briefly the importance of a work ethic concept to career planning and a career.
2. Secure labor market information for the area surrounding your place of residence. NOTE: This data is provided in such publications as labor market demand reports of State Departments of Commerce, Labor or Employment Security; "Occupational Outlook Handbook," and other national reports.
   a. State four economic sectors in the immediate labor market area.
   b. Name the predominant economic sector.
   c. Take one of the occupational constellations. Identify one major occupational cluster.
   d. Select and name one occupational field within the cluster.
   e. State four different job levels in the selected occupational field.
   f. Give an example of a representative job title for each of the four different job levels.

B. MATHEMATICS APPLIED TO CAREERS AND CAREER PLANNING

1. Describe briefly how awareness, orientation and exploratory learning experiences in the educational system are valuable in career planning.
2. Study a representative job title in a cluster at the skilled technician level and another at the unskilled level.
   a. List the unskilled job title in one column; the skilled technician in another.
   b. Take the table of contents of this book. Make a simple analysis of the mathematics needed by the unskilled worker and the technician. Then, name three sections in which the mathematics units are grouped for the unskilled worker and three other sections required by the technician.
3. Differentiate between "pure" mathematics and related mathematics as presented in this text.

C. MATHEMATICS NEEDED FOR CONTINUING CAREER DEVELOPMENT

1. Secure a U.S. Department of Labor, Bureau of Labor Statistics table or the latest annual "Manpower Report of the President," showing "employment by occupational group" for the nation.
   a. State the actual or projected total employment for 1960, 1970, and 1980.
   b. Review the data related to employment of: professional and technical workers, craftspersons and foreman, and operatives.
      (1) State the projected employment requirements for 1980.
      (2) Show the percent distribution of the employed work force represented by these requirements, and
      (3) Give the annual rate of change for 1970-1980.

2. Make a simple graphic of a career plan. Start with vocational preparation for an initial entry job. Assume a series of progressively higher level jobs over a period of years. Show three job levels at different career stages. Each level should require greater expertise in relating mathematics to practical occupational problems.
3. Review a wage rate and job level resource publication. Then, make a simple line graph showing generally the effect on wage rate (earnings) of (a) occupational level and (b) years of service.

APPENDIX

TABLE I STANDARD TABLES OF CUSTOMARY UNITS OF MEASURE

Linear Measure		
12 inches (in.)	=	1 foot (ft).
3 ft.	=	1 yard (yd.)
16 1/2 ft.	=	1 rod (rd.)
5 1/2 yd.	=	1 rd.
320 rd.	=	1 mile
1760 yd.	=	1 mile
5280 ft.	=	1 mile

Surface Measure		
144 sq. in.	=	1 sq. ft.
9 sq. ft.	=	1 sq. yd.
30 1/4 sq. yd.	=	1 sq. rd.
160 sq. rd.	=	1 acre
640 acres	=	1 sq. mile
43,560 sq. ft.	=	1 acre

Cubic Measure		
1728 cu. in.	=	1 cu. ft.
27 cu. ft.	=	1 cu. yd.
128 cu. ft.	=	1 cord

Angular (Circular) Measure		
60 sec. (″)	=	1 min. (′)
60′	=	1 degree (°)
90°	=	1 quadrant
360°	=	1 circle

Time Measure		
60 seconds (sec.)	=	1 minute (min.)
60 min.	=	1 hour (hr.)
24 hr.	=	1 day
7 days	=	1 week
52 weeks	=	1 year
365 days	=	1 year
10 years	=	1 decade

Liquid Measure		
4 gills	=	1 pint (pt.)
2 pt.	=	1 quart (qt.)
4 qt.	=	1 gallon (gal.)
231 cu. in.	=	1 gal.
31.5 gal.	=	1 barrel (bbl.)
42 gal.	=	1 bbl. of oil
8 1/2 lb.	=	1 gal. water
7 1/2 gal.	=	1 cu. ft.

Weights of Materials		
0.096 lb.	=	1 cu. in. aluminum
0.260 lb.	=	1 cu. in. cast iron
0.283 lb.	=	1 cu. in. mild steel
0.321 lb.	=	1 cu. in. copper
0.41 lb.	=	1 cu. in. lead
112 lb.	=	1 cu. ft. Dowmetal
167 lb.	=	1 cu. ft. aluminum
464 lb.	=	1 cu. ft. cast iron
490 lb.	=	1 cu. ft. mild steel
555.6 lb.	=	1 cu. ft. copper
710 lb.	=	1 cu. ft. lead

Avoirdupois Weight		
16 ounces (oz.)	=	1 pound (lb.)
100 lb.	=	1 hundredweight (cwt.)
20 cwt.	=	1 ton
2000 lb.	=	1 ton
8 1/2 lb.	=	1 gal. of water
62.4 lb.	=	1 cu. ft. of water
112 lb.	=	1 long cwt.
2240 lb.	=	1 long ton

Dry Measure		
2 cups	=	1 pt.
2 pt.	=	1 qt.
4 qt.	=	1 gal.
8 qt.	=	1 peck (pk.)
4 pk.	=	1 bushel (bu.)

Miscellaneous		
12 units	=	1 dozen (doz.)
12 doz.	=	1 gross
144 units	=	1 gross
24 sheets	=	1 quire
20 quires	=	1 ream
20 units	=	1 score
6 ft.	=	1 fathom

TABLE II
STANDARD TABLES OF METRIC UNITS OF MEASURE

Linear Measure		
Unit	**Value in Meters**	**Symbol or Abbreviation**
micron	0.000 001	μ
millimeter	0.001	mm
centimeter	0.01	cm
decimeter	0.1	dm
meter (unit)	1.0	m
dekameter	10.0	dam
hectometer	100.0	hm
kilometer	1 000.00	km
myriameter	10 000.00	Mm
megameter	1 000 000.00	
Surface Measure		
Unit	**Value in Square Meters**	**Symbol or Abbreviation**
square millimeter	0.000 001	mm^2
square centimeter	0.000 1	cm^2
square decimeter	0.01	dm^2
square meter (centiare)	1.0	m^2
square dekameter (are)	100.0	a^2
hectare	10 000.0	ha^2
square kilometer	1 000 000.0	km^2
Volume		
Unit	**Value in Liters**	**Symbol or Abbreviation**
milliliter	0.001	mL
centiliter	0.01	cL
deciliter	0.1	dL
liter (unit)	1.0	L
dekaliter	10.0	daL
hectoliter	100.0	hL
kiloliter	1 000.0	kL
Mass		
Unit	**Value in Grams**	**Symbol or Abbreviation**
microgram	0.000 001	μg
milligram	0.001	mg
centigram	0.01	cg
decigram	0.1	dg
gram (unit)	1.0	g
dekagram	10.0	dag
hectogram	100.0	hg
kilogram	1 000.0	kg
myriagram	10 000.0	Mg
quintal	100 000.0	q
ton	1 000 000.0	t
Cubic Measure		
Unit	**Value in Cubic Meters**	**Symbol or Abbreviation**
cubic micron	10^{-18}	μ^3
cubic millimeter	10^{-9}	mm^3
cubic centimeter	10^{-6}	cm^3
cubic decimeter	10^{-3}	dm^3
cubic meter	1	m^3
cubic dekameter	10^3	dam^3
cubic hectometer	10^6	hm^3
cubic kilometer	10^9	km^3

TABLE III

METRIC AND CUSTOMARY DECIMAL EQUIVALENTS FOR FRACTIONAL PARTS OF AN INCH

DECIMAL EQUIVALENTS					
Fraction	Decimal Equivalent		Fraction	Decimal Equivalent	
	Customary (in.)	Metric (mm)		Customary (in.)	Metric (mm)
1/64	.015625	0.3969	33/64	.515625	13.0969
1/32	.03125	0.7938	17/32	.53125	13.4938
3/64	.046875	1.1906	35/64	.546875	13.8906
1/16	.0625	1.5875	9/16	.5625	14.2875
5/64	.078125	1.9844	37/64	.578125	14.6844
3/32	.09375	2.3813	19/32	.59375	15.0813
7/64	.109375	2.7781	39/64	.609375	15.4781
1/8	.1250	3.1750	5/8	.6250	15.8750
9/64	.140625	3.5719	41/64	.640625	16.2719
5/32	.15625	3.9688	21/32	.65625	16.6688
11/64	.171875	4.3656	43/64	.671875	17.0656
3/16	.1875	4.7625	11/16	.6875	17.4625
13/64	.203125	5.1594	45/64	.703125	17.8594
7/32	.21875	5.5563	23/32	.71875	18.2563
15/64	.234375	5.9531	47/64	.734375	18.6531
1/4	.250	6.3500	3/4	.750	19.0500
17/64	.265625	6.7469	49/64	.765625	19.4469
9/32	.28125	7.1438	25/32	.78125	19.8438
19/64	.296875	7.5406	51/64	.796875	20.2406
5/16	.3125	7.9375	13/16	.8125	20.6375
21/64	.328125	8.3384	53/64	.828125	21.0344
11/32	.34375	8.7313	27/32	.84375	21.4313
23/64	.359375	9.1281	55/64	.859375	21.8281
3/8	.3750	9.5250	7/8	.8750	22.2250
25/64	.390625	9.9219	57/64	.890625	22.6219
13/32	.40625	10.3188	29/32	.90625	23.0188
27/64	.421875	10.7156	59/64	.921875	23.4156
7/16	.4375	11.1125	15/16	.9375	23.8125
29/64	.453125	11.5094	61/64	.953125	24.2094
15/32	.46875	11.9063	31/32	.96875	24.6063
31/64	.484375	12.3031	63/64	.984375	25.0031
1/2	.500	12.7000	1	1.000	25.4000

TABLE IV

DECIMAL AND MILLIMETER EQUIVALENTS

Millimeter Equivalents of Decimals (0.01″ to 0.99″)										
Dec.	0	1	2	3	4	5	6	7	8	9
0.0	....	0.254	0.508	0.762	1.016	1.270	1.524	1.778	2.032	2.286
0.1	2.540	2.794	3.048	3.302	3.556	3.810	4.064	4.318	4.572	4.826
0.2	5.080	5.334	5.588	5.842	6.096	6.350	6.604	6.858	7.112	7.366
0.3	7.620	7.874	8.128	8.392	8.636	8.890	9.144	9.398	9.652	9.906
0.4	10.160	10.414	10.688	10.922	11.176	11.430	11.684	11.938	12.192	12.446
0.5	12.700	12.954	13.208	13.462	13.716	13.970	14.224	14.478	14.732	14.986
0.6	15.240	15.494	15.748	16.022	16.256	16.510	16.764	17.018	17.272	17.526
0.7	17.780	18.034	18.288	18.542	18.796	19.050	19.304	19.558	19.812	20.066
0.8	20.320	20.574	20.828	21.082	21.336	21.590	21.844	22.098	22.352	22.606
0.9	22.860	23.114	23.368	23.622	23.876	24.130	24.384	24.638	24.892	25.146

Example 0.1″ = 2.540 mm, 0.75″ = 19.050 mm

Decimal Equivalents of Millimeters (1 mm to 99 mm)										
Mm.	0	1	2	3	4	5	6	7	8	9
0	....	0.0394	0.0787	0.1181	0.1575	0.1968	0.2362	0.2756	0.3150	0.3543
1	0.3937	0.4331	0.4724	0.5118	0.5512	0.5906	0.6299	0.6693	0.7087	0.7480
2	0.7874	0.8268	0.8661	0.9055	0.9449	0.9842	1.0236	1.0630	1.1024	1.1417
3	1.1811	1.2205	1.2598	1.2992	1.3386	1.3780	1.4173	1.4567	1.4961	1.5354
4	1.5748	1.6142	1.6535	1.6929	1.7323	1.7716	1.8110	1.8504	1.8898	1.9291
5	1.9685	2.0079	2.0472	2.0866	2.1260	2.1654	2.2047	2.2441	2.2835	2.3228
6	2.3622	2.4016	2.4409	2.4803	2.5197	2.5590	2.5984	2.6378	2.6772	2.7165
7	2.7559	2.7953	2.8346	2.8740	2.9134	2.9528	2.9921	3.0315	3.0709	3.1102
8	3.1496	3.1890	3.2283	3.2677	3.3071	3.3464	3.3858	3.4252	3.4646	3.5039
9	3.5433	3.5827	3.6220	3.6614	3.7008	3.7402	3.7795	3.8189	3.8583	3.8976

Example 10 mm = 0.3937″, 57 mm = 2.2441″

TABLE V

CONVERSION FACTORS FOR SI, CONVENTIONAL METRIC AND CUSTOMARY UNITS

	Conversion of Customary and Metric to Units of SI Metrics			Conversion of SI Metrics to Customary and Conventional Metric Units		
Category	**From ↓ Customary or Conventional Metric Unit →**	**To ↓ SI Metric ↓ →**	**Factor (A) (Multiply by)**	**From ↓ SI Metric ↓ →**	**To ↓ Customary or Conventional Metric Unit →**	**Factor ↓**
acceleration	ft/s^2	m/s^2	0.304 8*	m/s^2	ft/s^2	
	in/s^2		2.540 0 $\times 10^{-2}$*		in/s^2	
area	ft^2	m^2	9.290 3 $\times 10^{-2}$	m^2	ft^2	
	in^2		6.451 6 $\times 10^{-4}$*		in^2	
density	g/cm^3	kg/m^3	1.000 0 $\times 10^{3}$*	kg/m^3	g/cm^3	
	lb (mass)/ft^3		16.018 5		lb (mass)/ft^3	
	lb (mass)/in^3		2.768 0 $\times 10^{4}$		lb (mass)/in^3	
energy	Btu (thermochemical)	J	1.054 3 $\times 10^{3}$	J	Btu (thermochemical)	Multiply by the reciprocal of the multiplier (Factor A) which is used in conversion to the SI Metric unit
	cal (thermochemical)		4.184 0*		cal (thermochemical)	
	eV		1.602 1 $\times 10^{-19}$		eV	
	erg		1.000 0 $\times 10^{-7}$*		erg	
	ft • lb (force)		1.355 8		ft • lb (force)	
	kWh		3.600 0 $\times 10^{6}$*		kWh	
	Wh		3.600 0 $\times 10^{3}$*		Wh	
flow liquid and solid	ft^3/min	m^3/s	4.719 5 $\times 10^{-4}$	m^3/s	ft^3/min.	
	ft^3/s		2.831 7 $\times 10^{-2}$		ft^3/s	
	in^3/min		2.731 2 $\times 10^{-7}$		in^3/min	
	lb (mass)/s	kg/s	0.453 6	kg/s	lb (mass)/s	
	lb (mass)/min		7.559 9 $\times 10^{-3}$		lb (mass)/min	
	tons (short, mass)/h		0.252 0		tons (short, mass)/h	
force	dyne	N	1.000 0 $\times 10^{-5}$*	N	dyne	
	kg (force)		9.806 6		kg (force)	
	lb (force)		4.448 2		lb (force)	
heat	Btu (thermochemical)/ft^2	J/m^2	1.134 9 $\times 10^{4}$	J/m^2	Btu (thermochemical)/ft^2	
	cal (thermochemical) /cm^2		4.184 0 $\times 10^{4}$*		cal (thermochemical)/cm^2	
	ft^2/h	m^2/s	2.580 6 $\times 10^{-5}$	m^2/s	ft^2/h	
length	yd	m	0.914 4	m	yd	
	ft		0.304 8*		ft	
	in		2.540 0 $\times 10^{-2}$*		in	
	μ (micron)		1.000 0 $\times 10^{-6}$*		μ (micron)	
	mil		2.540 0 $\times 10^{-5}$*		mil	

TABLE V

CONVERSION FACTORS FOR SI, CONVENTIONAL METRIC AND CUSTOMARY UNITS (Con't.)

Category	Conversion of Customary and Metric to Units of SI Metrics			Conversion of SI Metrics to Customary and Conventional Metric Units		
	From ↓ Customary or Conventional Metric Unit →	To ↓ SI Metric ↓ →	Factor (A) (Multiply by)	From ↓ SI Metric ↓ →	To Customary or Conventional Metric Unit →	↓
mass	lb (mass avoirdupois)	kg	0.453 6	kg	lb (mass, avoirdupois)	
	oz (mass, avoirdupois)		2.835 0 x 10^{-2}		oz (mass, avoirdupois)	
	ton, long = 2 240 lb (mass)		1.016 0 x 10^{3}		ton, long = 2240 lb (mass)	
	ton, metric		1.000 0 x 10^{3} *		ton, metric	
	ton, short = 2 000 lb (mass)		0.907 2 x 10^{3}		ton, short = 2 000 lb (mass)	
power	Btu (thermochemical)/min	W	17.572 5	W	Btu (thermochemical)/min	Multiply by the
	cal (thermochemical)/min		6.973 3 x 10^{-2}		cal (thermochemical)/min	
	erg/s		1.000 0 x 10^{-7}*		erg/s	
	ft • lb (force)/min		2.259 7 x 10^{-2}		ft • lb (force)/min	reciprocal of the
	hp (550 ft • lb/s)		7.457 0 x 10^{2}		hp (550 ft • lb/s)	
pressure (stress)	atm (760 torr)	N/m^2	1.013 2 x 10^{5}	N/m^2	atm (760 torr)	multiplier (Factor A)
	$dyne/cm^2$		0.100 0*		$dyne/cm^2$	
	g $(force)/cm^2$		98.066 5*		g $(force)/cm^2$	which is used in
	kg $(force)/cm^2$		9.806 6 x 10^{4}		kg $(force)/cm^2$	
	lb $(force)/in^2$ (or psi)		6.894 8 x 10^{3}		lb $(force)/in^2$ (or psi)	
		kg $(force)/mm^2$	7.030 7 x 10^{-4}	kg $(force)/mm^2$		conversion to the SI
	torr (mm mercury at 0° C)	N/m^2	1.333 2 x 10^{2}	N/m^2	torr (mm mercury at 0° C)	
velocity	ft/min	m/s	5.080 0 x 10^{-3}*	m/s	ft/min	Metric unit
	in/s		2.540 0 x 10^{-2}*		in/s	
	mph		0.447 0		mph	
		km/h	1.609 3	km/h		
volume	ft^3	m^3	2.831 7 x 10^{-2}	m^3	ft^3	
	in^3		1.638 7 x 10^{-5}		in^3	
	liter		1.000 0 x 10^{-3}*		liter	
temperature	deg C	K	$t_K = t_C + 273.15$	K	deg C	

*Denotes exact value

TABLE VI

CONVERSION OF ENGLISH AND METRIC UNITS OF MEASURE

Linear Measure

Unit	Inches to millimetres	Millimetres to inches	Feet to metres	Metres to feet	Yards to metres	Metres to yards	Miles to kilometres	Kilometres to miles
1	25.40	0.03937	0.3048	3.281	0.9144	1.094	1.609	0.6214
2	50.80	0.07874	0.6096	6.562	1.829	2.187	3.219	1.243
3	76.20	0.1181	0.9144	9.842	2.743	3.281	4.828	1.864
4	101.60	0.1575	1.219	13.12	3.658	4.374	6.437	2.485
5	127.00	0.1968	1.524	16.40	4.572	5.468	8.047	3.107
6	152.40	0.2362	1.829	19.68	5.486	6.562	9.656	3.728
7	177.80	0.2756	2.134	22.97	6.401	7.655	11.27	4.350
8	203.20	0.3150	2.438	26.25	7.315	8.749	12.87	4.971
9	228.60	0.3543	2.743	29.53	8.230	9.842	14.48	5.592

Example 1 in. = 25.40 mm, 1 m = 3.281 ft., 1 km = 0.6214 mi.

Surface Measure

Unit	Square inches to square centimetres	Square centimetres to square inches	Square feet to square metres	Square metres to square feet	Square yards to square metres	Square metres to square yards	Acres to hectares	Hectares to acres	Square miles to square kilometres	Square kilometres to square miles
1	6.452	0.1550	0.0929	10.76	0.8361	1.196	0.4047	2.471	2.59	0.3861
2	12.90	0.31	0.1859	21.53	1.672	2.392	0.8094	4.942	5.18	0.7722
3	19.356	0.465	0.2787	32.29	2.508	3.588	1.214	7.413	7.77	1.158
4	25.81	0.62	0.3716	43.06	3.345	4.784	1.619	9.884	10.36	1.544
5	32.26	0.775	0.4645	53.82	4.181	5.98	2.023	12.355	12.95	1.931
6	38.71	0.93	0.5574	64.58	5.017	7.176	2.428	14.826	15.54	2.317
7	45.16	1.085	0.6503	75.35	5.853	8.372	2.833	17.297	18.13	2.703
8	51.61	1.24	0.7432	86.11	6.689	9.568	3.237	19.768	20.72	3.089
9	58.08	1.395	0.8361	96.87	7.525	10.764	3.642	22.239	23.31	3.475

Example 1 sq. in. = 6.452 cm^2 1 m^2 = 1.196 sq. yd., 1 sq. mi. = 2.59 km^2

Cubic Measure

Unit	Cubic inches to cubic centimetres	Cubic centimetres to cubic inches	Cubic feet to cubic metres	Cubic metres to cubic feet	Cubic yards to cubic metres	Cubic metres to cubic yards	Gallons to cubic feet	Cubic feet to gallons
1	16.39	0.06102	0.02832	35.31	0.7646	1.308	0.1337	7.481
2	32.77	0.1220	0.05663	70.63	1.529	2.616	0.2674	14.96
3	49.16	0.1831	0.08495	105.9	2.294	3.924	0.4010	22.44
4	65.55	0.2441	0.1133	141.3	3.058	5.232	0.5347	29.92
5	81.94	0.3051	0.1416	176.6	3.823	6.540	0.6684	37.40
6	98.32	0.3661	0.1699	211.9	4.587	7.848	0.8021	44.88
7	114.7	0.4272	0.1982	247.2	5.352	9.156	0.9358	52.36
8	131.1	0.4882	0.2265	282.5	6.116	10.46	1.069	59.84
9	147.5	0.5492	0.2549	371.8	6.881	11.77	1.203	67.32

Example 1 cm^3 = 0.06102 cu. in., 1 gal. = 0.1337 cu. ft.

Volume or Capacity Measure

Unit	Liquid ounces to cubic centimetres	Cubic centimetres to liquid ounces	Pints to litres	Litres to pints	Quarts to litres	Litres to quarts	Gallons to litres	Litres to gallons	Bushels to hectolitres	Hectolitres to bushels
1	29.57	0.03381	0.4732	2.113	0.9463	1.057	3.785	0.2642	0.3524	2.838
2	59.15	0.06763	0.9463	4.227	1.893	2.113	7.571	0.5284	0.7048	5.676
3	88.72	0.1014	1.420	6.340	2.839	3.785	11.36	0.7925	1.057	8.513
4	118.3	0.1353	1.893	8.454	3.170	4.227	15.14	1.057	1.410	11.35
5	147.9	0.1691	2.366	10.57	4.732	5.284	18.93	1.321	1.762	14.19
6	177.4	0.2029	2.839	12.68	5.678	6.340	22.71	1.585	2.114	17.03
7	207.0	0.2367	3.312	14.79	6.624	7.397	26.50	1.849	2.467	19.86
8	236.6	0.2705	3.785	16.91	7.571	8.454	30.28	2.113	2.819	22.70
9	266.2	0.3043	4.259	19.02	8.517	9.510	34.07	2.378	3.171	25.54

Example 1L = 2.113 pt., 1 gal. = 3.785 L

TABLE VII

NATURAL TRIGONOMETRIC FUNCTIONS

Angle	Sine	Cosine	Tangent	Angle	Sine	Cosine	Tangent
1°	.0175	.9998	.0175	46°	.7193	.6947	1.0355
2°	.0349	.9994	.0349	47°	.7314	.6820	1.0724
3°	.0523	.9986	.0524	48°	.7431	.6691	1.1106
4°	.0698	.9976	.0699	49°	.7547	.6561	1.1504
5°	.0872	.9962	.0875	50°	.7660	.6428	1.1918
6°	.1045	.9945	.1051	51°	.7771	.6293	1.2349
7°	.1219	.9925	.1228	52°	.7880	.6157	1.2799
8°	.1392	.9903	.1405	53°	.7986	.6018	1.3270
9°	.1564	.9877	.1584	54°	.8090	.5878	1.3764
10°	.1736	.9848	.1763	55°	.8192	.5736	1.4281
11°	.1908	.9816	.1944	56°	.8290	.5592	1.4826
12°	.2079	.9781	.2126	57°	.8387	.5446	1.5399
13°	.2250	.9744	.2309	58°	.8480	.5299	1.6003
14°	.2419	.9703	.2493	59°	.8572	.5150	1.6643
15°	.2588	.9659	.2679	60°	.8660	.5000	1.7321
16°	.2756	.9613	.2867	61°	.8746	.4848	1.8040
17°	.2924	.9563	.3057	62°	.8829	.4695	1.8807
18°	.3090	.9511	.3249	63°	.8910	.4540	1.9626
19°	.3256	.9455	.3443	64°	.8988	.4384	2.0503
20°	.3420	.9397	.3640	65°	.9063	.4226	2.1445
21°	.3584	.9336	.3839	66°	.9135	.4067	2.2460
22°	.3746	.9272	.4040	67°	.9205	.3907	2.3559
23°	.3907	.9205	.4245	68°	.9272	.3746	2.4751
24°	.4067	.9135	.4452	69°	.9336	.3584	2.6051
25°	.4226	.9063	.4663	70°	.9397	.3420	2.7475
26°	.4384	.8988	.4877	71°	.9455	.3256	2.9042
27°	.4540	.8910	.5095	72°	.9511	.3090	3.0777
28°	.4695	.8829	.5317	73°	.9563	.2924	3.2709
29°	.4848	.8746	.5543	74°	.9613	.2756	3.4874
30°	.5000	.8660	.5774	75°	.9659	.2588	3.7321
31°	.5150	.8572	.6009	76°	.9703	.2419	4.0108
32°	.5299	.8480	.6249	77°	.9744	.2250	4.3315
33°	.5446	.8387	.6494	78°	.9781	.2079	4.7046
34°	.5592	.8290	.6745	79°	.9816	.1908	5.1446
35°	.5736	.8192	.7002	80°	.9848	.1736	5.6713
36°	.5878	.8090	.7265	81°	.9877	.1564	6.3138
37°	.6018	.7986	.7536	82°	.9903	.1392	7.1154
38°	.6157	.7880	.7813	83°	.9925	.1219	8.1443
39°	.6293	.7771	.8098	84°	.9945	.1045	9.5144
40°	.6428	.7660	.8391	85°	.9962	.0872	11.4301
41°	.6561	.7547	.8693	86°	.9976	.0698	14.3007
42°	.6691	.7431	.9004	87°	.9986	.0523	19.0811
43°	.6820	.7314	.9325	88°	.9994	.0349	28.6363
44°	.6947	.7193	.9657	89°	.9998	.0175	57.2900
45°	.7071	.7071	1.0000	90°	1.0000	.0000	

TABLE VIII

POWERS AND ROOTS OF NUMBERS (1 through 100)

Number	Powers		Roots		Number	Powers		Roots	
	Square	Cube	Square	Cube		Square	Cube	Square	Cube
1	1	1	1.000	1.000	51	2,601	132,651	7.141	3.708
2	4	8	1.414	1.260	52	2,704	140,608	7.211	3.733
3	9	27	1.732	1.442	53	2,809	148,877	7.280	3.756
4	16	64	2.000	1.587	54	2,916	157,464	7.348	3.780
5	25	125	2.236	1.710	55	3,025	166,375	7.416	3.803
6	36	216	2.449	1.817	56	3,136	175,616	7.483	3.826
7	49	343	2.646	1.913	57	3,249	185,193	7.550	3.849
8	64	512	2.828	2.000	58	3,364	195,112	7.616	3.871
9	81	729	3.000	2.080	59	3,481	205,379	7.681	3.893
10	100	1,000	3.162	2.154	60	3,600	216,000	7.746	3.915
11	121	1,331	3.317	2.224	61	3,721	226,981	7.810	3.936
12	144	1,728	3.464	2.289	62	3,844	238,328	7.874	3.958
13	169	2,197	3.606	2.351	63	3,969	250,047	7.937	3.979
14	196	2,744	3.742	2.410	64	4,096	262,144	8.000	4.000
15	225	3,375	3.873	2.466	65	4,225	274,625	8.062	4.021
16	256	4,096	4.000	2.520	66	4,356	287,496	8.124	4.041
17	289	4,913	4.123	2.571	67	4,489	300,763	8.185	4.062
18	324	5,832	4.243	2.621	68	4,624	314,432	8.246	4.082
19	361	6,859	4.359	2.668	69	4,761	328,509	8.307	4.102
20	400	8,000	4.472	2.714	70	4,900	343,000	8.367	4.121
21	441	9,261	4.583	2.759	71	5,041	357,911	8.426	4.141
22	484	10,648	4.690	2.802	72	5,184	373,248	8.485	4.160
23	529	12,167	4.796	2.844	73	5,329	389,017	8.544	4.179
24	576	13,824	4.899	2.884	74	5,476	405,224	8.602	4.198
25	625	15,625	5.000	2.924	75	5,625	421,875	8.660	4.217
26	676	17,576	5.099	2.962	76	5,776	438,976	8.718	4.236
27	729	19,683	5.196	3.000	77	5,929	456,533	8.775	4.254
28	784	21,952	5.292	3.037	78	6,084	474,552	8.832	4.273
29	841	24,389	5.385	3.072	79	6,241	493,039	8.888	4.291
30	900	27,000	5.477	3.107	80	6,400	512,000	8.944	4.309
31	961	29,791	5.568	3.141	81	6,561	531,441	9.000	4.327
32	1,024	32,798	5.657	3.175	82	6,724	551,368	9.055	4.344
33	1,089	35,937	5.745	3.208	83	6,889	571,787	9.110	4.362
34	1,156	39,304	5.831	3.240	84	7,056	592,704	9.165	4.380
35	1,225	42,875	5.916	3.271	85	7,225	614,125	9.220	4.397
36	1,296	46,656	6.000	3.302	86	7,396	636,056	9.274	4.414
37	1,369	50,653	6.083	3.332	87	7,569	658,503	9.327	4.481
38	1,444	54,872	6.164	3.362	88	7,744	681,472	9.381	4.448
39	1,521	59,319	6.245	3.391	89	7,921	704,969	9.434	4.465
40	1,600	64,000	6.325	3.420	90	8,100	729,000	9.487	4.481
41	1,681	68,921	6.403	3.448	91	8,281	753,571	9.539	4.498
42	1,764	74,088	6.481	3.476	92	8,464	778,688	9.592	4.514
43	1,849	79,507	6.557	3.503	93	8,649	804,357	9.644	4.531
44	1,936	85,184	6.633	3.530	94	8,836	830,584	9.695	4.547
45	2,025	91,125	6.708	3.557	95	9,025	857,375	9.747	4.563
46	2,116	97,336	6.782	3.583	96	9,216	884,736	9.798	4.579
47	2,209	103,823	6.856	3.609	97	9,409	912,673	9.849	4.595
48	2,304	110,592	6.928	3.634	98	9,604	941,192	9.900	4.610
49	2,401	117,649	7.000	3.659	99	9,801	970,299	9.950	4.626
50	2,500	125,000	7.071	3.684	100	10,000	1,000,000	10.000	4.642

TABLE IX (A)

SQUARE ROOTS OF NUMBERS (1.000 through 5.490)

Number	0	1	2	3	4	5	6	7	8	9
1.0	1.000	$1.00\bar{5}$	1.010	$1.01\bar{5}$	1.020	$1.02\bar{5}$	1.030	1.034	1.039	1.044
1.1	1.049	1.054	1.058	1.063	1.068	1.072	1.077	1.082	1.086	1.091
1.2	1.095	1.100	$1.10\bar{5}$	1.109	1.114	1.118	1.122	1.127	1.131	1.136
1.3	1.140	$1.14\bar{5}$	1.149	1.153	1.158	1.162	1.166	1.170	$1.17\bar{5}$	1.179
1.4	1.183	1.187	1.192	1.196	1.200	1.204	1.208	1.212	1.217	1.221
1.5	$1.22\bar{5}$	1.229	1.233	1.237	1.241	$1.24\bar{5}$	1.249	1.253	1.257	1.261
1.6	$1.26\bar{5}$	1.269	1.273	1.277	1.281	$1.28\bar{5}$	1.288	1.292	1.296	1.300
1.7	1.304	1.308	1.311	1.315	1.319	1.323	1.327	1.330	1.334	1.338
1.8	1.342	1.345	1.349	1.353	1.356	1.360	1.364	1.367	1.371	$1.37\bar{5}$
1.9	1.378	1.382	1.386	1.389	1.393	1.396	1.400	1.404	1.407	1.411
2.0	1.414	1.418	1.421	$1.42\bar{5}$	1.428	1.432	1.435	1.439	1.442	1.446
2.1	1.449	1.453	1.456	1.459	1.463	1.466	1.470	1.473	1.476	1.480
2.2	1.483	1.487	1.490	1.493	1.497	1.500	1.503	1.507	1.510	1.513
2.3	1.517	1.520	1.523	1.526	1.530	1.533	1.536	1.539	1.543	1.546
2.4	1.549	1.552	1.556	1.559	1.562	1.565	1.568	1.572	$1.57\bar{5}$	1.578
2.5	1.581	1.584	1.587	1.591	1.594	1.597	1.600	1.603	1.606	1.609
2.6	1.612	1.616	1.619	1.622	$1.62\bar{5}$	1.628	1.631	1.634	1.637	1.640
2.7	1.643	1.646	1.649	1.652	1.655	1.658	1.661	1.664	1.667	1.670
2.8	1.673	1.676	1.679	1.682	1.685	1.688	1.691	1.694	1.697	1.700
2.9	1.703	1.706	1.709	1.712	$1.71\bar{5}$	1.718	1.720	1.723	1.726	1.729
3.0	1.732	$1.73\bar{5}$	1.738	1.741	1.744	1.746	1.749	1.752	$1.75\bar{5}$	1.758
3.1	1.761	1.764	1.766	1.769	1.772	$1.77\bar{5}$	1.778	1.780	1.783	1.786
3.2	1.789	1.792	1.794	1.797	1.800	1.803	1.806	1.808	1.811	1.814
3.3	1.817	1.819	1.822	$1.82\bar{5}$	1.828	1.830	1.833	1.836	1.838	1.841
3.4	1.844	1.847	1.849	1.852	$1.85\bar{5}$	1.857	1.860	1.863	1.865	1.868
3.5	1.871	1.873	1.876	1.879	1.881	1.884	1.887	1.889	1.892	$1.89\bar{5}$
3.6	1.897	1.900	1.903	1.905	1.908	1.910	1.913	1.916	1.918	1.921
3.7	1.924	1.926	1.929	1.931	1.934	1.936	1.939	1.942	1.944	1.947
3.8	1.949	1.952	1.954	1.957	1.960	1.962	$1.96\bar{5}$	1.967	1.970	1.972
3.9	$1.97\bar{5}$	1.977	1.980	1.982	$1.98\bar{5}$	1.987	1.990	1.992	$1.99\bar{5}$	1.997
4.0	2.000	2.002	$2.00\bar{5}$	2.007	2.010	2.012	$2.01\bar{5}$	2.017	2.020	2.022
4.1	$2.02\bar{5}$	2.027	2.030	2.032	$2.03\bar{5}$	2.037	2.040	2.042	$2.04\bar{5}$	2.047
4.2	2.049	2.052	2.054	2.057	2.059	2.062	2.064	2.066	2.069	2.071
4.3	2.074	2.076	2.078	2.081	2.083	2.086	2.088	2.090	2.093	2.095
4.4	2.098	2.100	2.102	$2.10\bar{5}$	2.107	2.110	2.112	2.114	2.117	2.119
4.5	2.121	2.124	2.126	2.128	2.131	2.133	2.135	2.138	2.140	2.142
4.6	$2.14\bar{5}$	2.147	2.149	2.152	2.154	2.156	2.159	2.161	2.163	2.166
4.7	2.168	2.170	2.173	$2.17\bar{5}$	2.177	2.179	2.182	2.184	2.186	2.189
4.8	2.191	2.193	2.195	2.198	2.200	2.202	$2.20\bar{5}$	2.207	2.209	2.211
4.9	2.214	2.216	2.218	2.220	2.223	$2.22\bar{5}$	2.227	2.229	2.232	2.234
5.0	2.236	2.238	2.241	2.243	$2.24\bar{5}$	2.247	2.249	2.252	2.254	2.256
5.1	2.258	2.261	2.263	$2.26\bar{5}$	2.267	2.269	2.272	2.274	2.276	2.278
5.2	2.280	2.283	$2.28\bar{5}$	2.287	2.289	2.291	2.293	2.296	2.298	2.300
5.3	2.302	2.304	2.307	2.309	2.311	2.313	2.315	2.317	2.319	2.322
5.4	2.324	2.326	2.328	2.330	2.332	$2.33\bar{5}$	2.337	2.339	2.341	2.343
	0	1	2	3	4	5	6	7	8	9

TABLE IX (B)

SQUARE ROOTS OF NUMBERS (5.500 through 9.990)

Number	0	1	2	3	4	5	6	7	8	9
5.5	2.345	2.347	2.349	2.352	2.354	2.356	2.358	2.360	2.362	2.364
5.6	2.366	2.369	2.371	2.373	2.375	2.377	2.379	2.381	2.383	2.385
5.7	2.387	2.390	2.392	2.394	2.396	2.398	2.400	2.402	2.404	2.406
5.8	2.408	2.410	2.412	2.415	2.417	2.419	2.421	2.423	2.425	2.427
5.9	2.429	2.431	2.433	2.435	2.437	2.439	2.441	2.443	2.445	2.447
6.0	2.449	2.452	2.454	2.456	2.458	2.460	2.462	2.464	2.466	2.468
6.1	2.470	2.472	2.474	2.476	2.478	2.480	2.482	2.484	2.486	2.488
6.2	2.490	2.492	2.494	2.496	2.498	2.500	2.502	2.504	2.506	2.508
6.3	2.510	2.512	2.514	2.516	2.518	2.520	2.522	2.524	2.526	2.528
6.4	2.530	2.532	2.534	2.536	2.538	2.540	2.542	2.544	2.546	2.548
6.5	2.550	2.551	2.553	2.555	2.557	2.559	2.561	2.563	2.565	2.567
6.6	2.569	2.571	2.573	2.575	2.577	2.579	2.581	2.583	2.585	2.587
6.7	2.588	2.590	2.592	2.594	2.596	2.598	2.600	2.602	2.604	2.606
6.8	2.608	2.610	2.612	2.613	2.615	2.617	2.619	2.621	2.623	2.625
6.9	2.627	2.629	2.631	2.632	2.634	2.636	2.638	2.640	2.642	2.644
7.0	2.646	2.648	2.650	2.651	2.653	2.655	2.657	2.659	2.661	2.663
7.1	2.665	2.666	2.668	2.670	2.672	2.674	2.676	2.678	2.680	2.681
7.2	2.683	2.685	2.687	2.689	2.691	2.693	2.694	2.696	2.698	2.700
7.3	2.702	2.704	2.706	2.707	2.709	2.711	2.713	2.715	2.717	2.718
7.4	2.720	2.722	2.724	2.726	2.728	2.729	2.731	2.733	2.735	2.737
7.5	2.739	2.740	2.742	2.744	2.746	2.748	2.750	2.751	2.753	2.755
7.6	2.757	2.759	2.760	2.762	2.764	2.766	2.768	2.769	2.771	2.773
7.7	2.775	2.777	2.778	2.780	2.782	2.784	2.786	2.787	2.789	2.791
7.8	2.793	2.795	2.796	2.798	2.800	2.802	2.804	2.805	2.807	2.809
7.9	2.811	2.812	2.814	2.816	2.818	2.820	2.821	2.823	2.825	2.827
8.0	2.828	2.830	2.832	2.834	2.835	2.837	2.839	2.841	2.843	2.844
8.1	2.846	2.848	2.850	2.851	2.853	2.855	2.857	2.858	2.860	2.862
8.2	2.864	2.865	2.867	2.869	2.871	2.872	2.874	2.876	2.877	2.879
8.3	2.881	2.883	2.884	2.886	2.888	2.890	2.891	2.893	2.895	2.897
8.4	2.898	2.900	2.902	2.903	2.905	2.907	2.909	2.910	2.912	2.914
8.5	2.915	2.917	2.919	2.921	2.922	2.924	2.926	2.927	2.929	2.931
8.6	2.933	2.934	2.936	2.938	2.939	2.941	2.943	2.944	2.946	2.948
8.7	2.950	2.951	2.953	2.955	2.956	2.958	2.960	2.961	2.963	2.965
8.8	2.966	2.968	2.970	2.972	2.973	2.975	2.977	2.978	2.980	2.982
8.9	2.983	2.985	2.987	2.988	2.990	2.992	2.993	2.995	2.997	2.998
9.0	3.000	3.002	3.003	3.005	3.007	3.008	3.010	3.012	3.013	2.015
9.1	3.017	3.018	3.020	3.022	3.023	3.025	3.027	3.028	2.030	3.032
9.2	3.033	3.035	3.036	3.038	3.040	3.041	3.043	3.045	3.046	3.048
9.3	3.050	3.051	3.053	3.055	3.056	3.058	3.059	3.061	3.063	3.064
9.4	3.066	3.068	3.069	3.071	3.072	3.074	3.076	3.077	3.079	3.081
9.5	3.082	3.084	3.085	3.087	3.089	3.090	3.092	3.094	3.095	3.097
9.6	3.098	3.100	3.102	3.103	3.105	3.106	3.108	3.110	3.111	3.113
9.7	3.114	3.116	3.118	3.119	3.121	3.122	3.124	3.126	3.127	3.129
9.8	3.130	3.132	3.134	3.135	3.137	3.138	3.140	3.142	3.143	3.145
9.9	3.146	3.148	3.150	3.151	3.153	3.154	3.156	3.158	3.159	3.161
	0	1	2	3	4	5	6	7	8	9

TABLE IX (C)

SQUARE ROOTS OF NUMBERS (10.00 through 54.90)

Number	0	1	2	3	4	5	6	7	8	9
10.	3.162	3.178	3.194	3.209	3.225	3.240	3.256	3.271	3.286	3.302
11.	3.317	3.332	3.347	3.362	3.376	3.391	3.406	3.421	3.435	3.450
12.	3.464	3.479	3.493	3.507	3.521	3.536	3.550	3.564	3.578	3.592
13.	3.606	3.619	3.633	3.647	3.661	3.674	3.688	3.701	3.715	3.728
14.	3.742	3.755	3.768	3.782	3.795	3.808	3.821	3.834	3.847	3.860
15.	3.873	3.886	3.899	3.912	3.924	3.937	3.950	3.962	3.975	3.987
16.	4.000	4.012	4.025	4.037	4.050	4.062	4.074	4.087	4.099	4.111
17.	4.123	4.135	4.147	4.159	4.171	4.183	4.195	4.207	4.219	4.231
18.	4.243	4.254	4.266	4.278	4.290	4.301	4.313	4.324	4.336	4.347
19.	4.359	4.370	4.382	4.393	4.405	4.416	4.427	4.438	4.450	4.461
20.	4.472	4.483	4.494	4.506	4.517	4.528	4.539	4.550	4.561	4.572
21.	4.583	4.593	4.604	4.615	4.626	4.637	4.648	4.658	4.669	4.680
22.	4.690	4.701	4.712	4.722	4.733	4.743	4.754	4.764	4.775	4.785
23.	4.796	4.806	4.817	4.827	4.837	4.848	4.858	4.868	4.879	4.889
24.	4.899	4.909	4.919	4.930	4.940	4.950	4.960	4.970	4.980	4.990
25.	5.000	5.010	5.020	5.030	5.040	5.050	5.060	5.070	5.079	5.089
26.	5.099	5.109	5.119	5.128	5.138	5.148	5.158	5.167	5.177	5.187
27.	5.196	5.206	5.215	5.225	5.235	5.244	5.254	5.263	2.273	5.282
28.	5.292	5.301	5.310	5.320	5.329	5.339	5.348	5.357	5.367	5.376
29.	5.385	5.394	5.404	5.413	5.422	5.431	5.441	5.450	5.459	5.468
30.	5.477	5.486	5.495	5.505	5.514	5.523	5.532	5.541	5.550	5.559
31.	5.568	5.577	5.586	5.595	5.604	5.612	5.621	5.630	5.639	5.648
32.	5.657	5.666	5.675	5.683	5.692	5.701	5.710	5.718	5.727	5.736
33.	5.745	5.753	5.762	5.771	5.779	5.788	5.797	5.805	5.814	5.822
34.	5.831	5.840	5.848	5.857	5.865	5.874	5.882	5.891	5.899	5.908
35.	5.916	5.925	5.933	5.941	5.950	5.958	5.967	5.975	5.983	5.992
36.	6.000	6.008	6.017	6.025	6.033	6.042	6.050	6.058	6.066	6.075
37.	6.083	6.091	6.099	6.107	6.116	6.124	6.132	6.140	6.148	6.156
38.	6.164	6.173	6.181	6.189	6.197	6.205	6.213	6.221	6.229	6.237
39.	6.245	6.253	6.261	6.269	6.277	6.285	6.293	6.301	6.309	6.317
40.	6.325	6.332	6.340	6.348	6.356	6.364	6.372	6.380	6.387	6.395
41.	6.403	6.411	6.419	6.427	6.434	6.442	6.450	6.458	6.465	6.473
42.	6.481	6.488	6.496	6.504	6.512	6.519	6.527	6.535	6.542	6.550
43.	6.557	6.565	6.573	6.580	6.588	6.595	6.603	6.611	6.618	6.626
44.	6.633	6.641	6.648	6.656	6.663	6.671	6.678	6.686	6.693	6.701
45.	6.708	6.716	6.723	6.731	6.738	6.745	6.753	6.760	6.768	6.775
46.	6.782	6.790	6.797	6.804	6.812	6.819	6.826	6.834	6.841	6.848
47.	6.856	6.863	6.870	6.877	6.885	6.892	6.899	6.907	6.914	6.921
48.	6.928	6.935	6.943	6.950	6.957	6.964	6.971	6.979	6.986	6.993
49.	7.000	7.007	7.014	7.021	7.029	7.036	7.043	7.050	7.057	7.064
50.	7.071	7.078	7.085	7.092	7.099	7.106	7.113	7.120	7.127	7.134
51.	7.141	7.148	7.155	7.162	7.169	7.176	7.183	7.190	7.197	7.204
52.	7.211	7.218	7.225	7.232	7.239	7.246	7.253	7.259	7.266	7.273
53.	7.280	7.287	7.294	7.301	7.308	7.314	7.321	7.328	7.335	7.342
54.	7.348	7.355	7.362	7.369	7.376	7.382	7.389	7.396	7.403	7.409
	0	1	2	3	4	5	6	7	8	9

TABLE IX (D)

SQUARE ROOTS OF NUMBERS (55.00 through 99.90)

Numbers	0	1	2	3	4	5	6	7	8	9
55.	7.416	7.423	7.430	7.436	7.443	7.450	7.457	7.463	7.470	7.477
56.	7.483	7.490	7.497	7.503	7.510	7.517	7.523	7.530	7.537	7.543
57.	7.550	7.556	7.563	7.570	7.576	7.583	7.589	7.596	7.603	7.609
58.	7.616	7.622	7.629	7.635	7.642	7.649	7.655	7.662	7.668	7.675
59.	7.681	7.688	7.694	7.701	7.707	7.714	7.720	7.727	7.733	7.740
60.	7.746	7.752	7.759	7.765	7.772	7.778	7.785	7.791	7.797	7.804
61.	7.810	7.817	7.823	7.829	7.836	7.842	7.849	7.855	7.861	7.868
62.	7.874	7.880	7.887	7.893	7.899	7.906	7.912	7.918	7.925	7.931
63.	7.937	7.944	7.950	7.956	7.962	7.969	7.975	7.981	7.987	7.994
64.	8.000	8.006	8.012	8.019	8.025	8.031	8.037	8.044	8.050	8.056
65.	8.062	8.068	8.075	8.081	8.087	8.093	8.099	8.106	8.112	8.118
66.	8.124	8.130	8.136	8.142	8.149	8.155	8.161	8.167	8.173	8.179
67.	8.185	8.191	8.198	8.204	8.210	8.216	8.222	8.228	8.234	8.240
68.	8.246	8.252	8.258	8.264	8.270	8.276	8.283	8.289	8.295	8.301
69.	8.307	8.313	8.319	8.325	8.331	8.337	8.343	8.349	8.355	8.361
70.	8.367	8.373	8.379	8.385	8.390	8.396	8.402	8.408	8.414	8.420
71.	8.426	8.432	8.438	8.444	8.450	8.456	8.462	8.468	8.473	8.479
72.	8.485	8.491	8.497	8.503	8.509	8.515	8.521	8.526	8.532	8.538
73.	8.544	8.550	8.556	8.562	8.567	8.573	8.579	8.585	8.591	8.597
74.	8.602	8.608	8.614	8.620	8.626	8.631	8.637	8.643	8.649	8.654
75.	8.660	8.666	8.672	8.678	8.683	8.689	8.695	8.701	8.706	8.712
76.	8.718	8.724	8.729	8.735	8.741	8.746	8.752	8.758	8.764	8.769
77.	8.775	8.781	8.786	8.792	8.798	8.803	8.809	8.815	8.820	8.826
78.	8.832	8.837	8.843	8.849	8.854	8.860	8.866	8.871	8.877	8.883
79.	8.888	8.894	8.899	8.905	8.911	8.916	8.922	8.927	8.933	8.939
80.	8.944	8.950	8.955	8.961	8.967	8.972	8.978	8.983	8.989	8.994
81.	9.000	9.006	9.011	9.017	9.022	9.028	9.033	9.039	9.044	9.050
82.	9.055	9.061	9.066	9.072	9.077	9.083	9.088	9.094	9.099	9.105
83.	9.110	9.116	9.121	9.127	9.132	9.138	9.143	9.149	9.154	9.160
84.	9.165	9.171	9.176	9.182	9.187	9.192	9.198	9.203	9.209	9.214
85.	9.220	9.225	9.230	9.236	9.241	9.247	9.252	9.257	9.263	9.268
86.	9.274	9.279	9.284	9.290	9.295	9.301	9.306	9.311	9.317	9.322
87.	9.327	9.333	9.338	9.343	9.349	9.354	9.359	9.365	9.370	9.375
88.	9.381	9.386	9.391	9.397	9.402	9.407	9.413	9.418	9.423	9.429
89.	9.434	9.439	9.445	9.450	9.455	9.460	9.466	9.471	9.476	9.482
90.	9.487	9.492	9.497	9.503	9.508	9.513	9.518	9.524	9.529	9.534
91.	9.539	9.545	9.550	9.555	9.560	9.566	9.571	9.576	9.581	9.586
92.	9.592	9.597	9.602	9.607	9.612	9.618	9.623	9.628	9.633	9.638
93.	9.644	9.649	9.654	9.659	9.664	9.670	9.675	9.680	9.685	9.690
94.	9.695	9.701	9.706	9.711	9.716	9.721	9.726	9.731	9.737	9.742
95.	9.747	9.752	9.757	9.762	9.767	9.772	9.778	9.783	9.788	9.793
96.	9.798	9.803	9.808	9.813	9.818	9.823	9.829	9.834	9.839	9.844
97.	9.849	9.854	9.859	9.864	9.869	9.874	9.879	9.884	9.889	9.894
98.	9.899	9.905	9.910	9.915	9.920	9.925	9.930	9.935	9.940	9.945
99.	9.950	9.955	9.960	9.965	9.970	9.975	9.980	9.985	9.990	9.995
	0	1	2	3	4	5	6	7	8	9

TABLE X

CIRCUMFERENCES AND AREAS (0.2 to 9.8; 10 to 99)

Diameter	Circum.	Area
0.2	0.628	0.0314
0.4	1.26	0.1256
0.6	1.88	0.2827
0.8	2.51	0.5026
1	3.14	0.7854
1.2	3.77	1.131
1.4	4.39	1.539
1.6	5.02	2.011
1.8	5.65	2.545
2	6.28	3.142
2.2	6.91	3.801
2.4	7.53	4.524
2.6	8.16	5.309
2.8	8.79	6.158
3	9.42	7.069
3.2	10.05	7.548
3.4	10.68	8.553
3.6	11.3	10.18
3.8	11.93	11.34
4	12.57	12.57
4.2	13.19	13.85
4.4	13.82	15.21
4.6	14.45	16.62
4.8	15.08	18.1
5	15.7	19.63
5.2	16.33	21.24
5.4	16.96	22.9
5.6	17.59	24.63
5.8	18.22	26.42
6	18.84	28.27
6.2	19.47	30.19
6.4	20.1	32.17
6.6	20.73	34.21
6.8	21.36	36.32
7	21.99	38.48
7.2	22.61	40.72
7.4	23.24	43.01
7.6	23.87	45.36
7.8	24.5	47.78
8	25.13	50.27
8.2	25.76	52.81
8.4	26.38	55.42
8.6	27.01	58.09
8.8	27.64	60.82
9	28.27	63.62
9.2	28.9	66.48
9.4	29.53	69.4
9.6	30.15	72.38
9.8	30.78	75.43
10	31.41	78.54
11	34.55	95.03
12	37.69	113
13	40.84	132.7
14	43.98	153.9
15	47.12	176.7
16	50.26	201
17	53.4	226.9
18	56.54	254.4
19	59.69	283.5
20	62.83	314.1
21	65.97	346.3
22	69.11	380.1
23	72.25	415.4
24	75.39	452.3
25	78.54	490.8
26	81.68	530.9
27	84.82	572.5
28	87.96	615.7
29	91.1	660.5
30	94.24	706.8
31	97.39	754.8
32	100.5	804.2
33	103.7	855.3
34	106.8	907.9
35	110	962.1
36	113.1	1,017.9
37	116.2	1,075.2
38	119.4	1,134.1
39	122.5	1,194.6
40	125.7	1,256.6
41	128.8	1,320.3
42	131.9	1,385.4
43	135.1	1,452.2
44	138.2	1,520.5
45	141.4	1,590.4
46	144.5	1,661.9
47	147.7	1,734.9
48	150.8	1,809.6
49	153.9	1,885.7
50	157.1	1,963.5
51	160.2	2,042.8
52	163.4	2,123.7
53	166.5	2,206.2
54	169.6	2,290.2
55	172.8	2,375.8
56	175.9	2,463
57	179.1	2,551.8
58	182,2	2,642.1
59	185.4	2,734
60	188.5	2,827.4
61	191.6	2,922.5
62	194.8	3,019.1
63	197.9	3,117.3
64	201.1	3,217
65	204.2	3,318.3
66	207.3	3,421.2
67	210.5	3,525.7
68	213.6	3,631.7
69	216.8	3,739.3
70	219.9	3,848.5
71	223.1	3,959.2
72	226.2	4,071.5
73	229.3	4,185.4
74	232.5	4,300.8
75	235.6	4,417.9
76	238.8	4,536.5
77	241.9	4,656.6
78	245	4,778.4
79	248.2	4,901.7
80	251.3	5,026.6
81	254.5	5,153
82	257.6	5,281
83	260.8	5,410.6
84	263.9	5,541.8
85	267.0	5,674.5
86	270.2	5,808.8
87	273.3	5,944.7
88	276.5	6,082.1
89	279.6	6,221.2
90	282.7	6,361.7
91	285.9	6,503.9
92	289.0	6,647.6
93	292.2	6,792.9
94	295.2	6,939.8
95	298.5	7,088.2
96	301.6	7,238.2
97	304.7	7,389.8
98	307.9	7,543.0
99	311.9	7,697.7

TABLE XI

TAP DRILL SIZES FOR AMERICAN NATIONAL FORM THREADS (CUSTOMARY AND METRIC DRILL SIZES)

Diam. of Thread	Threads per Inch	Drill*	Decimal Equiv.
No. 0–.060	80 NF	3/64	.0469
1–.073	64 NC	1.5 mm	.0591
	72 NF	53	.0595
2–.086	56 NC	50	.0700
	64 NF	50	.0700
3–.099	48 NC	5/64	.0781
	56 NF	45	.0820
4–.112	40 NC	43	.0890
	48 NF	42	.0935
5–.125	40 NC	38	.1015
	44 NF	37	.1040
6–.138	32 NC	36	.1065
	40 NF	33	.1130
8–.164	32 NC	29	.1360
	36 NF	29	.1360
10–.190	24 NC	25	.1495
	32 NF	21	.1590
12–.216	24 NC	16	.1770
	28 NF	14	.1820
1/4	20 NC	7	.2010
	28 NF	3	.2130
	32 NEF	7/32	.2188
5/16	18 NC	F	.2570
	24 NF	I	.2720
	32 NEF	9/32	.2812
3/8	16 NC	5/16	.3125
	24 NF	Q	.3320
	32 NEF	11/32	.3438
7/16	14 NC	U	.3680
	20 NF	25/64	.3906
	28 NEF	Y	.4040
1/2	12 N	27/64	.4219
	13 NC	27/64	.4219
	20 NF	29/64	.4531
	28 NEF	15/32	.4687
9/16	12 NC	31/64	.4844
	18 NF	33/64	.5156
	24 NEF	33/64	.5156
5/8	11 NC	17/32	.5312
	12 N	35/64	.5469
	18 NF	14.5 mm	.5709
	24 NEF	37/64	.5781

Diam. of Thread	Threads per Inch	Drill*	Decimal Equiv.
11/16	12 N	39/64	.6094
	24 NEF	16.5 mm	.6496
	10 NC	16.5 mm	.6496
3/4	12 N	17 mm	.6693
	16 NF	17.5 mm	.6890
	20 NEF	45/64	.7031
13/16	12 N	18.5 mm	.7283
	16 N	3/4	.7500
	20 NEF	49/64	.7656
7/8	9 NC	49/64	.7656
	12 N	20 mm	.7874
	14 NF	20.5 mm	.8071
	16 N	13/16	.8125
	20 NEF	21 mm	.8268
15/16	12 N	55/64	.8594
	16 N	7/8	.8750
	20 NEF	22.5 mm	.8858
1	8 NC	7/8	.8750
	12 N	59/64	.9219
	14 NF	23.5 mm	.9252
	16 N	15/16	.9375
	20 NEF	61/64	.9531
1 1/2	6 NC	1 21/64	1.3281
	8 N	1 3/8	1.3750
	12 NF	36 mm	1.4173
	16 N	1 7/16	1.4375
	18 NEF	1 29/64	1.4531
2	4 1/2 NC	1 25/32	1.7812
	8 N	1 7/8	1.8750
	12 N	1 59/64	1.9219
	16 NEF	1 15/16	1.9375
2 1/2	4 NC	2 1/4	2.2500
	8 N	2 3/8	2.3750
	12 N	61.5 mm	2.4213
	16 N	2 7/16	2.4375
3	4 NC	2 3/4	2.7500
	8 N	2 7/8	2.8750
	12 N	74 mm	2.9134
	16 N	2 15/16	2.9375

TABLE XII

DRILL SIZES (Letters Z-A, Numbers 1-80)

Letter Size	Decimal Value	Number Size	Decimal Value	Number Size	Decimal Value	Number Size	Decimal Value
Z	0.413	1	0.228	28	0.1405	55	0.052
Y	0.404	2	0.221	29	0.136	56	0.0465
X	0.397	3	0.213	30	0.1285	57	0.043
W	0.386	4	0.209	31	0.12	58	0.042
V	0.377	5	0.2055	32	0.116	59	0.041
U	0.368	6	0.204	33	0.113	60	0.04
T	0.358	7	0.201	34	0.111	61	0.039
S	0.348	8	0.199	35	0.11	62	0.038
R	0.339	9	0.196	36	0.1065	63	0.037
Q	0.332	10	0.1935	37	0.104	64	0.036
P	0.323	11	0.191	38	0.1015	65	0.035
O	0.316	12	0.189	39	0.0995	66	0.033
N	0.302	13	0.185	40	0.098	67	0.032
M	0.295	14	0.182	41	0.096	68	0.031
L	0.290	15	0.18	42	0.0935	69	0.0292
K	0.281	16	0.177	43	0.089	70	0.028
J	0.277	17	0.173	44	0.086	71	0.026
I	0.272	18	0.1695	45	0.082	72	0.025
H	0.266	19	0.166	46	0.081	73	0.024
G	0.261	20	0.161	47	0.0785	74	0.0225
F	0.257	21	0.159	48	0.076	75	0.021
E	0.25	22	0.157	49	0.073	76	0.02
D	0.246	23	0.154	50	0.07	77	0.018
C	0.242	24	0.152	51	0.067	78	0.016
B	0.238	25	0.1495	52	0.0635	79	0.0145
A	0.234	26	0.147	53	0.0595	80	0.0135
		27	0.144	54	0.055		

TABLE XIII

SIZES OF TAPERS AND ANGLES

Taper per foot	Included angle			Taper per inch
	Deg.	Min.	Sec.	
1/8	0	35	48	0.010416
3/16	0	53	44	0.015625
1/4	1	11	36	0.020833
5/16	1	29	30	0.026042
3/8	1	47	24	0.031250
7/16	2	5	18	0.036458
1/2	2	23	10	0.014667
9/16	2	41	4	0.046875
5/8	2	59	42	0.052084
11/16	3	16	54	0.057292
3/4	3	34	44	0.06250
13/16	3	52	38	0.067708
7/8	4	10	32	0.072917
15/16	4	28	24	0.078125
1	4	46	18	0.083330

Taper per foot	Included angle			Taper per inch
	Deg.	Min.	Sec.	
1 1/4	5	57	48	0.104666
1 1/2	7	9	10	0.125000
1 3/4	8	20	26	0.145833
2	9	31	36	0.166666
2 1/2	11	53	36	0.208333
3	14	15	0	0.250000
3 1/2	16	35	40	0.291666
4	18	55	28	0.333333
4 1/2	21	14	2	0.375000
5	23	32	12	0.416666
6	28	4	2	0.500000

TABLE XIV

COMPOUND INTEREST TABLE

n	1%	2%	3%	4%	5%	6%
1	1.010 000	1.020 000	1.030 000	1.040 000	1.050 000	1.060 000
2	1.020 100	1.040 400	1.060 900	1.081 600	1.102 500	1.123 600
3	1.030 301	1.061 208	1.092 727	1.124 864	1.157 625	1.191 016
4	1.040 604	1.082 432	1.125 509	1.169 859	1.215 506	1.262 477
5	1.051 010	1.104 081	1.159 274	1.216 653	1.276 282	1.338 226
6	1.061 520	1.126 162	1.194 052	1.265 319	1.340 096	1.418 519
7	1.072 135	1.148 686	1.229 874	1.315 932	1.407 100	1.503 630
8	1.082 857	1.171 659	1.266 770	1.368 569	1.477 455	1.593 848
9	1.093 685	1.195 093	1.304 773	1.423 312	1.551 328	1.689 479
10	1.104 622	1.218 994	1.343 916	1.480 244	1.628 895	1.790 848
11	1.115 668	1.243 374	1.384 234	1.539 454	1.710 339	1.898 299
12	1.126 825	1.268 242	1.425 761	1.601 032	1.795 856	2.012 196
13	1.138 093	1.293 607	1.468 534	1.665 074	1.885 649	2.132 928
14	1.149 474	1.319 479	1.512 590	1.731 676	1.979 932	2.260 904
15	1.160 969	1.345 868	1.557 967	1.800 944	2.078 928	2.396 558
16	1.172 579	1.372 786	1.604 706	1.872 981	2.182 875	2.540 352
17	1.184 304	1.400 241	1.652 848	1.947 900	2.292 018	2.692 773
18	1.196 147	1.428 246	1.702 433	2.025 817	2.406 619	2.854 339
19	1.208 109	1.456 811	1.753 506	2.106 849	2.526 950	3.025 600
20	1.220 190	1.485 947	1.806 111	2.191 123	2.653 298	3.207 135
21	1.232 392	1.515 666	1.860 295	2.278 768	2.785 963	3.399 564
22	1.244 716	1.545 980	1.916 103	2.369 919	2.925 261	3.603 537
23	1.257 163	1.576 899	1.973 587	2.464 716	3.071 524	3.819 750
24	1.269 735	1.608 437	2.032 794	2.563 304	3.225 100	4.048 935
25	1.282 432	1.640 606	2.093 778	2.665 836	3.386 355	4.291 871
26	1.295 256	1.673 418	2.156 591	2.772 470	3.555 673	4.549 383
27	1.308 209	1.706 886	2.221 289	2.883 369	3.733 456	4.822 346
28	1.321 291	1.741 024	2.287 928	2.998 703	3.920 129	5.111 687
29	1.334 504	1.775 845	2.356 566	3.118 651	4.116 136	5.418 388
30	1.347 849	1.811 362	2.427 262	3.243 398	4.321 942	5.743 491
31	1.361 327	1.847 589	2.500 080	3.373 133	4.538 039	6.088 101
32	1.374 941	1.884 541	2.575 083	3.508 059	4.764 941	6.453 387
33	1.388 690	1.922 231	2.652 335	3.648 381	5.003 189	6.840 590
34	1.402 577	1.960 676	2.731 905	3.794 316	5.253 348	7.251 025
35	1.416 603	1.999 890	2.813 862	3.946 089	5.516 015	7.686 087
36	1.430 769	2.039 887	2.898 278	4.103 933	5.791 816	8.147 252
37	1.445 076	2.080 685	2.985 227	4.268 090	6.081 407	8.636 087
38	1.459 527	2.122 299	3.074 783	4.438 813	6.385 477	9.154 252
39	1.474 123	2.164 745	3.167 027	4.616 366	6.704 751	9.703 507
40	1.488 864	2.208 040	3.262 038	4.801 021	7.039 989	10.285 718
41	1.503 752	2.252 200	3.359 899	4.993 061	7.391 988	10.902 861
42	1.518 790	2.297 244	3.460 696	5.192 784	7.761 588	11.557 033
43	1.533 978	2.343 189	3.564 517	5.400 495	8.149 667	12.250 455
44	1.549 318	2.390 053	3.671 452	5.616 515	8.557 150	12.985 482
45	1.564 811	2.437 854	3.781 596	5.841 176	8.985 008	13.764 611
46	1.580 459	2.486 611	3.895 044	6.074 823	9.434 258	14.590 487
47	1.596 263	2.536 344	4.011 895	6.317 816	9.905 971	15.465 917
48	1.612 226	2.587 070	4.132 252	6.570 528	10.401 264	16.393 872
49	1.628 348	2.638 812	4.256 219	6.833 349	10.921 333	17.377 504
50	1.644 639	2.691 588	4.383 906	7.106 683	11.467 400	18.420 154

TABLE XV

CALCULATOR PROCESSES FOR COMMON GEOMETRIC CONSTRUCTIONS

Geometric Calculation		Formula	Calculator Processes	Measurement Unit Value
Areas	Square	$A = s^2$	(s) x (s)	square units
	Rectangle	$A = (\ell)\ (w)$	(ℓ) x (w)	" "
	Circle	$A = \pi r^2$	π to required accuracy (π) x (r) x (r)	" "
	Triangle	$A = \frac{(b \times h)}{2}$	(b x h) ÷ 2	" "
Perimeter	Square	$P = 4(s)$	(s) x (4)	base unit
	Rectangle	$P = 2\ (\ell \times w)$	$(\ell$ x w) x 2	" "
	Triangle	$P = s_1 + s_2 + s_3$	$s_1 + (s_2) + (s_3)$	" "
	Cirumference	$C = \pi d$	(π) x (d)	" "
Degrees and Radians	Angle (as a radian value)	$\angle A = \frac{n^\circ}{57.295\ 78^\circ}$	n° ÷ 57.295 78	radian
	Radian angle (r) (in degrees)	d = r x 57.295 78	(r) x (57.295 78)	degrees
Volume	Cube	$V = s^3$	(s) x (s) x (s)	cubic units
	Rectangular solid	$V = (\ell) \times (w) \times (h)$	(ℓ) x (w) x (h)	" "
	Cylindrical solid	$V = \pi r^2 h$	(π) x (r) x (r) x (h) (π to required accuracy)	" "
	Sphere	$V = \frac{4 \pi r^3}{3}$	(4) x (π) x (r) x (r) x (r) ÷ 3	" "
	Cone	$V = 0.2618 h\ (D^2 + Dd + d^2)$	(D x D+ (D x d) + (d x d) x (h) x (0.2618)	" "

GLOSSARY

Algebraic Entry The sequence in which the numerals of a problem are entered on a calculator.

Algorithm A set of mathematical rules, numerical procedures, or logical decisions which also may be used with an electronic calculator to solve advanced problems.

Angular Measure The size of an opening formed by two intersecting lines or surfaces. Angles are measured in radians or steradians and in degrees (°) minutes ('), and seconds ("). Angular measure involves the four basic arithmetical processes with angles and parts of angles.

Area of a Circle $A = \pi\ (\text{radius})^2$ or $A = 0.7854\ (\text{diameter})^2$

Area of a Triangle The surface area of a triangle equals the base x 1/2 altitude.

Avoirdupois Units of weight based on 16 drams being equal to one ounce. Sixteen ounces equal one pound.

Balanced Equation The values on both sides of an equation are equal.

Bar Graphs Heavy lines or bars of a definite length to represent specific quantitites on a grid having vertical and horizontal lines. A scale indicates the value between each line.

Base Units in SI Metrics Seven base units circumscribe all physical science measurements. The base units include: meter, kilogram, second, ampere, candela, kelvin, and mole.

Basic Arithmetical Processes The four processes of adding, subtracting, multiplying, and dividing. Included, also, is any combination of the four processes.

Calculator Display A lighted numerical readout on a calculator.

Celsius (C) A derived unit of temperature measurement in SI Metrics, expressed as degrees Celsius (°C). Celsius temperatures replace Centigrade temperatures.

Circle A closed curved line on a flat surface. Every point on the closed curved line is the same distance from a fixed given point called a center. "Concentric circles" have a common center. "Eccentric circles" are "off-center" and do not originate from the same center.

Circle Graph The division of a circle into a specific number of parts, each sector denoting a fixed relationship to all other data presented.

Circular Measure The measurement of circles, curved sufaces, cylinders, and other circular shapes.

Circumference The distance around the periphery of a circle, measured either in standard units of linear measure or in degrees.

Clear-entry Key A key used to correct number-entry errors without interfering with any previous part of the calculating sequence. A "clear-entry" key on some models performs this same function.

Collecting Terms The process of combining letters, symbols, or numbers within grouping symbols.

Congruence A geometric term indicating that all the physical properties of size and shape in one part are identical in another part. Two figures are congruent if they differ only in location. Two lines segments of equal length or two circles of equal diameter are congruent.

Constant A fixed mathematical relationship for which a specific symbol is used universally.

Conventional Units French and European metric systems using the meter as the basic unit of measure. Unit designations, standards, values, and derivation of base and other units differ from SI Metrics.

Conversion of Quantities The changing of a quantity from a unit of measure to an equivalent value in another unit of measure. The process of multiplying or dividing (as may be required) a specified quantity by a conversion factor.

Credit Financing Securing a product or service on credit terms which require paying additional financing costs.

Cubical Solid A figure formed by extending an original square surface so that all corners are square and the edges are the same length.

Cubic Measure (Also Volume Measure) Measurement of the space occupied by a body that has three linear dimensions of length, height, and depth. Cubic measure is the product of these three dimensions, expressed in cubic units.

Customary Units United States units of measure based upon the inch, yard, and pound, similar to the British Standard units.

Cylinder of Revolution (Right Cylinder) Two equal and perpendicular bases with a lateral (vertical outside) surface around the bases. The area of the lateral surface of a cylinder of revolution equals the circumference x height.

Decimal Equivalent The conversion of a customary unit of measure to its equivalent value as a decimal.

Decimal Fraction A fraction whose denominator is a multiple of ten; like, 100; 1000; and 10,000. Decimal fractions are written on one line with a decimal point in front of the numerical value.

Decimal Places The number of digits to the right of the decimal point. The number of places is usually related to the degree of accuracy required in the answer.

Depreciation The loss in value of a process, material or product.

Derived SI Metrics Unit Units which are derived from the base units in SI Metrics to satisfy varying computational needs. The complementary derived units relate to quantities of length, mass, time, electric current. thermodynamic temperature, luminous intensity, and amount of substance.

Discounts A reduction in the price of materials, parts and mechanisms. Discounts may be "single" or "multiple," involving successive discounts.

Division The process of determining how many times one value is contained in another. Division is a simplified method of subtraction.

Economic Sector A major grouping of occupations in the labor market. For example, agriculture, health industries, and trade and industries.

Electronic Calculator A computing machine which performs the four basic mathematical processes. Higher mathematical processes may be carried on with more sophisticated calculators.

Equation A mathematical statement indicating that the quantities or expressions on both sides of an equality (=) sign are equal.

Estimating A short cut mathematical process of determining a range against which an actual answer may be checked for accuracy.

Exponent A simple mathematical statement that a quantity is to be multiplied by itself a number of times. The exponent is a small number written to the right and slightly above a quantity. The exponent indicates the power to which the number is to be raised (multiplied by itself).

Expressing Quantities Stating a quantity either in terms of numbers, or a combination of numbers and symbols. "Numerical terms" signifies that numbers are used to express a quantity. "Literal terms" relate to the use of numbers and symbols to express a quantity.

Expression The statement of a problem in abbreviated form using numerical and literal terms.

Extracting the Square Root The process of determining the equal factors which, when multiplied together, give the original value.

Factoring The steps used in determining the series of smaller numbers which, when multiplied by each other, produce the original number.

Formula A shortened method of expressing relationships and a combination of mathematical processes which consistently give the same solution.

Gage Block Measurement A system for establishing a precise measurement by "wringing" together hardened and precisely finished steel blocks against which measurements may be established.

Geometry A branch of mathematics relating to points, lines, planes, closed flat shapes, and solids. These elements may be used alone or in combination to describe, design, construct, and test every visible object.

Grouping Symbols Symbols which are used to group quantities together to simplify reading and mathematical processes. The four common grouping symbols are: parentheses, brackets, braces, and a bar to cover a quantity.

Hertz The frequency of one cycle per second.

Improper Fraction A fraction with a numerator greater than the denominator.

Indirect (Inverse) Proportion Ratios that vary inversely. The two terms in the first or second ratio are reversed.

Interest A payment for the use of money. Compound interest produces a continuous growth in principal. The rate of interest at each interest posting date is applied to the accumulated interest and principal.

Interpolation The process of calculating an intermediate value of a function which lies between two known values.

Job Levels Clusters of jobs within each economic sector. These range from unskilled to operative to semiskilled to skilled technician.

Joule The work done when a force of one newton is moved a distance of one meter in the direction of the force.

Kilogram A base unit of mass in SI Metrics. A kilogram is equal to 2.2 pounds or 1,000 grams.

Law of Cosines The square of any side of a triangle is equal to the sum of the squares of the other sides minus twice the product of the two sides and the cosine of their included angle.

Law of Sines An abbreviated method of expressing that the sides of a triangle are proportional to the sines of the opposite angles.

Line Graph A grid of lines at fixed values on which straight, curved, or broken lines are plotted to present information visually.

Line Segment The working length of a line defined by end points.

Lowest Common Denominator The smallest number into which each number in a set of denominators will divide exactly.

Members (Equation) The expressions that appear on either side of the equality sign in an equation. The quantity on the left side is the "first member." The "second member" appears on the right side.

Meter A base unit of length in SI Metrics and conventional metric measurements. For most practical purposes the meter equals 39.37 inches.

Metrication Any policy, act, or process which tends to increase the changeover from customary (United States) and conventional Metric units of measure to SI Metrics.

Metricize The process of converting any other unit of measure to its SI Metric equivalent.

Micrometer A precision instrument for taking linear measurements in any one of the measurement systems, depending on the calibrations on the micrometer. The distance between the anvil and a spindle are accurately read from a calibrated barrel and thimble. Vernier micrometers have an additional set of graduated lines. These make it possible to read to a more precise degree (0.002 mm and 0.000.") than regular micrometers.

Money Management The setting up of a budget and a system of records and maintaining them; controlling and managing income and expenses.

Multiplication A simplified method of addition.

Multiplying and Dividing Quantities The product of multiplying two like negative terms or any number of positive terms is (+). The product is (-) when an odd number of negative terms is multiplied. These rules for the use of signs apply also to division.

Newton A force which, when applied to a body of one kilogram mass, produces an acceleration of the body of one meter per second.

Overflow A condition where the numerical capacity of the calculator is exceeded. "Underflow" also denotes a condition beyond the calculator capacity where least significant digits may be lost.

Parallelogram A figure having two pairs of parallel sides. The area = length x height.

Percent A short way of relating a given number of parts to a whole, which is equal to 100 (percent). One percent is 1/100 of the whole.

Percentage The product of the base times the rate.

Plane (Plane Surface) A flat surface on which a straight line connecting two points lies.

Positive and Negative Quantities "Positive numbers" refer to all numbers that are greater than zero. "Negative numbers" relate to values that are less than zero.

Prefixes and Symbols (SI Metrics) Multiple and submultiple values of the base-ten notation stem are identified by a system of prefixes. Each prefix is identified by an SI symbol. SI Metric quantities are usually defined by the appropriate prefix followed by the unit of measure.

Programmable Calculators Calculators that contain a "memory" to store numbers and instructions for performing a sequence of operations.

Probability The number of ways an event can occur divided by the total number of ways the event can occur.

Proper Fraction A fraction with a numerator smaller than the denominator.

Proportion Two ratios, equal in value, that are placed on opposite sides of an equality sign.

Protractor A measuring tool for angles. Protractors vary from simple flat tools graduated in degrees to more precise instruments. A movable blade protractor and the universal-bevel protractor are graduated to permit readings in degrees and minutes. The vernier protractor with vernier scales is used for still greater degrees of accuracy.

Radical Sign A mathematical shorthand way of indicating that the equal factors of the value under the radical symbol ($\sqrt{\quad}$) are to be determined.

Ratio A comparison of one quantity with another like quantity or value.

Rectangle A figure whose opposite sides are parallel and the adjacent sides are at right angles to each other. The area = length x height.

Right Prism A solid formed by a flat form as it moves perpendicular to its base to a specified altitude. The shape of the base determines the name of the right prism.

Rounding (Rounding Off) Reducing the number of digits to a lesser number than the total number available. A quantity is reduced to the number of significant digits which produces a desired degree of accuracy in the result.

Sector of a Circle The surface or area between the center and the circumference of a circle which is included within a given angle. The area of a sector equals the area of the circle multiplied by the fractional part which the sector occupies.

Significant Digits Any digit that is needed to define a specific value or quantity. The number of significant digits is based on the implied or required precision associated with the problem.

SI Metrics (SI) An up-to-date "International System of Units" of measurement established cooperatively among most industrialized nations. SI measurements depend on base, supplementary, derived, and combinations of these units to accurately measure and quantitatively define all measurable objects. SI is a standard abbreviation for the "Systemé Internationale D'Unites."

Solids of Revolution The shape that the outside line or lines of flat form take when revolved around an axis.

Supplementary Units in SI Metrics The radian and steradian constitute the two supplementary units for measuring angles in SI Metrics. The radian relates to a plane angle; the steradian, a solid angle.

Surface Measure The measurement of a part, object, mechanism, or other physical mass which has length and height. A surface is "measured" when its length and height (in the same unit of measure) are multiplied. The product is the "area" in square units.

Symbols A simplified way of identifying and working with quantities, units of measure, mathematical processes, and communicating information.

Symmetrical The corresponding points of an object are equidistant from an axis.

Take-home Pay The actual money a worker receives after all deductions for taxes and other payments are made.

Terms Parts in a mathematical expression that are separated by such signs as (+) and (–). "Like terms" relate to the different terms in an expression that have the same literal factor. When the literal factors are different or unlike, they are called "unlike terms."

Terms (Proportion) The two outside terms of a proportion are the "extreme." The two inner terms of a proportion are the "means."

Transposing Terms A method of moving all known terms to one side of an equation and all unknown terms to the other side. The sign of each transposed quantity is changed.

Trapezoid A four-sided figure in which two of the sides (called bases) are parallel. The area = sum of the two bases x 1/2 altitude.

Triangle Three straight line segments joined at the ends to form a closed flat shape.

Trigonometric Functions An equation expressing the ratio between two sides. The six common ratios are sine (sin), cosine (cos), tangent (tan), cotangent (cot), secant (sec), and cosecant (csc).

Trigonometry A branch of mathematics which deals with the measurement of angles, triangles, and distances.

True-credit Balance (Calculator) The display indicates whether the resulting numerical value is positive or negative.

Variable Expenditures Expenses that may be changed.

Venier Caliper Micrometer An instrument on which linear measurements are determined by adding the reading on a graduated beam and a graduation on the vernier scale, of a movable leg.

Volt The difference of electrical potential between two joints of a conductor carrying a constant current of one ampere. The power dissipated between these two points equals one watt.

279 (8C700)